The Atom and the Universe

The ATOM and

the UNIVERSE

JAMES S. PERLMAN
San Francisco State College

WADSWORTH PUBLISHING COMPANY, INC.
Belmont, California

To Beatrice

Preface

However abstract science may become, it is essentially human in its origin and growth. Each scientific result is a fruit of humanity. Show the deep human interest of science and the study of it becomes the best vehicle of humanism one could devise; exclude that interest, teach scientific knowledge only for the sake of information and professional instruction, and the study of it, however valuable from a purely technical point of view, loses . . . educational value.

GEORGE SARTON, 1938

This text is written from the liberal arts point of view that science is a dynamic human enterprise. Man is a product of nature, and science a product of man. But science is more than an accumulation of facts and gadgets. Bricks alone do not make a house; design is necessary, too. In the same way, the data and tools of science must be structured by the general principles that are part of its content. Science, man's product, also includes unique processes of investigation in which men use everything they have—senses, mind, imagination, and muscles—to come to grips with their surroundings. Through their search for order, men in science develop major concepts and techniques with which they approach nature. Ideas are tested by experience, generally by the organized experience of experiment. In the text, the open-ended structure and processes of science emerge directly and inductively from specific materials within the chapters, just as the form of a house emerges from bricks. Then Chapter 26 fully summarizes the idea of science as a human enterprise through references to earlier chapters.

Specific subject areas treated here are astronomy, physics, chemistry, and atomic science. Physical science may be seen as an investigation of matter and energy at interrelated levels. For the intermediate visible world of experience, astronomy offers setting and perspective, physics and chemistry provide insights, and the unseen, minute atom provides analysis of process and composition. That analysis and perspective are both indispensable for understanding is reflected in the title, *The Atom and the Universe*. Astronomy is handled in Part 1, World System and Motion; physics in Part 2, Force and Motion, and in Part 3, Energy and Its Transformations; and chemistry and nuclear science in Part 4, Matter and Its Transformations.

Comprehensiveness is attained in this text by the expansion of a number of related basic ideas rather than by a survey of a multitude of separate topics. Our key to the physical universe is in the development of such major ideas, or conceptual models, as the following: the Copernican world view, Newton's mechanical world system, kinetic-molecular theory, atoms and molecules as chemical units, the law of conservation of matter, the periodic table, the law of conservation of energy, electromagnetic fields, the electromagnetic spectrum, relativity, and the Rutherford-Bohr atom. Concepts are seen to develop in systems rather than in isolation. And the observations, ideas, and imagination of many men from many times and places are fused in the development of such conceptual systems. Data, concepts, theories, techniques, and apparatus fall into place in the open-ended structure and processes of science. Science in the dimension of time is an on-going, developing enterprise.

The handling of text material is inductive. Natural phenomena precede theories. "Observations of the Heavens" (Chapter 1) precedes "Theories of the Heavens" (Chapters 2 and 3); "Heat Phenomena" precedes "Caloric Theory" in Chapter 11 and "Kinetic-Molecular Theory" in Chapters 12 and 13. Progression is from the simple observational origins of a given science to modern complexities of theory. Ontogeny recapitulates phylogeny—the development of the individual repeats the history of the race. The student beginning a main section of the text is like one of his own ancestors several centuries ago confronting lightning, a rainbow, or other physical phenomena. His degree of scientific knowledge and intelligence may be comparable. But the student has the benefit of collective experience since antiquity. First projected by the text into the simpler world of his ancestors, the student bridges the historical gap by tracing the development of early impressions to modern ideas and evidence. If the student is a science major, he may be somewhat familiar with present theories of lightning or of rainbows, but future specialists also need perspective and the opportunity to see how and why ideas change.

Although the text is developmental, the reader is not limited to history. Ideas and methods are brought up to date. For example, two chapters on relativity (Chapter 22, The Special Theory, and Chapter 25, The General Theory) emphasize its impact on ideas about the physical world. Chapters 21, 23, and 24, concerned with atomic structure, atomic energy, and their social impacts, speak for themselves.

A "power" arrangement from simple to complex, within chapters and from chapter to chapter within many sections of the book, permits considerable flexibility in selecting materials without sacrificing basic continuity. For example, in the three chapters on electricity and magnetism starting with Chapter 14, reading may be cut off after Chapter 15 or anywhere within Chapter 16 without disturbing overall unity and coherence. Or Chapters 22 and 25 on relativity may be eliminated, in part or entirely, without difficulty.

Two sets of questions complete each chapter. The first set, entitled "Chapter Review," outlines the main points of the chapter in question form. In keeping with science itself as a constant questioning of nature, one key question leads to another to cover the chapter. Questions in the second set, labeled "Problems," are more specific and applied. The text requires only one year of high school algebra, but in it mathematics is seen as a language and logic of science, and equations as a symbolic form for physical laws.

My primary acknowledgments are to the thinking, observing, imaginative men of many nations who through centuries have shaped and reshaped the physical sciences as we know them. More immediately, the writer was fortunate in having available the artistic talents of Dale Johnson as illustrator. My wife, Beatrice, typed and retyped the original manuscript as it was continually refined, and otherwise assumed responsibility for countless details in its completion. A number of reviewers, especially Frank X. Sutman of Temple University, contributed many helpful comments and suggestions. My personal thanks also to naturalist Ansel Adams, colleague Charles Hagar, and friend Carl Hunter for photographs of a Yosemite rainbow, high and low tides (Bay of Fundy), and the ancient Stonehenge observatory, respectively.

Contents

Part Three   Energy and Its Transformations

The Atom and the Universe

PART ONE

World System and Motion

THE AUTHOR AND CHAPTER 26

The author strongly recommends that for an overview of the text the student read Chapter 26, Science as a Human Enterprise, before starting Chapter 1.

1 *Observation of the Heavens*

Science arose in the main from early human contact with nature and the necessity of anticipating certain of her events as a condition of survival.

LLOYD W. TAYLOR, 1941

OUR DYNAMIC UNIVERSE OF MOTION AND CHANGE

We live in a dynamic universe. Everything is ceaselessly moving or changing. Electrons, the smallest units of matter, are said to spin as they revolve around protons within atoms. Atoms either dart about freely as gases or vibrate within molecules. They combine and recombine continuously to form hundreds of thousands of different molecules. Molecules themselves seemingly are always in random motion, whether in solids, liquids, or gases. Or they in turn break down into atoms and re-form into hundreds of thousands of changing substances.

This constant motion is not always apparent. The book in your hand may seem to be at rest. But the impression is only illusory. The molecules within its pages are vibrating; some are uniting with oxygen in the slow aging of the paper. Further, the book is speeding: It is carried by the earth spinning daily on its axis and orbiting at 67,000 miles an hour around the sun. The fact that you and everything else on the earth travel together at the same rate gives the illusion of rest.

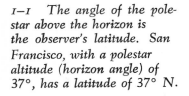

Winds and swift waters relentlessly wear down the land; earthquakes and volcanoes force it again above the sea. Individual plants, animals, and men live and die in groups that undergo evolutionary change. In the heavens the planets, moons, suns, and stars revolve endlessly in orbits of their own—much on the pattern of the tiny electron. Nothing ever seems free of motion.

In so dynamic, vast, and seemingly capricious a universe, man has always needed some degree of order, prediction, and control. Without these, he is reduced to insignificance. Worse than that, without some basis for anticipating and controlling natural events, man could not long survive in a universe of motion and change.

REGULARITY OF MOTION IN THE HEAVENS

Man's earliest search for order was in the heavens. Little wonder! The heavens are a vast natural laboratory open to any creature that can observe, wonder, think, and record. The beauty, sparkle, and mystery of this immense laboratory are even now being explored by rockets and space-ships. But even the earliest of men saw that motion in the heavens was not chaotic. Motion and change there were generally periodic and regular. It wasn't that the sun moved, but that it did so daily across the same belt in the sky. It wasn't that the moon had phases, but that the phases exactly repeated themselves. When the seasons alternated, they always alternated in the same way: Spring always followed winter, and summer, spring. Such regularities suggested order, natural law, and system. They encouraged calendar and chart making; they stimulated questions. It was perhaps in the observation of regularity in the motion of celestial objects that astronomy as a science was born.

In addition to the sun and moon, men observed myriads of stars daily rising and setting in fixed patterns. Each star retraced its own particular path in the sky. The ancients imaginatively translated these patterns into easily comprehensible terms and gave them life in the forms we know as constellations (Fig. 1–3)—Taurus the Bull, Leo the Lion, Scorpius the Scorpion and many others. Ancient men also observed that these stars daily revolve around a central star, or pole star.

Continued observation revealed five "stars" in addition to the sun and moon, apparently wandering in and out of fixed constellations. The Greeks applied their word *planets,* meaning "wanderers," to the bodies we know today as Mercury, Venus, Mars, Jupiter, and Saturn and to the sun and moon. Soon the first five were seen as decidedly different in motion, size, and brightness from the other two, and celestial objects were grouped into fixed stars, planets, sun, and moon.

1–1   The angle of the pole-star above the horizon is the observer's latitude. San Francisco, with a polestar altitude (horizon angle) of 37°, has a latitude of 37° N.

As early as 3,000 B.C. in Babylonia, movements of heavenly bodies were charted accurately enough for the astronomers of that period to develop calendars. This meant relating time to motions of heavenly bodies. The first Babylonian calendars were lunar ones, based on phases of the moon. Those calendars provided 12 lunar months of 29½ days each for a total of 354 days, a system like the Mohammedan calendar today. A thirteenth month was added from time to time for reconciliation of the calendar with the seasons. By the 8th century B.C., the Babylonians—and before them, the Egyptians—recognized the regularity of the *heliacal rising* of stars fully enough to develop a solar calendar. "Regularity of heliacal rising" refers to the specific observations that any given star rising with the sun does so again only after a certain interval of time. This interval of time between the heliacal risings of a star is so exact, so regular, and so general that it became the basis for the year as a unit of time. We shall discuss these risings further in connection with the *eastward drift* and the *ecliptic* of the sun. Be that as it may, through measurements, charts, and calendars, the Babylonians first predicted eclipses of the sun and moon. Regularity of celestial motions thus meant that time could be systematized and that events could be predicted on a natural basis. The flooding of the Nile was not a caprice of an Egyptian god but a predictable yearly event associated with the heliacal rising of the star Sirius. A calendar associated periodic floods with regular motions of sun and stars.

A SPHERICAL EARTH

The concept of a spherical earth did not originate with either Columbus or Copernicus. Ancient Greek astronomers emphasized the following evidences for a spherical earth:

1. The elevation (angular distance) of the North Star and other stars above the *horizon* is directly related to the observer's *latitude* (angular distance north or south of the equator). This is possible only on a spherical earth (Fig. 1–1).
2. During lunar eclipses, the shadow of the earth on the moon is circular.
3. Ships at sea appear on the horizon mast first. If the earth were flat, the entire ship would come into view at once.

Eratosthenes, head of the great Alexandrian Library, in about 240 B.C. conceived the idea of using the angle of the sun to calculate the circumference of the earth (Fig. 1–2). He had been informed that in the Egyptian city of Syene on a certain day, the noon sun would light up a well through all its depth. In Alexandria at the same hour of the same

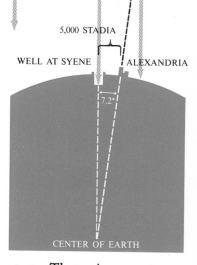

LIGHT RAYS FROM SUN

5,000 STADIA

WELL AT SYENE   ALEXANDRIA

7.2°

CENTER OF EARTH

1–2 The sun's rays were direct at Syene when arriving at 7.2° from the perpendicular at Alexandria. This angular difference reveals the earth's circumference.

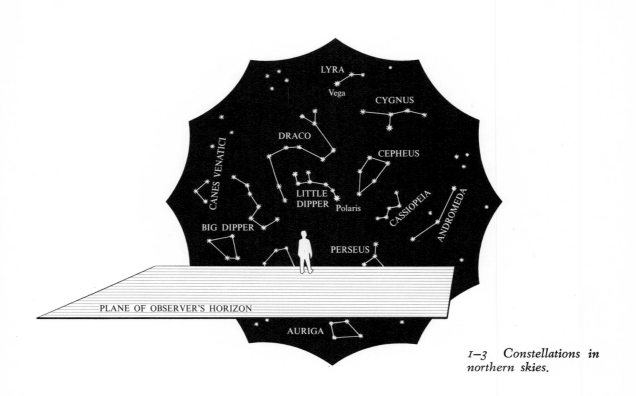

LYRA
Vega
CYGNUS
CANES VENATICI
DRACO
CEPHEUS
LITTLE DIPPER
Polaris
CASSIOPEIA
ANDROMEDA
BIG DIPPER
PERSEUS
PLANE OF OBSERVER'S HORIZON
AURIGA

1–3   Constellations in northern skies.

day, he measured the sun's rays at 7.2° from the perpendicular. He knew that Syene is 5,000 stadia (about 490 miles) due south of Alexandria. Assuming the earth to be a sphere, he then developed the following relationship:

$$\frac{360°}{7.2°} = \frac{\text{earth's circumference}}{5,000 \text{ stadia } (490 \text{ mi})}.$$

By this equation, the earth's circumference should be about 50 times 490 miles, or 24,500 miles (250,000 stadia). Eratosthenes later increased his value to about 24,750 miles (252,000 stadia) and so came remarkably close to our present approximation of 25,000 miles.

Photographs from present-day probing rockets provide final evidence for the sphericity of the earth and a circumference close to 25,000 miles. The earth is actually a spheroid, or slightly flattened sphere; its diameter from pole to pole has been found to be about 12 miles shorter than its diameter at the equator.

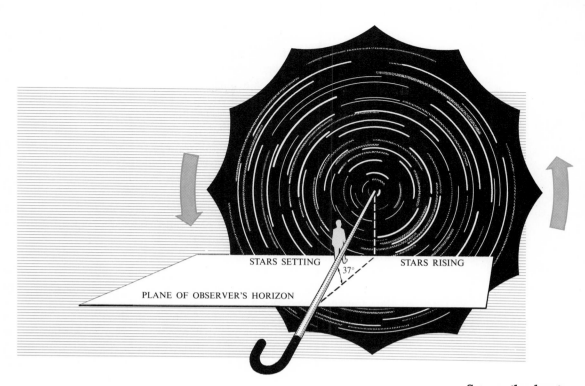

STARS SETTING

37°

PLANE OF OBSERVER'S HORIZON

STARS RISING

1–4 Star trails showing apparent daily motion of stars. Such trails are photographed through time exposure techniques.

SPECIFIC CELESTIAL CYCLES

What particular patterns of motion can men see with the naked eye from their frame of reference, the earth?

1. Daily East-to-West Motion of Celestial Objects

Apparent first of all, is the general east-to-west motion of celestial objects. Sun, moon, planets, and stars rise daily in the east, trace a semicircle across the sky, and disappear beneath the western horizon. The sun clearly brings the day; the moon often reduces the darkness of the night. There are no exceptions to the uniformity of direction. All objects in their daily half-circles seem to move from east to west; none from west to east with respect to the horizon. And what is more, the sun, the moon, and all the planets apparently move across the same narrow belt of the star-studded sky.

In a sense, the heavens are like an open umbrella with white dots. It is as if the umbrella shaft is stretched horizontally across a table, with the white-spotted top hanging over the end of the table, half in and half out of sight (Fig. 1–4). When the umbrella is rotated,* the tabletop becomes the observer's horizon, across which the patterns of dots rise and set, unfailingly and always in the same direction.

Then, raising the handle of the rotating umbrella to some angle—for example, 30°—to the tabletop (horizon) also raises the center of the umbrella dome to a point 30° above the table horizon. Dots near the center of the dome revolve around the dome center instead of appearing and disappearing across the tabletop. As the umbrella handle is tilted to an ever greater degree, more and more dots are seen in their complete circles. Finally, even the outermost dots can be seen moving in complete circles rather than "setting" beneath the table. This analogy explains the orbits that stars are seen to make around the polestar. From the equator, the North Star, Polaris, appears at the horizon, and all the stars in the Northern Hemisphere seem to rise and set in partial circles around it. As the observer travels north, the North Star appears ever higher above the horizon in accordance with the latitude of the observer. In San Francisco, for example, at 37° North latitude, the North Star appears at 37° above the northern horizon. Or from Chicago, 42° North latitude, the North Star appears at 42° above the northern horizon. With this increase in altitude of the North Star above the horizon, more and more stars around it that formerly disappeared under the horizon can be observed making complete circles around this central star. For an observer at the North Pole, no stars would rise and set. He would see all the stars moving in complete circles around the polar star like dots in a mammoth umbrella rotating directly overhead.

The location of an observer thus partly determines what he sees. Every observer has a frame of reference that must be taken into account in scientific observation. In the above case, the *observer's frame of reference* was his position on the earth's surface, his latitude. The observer's latitude determined what he saw of the stars' apparent motions around the North Star or around his own horizon.

Of importance equal to the frame of reference of the observer is another one related to it. This second frame of reference is a *background frame for the object observed*. In the daily motions of sun, moon, or stars described above, the North Star is a background point of reference for the sun, moon, or stars regardless of where the observer is in the

---

*An object *rotates* when spinning around its own axis but *revolves* when circling around an outside center. The umbrella as a unit thus rotates around its own axis, but a white spot revolves around a point on that axis. An object can both rotate and revolve at the same time: The moon rotates on its axis as it revolves around the earth. Otherwise, the moon could not always show the same face to the earth.

Northern Hemisphere. The angle at which an observer sees the North Star above his horizon depends upon his latitude; when the angle between the North Star and any given star is equal to or less than the angle between the North Star and the horizon, the star is seen in a complete circular orbit daily. Otherwise, the circle around the North Star appears to be broken at the points on the horizon where the star seems to disappear and reappear. The horizon gets in the way.

The above ideas apply to groups of stars as well as to individual ones. All the stars forming the Little Dipper, for example, revolve together as a unit around the North Star, with the angular distances among themselves remaining the same. The revolution is only partially seen when the horizon gets in the way. Because the North Star is at the tail end of the Little Dipper, this Dipper seems to be completely rotating around its own end when seen from most of the Northern Hemisphere. Close observation would show, however, that even this end makes a slight circular orbit around an imaginary *north celestial pole*, described later. The polestar at present is not far enough from the celestial pole to diminish this star's great importance as a point of reference for stars and navigation in the Northern Hemisphere.

2. *Yearly Eastward Drifts of the Sun*

Each morning the twinkle of any given star rising with the sun is quickly lost in the bath of the sun's light. Careful observation at dawn the next morning shows that now the same star rises about 4 minutes before the sun or that, conversely, the sun falls behind the star by about 4 minutes. If the sun makes a complete cycle in 24 hours, the star does so in 23 hours and 56 minutes. You can easily observe this phenomenon yourself. Check the position of any star at say, 8:00 P.M. tonight. Check again tomorrow night, and you will observe the star to be at the same position at 7:56 P.M., since we base our 24-hour day and our clocks on the sun's apparent movement.

This daily falling behind of the sun with respect to the stars is known as the *eastward drift* of the sun. Thus, the sun appears to move westward with respect to the earth's horizon; it does so more slowly than the stars by 4 minutes in every 24 hours and therefore appears to move eastward with respect to the stars. An analogy is two cars moving westward on a highway at 50 and 60 miles per hour. With respect to a ground observer, the slower car (the sun) is moving *westward;* with respect to an observer in the faster car (a star), the slower car is receding *eastward.*

On each succeeding day, the gap between a given star and the sun widens by an additional 4 minutes of time or 1° of space. The sun is about

2° behind the star in 2 days, 3° behind in 3 days, and so on. After 365¼ days, the sun will have fallen back 360° to the position of the given star again. The sun will have fallen one cycle (or lap) behind the star in its "race." The daily cycles of the star around the earth will have been counted at 366¼, while that of the sun will have been counted at 365¼.

This interval between the two heliacal risings of the star—that is, between the two occasions when the sun and any given star rise together—is arbitrarily defined as 1 year. Thus, the eastward drift involves a yearly cycle. To summarize, there is the original daily cycle of the sun and of the stars around the earth; but because the sun slowly falls behind the stars in the daily cycles, the sun also has a yearly cycle of eastward drift with respect to the stars as all seem to move about the earth.

The particular belt of stars through which the sun drifts in yearly cycles is called the zodiacal belt (Fig. 1–8). The belt is 18° wide, extending 9° on each side of the sun's observed path of drift, known as the *ecliptic*. In this area are always found the same stars in patterns that were arbitrarily grouped by the Greeks into twelve constellations, or *"signs" of the zodiac*. These constellations stretch along the belt at equal lengths of 30° for the total 360°. "Zodiac" means "zone of animals"; all constellations in it except one, Libra, appeared to the ancients to be figures of living creatures, such as the Lion, the Fishes, the Scorpion, the Bull, and the Water Bearer. The sun in its ecliptic slowly drifts eastward into and out of each one of these signs during 1 year. Thus, the zodiacal belt is really a background frame of reference of the sun in its eastward drift.

3. *"Faster" Eastward Drift of the Moon*

The moon, like the sun, daily appears to move *westward* with respect to the earth and to drift *eastward* with respect to the moving zodiacal belt of stars. If the moon rises on any evening with a given star, on the following evening the moon will be 54.5 minutes behind the star instead of only 4 minutes late like the sun. The moon is found in about the same position in 24 hours and 50.5 minutes. The star is already 13.2° above the eastern horizon on the second evening when the moon shows itself. With the moon drifting behind the stars 54.5 minutes or 13.2° daily, it takes the moon 27.3 days—divide 360° by 13.2° per day—to fall back to any given star. These 27.3 days constitute the cycle of eastern drift for the moon, as against the period of 1 year for the sun. That is, the moon rises (or sets) with any given star once in every 27.3 days, or about once a month.

4. Retrograde Motion of the Planets

Each of the planets also shows a general eastward drift in the zodiacal belt. Mars, for example, at the same hour from one evening to the next, falls behind any given star in the zodiacal belt without fail—almost. It was this "almost" that made certain "wanderers" a special source of interest to ancient man, for from time to time, the eastward drift of five planets was reversed. During approximately 2 months in every 26, Mars was seen to reverse its direction from east to west relative to the stars. Instead of drifting further behind surrounding stars as expected, Mars strangely seemed to gain on them and even catch up. If plotted, this seemingly reversed motion relative to the stars forms a loop, as indicated in Fig. 1–5. Then, after about 2 months, Mars again settled back to the customary eastward drift for about 2 years. Such reversed motion, seen for planets only, is known as *retrograde motion*. The sun and moon do not show retrograde motion in their zodiacal "wanderings" and by the 17th century were removed from the (ancient) list of planets. The intervals between successive retrograde motions of planets known today are listed as follows and can be seen to vary from one planet to another:

Mercury	116 days
Venus	584 days
Mars	780 days
Jupiter	399 days
Saturn	378 days
Uranus	370 days
Neptune	367 days
Pluto	367 days

Notice, as did the ancients, that Mars is the only planet whose interval between periods of retrograde motion is more than 2 years and that Mercury is the only "wanderer" with an interval of less than 1 year. The planets Uranus, Neptune, and Pluto, of course, were unknown until recent times.

1–5 Mars in apparent retrograde (reversed) motion.

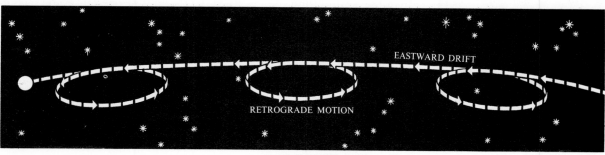

EASTWARD DRIFT

RETROGRADE MOTION

FACING SOUTH

5. Proximity of Mercury and Venus to the Sun

Mercury and Venus have long been of special fascination as morning and evening stars. Even Wagner's opera *Tannhäuser* has it, "Song to the Evening Star," a song to brilliant Venus. These two planets are always seen close to the sun. This is true regardless of where the sun may be during the year in its apparent eastward drift through the zodiacal belt. As morning stars, these planets are periodically close to the eastern horizon just before sunrise. As evening stars, they are not far from the western horizon at sundown. They pass in front of the sun and slip behind it. But the two morning or evening stars do not travel together. Each planet takes a different length of time to reach its point of maximum distance (maximum elongation) from the sun. The greatest distance from the sun observed for Venus is about 48°. Mercury is seen up to 28° from the sun. Remember that these values are relative to the earth as the observer's frame of reference. The angle measurements would be different for an observer in a spaceship. From the earth, the zodiac, of course, is the background frame of reference through which Mercury and Venus seemingly parade with the sun in general eastward drift.

6. Varying Size and Brightness of Celestial Objects

A sixth type of significant observation of sun, moon, and planets is that the diameters of the sun and moon and brightness of the planets appear to change as they move. All apparent changes in size or brightness of celestial objects are assumed to mean that these bodies vary in their distances from the earth. The change in diameters is small to the eye but observable and periodic. The sun's change of size and therefore distance from the earth has a yearly periodicity. The moon appears to change in size on a monthly basis. The planets vary in brightness and therefore in distance from the earth during the interval from the start of one retrograde motion to that of another.

7. Phases of the Moon

Observations of the phases of the moon are as old as man himself. How could the gradual daily change in the appearance of the moon not be noticed? Or the monthly repetition of this cycle from new to full and back to new moon?

Phases of the moon. (Photographs from the Mount Wilson and Palomar Observatories)

We have seen that with respect to rising with any given star, the moon has a cycle of 27.3 days of eastward drift before rising with that star again. If we change the point of reference *from a star to the sun,* the moon has a cycle of 29.5 days of eastern drift before rising with the sun again. The reason for this longer cycle is that the moon falls less behind the sun daily than behind the stars. More days would be required, therefore, for the moon to fall back to the sun than to the given star. Obviously, the background point of reference for comparison—star or sun—determines the moon's monthly cycle of observed eastward drift (that is, with respect to the stars, 27.3 days; with respect to the sun, 29.5 days).

The 29.5-day cycle of drift with respect to the sun early became the basis of our month (moonth); it exactly corresponds to the easily observed regular cycle of phases of the moon. Each new moon occurs when the moon rises with the sun. On the morning when the moon does rise with the sun, the moon is between the sun and the earth (Fig. 1–6). The half of the moon directly lit by the sun is therefore turned away from the earth. The half facing the earth is unlit, or "new." The next morning, when the moon rises about 50.5 minutes or about 12° behind the sun, the moon shows a bright, slim crescent with horns pointed away from the sun. Each day as the moon rises ever later behind the sun, the crescent increasingly fills in. The eighth rising of the moon is at noon, with the sun overhead at 90°. At that point the crescent is almost completely filled in, and one-half of the observable side of the moon facing us is brightly lit. This is the first-quarter phase.

The face of the moon now continues to wax fuller each day, and the moon is said to be gibbous. On the fifteenth day when the sun is setting, the moon is rising. At this point, the second quarter, the entire face of the moon brightens the earth in a full phase.

After full phase, the face of the moon wanes, and the phases are in reverse. The moon is again gibbous until the third quarter, after which

1–6 The moon changes phases as it apparently drifts eastward with respect to the sun.

it again shows a crescent. The fourth-quarter crescent becomes ever slimmer, with its horns pointed toward the sun. After 29.5 days, the moon is again new, and the phases are complete. The moon has fallen back to the sun's position, and both bodies rise together again.

8. *Eclipses of the Sun and Moon*

Eclipses of the sun and moon early threw terror into the hearts of men. At a new-moon phase, the moon at times blotted out the sun, and a chilly, foreboding darkness prevailed. As the sun slowly forged ahead, light, heat, and better spirits returned. Such solar eclipses can be total or partial according to whether the face of the sun is completely or partly hidden.

At full-moon phase, a round shadow of the earth can gradually creep totally across the face of the moon, as if some monster rat is quickly eating a piece of cheese. When man's fate was rigidly bound up with celestial events, fear became rampant. With the later Babylonians and with the Greeks, however, eclipses were viewed as regular and predictable, and men could begin to separate eclipses from bad omens.

9. *Seasonal North-South Motion of the Sun*

Ancient man recognized that when the sun is most nearly overhead, objects have the shortest shadows. The shortest shadows are identified with midday or noon and, in the Northern Hemisphere, with a due north direction. Also easily observable to early man is the seasonal north-south motion of the sun. Sundials in ancient Egypt (or anywhere north of 23½° North latitude) clearly showed that on June 22 (by today's calendar), the noon sun throws the shortest shadow of the year and is itself furthest north (Fig. 1–7). After that day, the noon shadow increases in length as the noon sun moves further south. A maximum length of shadow is reached on December 22, the first day of winter in the Northern Hemisphere, when the sun is furthest south (*winter solstice*). After that date, the noon shadow of the gnomon (the upright stick on the sundial) daily becomes shorter until again reaching a minimum size on June 22 (*summer solstice*). The sun is midway in its north-south journey on March 21 and September 23, when days and nights are of equal length (*vernal* and *autumnal equinoxes*) and shadows are intermediate in length.

The length and direction of the shadow on any day at noon varies according to the latitude of the locale. At the equator, for example, on

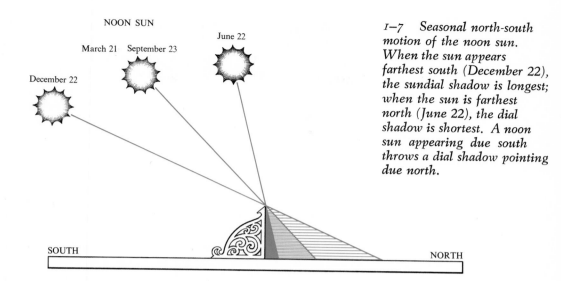

NOON SUN

December 22 March 21 September 23 June 22

SOUTH

NORTH

1–7   Seasonal north-south motion of the noon sun. When the sun appears farthest south (December 22), the sundial shadow is longest; when the sun is farthest north (June 22), the dial shadow is shortest. A noon sun appearing due south throws a dial shadow pointing due north.

March 21 and on September 23, the sun is directly overhead at noon, so that no shadow appears. In fact, the equator was early established as a 0°, or base line, for latitude through this disappearance of the noon shadow on those days. At this location after March 21 to September 23, there is a shadow thrown south of the gnomon. After September 23 to March 21, the noon shadow at the equator is thrown north of the sundial. When the sun is south after March 21, the shadow at noon increases in size until it is at a maximum on June 22. After that, the shadow decreases in length. When the sun is north after September 23, the shadow at the equator also increases in length until it reaches its maximum length on December 22.

The understanding and measurement of angles gave the sundial added importance in ancient civilizations. Through it a daily change in the length of the sun's shadow came to mean that the sun itself is daily changing its overhead position and angle from north to south to north in a yearly cycle. The limits of this north-south motion of the sun were determined at 23½° north and 23½° south of the equator. Latitude parallels of 23½° north and 23½° south were established at these limits and called the Tropics ("turning points") of Cancer and Capricorn, respectively; about 2,200 years ago at these "turning points" of the sun, there were star constellations known as Cancer and Capricorn. At the tropic of Cancer, the sun is directly overhead at noon on June 22, and at the Tropic of Capricorn, the noon sun is directly overhead on December 22. With the shifting of the sun went an observed shifting of its direct rays upon the earth. It became clear to ancient peoples that seasonal changes result from the apparent shifting of the sun and its direct rays from north to south.

10. *Precession of the Equinoxes*

The *precession of the equinoxes* was perhaps one of the most difficult observations in ancient, naked-eye astronomy. It is the observation that the equinoxes, or points of crossing between the celestial equator and the ecliptic circle, are not fixed. They shift slowly westward with respect to the constellations. That is, the sun crosses the celestial equator each year at the vernal equinox at a very slightly changed position with respect to the stars (Fig. 1–8). So slight is this shift that it takes about 26,000 years for this point of intersection to describe a complete circle around the celestial equator. This means that during the 26,000 years, each day of the calendar year has the opportunity to be the first day of spring! It also means that different stars become the polestar during this period.

The ancient Greek astronomer Hipparchus was the first to call attention to this precession of the equinoxes. His estimate of the precession was at 1° in 100 years, as against our value of 0.72° today. That is, our North Star today, Polaris, will be 0.72° from its present position just off the north celestial pole in 100 years. Hipparchus, perhaps one of the greatest astronomical observers of all time, died about 125 B.C.

FRAMES OF REFERENCE IN ASTRONOMY

Frames of Reference and Relativity of Motion

The importance of frames of reference in astronomy warrants further attention. There can be no science without observation, and no observation without frames of reference. In the previous section we observed motions of different celestial bodies in some detail. In so doing, we found it necessary to relate the moving bodies to other objects. The sun "rises" with respect to the eastern horizon and moves *westward* with respect to it; but the sun also has an *eastward* drift with respect to zodiacal stars as it falls behind them. Planets sometimes reverse their motions with respect to the stars but always move from east to west with respect to the horizon. *Motion cannot be observed except in reference to other objects.* Whether the sun moves eastward or westward depends upon whether its apparent motion is with respect to the stars, the horizon, or the moon. But if the direction and speed of an object depend upon the moving object to which it is referred—and all objects move—then all motion is relative. That is, in our dynamic universe of relative motion, any object moves with respect to a second object, which moves relative to a third, and so on. The moon, let us say, moves relative to the stars, which move relative to the earth. Such a chain of relative motion could be broken only if the earth were stationary and the motion of all objects

could be compared to it. How fast or in what direction any object is actually moving can be determined only if there is something in the universe that is at rest. The motion of other objects compared to it would then give a true, or absolute, motion. Thus, we must emphasize with Copernicus that "it is the Earth from which the rotation of the Heaven is seen." The earth is the astronomer's frame of reference, and what the astronomer sees depends on the earth's position and motion in space. In art or photography when the observer changes his position, he changes the background of the objects he observes. If, of course, the background should also be moving independently, what is photographed or observed is further changed. In astronomy it is the same: Each position on the earth has its own horizon; every motion or apparent lack of it is expressed in terms of the observer's location. The sun rises at one person's horizon after it has risen for a person to the east or before it does so for an observer to the west. This, of course, has resulted in 24 hourly time belts around the earth. Or you will recall that at different latitudes on the earth's surface, the North Star is seen at different altitudes above the horizon. This fact again is in accordance with different horizons for different observers on a curved earth. Another example is that from the earth, the monthly path of the moon in its eastward drift against the zodiacal belt is a circle. From the sun, the path of the moon would appear more like a cycloid than a circle.* Which observer would be correct—the one on the earth or an imaginary one on the sun? In an

Prehistoric observatory at Stonehenge. Thirty-five hundred years ago, Stone Age men determined the winter solstice by accurately aligning two huge stone archways. When the sun was southernmost, the rays of the rising sun shone through a long, narrow slit formed by the archways. Other astronomical events were also predicted at Stonehenge, perhaps including lunar eclipses. (Photograph by Carl Hunter)

*Whether the system is sun-centered or earth-centered would not matter.

absolute sense, neither would be correct; in a relative sense, each would be correct from his own frame of reference. It is like the case of a passenger in a moving automobile who drops a stone from the window. He sees the stone fall in a straight line. But a pedestrian at the side of the highway sees the stone fall in a parabolic curve. Whether the path of fall is a straight line or a parabola depends upon whether the observer is in the moving car or on the highway. Similarly, the astronomer must be concerned with his own frame of reference, the earth, and how its motion (or lack of it) and his position on it determine what he sees.

Background Frames of Reference: The Celestial Sphere

From the earliest times men have used apparent groupings of stars as frames of reference to locate particular stars. You will remember, for example, that the Little Dipper was a frame of reference for the North Star. As men came to accept the concept of a spherical earth, they established what is known as a system of coordinates to locate positions on its surface. They halved the earth with the imaginary line that is the equator. They subdivided it further with lines of latitude as measurements of distance north and south of the equator.

They also sectioned the earth with longitudinal lines running north and south and subdivided it into degrees of longitude east or west of an arbitrary *prime meridian*. The 0° (or "prime") meridian we use today is the line running from pole to pole through the Greenwich Observatory, outside London.

Greek astronomers projected upon the heavens a celestial sphere that completely encompassed the earth. After all, do not the heavens appear to be a huge dome? With the sphere was projected a celestial equator above that of the earth and a celestial prime meridian as coordinate axes for mapping the sky. As part of this coordinate system, a number of other reference points and lines were projected upon the celestial sphere directly above their earthly counterparts. These included the celestial poles, zenith, nadir, celestial meridians, parallels of declination, ecliptic, and zodiacal belt (Fig. 1–8). Such systematic mapping of the heavens was invaluable in the location of stars and in navigation.

The *horizon* is the imaginary circle where the sky seems to meet the earth. It is shaped by the curvature of the earth, and every position on the earth has its own horizon. On an even surface at an eye level of 5 feet, the horizon is only 4 miles away.

The *celestial north and south poles,* to the Greeks, were points on the sphere connected by an imaginary axis around which the supposed celestial sphere and its embedded stars rotated. The celestial poles are

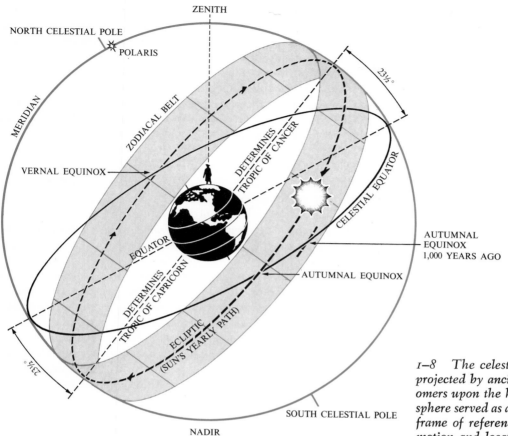

The figure is labelled with:

ZENITH

NORTH CELESTIAL POLE

POLARIS

MERIDIAN

ZODIACAL BELT

VERNAL EQUINOX

DETERMINES TROPIC OF CANCER

CELESTIAL EQUATOR

23½°

EQUATOR

DETERMINES TROPIC OF CAPRICORN

AUTUMNAL EQUINOX

AUTUMNAL EQUINOX 1,000 YEARS AGO

ECLIPTIC (SUN'S YEARLY PATH)

23½°

SOUTH CELESTIAL POLE

NADIR

1–8   The celestial sphere projected by ancient astronomers upon the heavens. This sphere served as a background frame of reference for the motion and location of celestial objects. (Note the shift westward that the autumnal equinox has made along the celestial equator during the last 1,000 years.)

projections of the earth's poles and therefore are points directly above them in the celestial sphere. The North Star, although now about 1° from the true celestial pole, nevertheless makes a good reference point. Due north on the earth can be established by sighting this star with a vertically pivoted rod. If the rod is then rotated down toward the horizon, it will be pointing north.

The *celestial equator*, similarly, is a projection of the earth's equator on the celestial sphere and is parallel to it.

The *lines of declination* are the projections of the earth's parallels of latitude on the celestial sphere. These imaginary lines, as on earth, are used to describe the location of a celestial object in degrees north or south of the celestial equator.

The *zenith* is the point on the celestial sphere directly above the head of the observer.

The *nadir* is the point on the celestial sphere exactly opposite to the zenith. It is a point directly below the observer, but through the earth and out to the "lowest" point on the celestial sphere. Every point on the earth has its own zenith and nadir.

The *celestial meridian* line connects the observer's zenith with the two celestial poles and is therefore imagined as directly above the observer's head on the celestial sphere. These lines correspond to longitude on earth. They are also measurements east and west of the celestial prime meridian, which is described below.

The zodiacal belt, established by the Babylonians, is the background belt of stars previously discussed as one in which the sun, the moon, and all the planets are always found. The apparent annual path of the sun, referred to earlier as its ecliptic, is the center line of the belt. The belt, extending 9° on each side of this center line, is 18° wide. As a background frame of reference for the sun's yearly motion, the belt, like the sun in its ecliptic, crosses the celestial equator twice at an angle of 23½° (see Fig. 1–8).

Since the belt entirely circles the earth, the Greeks divided the 360° into twelve equal sections of 30° each. These sections are called the signs of the zodiac. Each sign includes its own grouping or constellation of stars with such names as Leo the Lion and Taurus the Bull. The stars in these constellations and others are "fixed" relative only to one another, not to the earth: The angular distances among stars remain constant as they appear to rotate around the earth. Their apparent fixed positions relative to one another early provided backgrounds for locating individual stars.

The two points where the sun's ecliptic crosses the celestial equator are called *equinoxes* because when the sun is at these points, the day and night are equal in length. From one crossing point, called the vernal equinox, the sun travels north, and its direct rays shift toward the Tropic of Cancer. From the other crossing point, the autumnal equinox, the sun moves south across the equator. The vernal equinox is the first day of spring, and the autumnal equinox, the first day of fall. The north-south motion of the sun and its connection with the seasons have been discussed previously.

Coordinate Systems in Astronomy

Any two perpendicular lines can be arbitrarily used for convenience as base (zero) lines for a coordinate system. The celestial sphere, like the earth, has a prime meridian as well as an equator for base lines. The *celestial prime meridian* is an imaginary line connecting the vernal equinox to the celestial poles. This meridian also circles through the autumnal equinox.

Parallels of declination is another term referring to this celestial coordinate system. These parallels include both the celestial lines of declination (latitude) and the meridian lines. A star can be located through this coordinate system by determining its declination, or angular distance, north or south of the celestial equator, and its *right ascension,* or angular distance east of the celestial prime meridian.

The horizon and a north-south line have also been used as base lines for another celestial coordinate system. *Altitude* is the vertical angle from the horizon to a given celestial body, and *azimuth* is the horizontal angular distance west from due south on the horizon. (The azimuth is thus a measurement along the horizon; the altitude is distance above the horizon.) By knowing these two values, we can establish the position of any given star. The north-south line is determined from the North Star or the noon sun, as described earlier. An *astrolabe* is a simple, ingenious starfinder dating back to antiquity that consists essentially of vertical and horizontal protractors, a plumb line, and a pointer (Fig. 1–9). A plumb line against an upraised vertical protractor gives the altitude of a celestial body, and a pointer on a horizontal protractor gives the azimuth.

1–9 *Astronomer determining the azimuth angle of a star.* (*The Bettmann Archive, Inc.*)

According to Aristotle, "men are political animals." But Aristotle did not go far enough: Men are system-building animals; "political" organization is only one form of system building. In fact, as system builders, men are unique. Bees construct hives, and beavers dam streams. Both operate by instinct and senses to build systems of things. They do not learn these techniques, nor have they been capable of altering or adapting them over countless centuries. The habits of bee and beaver, ant and eagle, nut-gathering squirrel and bone-hiding dog, are the same now as they were 10,000 years ago. Changes in habit occur only as the species themselves change.

But men have minds and imagination. They not only learn, adapt, and invent but also build systems of ideas as well as of things. Some of men's idea systems we know as philosophy, religion, literature, music, art, politics, and social theory. And, of course, we have houses, furniture, bridges, spaceships, and all the other wonders of technology resulting from men's building systems of things. None of these tangible products, however, is possible without the ideas behind them. Science is a synthesis of a world of ideas and a world of things, and man is the synthesizer. Specifically, in astronomy, when men projected frames of reference and celestial spheres upon the heavens to locate moving objects there, they were scientifically building a system. They were projecting ideas upon nature to systematize nature.

Frames of Reference
and the Question of a Moving Earth

Even more important than the shape of the earth in determining what is seen from it is the question of whether or not the earth is moving. If the earth is stationary, the observations of the speeds, directions, and paths of all other objects are true ones. If the earth is moving, then "diurnal rotation is only apparent in the Heavens and real on Earth" (Copernicus). We must therefore have something else fixed in the universe to determine our own position and velocity. We otherwise cannot make the proper allowances in determining the motions of all other objects and must accept all motion as relative. In other words, with all else in motion, only a stationary earth could provide the fixed frame of reference necessary to determine the true, or absolute, motions of all objects in the universe. It certainly would be of advantage to have the earth fixed, with all other objects in absolute motion around it. Upon what basis, even against our immediate senses, do we disclaim a stationary earth and with it an earth-centered universe? This is a question that leads to the famous Ptolemaic-Copernican issue. Does the sun revolve around the earth or the earth around the sun? In approaching this question in the next chapter, we will need to refer back to the specific motions in the heavens already discussed. They represent observations from the earth that any theory of the universe would have to take into account. Perhaps in the process we can gain some insight into the nature, content, and structure of the universe as well as of science itself.

In summary, motion and change are characteristic of all things, but observation shows that, at least in the heavens, motions are not random or chaotic. And at least from the standpoint of men on earth, it has long been apparent that a regularity, a periodicity, exists in the motions of heavenly bodies. Things move in patterns or cycles. This regularity provides a basis for some kind of order; and order enables prediction, both prerequisites to science. Thus, astronomy became one of the earliest of sciences.

But we have also seen that there is no meaningful observation without two related frames of reference: one for the object observed and another for the observer. When characteristic motions of various heavenly bodies are considered in detail, a relativity of motion becomes obvious. That is, the specific orbit of any given object can be observed and described only relative to a background of other moving objects. The earth, our particular frame of reference as observers, also has to be considered with respect to its shape, and with respect to the question of its own motion. Whether the earth is fixed or moving is a particularly important question, for the earth influences what men observe and interpret in an apparent universe of motion.

CHAPTER REVIEW

The key questions completing each chapter are intended for review and reflection. These questions also serve to emphasize the basically investigative, dynamic character of science. Early questions in observation of nature led to facts, concepts, and theories, which in turn led to further questions in a continuing reciprocal process that ever extends horizons. Astronomy, perhaps the most ancient science, affords excellent illustrations of this process, which dynamically pushes back the boundaries of the known into the unknown.

1. Can you think of anything in the universe that is not moving and changing?

2. If everything is apparently moving and changing, what basis is there for order or law in nature?

3. Is a consistent, general, east-to-west motion of objects apparent in the heavens? Do stars seen in circular paths around the pole star contradict this general westward motion? Explain.

4. To what phenomena or observations does the "eastward drift" of the sun and moon refer?

5. How can the sun and moon have a daily westward motion and still have an "eastward drift"? What significance does the idea of "frame of reference" have in this seeming contradiction?

6. To what observations does the "retrograde motion" of planets refer? What significance does frame of reference have in this case?

7. What apparent celestial cycles of motion other than those in questions 3–6 suggested some order in the physical universe to ancient observers?

8. Describe the Babylonian and Egyptian calendars, and relate them to specific celestial patterns of motion.

9. What do you think is meant by the statement that such ancient calendars helped "call the world to order" scientifically? Do you agree? Why or why not? What is meant by "scientifically"?

10. Describe the location of Polaris in the Little Dipper. Where does observation end and organization (and imagination) begin in locating Polaris in this background frame of reference?

11. The earth is our frame of reference as observers. How does the sphericity of the earth affect what we see in the heavens or otherwise?

12. State the background frame of reference for each of the following observations, and describe those you have not discussed in former questions: (a) succession of day and night, (b) general westward motion of celestial objects, (c) eastward drift of the sun, (d) eastward drift of the moon, (e) retrograde motion of Mars, (f) changing diameters of the sun and moon, (g) changing brightness of Venus, (h) Mercury's constant

nearnesss to the sun, (i) the sun's north-south motion, (j) phases of the moon, (k) eclipses of the sun and moon, and (l) precession of the equinoxes.

13. Describe the main features of the celestial sphere, and show how these features in a sense are an "ordering" of the universe by man. Where does observation end and organization begin in locating an object—for example, Polaris—in the celestial sphere?

14. What distinctions can you make among the following: observed cycles of motion, order, and design in the universe?

15. Discuss two other areas of human experience besides astronomy in which you believe "frames of reference" is a significant concept. Can observation be meaningful without a frame of reference for both the observer and the thing observed?

16. How do astronomical observations as emphasized in this chapter illustrate that science is a human enterprise?

PROBLEMS

Diagrams often help in answering such specific questions as those in this group.

1. Explain how the sun can be used to determine north. How can the North Star be used instead? What errors arise in both cases?

2. At what angle would Polaris be if you were at the North Pole? Explain how the North Star can be used to determine your latitude. Why must you assume a spherical earth in using the North Star to determine your latitude?

3. How can stars be called "fixed" if they are always seen moving from east to west or in concentric circles around celestial poles? Are stars "fixed" by observation, by definition, or by what?

4. Suppose that you watch the moon, Venus, and nearby stars apparently moving westward during a number of evenings. How can you tell that the moon and Venus are not just stars closer or larger than the rest?

5. Explain how the apparent eastward drift of the sun is related to the calendar year.

6. How is the apparent eastward drift of the moon related to the month as a unit of time?

7. How can an astrolabe be used to measure the angle of eastward drift of the moon in 24 hours?

8. What are the approximate declinations and right ascensions of the sun on March 21, June 22, September 23, and December 22 (Fig. 1–8)?

9. The moon always shows the same face to the earth. Does the moon rotate on an axis with respect to you? Explain.

10. Use two illustrations from astronomy to show the importance of using frames of reference for describing motion.

SUGGESTIONS
FOR FURTHER READING

Bernhard, Hubert J., et al., *New Handbook of the Heavens,* Mentor paperback, New York, 1959, Chs. 1–3.

Childe, V. Gordon, *Man Makes Himself,* Mentor paperback, New York, 1963.

Clagett, Marshall, *Greek Science in Antiquity,* Collier paperback, New York, 1963, Ch. 1.

Farrington, Benjamin, *Greek Science,* Penguin paperback, Baltimore, 1961, Ch. 1.

Hogben, Lancelot, *Science for the Citizen,* Unwin, London, 1951, Chs. 1–2.

Kuhn, Thomas, *The Copernican Revolution,* Vintage paperback, New York, 1959, Chs. 1–2.

Sarton, George, *A History of Science: Ancient Science through the Golden Age of Greece,* Wiley paperback, New York, 1964, Chs. 1–3.

2 Theories of the Heavens — Earth-Centered

...like a floating iceberg whose bulk is largely hidden in the sea, only the smallest part of the physical world impresses itself upon us directly. To help us grasp the whole picture is the supreme function of *theory*.

GERALD J. HOLTON, 1953

FROM OBSERVATION TO WORLD SYSTEM

Observation in science is basic but insufficent. Necessary also are ideas that relate and explain what is seen. With ideas we can relate what we observe; we can draw conclusions from our observations; we can explain and even predict events.

Together with the above quote, Holton expressed the role of theory in science well in this remark: "The task of science as that of all thought is to penetrate beyond the immediate and visible, to formulate connections, and thereby to place the observable phenomena into a new and larger context." But in astronomy, how can we attain such a larger context? Even with space travel, no man will be able to get above or beyond the universe to observe it from some neutral point.

We can start with ourselves and our earth. Just as ancient man did, we can project a celestial sphere to assist us in observing the stars. In that sphere we can establish a zodiacal belt in which we locate the wandering planets, sun, and moon. Our first model at least permits the careful observation and accurate measurement of time and place: where the heavenly bodies are, where they have been, where they will be, and when they will be there.

Charting the movements of these objects, we can determine orbits and periodicity; upon these movements we can calculate time, organize calendars, and make predictions, but working within our frames of reference by observation, we learn only *how* objects move—not *why*. When we inquire *why*, we advance not so much beyond as into the problem of *how*. To take such a step requires forming a larger picture or a model of the universe that can relate our observations in a unified, coherent manner. But how do we obtain this more comprehensive model?

GEOMETRY
SHAPES ASTRONOMY

As the ancient Greeks did, we can let geometry provide the model. While they were studying the skies, the Greeks were also developing geometry into a very substantial mathematical system. Euclid brought this science to a pinnacle about 300 B.C. The Greek mind, with its interest in logic and the abstract, found rationality, order and consistency in geometry. In fact, here were all the most desirable elements for a logical, understandable universe, predictable to human beings.

Pythagoras (500 B.C.) and his followers had been eager to fit a number system to the universe and then proceed mystically, almost religiously, to ascribe a geometric order, truth, and beauty to the essence and structure of the universe itself. The numbers and geometric patterns became the underlying realities. After all, aren't spheres and circles characteristic of celestial objects and motion? Aren't spheres and circles perfect geometric figures? And isn't perfection to be associated with the heavens?

In this way, it becomes a simple matter to treat the celestial sphere less as a projected conceptual frame of reference of many moving points of light and more as a large, geometric, mechanically rotating structure of which the stars are a part. In other words, the stars would not be objects that moved and rotated on their own. Rather, the sphere becomes the unit, and the stars become points of light carried within it. Once a celestial sphere has been imagined and projected for observing the heavens, it is but one more step in theoretical system building to consider the sphere a mathematical reality. Besides, ideas were realities to the Greeks.

This conception of a rotating sphere might again be compared to the large, transparent plastic umbrella previously described, on which the stars were only spots. But this time—more literally—there can be an actual sphere to do the rotating. According to Aristotle (384–322 B.C.), the "umbrella" can be composed of an ethereal crystal sphere, a fifth element, distinctly different from the terrestrial elements of air, earth, water, and fire. Or, according to a contrasting theory introduced about 373 B.C. by Hicetas, Ecphantus, and Heraclides, the celestial sphere and points of light can remain stationary while the spherical earth at its center keeps rotating. Because of relative motion, what would be observed from the earth would be the same under either theory. To illustrate, have you ever been in a train watching another on a neighboring track when suddenly you observed it to be moving backward? Then, you look around and observe that your own train has gently begun to move forward.

An important consideration in all the above, however, is the fact that these ancient scientists had made an interpretation beyond observation in their attempt to answer the *why*. The celestial sphere originating as a convenient background frame of reference for locating stars became an imaginary theoretical structure in the heavens, a rotating geometric system. The rotating structure could be used to explain why moving objects were where seen and when seen. Such a theoretical system is an idea; it is a conceptual model of the world. Such a model as theory should be distinguished from the observations that suggest it and that are related to it.

From Plato's 4th century B.C. work *Phaedo* comes this quotation: "This was the method I adopted: I first assumed some principle which I judged to be the strongest and then I affirmed as true whatever seemed to agree with this, whether relating to the cause or to anything else; and that which disagreed, I regarded as untrue." (Doesn't this sound like a great deal of our personal, social, and cultural thinking today?) In further comment, let us quote Alfred Whitehead: "The Greeks thought that metaphysics was easier than physics and tended to deduce scientific principles from *a priori* conceptions of the nature of things. They were restrained in this disastrous tendency by their vivid naturalism, their delight in first-hand perception. [Later] Medieval Europe shared the tendency without the restraint."

With respect to astronomy, Plato advised further: Determine "what uniform and ordered movements must be assumed for each planet to explain its apparently irregular paths." This was a specific directive to his students in their attempts to call the heavens to order. Implied in his words is a sophisticated recognition that things as they *appear* ("apparently irregular movements of the planets") may not be as they actually are ("uniform and ordered movements"). Perfection was to be expected in the heavens. Yet retrograde motions involved irregular, changing paths for planets easily observed. The problem was this: How can the idea of perfection of the heavens be reconciled with the imperfection of what is seen? How can only circular motions or combinations of them be used to explain apparent motions of celestial objects that are not circular? To Plato, perfection of all things in the heavens was the reality to be reconciled with the imperfect shadows that we observe. The perfect forms of geometry could do the job of reconciliation, but specifically, how? Plato meanwhile inscribed these words above the entrance of his academy: "Let no one enter here unless he has a taste for geometry and mathematics."

ROTATING CONCENTRIC SPHERES

Of Plato's various students, Eudoxus (409–350 B.C.) developed perhaps the most ingenious answer to his master's problem of reconciling or "saving the phenomena." In considerable detail, he developed a model in which he placed the sun, moon, and each of the other "wanderers," or planets, into separate concentric spheres within the regular, celestial sphere of stars (Fig. 2–1). After all, if stars have a celestial sphere, it is consistent with perfection for the sun, moon, and planets to have spheres, too. The fixed earth was at the center of these eight spheres, arranged like the layers of an onion. All the spheres were assumed to be rotating at different speeds and in different directions around different axes. Each sphere was imbedded through an axis to the adjacent sphere further out and was carried around by this outer sphere. Its own motion was in this way compounded by those of the other spheres. The motion of the outermost star-bearing sphere was simple: It turned about its celestial poles daily. The motions of sun and moon were also comparatively easy. The imbedded axes of the solar and lunar spheres were tilted each at the proper angle, so that the observed paths of the sun and moon relative to the stars could be accounted for. The speeds of these two spheres were easily determined to account for the sun falling 4 minutes behind the stars daily and for the moon drifting about 50.5 minutes per day behind the sun. The planets* were a more difficult problem. To account for retrograde motion, each planet needed several special auxiliary spheres in connection with its own to show how several interconnected objects in uniform circular motion can give the appearance of changing speed and direction.

Eudoxus ascribed a total of 26 simultaneous uniform motions—and Aristotle, later, 55—to account for the particular motions of the sun, moon, and planets. As discrepancies accumulated between the positions of planets predicted by the model and the actual observed positions, more auxiliary spheres thrown into the system eliminated the differences between prediction and observation. There was, however, an Achilles' heel in Eudoxus's world system. His model could not explain why planets appear to vary in brightness as time goes by. No matter how many auxiliary spheres were used to account for apparent positions or directions of a planet, the planet itself would always in this system of concentric spheres have to be at the same distance from the observer and, therefore, should always show the

*The term "planets" is used here in the modern sense. Recall that to the Greeks the sun and moon as "wanderers" in the zodiacal belt were also planets.

DAILY MOTION

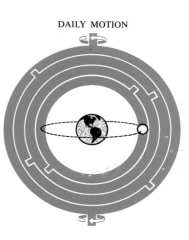

2–1 *Concentric spheres model of the universe. The model explained various apparent celestial motions by embedding sun, moon, and planets within separate rotating spheres enclosed by an outermost sphere of fixed stars. Spheres were connected by axes rotating at various angles and velocities.*

same brightness. After all, the observer is at the center of the original sphere carrying the planet itself and, therefore, always at an equal distance from it.

In spite of its weakness, Eudoxus's model of the universe was an important scientific development for the following reasons:

1. It was an ingenious conceptual device. Although his model was inadequate to attain his objectives of highly accurate predictions with the assumption of the perfection of the heavens, Eudoxus established a significant precedent of using mental models to explain, unify, and predict phenomena of nature.

2. By establishing such use of geometric models as bridges between astronomical theory and observation, Eudoxus stimulated such successors as Aristotle (also a student of Plato), Hipparchus, and Ptolemy to work for modifications or for more adequate models.

3. His model gave further promise for mathematics as a language of nature and of science.

4. Through the model, explanations of events were possible in terms of natural causes. That is, most known astronomical events could be explained in terms of the immediate workings of nature itself.

5. Concretely and ingeniously, Eudoxus, through this model, spelled out differences between apparent and actual motions. Apparent motions were what was observed, including such irregularities as retrograde motion, whereas actual motions were represented by perfect geometric models, befitting perfection of the heavens. Retrograde motion as an observation of imperfect motion was a combination of actually perfect motions of spheres.

THE PTOLEMAIC MODEL OF THE UNIVERSE

Greek astronomy reached its culmination in Claudius Ptolemy (100–178 A.D.) some 400 years after the decline of the Grecian states themselves. This meticulous scientist, like Hipparchus before him, set a pattern for all future astronomers in the extent and care of his observations. He cataloged some 1,080 stars, almost half of those visible to the naked eye. More than that, using earlier concepts of Hipparchus, he developed in great detail from his observations a world system powerful in its ability to predict future motions of celestial objects with precision. His great synthesizing work, the *Almagest,* dominated astronomy until the time of Copernicus, 1,400 years later. Ptolemaic tables are still used in navigation today.

The Ptolemaic world system (Fig. 2–2) is based on common sense. Like Aristotelian cosmologists before him, Ptolemy placed the earth at the center of the universe, and although he acknowledged its sphericity, his earth was stationary (Fig. 2–2). This is easy to understand. The earth appeared to be at the center of the universe and fixed; therefore, he assumed that it was so. Similarly, the stars appeared to be revolving; therefore, he assumed that they were. Even today in common conversation we attribute movement to the sun when we say that it rises—and not that we are turning toward the sun. That appearances are deceiving is still in many ways to be learned today. Observation is still often confused with fact; the problem is not an easy one. Apparent motions of stars were thus interpreted by Ptolemy and other geocentric astronomers as *actual* motions.

Between the earth and the celestial sphere in the Ptolemaic model (Fig. 2–2) are the moon, Mercury, Venus, the sun, Mars, Jupiter, and Saturn in the order given. The circles, called deferents, represent the orbit of drift, with respect to the stars, of the various bodies around the earth, the observer's frame of reference. In the case of the sun, Mercury, and Venus, these primary circles represent a 1-year revolution with respect to the stars. For Mars, the revolution takes 687 days; for Jupiter, 12 years; for Saturn, 30 years; for the moon, 27.3 days. When we *observe* the sun's eastward drift with respect to the stars, we refer to the path as the ecliptic. When we *explain* the ecliptic by means of the Ptolemaic model of the universe, the ecliptic becomes the deferent.

Epicycles, Eccentrics, and Equants

To solve the basic problem of the planets, their varying brightness, however, Ptolemy replaced the concentric spheres of the planets with a mathematical representation of their orbits by circles, also a perfect geometric form. The use of circles solved the problem in the following way: Imagine a planet P to orbit in a circle around the point O' (Fig. 2–3). If meanwhile the center O' moves in a larger circle around a center O,

2–2 Ptolemaic world system. Ptolemy replaced planetary concentric spheres with circles representing planetary orbits around the earth.

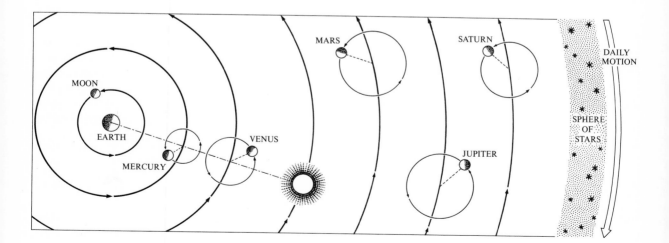

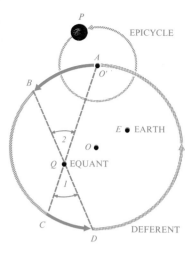

2–3   Epicycles, eccentrics, and equants reconciled observation and theory. These geometric devices involved three different centers around which planets moved. The earth, of course, was the universal center. Angular speed was constant ($\angle 1 = \angle 2$) around a nearby equant center Q. Direction was symmetrical around a deferent center O.

the smaller circle is called an *epicycle,* and the larger, a deferent. If the deferent center O is not on the earth, the point O becomes an *eccentric* center in relation to the earth. Because of the displacement of the center O from E, an object moving on the deferent would appear to be changing its distance from the earth. The object would be following an eccentric path. Still another center Q, called an *equant,* is an imaginary point from which the epicycle center O' moves at a uniform angular rate. That is, from it a given angle AQB will change at a constant rate as point O' revolves. Or if O' moves from A to B in the same time that O' later moves from C to D, the two angles formed, AQB and CQD, are equal. (That is, $\angle 1 = \angle 2$.) The angle AQB changes at a constant rate as O' moves around the circle. *Constant angular speed* exists with respect to equant center Q, and *circular motion* with respect to deferent center O. The assumption of uniform circular motion was thus satisfied while allowing the planets to vary in brightness. We shall also see that through the use of deferents, epicycles, eccentrics, and equants as geometric devices, the Ptolemaic model could predict motions of celestial bodies with precision.

Assumptions of the Ptolemaic Model

All ideas, beliefs, theories, or statements rest upon assumptions of some kind. Since no idea can be stronger than the assumptions it rests on, assumptions are extremely important in the examination of ideas. In fact, science in large part, as we shall see, is a matter of testing assumptions. We can consider the Ptolemaic model to have been based upon the following main assumptions. Only the last still holds today.

1. A stationary, spherical earth exists at the center of the universe. There are actually three assumptions here, based on observation and Aristotelian cosmology: a fixed earth, a spherical earth, and the earth's location at the "center of the heavens."

2. All heavenly bodies move in perfect circles or in systems of perfect circles around the earth. This assumption was in tune with prevailing ideas associating the heavens with divinity and with mathematical perfection.

3. All circular motions of celestial bodies are at constant angular speeds. This assumption was also in line with the Aristotelian doctrine of the perfection of the heavens.

4. All "fixed" stars move in one outermost sphere. This assumption was also based on observation. The difficulty of observing the third dimension, depth, permitted the placement of all stars in a single sphere. Observations of unchanging angles among stars as they apparently moved also substantiated this assumption at the time.

5. The sun, moon, and planets occupy their own individual orbits daily around the earth. As with Eudoxus's assumption of concentric

spheres, more careful observation (for example, noting that one body passes in front of another in transits or eclipses) justified removing the sun, moon, and planets individually from the sphere of stars.

6. The individual orbits of sun, moon, and planets are at considerable distances from one another. By the time of Ptolemy, geometric technique had become far enough advanced to give some idea of this distance. In the 3rd century B.C., for example, Aristarchus had already used triangulation methods with the sun, moon, and earth to determine the relative distances of the first two from the earth.

7. The size of the earth compared to its distance to the sphere of stars is so insignificant as to permit treating the earth as a mathematical point in the universe. Here again, the application of geometry to astronomy gave ever increasing respect for distance in astronomy as compared to the size of objects.

In examining the above assumptions from the vantage point of today's knowledge, only the last assumption is without fallacy. The first six assumptions, one by one, are based upon observation, beliefs, or mathematical reasoning but have not lasted. Obviously, the senses, the mind, or the imagination alone is not enough for the advancement of knowledge and understanding of the universe. We need to use everything we have, senses, mind, and imagination, in a system of checks and balances to attain a solid hold on the universe. It is a matter of using over time everything we have with more and more precision of observation, refinement of ideas, and fertility of imagination. Mathematics in the physical sciences early became intimately involved with accuracy of observation or measurement, with systematizing, and with reasoning.

PTOLEMAIC EXPLANATION AND PREDICTION OF CELESTIAL MOTIONS

We have previously discussed conceptual models as theoretical systems or schemes. A first main function of such models is to systematize and explain data already known. A second main function is accurately to predict future events. Such models also serve as conceptual rather than observed frames of reference, like the constellations or the horizon. In performing these functions, conceptual models must be comparatively accurate, simple, reasonable, flexible, and fruitful of new developments. Otherwise, as we shall see, they do not survive. Let us therefore return to the ten basic astronomical observations outlined in Chapter 1. Our purpose is to see how effectively the Ptolemaic model systematizes, explains, and predicts these particular phenomena.

1. Daily East-to-West
Motion of Celestial Objects

The Ptolemaic model easily explains the daily east-to-west motion of all celestial objects. The general diagram of the Ptolemaic system (Fig. 2–2) is from the vantage point of an observer on the north celestial pole. All objects move in the same *clockwise* direction around the earth. This revolution, indicated by the blue arrow at the sphere of stars, occurs daily. The celestial sphere carries all the stars imbedded in it. The sun, moon, and planets move as if carried in separate, inner spheres of their own. Their paths are also clockwise ones daily around the earth. (The counter-clockwise black arrows in Fig. 2–2 will be explained in succeeding sections.)

Let us now reverse the frames of reference by placing the observer back on the earth. In the Northern Hemisphere he looks toward the North Star and sees all the stars near it moving *counterclockwise* around it. As he glances from the North Star toward the horizon, he notices that the latter is in the way of his seeing the entire orbits below that line. What was a complete counterclockwise motion to the horizon becomes an east-to-west motion at this reference line. The sun and moon in this change of the observer's frame of reference from the north celestial pole to the earth also are not seen in their entire circles, but only east-to-west above the horizon.

2. Yearly Eastward Drift
of the Sun in the Zodiacal Belt

You will recall from Chapter 1 that the sun in its observed daily cycle around the earth falls behind any given star to the extent of about 1° of space and 4 minutes of time daily. If the sun rises with a given star today, tomorrow the sun will rise behind the star. How did Ptolemaic theory explain this eastward drift of the sun with respect to the stars?

The earlier concentric-spheres theory of Eudoxus would simply have had the sun in an invisible, moving sphere. The sun would be carried through its 360° daily a trifle more slowly than the stars would be in their sphere. It would be like a race in a circular track. The "vehicle" carrying the sun in a complete circle daily would fall behind that carry-ing the stars by about 1° a day. After 365¼ turns (or 1 year), the sun as a "passenger" would have fallen behind by one complete lap to the position of the given star in the race.

The Ptolemaic explanation is somewhat more involved. The sun is also treated as if carried around clockwise daily in a celestial sphere of its own. In this case, however, the sphere of the sun is not considered to be moving more slowly than the rotating sphere of the stars. Rather than a passive passenger on a merry-go-round, the sun is an active one moving against the motion of its vehicle. The sun moves about 1° within its sphere during the 23 hours and 56 minutes that the sphere moves 360°. Therefore, the sun is 1° from its position of the day before in the vehicle and thus 1° short of a complete turn. Creeping about 1° a day in this way, it takes the sun 365¼ days, or turns of its sphere, to go completely around its sphere. This slow path traced within its sphere is the sun's ecliptic or deferent and represents a yearly cycle of eastward drift.

To summarize, in Ptolemaic theory the sun has two cycles of motion: first, a daily one as it is carried around the earth by its rotating sphere; and second, a yearly one as it drifts within its sphere. The second cycle of drift within the sphere would exist even if the sphere bearing the sun were stationary. After 365¼ days the sun is back to its original relationship with the stars, exactly one complete revolution behind. In all this, the Ptolemaic theory was a successful model. It explained motions observed; it afforded a mathematical basis for day-to-day prediction.

3. Monthly Eastward Drift of the Moon in the Zodiacal Belt

As noted in Chapter 1, the moon, like the sun, is observed in two separate cycles: its daily westward one across the horizon and a rapid eastward drift with respect to the stars. In this case the eastward drift is so rapid that it can be easily observed in a single night. Its rate, you will recall, is 13° of space or 54.5 minutes of time per day, as compared to the 1° or 4 minutes per day of the sun. Falling behind at such a rate, the moon "loses" a complete revolution once every 27.3 days, when it is again in its original position with respect to any given fixed star.

The Ptolemaic explanation of the observed eastward drift of the moon is similar to that of the sun's drift. The moon is also treated as if carried around clockwise daily in its own sphere. The moon, however, moves against the motion of its sphere to the extent of 13° a day and therefore loses the 54.5 minutes a day. Every 27.3 days, the moon falls back to its original position within the sphere. This explains the faster, 27.3-day cycle of the moon's eastward drift, as against the 365¼ days of the sun. This path of the moon's eastward drift traced within its sphere is also with respect to the sphere of stars and constitutes the deferent of the moon.

4. Retrograde Motion of the Planets in the Zodiac

The basic movements of the planets are explained in the same way. Each is borne on a separate sphere for a daily cycle around the earth.

Each also moves within its sphere for a separate cycle of eastward drift against the background of stars. Each has a deferent representing a complete circular path of eastward drift within its sphere.

An explanation was also necessary for the retrograde motion of the planets. You will recall that this motion is a temporary reversal of eastward drift of the planets to a westward gaining on the stars. At this time the planets are observed to catch up to stars west of them rather than to fall behind. According to Ptolemaic theory, the planet, instead of moving against the motion of its sphere, still moves in the same direction.

For a planet actually to reverse itself in this way would be contradictory to the Ptolemaic assumption of perfection of the heavens. Celestial objects must consistently move in circles and at constant speeds. How were the irregularities of retrograde motion to be reconciled with these Ptolemaic assumptions? Once again, how were the "phenomena to be saved"? Mind you, it wasn't the theory of perfection that was in jeopardy, but the phenomena of observation! Ptolemy's answer was the ingenious one of epicycles. The use of this geometric device would permit the planets actually to move in a system of perfect circles at constant speed and yet appear to retrogress. A point on the rim of a wheel rolling at constant speed always moves in a circle around the hub at constant speed. When this point approaches the ground for a short time, it can appear to be moving backward even though the wheel as a whole moves forward. This reversal can be photographed by attaching a lamp on a point of the rim of a wheel properly rolling on a rotating disk.

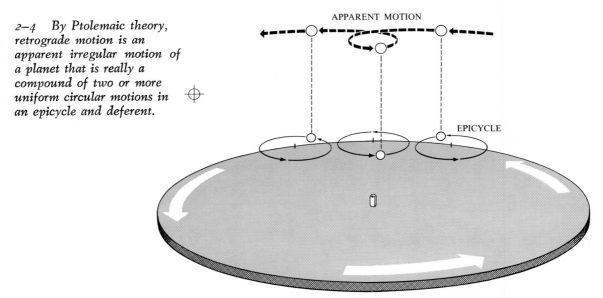

2-4   By Ptolemaic theory, retrograde motion is an apparent irregular motion of a planet that is really a compound of two or more uniform circular motions in an epicycle and deferent.

APPARENT MOTION

EPICYCLE

ACTUAL MOTION BY PTOLEMAIC THEORY

For the Ptolemaic explanation of retrograde motion, place a planet on the rim of a small merry-go-round, and call the planet's circular path an epicycle (Fig. 2–4). Then place the center of the small merry-go-round on the rim of a large merry-go-round, and identify the circular path of the epicycle center as the cycle of eastward drift of the planet in the zodiacal belt. The planet, like any point or lamp on a wheel, will show a retrogression that is really a compound of two uniform circular motions. *Uniform circular motion* is defined as circular motion at constant speed.

Here Ptolemy and his followers, in their passion for perfect order, made the universe conform to that passion. Ptolemy based his thinking on Plato's assumption of perfection of the heavens, just as we today base our thinking on other assumptions that may be rejected in the future. Ptolemy attributed the irregular motions of the planets to their supposed epicyclic movements and ingeniously reconciled these imperfect movements with prevalent perfect-circle theories.

This reconciliation took several forms:

a. The radius and constant speed of each epicycle upon each deferent were varied. If the observed position of a planet at a given time varied from the position predicted by the theory, the theoretical position could be adjusted to that observed by varying the radius or speed of the planet's epicycle.

b. Systems not merely of epicycles upon deferents, but of epicycles upon epicycles upon epicycles . . . . upon deferents were devised. (Picture a small merry-go-round twirling about on the edge of a larger one upon a still larger one—and then add a still smaller one upon the smallest.) This gave greater flexibility in reconciling predicted positions of planets with observed positions.

c. The eccentrics, previously described, were used and adjusted; that is, the deferent centers of sun, moon, and planets could fall near rather than on the earth. The angular speed of a celestial object could then be observed to vary from the earth and yet be constant with respect to its true geometric center nearby.

d. The equant center, also previously described, was used and adjusted. This center was used primarily when the assumption of a constant angular speed for a planet from a true center did not allow accurate predictions. Using an adjustable point near the geometric center as a theoretical point from which angular speeds would be equal could be effective.

By using combinations of the above devices, the Ptolemaic theory supplied answers for all observed movements of planets without changing the basic theory. Major epicycles and equants were not necessary for the sun and moon. The eccentric and the equant placed considerable strain upon the original assumption of the perfect-circle theory of the heavens. As we shall see later, it was the equant in particular that disturbed Copernicus.

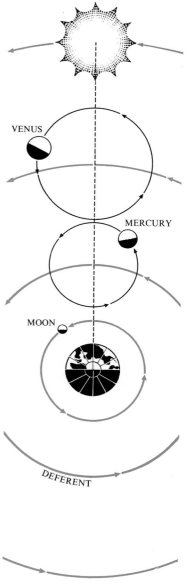

2–5 *Ptolemaic explanation of why Venus and Mercury are always seen near the sun. The epicycles of these planets are on a line of centers between the earth and sun as the sun yearly moves in its deferent around the earth.*

5. *Proximity of Mercury and Venus to the Sun*

The two planets Mercury and Venus are always seen near the sun. This phenomenon required an explanation. Mercury is hardly ever visible except just at sunset or before sunrise, and then it is quite close to the sun. Its distance from the sun is now known to average 36 million miles. Venus, at a distance of about 67 million miles, is the brightest object in the heavens, after the sun and moon, whenever its position in its orbit is close to ours—about 30 million miles away.

In the Ptolemaic model both of these planets are placed in epicycles the centers of which form a line of centers with the moving sun (Fig. 2–5). This means that the centers of the epicycles of both planets travel completely around their respective deferents in a line of centers with the sun yearly. With the planets placed on large enough epicycles, it is easy to explain how each of these planets can be observed to lead the sun as morning stars or trail it as evening stars. They are morning stars when in their epicycles they are far enough east of the line of centers to lead the sun, and evening stars when far enough west of the same line to trail it.

6. *Varying Size and Brightness of Celestial Objects*

The apparent changes in diameter and brightness of the seven wandering objects are explained by the varying distance of each of them from the earth. Objects appear smaller or less bright with distance. In the cases of the sun and moon, slightly varying sizes result from their eccentrics, or off-center positions. With the earth off the true centers of those two bodies, their distances to the earth must vary, and so must their apparent sizes. Minor epicycles are used, too. The explanation for the changing brightness of the other "wanderers," or planets, emphasizes a change of distance from the earth as each orbits in a large epicycle. The eccentric is an additional factor with all the planets.

2–6 A lunar eclipse occurs when the moon moves into the earth's shadow.

7. *Phases of the Moon*

The background frame of reference for the changing phases of the moon is that half of the moon ever visible from the earth. Ptolemy came remarkably close to present theories in explaining this phenomenon as follows:

a. The moon is a sphere and shines by reflected light from the sun. Therefore, the half facing the sun is always lighted, while the other half is always in darkness.

b. How much of the lighted half we see depends upon the relative positions of sun, moon, and earth.

c. Since both sun and moon revolve in a regular, describable pattern around the earth, the relative positions of the three bodies change in a constant, predictable manner. These phases, as we know, vary from new moon (no lighted portion facing the earth) to full moon (fully lighted on the earth's side).

d. A very dimly lighted section of the moon can also be seen during all phases except full moon. This is caused by earthshine reflected from the sun and back to the earth again.

e. The moon is new when it has dropped back in its sphere to occupy an identical position with the sun with respect to the earth. That is, there is a line of centers from earth to moon to sun, and the sun and moon rise and set together. As the moon drifts further eastward behind the sun, it waxes toward fullness. The moon becomes full when it is directly opposite the sun and starts to wane as further drift brings it again closer to the sun's position.

f. The complete cycle from new moon to new moon takes about 29.5 days. This is caused by the combined effect of the eastward drift of the moon with respect to the stars (13° per day) and the eastward drift of the sun (1° per day). The moon thus falls behind the sun at the rate of 12° per day and takes about 29.5 days to return to its original position with respect to the sun, as against 27.3 days with respect to the stars.

8. Eclipses of the Sun and Moon

The background frame of reference here is the half of the eclipsed object facing the earth.

a. Eclipses of both sun and moon occur only when the centers of the earth, sun, and moon are in approximate line—thus only during either a full-moon or a new-moon phase.

b. A lunar eclipse (Fig. 2–6) occurs when the earth is in line between the sun and the moon (full phase) and the earth's shadow covers the visible face of the moon.

c. A solar eclipse (Fig. 2–7) occurs when the moon is in line between the sun and the earth (new phase), blocking out the sun from the earth, and casting its shadow upon the earth.

d. You will recall that in Ptolemaic theory, the sun and moon move in deferents that cross the celestial equator. From one new or full phase to another, these two bodies are at different distances above or below the equators of their spheres. They are therefore at different

2–7   A solar eclipse occurs whenever the moon casts its shadow upon the earth.

distances above or below each other. The earth is also off the center of the moon's and sun's deferents. Thus, it is not to be expected that at every full moon the earth will cast its shadow upon the moon or that the moon will eclipse the sun at every new phase.

9. Seasonal North-South Cycle of the Sun

As the celestial sphere turns a full 360° per day, the sun in its ecliptic, or deferent circle, moves on the surface of its sphere eastward at the rate of about 1° per day. The ecliptic itself extends 23½° north and south of the celestial equator, respectively, to define the north-south limits of the sun's travel.

The equinoxes occur for spring and fall alike when the sun is in that point of the ecliptic circle which intersects with the equator of the sun's sphere. Whether it is the vernal or the autumnal equinox depends upon the direction of the sun's actual movement north or south of its celestial equator. It also depends upon the hemisphere of the earth from which the observation is made. This north-south movement of the sun, of course, causes a shifting in the direct rays of the sun upon the earth that results in the seasons.

10. Precession of the Equinoxes

Ptolemaic astronomy recognizes the very slight yearly shift westward of about 0.01° in the position of the crossing of the sun's celestial equator by the sun in its ecliptic. It was Hipparchus who first observed that the vernal equinox shifts slightly from year to year at such a slow rate as to describe a complete rotation, or cycle, around the equator of the celestial sphere every 36,000 years, as compared to our value today of 26,000 years. And it was also Hipparchus who recognized that during this cycle, each day in the year from January 1 through December 31 would serve in turn as the first day of spring and, similarly, for the corresponding first days of summer, autumn, and winter. The Ptolemaic explanation is simply that an unknown motion of the celestial sphere causes this precession.

EVALUATION OF PTOLEMAIC THEORY

The Ptolemaic model of the universe was a dominant, successful theory for 14 centuries. Why was it successful?

1. The Ptolemaic theory appealed so widely and for so long a time because it was based upon immediate sensory impressions or appearances. It contained so much "common sense." The earth certainly seemed to be fixed, and the heavenly bodies seemed to move around it.

2. The system exerted a strong psychological appeal to man's necessary egoism and unnecessary vanity by putting man and his earth at the center.

3. The system was aesthetically pleasing because of its coherence, unity, and symmetry.

4. A perfection-of-the-heavens doctrine exerted considerable philosophic-religious appeal, whether reflected in the Pythagorean Brotherhood, Plato, the Old Testament, or Milton's *Paradise Lost*.

5. The scientific appeal was also strong. The Ptolemaic theory seemed to satisfy criteria of a good theory even today. It provided a working model for the universe that offered a neat, unified explanation and a basis for prediction of movements, with built-in means of self-correction and modification. The theory had a definite sophistication in distinguishing between the observed motion and the (supposed) actual motion of celestial bodies. The difference is one between what is *seen* and what *is*, between *data* and *facts*—in today's terms, between arriving *signals* and actual *events*.

By systematizing what was observed through the use of well-ordered celestial circles, the theory successfully met all challenges, even to account for the unusual phenomenon of varying brightness of the planets. In using epicycles, eccentrics, and equants as special geometric devices for reconciling assumptions and observations, the Ptolemaic model was able to unify and to predict with considerable detail, precision, and self-correction. Thus, it satisfied prerequisites for any good scientific theory.

It is easy for us today in our 20th century sophistication to look back upon Ptolemy and his followers condescendingly. After all, we know the absolute truth! Or do we really? Does his well-ordered geocentric universe look ridiculous to us? Well, how will our theories appear to scientists in the year 2470? Even today, in accordance with Einstein's theory of relativity, whether the earth revolves around the sun or the sun around the earth depends upon where we are as observers.

We respect Ptolemy for his great contributions to science and astronomy in terms of his period in history. He lived 1,800 years ago, still over 1,400 years before the invention of even so early and relatively simple a scientific instrument as the Galilean telescope. Using his unaided sight only, Ptolemy was able meticulously to classify, to locate, and to describe accurately the apparent movement of some 1,080 or more celestial bodies. If he made interpretations that we do not accept today, we can understand why. From what point of reference was he able to observe the turning of the earth? How could he or any man, dependent upon senses alone, comprehend the turning earth? In the light of the limited knowledge of astronomy in Ptolemy's day, the apparent motions of the heavenly bodies were more explainable by a stationary earth. His geocentric model of the universe represents an earlier stage in the development of the same science that later efforts have brought to a more advanced stage. Men had to exhaust the strong commonsense possibilities of an earth-centered universe before seriously entertaining present ideas of an ever expanding universe with the earth a mere speck in all this vastness.

Besides, as expressed in Lardner's *Cabinet Encyclopedia* of 1831: "If the admission of this or any other [theoretical] structure tenfold more artificial and complicated will enable anyone to present in a general point of view a great number of particular facts—to make them a part of one system, and enable us to reason from the known to the unknown, and actually to *predict facts before trial*—we would ask, "Why should it *not* be granted?"

Ptolemy's system satisfied the above requirements set up by Lardner. Why didn't it suffice? Why not accept what we directly see, a universe moving around a stationary earth? Why look further? At any rate, Copernicus did look further about 1,400 years after Ptolemy. For what reasons does a man give up a system that works for the development and uncertainties of another system?

CHAPTER REVIEW

Answer the following questions concisely but with reasonable completeness. Diagrams often help. See chapter illustrations.

1. What "commonsense" observations of the earth, sun, moon, planets, and stars suggest that the earth is the stationary center of the universe?

2. What psychological and religious considerations favor an earth-centered universe?

3. Define a theory. Illustrate the use of the celestial sphere as a frame of reference and then as a theory. Explain the difference between the two uses.

4. Explain why Eudoxus and Aristotle added concentric spheres between the earth and the sphere of stars.

5. What are basic assumptions of the concentric-spheres model? What cultural aspects of the time are reflected in these assumptions? What problems did this model solve?

6. What did Plato mean by "Determine what uniform and ordered movements must be assumed for each planet to explain its apparently irregular yearly paths"? Is this advice of Plato to his students in keeping with science? Why or why not? What aspects of this statement, if any, are unscientific?

7. Explain with a diagram why Eudoxus's concentric-spheres model could not explain the varying brightness of Venus or Jupiter.

8. Describe with a drawing the Ptolemaic earth-centered model. How did this model solve the problem of the varying brightness of planets?

9. List four or five main assumptions of the Ptolemaic system, and indicate in each case how each assumption reflects mathematical, artistic, philosophic, religious, and scientific influences of the times. Which of these assumptions were retained from the Eudoxus model?

10. How did the Ptolemaic model explain the following observations: (a) succession of day and night, (b) general westward motion of objects in the sky, (c) eastward drift of the sun and moon, (d) retrograde motion of the planets, (e) changing diameters of the sun and moon, (f) constant nearness of Mercury and Venus to the sun, (g) phases of the moon, (h) solar and lunar eclipses, (i) seasons, and (j) precession of the equinoxes.

11. Explain the differences among epicycles, eccentrics, and equants. Show how these geometric devices gave Ptolemaic theory flexibility.

12. Define a hypothesis. Why call the Ptolemaic system a theory rather than a hypothesis?

13. Would you consider the Ptolemaic model to have been scientific in its time? Why or why not?

PROBLEMS

Here again, diagrams will help.

1. How could Ptolemaic theory explain the slight circular motion of the polestar around the north celestial pole?

2. How could Ptolemaic theory account for the fact that all planets are seen in the same belt in the sky?

3. Does the deferent of the sun in the Ptolemaic model represent the sun's apparent daily motion around the earth or its yearly cycle of eastward drift among the stars? Explain.

4. Explain what the deferent of a planet represents in the Ptolemaic scheme.

5. Show by a Ptolemaic diagram how epicycles explained the varying brightness of planets.

6. Use the Ptolemaic model to explain why the moon rises almost an hour later each day.

7. We say, "The moon rises." Is that apparent motion, actual motion, interpretation, or what? Explain.

8. Use the Ptolemaic explanation of retrograde motion to explain (a) the difference between apparent motion and actual motion and (b) the difference between observation and interpretation.

9. Why were major epicycles necessary for the planets and not for the sun and moon in the Ptolemaic model?

10. Use the sun's apparent motion in its ecliptic to show how the Ptolemaic theory's explanation of seasons differs from its explanation of eastward drift.

SUGGESTIONS FOR FURTHER READING

Kuhn, Thomas, *The Copernican Revolution*, Vintage paperback, New York, 1959, Ch. 2.

American Foundation for Continuing Education, *Exploring the Universe*, ed. Louise B. Young, McGraw-Hill, New York, 1963, Part 3.

Milton, John, *Paradise Lost*, Book 8.

Wightman, W. P. D., *The Growth of Scientific Ideas*, Yale Univ. Press, New Haven, Conn., 1951, Chs. 1–4.

Whitehead, Alfred, *Science and the Modern World*, Mentor paperback, New York, 1958, Chs. 1–2.

Holton, Gerald J., and D. H. D. Roller, *Foundations of Modern Physical Science*, Addison-Wesley, Reading, Mass., 1958, Ch. 6.

Omer, Guy C., Jr., et al., *Physical Science: Men and Concepts*, Heath, Boston, 1962, Chs. 4–6.

3   Theories
of the Heavens —
Sun-Centered

In the midst of all, the sun reposes, unmoving. Who, indeed, in this most beautiful temple would place the light-giver in any other part than that whence it can illumine all other parts?

COPERNICUS, 1543

FROM PTOLEMY
TO COPERNICUS

With the fall of the ancient Greco-Roman civilization, Western science was lost in the barbarism of the Dark Ages and the otherworldliness of Christianity. Astronomy did not advance for about 1,400 years after Ptolemy. In 389 A.D., Theophilus, Patriarch of Alexandria, had ordered the temple and library of Serapia burned to the ground as pagan, books and all. This library had been well known in the classical world. The even more famous library of Alexandria was completely destroyed by Moslems in 641 A.D., but not before it had been badly depleted by drives against paganism.

Fortunately, copies of Ptolemy's *Almagest*, together with works of Aristotle and Plutarch, had found their way into the hands of appreciative Arabian scholars, who translated them into their own language. In the 13th century, Thomas Aquinas (1225–1274) scholastically reconciled Christian theology with Greek science and philosophy. By this time, a

Nicolaus Copernicus, 1473–1543. (Brown Bros. photograph)

number of churchmen had been retranslating Aristotle, Ptolemy, and other Greek authorities from Arabic to Latin. Then, with the Renaissance, came a humanistic search for classics in the original Greek language.

This brings us to Nicolaus Copernicus (1473–1543), born in the Polish town of Thorn, near the Prussian border, 30 years after the invention of the printing press. While Columbus was busy with another earth-shaking discovery, that of America, Copernicus was a student at the Universities of Cracow and Bologna. The young Copernicus pursued studies of law, medicine, astronomy, mathematics, and Greek. In 1503, his uncle, the Bishop of Ermland, appointed his well-educated young nephew, who now had the degree of Doctor of Ecclesiastical Law, as a canon in the Cathedral of Frauenburg. As a church dignitary and assistant to his uncle in governing Ermland, Copernicus was able to devote considerable time to astronomical observation and theory.

Knowing Greek and Latin, Copernicus read ancient classics directly. In establishing a sun-centered system of the world, he used Ptolemy's recorded observations as well as observations of his own. Copernicus worked quietly and published his great work, *Revolutions of the Celestial Spheres,* at the very end of his life. The first copy of this book was brought to him from the printer the day he died.

Although we give credit to Nicolaus Copernicus for developing the concept of the sun-centered universe and a revolving, rotating earth, he was not the first to hold such theories. In Greece, 4 centuries before Christ, Heracleides of Pontus introduced the idea of a rotating earth, as we have already noted. However, he placed his earth at the center of the universe, with the planets Mercury and Venus revolving about the sun.

A century later, Aristarchus of Samos became an "ancient Copernicus" by positioning the sun at the center and sending his earth in an orbit about it, rotating as it revolved. But his ideas did not prevail against Aristotle, a contemporary of Heracleides, or against Ptolemy, 400 years later, for several probable reasons:

1. From what we understand of the Aristarchan theory—the records are meager—he handled his proposition qualitatively only. That is, unlike Copernicus much later, he did not base his theory on quantitative detail involving observations, tables, and predictions.

2. Aristarchus also was not fortunate enough to have a Galileo come shortly after his time with a telescope that improved observations of the heavens. Technology had not yet developed to the stage where a bold new theory could be supported (or rejected) by evidence from a telescope.

3. Hipparchus and Ptolemy, unlike Aristarchus, made elaborate use of mathematics and observation to establish their opposite system in a quantitative treatment. Their theory was grounded in tables, charts, and predictions. In this way, their theory was able to function in navigation. Aristarchus was forgotten.

Our ideas of the original Copernican theory are based upon three of Copernicus's astronomical publications: *The Commentariolus* (small comments), a *Letter against Werner*, and *De Revolutionibus Orbium Celestium* (concerning revolutions of the celestial spheres). The first two are lengthy letters sent by Copernicus to friends, who quietly copied and circulated them. These two are really preludes to his monumental *Revolutions*.

Copernicus had great respect for Ptolemy and his work. He used Ptolemy's observational data without ever questioning its accuracy. And he recognized the great value of the Ptolemaic tables, based upon his predecessor's data. Through the tables, men could still predict future positions of moon, planets, and stars; and navigators like Columbus could sail far and wide on a spherical earth. But Copernicus also knew that the Ptolemaic system would be inadequate for predicting celestial motions in his own day unless about 80 circles were used, mostly epicycles upon epicycles upon epicycles.... Copernicus was too convinced of a mathematical simplicity and harmony in the universe to be satisfied with so complicated a system, even if it was successful. He had read what there was about Aristarchus and other ancient writers; he believed that a sun-centered system would be more simple and appealing.

Copernicus also deeply respected the Ptolemaic assumption of perfection of the heavens, and so he believed that all moving astronomical objects definitely must orbit in perfect circles and at constant speeds. Concentric crystal spheres could well provide the celestial mechanism for this kind of movement. If the earth is moving, as proposed by Aristarchus, the earth is part of the universe and should be sphere-borne to conform to the master plan. It therefore was not the assumption of perfection that disturbed Copernicus. On the contrary, the dissatisfaction was that Ptolemy's equant violated it. Let Copernicus speak for himself in the *Commentariolus*:

> Yet the planetary theories of Ptolemy and most other astronomers, although consistent with the numerical data, seemed likewise to present no small difficulty. For these theories were not adequate unless certain equants were also conceived; it then appeared that a planet moved with uniform velocity neither in its deferent nor about the center of its epicycle. Hence, a system of this sort seemed neither sufficiently absolute nor sufficiently pleasing to the mind.

Copernicus could not with Ptolemy "allow that a circular motion may take place uniformly about a foreign center and not about its own center." The equant described in Chapter 2 was not only cumbersome; for Copernicus, it placed too much strain upon the basic Aristotelian assumption of perfect order in the heavens. The calendar was also a cause for restlessness. In the 1,400 years since Ptolemy, discrepancies in the calculation of the calendar had been accumulating, and there was no adequate explanation for them. Spotlighting Ptolemaic errors, the fact that the calendar had lagged behind by as much as 11 days was discovered during the 16th century. Just building more epicycles upon epicycles did not meet the problem. Copernicus had his feet in the past and his eyes in the future.

CHARACTERISTICS OF THE ORIGINAL COPERNICAN MODEL

Copernicus thus was distressed with the Ptolemaic system as too complex, with its 79 or 80 circles, and too inconsistent, with its use of the equant. In the name of simplicity and consistency, he proposed that the earth and the sun be switched with respect to both position and motion. Copernicus did not give us our present simple solar system of ellipses. As we shall see below, his proposal at first glance is more like a concentric-spheres model of Eudoxus and Aristotle in which the sphere bearing the sun—yes, literally, sphere!—is interchanged with a sphere bearing the earth.

But perhaps it would be best if, at this point, we let Copernicus describe his own system. The following famous excerpt is from the *Revolutions*:

> The first and highest of all the spheres is the sphere of the fixed stars. It encloses all the other spheres and is itself self-contained; it is immobile; it is certainly the portion of the universe with reference to which the movement and positions of all the other heavenly bodies must be considered. If some people are yet of the opinion that this sphere moves, we are of a contrary mind; and after deducing the motion of the earth, we shall show why we so conclude. Saturn, first of the planets, which accomplished its revolution in thirty years, is nearest to the first sphere. Jupiter, making its revolution in twelve years, is next. Then comes Mars, revolving once in two years. The fourth place in the series is occupied by the sphere which contains the earth and the sphere of the moon, and which performs an annual revolution. The fifth is that of Venus, revolving in seven months. Finally, the sixth place is occupied by Mercury, revolving in eighty days.

> In the midst of all, the sun reposes, unmoving. Who, indeed, in this most beautiful temple would place the light-giver in any other part than that whence it can illumine all other parts?

And now with respect to his "deducing the motion of the earth" as he reports in *Commentariolus*:

> Having become aware of these defects, I often considered whether there could perhaps be found a more reasonable arrangement of circles, from which every apparent inequality would be derived and in which

everything would move uniformly about its proper center, as the rule of absolute motion requires. After I had addressed myself to this very difficult and almost insoluble problem, the suggestion at length came to me how it could be solved with *fewer and much simpler constructions* than were formerly used if some assumptions (which are called axioms) were granted me. They follow in this order.

1. There is no one center of all the celestial circles of spheres. [That is, the centers of the various spheres could be in various eccentric positions around the center of the universe.]

2. The center of the earth is not the center of the universe, but only of gravity and of the lunar sphere.

3. All the spheres revolve about the sun as their midpoint, and therefore the sun is the center of the universe.

4. ...the distance from the earth to the sun is imperceptible in comparison with the height of the firmament. [That is, imperceptible in comparison with the distance from the earth or the sun to the stars.]

5. Whatever motion appears in the firmament arises not from any motion of the firmament, but from the earth's motion. The earth ...performs a complete rotation on its fixed poles in a daily motion, while the firmament and highest heaven abide unchanged.

6. What appears to us as motions of the sun arise not from its motion but from the motion of the earth and our sphere, with which we revolve about the sun like any other planet. The earth has, then, more than one motion.

7. The apparent retrograde [motion] and direct motion of the planets arise not from their motion but from the earth's. The motion of the earth alone therefore suffices to explain so many apparent inequalities in the heavens.

And then in his preface to the *Revolutions*:

...I found after much and long observation that if the motions of the other planets were added to the motions of the earth [its daily rotation on an axis and yearly revolution around the sun] ...not only did the apparent behavior of the others follow this, but the [new] system so connects the orders and sizes of the planets and their orbits, and of the whole heaven, that no single feature can be altered without confusion among the other parts and in all the universe. For this reason, therefore ...have I followed this system.

The seven assumptions listed above differentiate Copernicus's sun-centered system from Ptolemy's earth-centered system. Two further very important assumptions of Copernicus, however, must be mentioned; they are the same as for Aristotelian-Ptolemaic theory. These are the assumptions that all actual motions in the heavens must involve (1) perfect circles and (2) constant speeds.

With the first seven assumptions, Copernicus paves the way for a scientific revolution; with the last two assumptions, he remains tied to the past. He was a medieval man in transition to modern times.

In summary, remove the equants from the Ptolemaic system, and the Copernican system becomes much like the Ptolemaic with the positions of the sun and earth exchanged. The moon, of course, accompanies the earth as a true satellite. Celestial spheres remain, epicycles remain, and so do eccentrics. Deferents are still there but have become "yearly orbits" around the sun. True, the earth has been removed from the center of the universe, but not far from it; for the distance from the earth to the sun is almost negligible compared to the distance between the earth and the sphere of stars. Besides, the sun, to Copernicus, belongs at the center. As the source of all light, the sun should be placed there for greater simplicity and harmony in the heavens. Moreover, with the sun in the center of the universe and the earth circling around it, the despised equant could be eliminated.

COPERNICAN EXPLANATION AND PREDICTION OF CELESTIAL MOTIONS

A crucial test of any theory is its ability to explain and predict specific events. Let us now see how the original Copernican theory could account for the ten basic observations of the heavens described in Chapters 1 and 2.

1. Daily East-to-West Motion of Celestial Objects

"It is Earth from which the rotation of the Heavens is seen," said Copernicus. But the earth is the observer's frame of reference. This frame of reference actually is rotating on its axis every 23 hours and 56 minutes counterclockwise, from west to east, and of course, all observers travel with it. But by relative motion, the sun, moon, stars, and planets appear to move in an opposite direction around the earth from east to west and around the North Star counterclockwise. The North Star becomes the stars' point of reference because this star is almost in line with the axis of the earth and the zenith of the earth's North Pole. By illustration, a child rotating counterclockwise under the dome of a huge, stationary umbrella will see dots on the umbrella seemingly move clockwise with respect to himself but counterclockwise around the central, uppermost

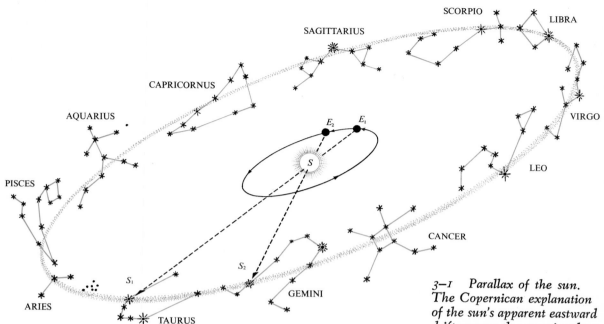

SCORPIO

LIBRA

SAGITTARIUS

VIRGO

CAPRICORNUS

AQUARIUS

E_2 E_1

S

LEO

PISCES

CANCER

S_2

ARIES

S_1

GEMINI

TAURUS

3–1 *Parallax of the sun.*
The Copernican explanation
of the sun's apparent eastward
drift among the stars involves
solar parallax. As the earth
moves from E_1 to E_2, the sun
appears to move eastward
from star S_1 to S_2 in the
background.

point of the umbrella. Thus, "the diurnal rotation is only apparent in the Heavens, but real [actual] on earth." And relative motion makes it difficult for an observer to distinguish between apparent motion and real motion.

It is obvious that both Ptolemy and Copernicus had adequate mechanisms of explanation and prediction for daily rotation of the heavens. Ptolemy had all objects carried in circles around the earth; Copernicus had the earth rotating instead. The only advantage that Copernicus could claim here is one of simplicity: Just rotating the earth dispenses with the need for the sun, moon, planets, and stars to make complete daily circles in the heavens. If Ptolemaic people would be concerned with a rotating earth flying apart because of speed, "what about the celestial sphere of stars?" asked Copernicus. Under the Ptolemaic theory, the celestial sphere would be required to revolve through much greater distances at fantastic speeds to get around in 24 hours. As for the anticipated Ptolemaic argument that with a rotating earth, relative winds would blow everything off the face of the earth, Copernicus's answer was that there is no problem: There is no relative wind because the atmosphere turns with the earth. Why the atmosphere should turn with the earth Copernicus would not have been able to answer. Galileo and Newton had not yet arrived with a new concept of gravity and a new science of mechanics. The Ptolemaic people, however, did have Aristotle's mechanics to support an earth-centered universe, as we shall see later.

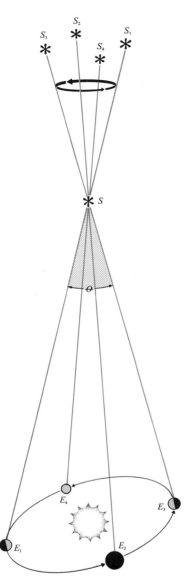

2. Yearly Eastward Drift of the Sun

The eastward drift of the sun in its ecliptic was easily predicted and explained by Copernicus. The earth is not only rotating on its axis but also revolving around the sun at the rate of about 1° a day, or 360° a year (Fig. 3–1). Both the sun and the stellar sphere are stationary. This revolution of the earth results in the sun's being seen against a slightly changed background of stars after each rotation. Since the earth's revolution is counterclockwise, or in the same direction as its rotation, it has to continue rotating 1° or 4 minutes of time more than a complete circle for the next sunrise. This extra amount of turn accounts for eastward drift. When the earth is at point E_1, there is a line of sight to the sun E_1S. Note the extension of this line back to any star S_1 in the stellar sphere. The sun then rises with the star S_1 in the zodiacal constellation, let us say, of Taurus the Bull. A day or preferably a month later, when the earth is at E_2, there would be a line of sight E_2SS_2 from the earth to the sun to the star S_2. The sun would then be rising with the star S_2 in the zodiacal constellation Gemini the Twins, adjacent to Taurus the Bull. Star S_1 is now about 30° above the horizon when the sun rises instead of at the horizon. Since the earth revolves only about 1° a day, the above illustration is based on a period of 1 month for clarity.

The *parallax* of an object is an angle made at the object by two lines of sight. The angle E_1SE_2 (Fig. 3–1) is a parallax of the sun. According to Copernicus, therefore, observed arcs of eastward drift of the sun in the zodiacal belt are really parallax angles of the sun due to revolution of the earth. As the earth moves from E_1 to E_2, the sun appears to move from star S_1 to S_2 in the background.

Stellar parallax, similarly, is an angle made at a star by two lines of sight. Let us again consider Copernicus's assumption or hypothesis that the earth is revolving. In Fig. 3–2, when the earth is at position E_1, there should be a line of sight E_1S to star S. When the earth is at position E_3 six months later, there should be a line of sight E_3S to star S. The angle E_1SE_3 is a parallax angle.

Consider star S to be a closer star against a background of farther stars S_1, S_2, S_3, S_4, and others in its sphere. During a complete revolution of the earth around the sun, the closer star S should appear to describe a small circle among the more distant stars. This is shown in Fig. 3–2 through the extension of the line of sight E_1S to S_1, E_2S to S_2, E_3S to S_3, and E_4S to S_4. The circular arrow through S_1, S_2, S_3, and S_4 indicates apparent positions of star S against the background of farther stars if the earth is revolving.

Astronomers from Aristarchus to Copernicus, Galileo, and others much later looked for stellar parallax. It was not to be found. To Ptolemaic astronomers, this was evidence that the earth does not revolve. To them, the hypothesis of a sun-centered universe failed to pass the test of stellar

3–2 Stellar parallax. As the earth revolves from E_1 to E_3, star S appears to move against the background of farther stars from S_1 to S_3. The parallax angle θ is tinted.

parallax. The answer of Copernicus, as well as of Aristarchus long before him, was that the stars are too far away for detection of annual parallax. The naked eye cannot detect it if it is there.

It wasn't until 1838, of course, that stellar parallax was finally discovered officially by the astronomer Bessel. The telescope had become a powerful enough instrument for Bessel to determine slight apparent shifts of the star 61 Cygni. Earlier astronomers had been handicapped by astrolabes or by telescopes of less resolving power and had been unsuccessful in discovering parallax. The importance of the development of tools and apparatus in the history of ideas in science cannot be overemphasized.

Back in the 16th century, however, before the discovery of parallax, Copernican and Ptolemaic theory could about equally well explain and predict the eastward drift of the sun. Certainly in this regard, the Copernican approach had no decisive advantage. And even if parallax had been observed at that time, Ptolemaic astronomers could have attributed it to epicyclic motions of the particular stars in the stellar sphere. And with respect to simplicity, Copernicus's earth, carried by a sphere yearly around the sun as it also rotates is hardly simpler than Ptolemy's sun, slowly moving within its sphere as its sphere carries it daily around the earth.

3—3 Copernican explanation of the moon's apparent eastward drift among the stars. Suppose the moon is seen rising with a given star on May 10 from point O. In one day the earth makes a complete rotation on its axis while the moon revolves only 13°. Thus, when next seen rising (May 11), the moon appears to have drifted 13° to the east with respect to the stars.

3. Monthly Eastward Drift of the Moon

The Copernican theory explains the eastward drift of the moon mainly through three motions occurring at the same time: (a) the earth's counterclockwise rotation on its axis, (b) the earth's counterclockwise revolution about the sun, and (c) the moon's counterclockwise revolution around the earth.

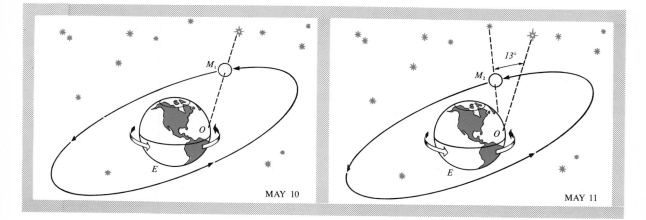

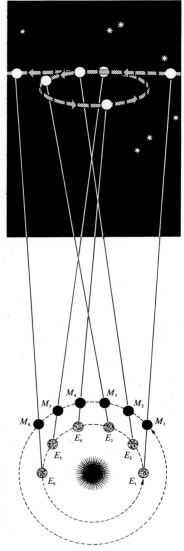

In Fig. 3–3, let us start on a given evening, say May 10, with the earth at E_1 and the moon at M_1. If the observer is at O, he will see the moon rising. As the earth rotates once daily through 360° with respect to the stars, the moon meanwhile moves about 13° around the earth from point M_1 to M_2. That is, when the earth has completed its rotation on May 11, the moon has meanwhile moved on. The earth must rotate about another 13° or 54.5 minutes for the same observer to sight again the moon rising—but it is now against a different background of stars. The moon seems to have fallen behind or drifted to the east considerably. Meanwhile, of course, the earth has revolved through only 1° around the sun.

This should be enough to show that Copernicus could predict an eastward drift of the moon against the stars as effectively as Ptolemy and could explain why the drift of the moon is greater than that of the sun. Ptolemy's explanation seems simpler, however, because only two motions are involved: a daily cycle of the moon around a fixed earth and a monthly cycle of the moon in a deferent. It is as if the moon moves 13° within its sphere as the sphere itself turns 360° a day. Copernicus, like Ptolemy, found it necessary to use a minor epicycle for the moon to reconcile differences between predicted and observed positions of the moon.

4. Retrograde Motion of the Planets

As with the moon, there are three simultaneous motions involved in understanding the movement of the planets: the earth's own rotation, its revolution about the sun, and the revolution of the planets. The basic explanation in Copernican theory for their apparent eastward drift against the background of the zodiacal belt is the same as for the sun and moon.

The earth and any observed planet are both revolving as the earth rotates. Therefore, when the earth completes a daily rotation, the planet is seen against a changed star background. Thus, for example, Mars will "rise" with a different star from one evening to the next, generally later according to its rate of revolution. Perhaps it would be preferable to say that Mars will appear above the horizon with a different star, rather than "rise," to emphasize the fact of the moving horizon.

In regard to retrograde motion, as with other observations, the earth is the frame of reference of the observer, and the zodiacal belt is the background frame of reference of the planet. There is a changing line of sight against the background of stars between any planet and the earth as both revolve around the sun. Where an earthly observer sees a planet in the zodiacal belt depends upon this line of sight. For illustration, note Fig. 3–4, which shows the retrograde motion of Mars. This

3–4 Retrograde motion of Mars. The Copernican explanation is that the earth revolves more rapidly than Mars. Each time the earth "catches up" to Mars (just after the E_3M_3 line of sight), Mars appears to reverse its eastward drift in the zodiacal belt of stars.

planet is beyond the earth and therefore moves more slowly around the sun than the earth does. Mars takes almost 2 years instead of 1 for a revolution. Notice that as the earth moves from E_1 to E_2 in the diagram, Mars circles from M_1 to M_2. The line of sight between them extended to the fixed background of stars shows Mars to be in an eastward drift with respect to the stars. Next, as the earth approaches E_3 in opposition to Mars, which is at M_3, the line of sight gives Mars the appearance of reversing direction toward the west with respect to the background of stars. In swinging from M_1 to M_3, Mars, of course, has not actually changed its uniform circular motion. By the time the earth and Mars have reached M_5 and E_5, respectively, the apparent path of Mars reverts to the original eastward drift.

In the Ptolemaic theory, with the planets revolving about a stationary earth, epicycles were necessary to explain an apparent reversed motion. Then other epicycles upon epicycles had to be added upon the original ones to account for other irregularities. At first glance, the Copernican answer is much simpler: Epicycles are not necessary for the original explanation of the observed reversed motions of planets. A changing line of sight with a revolving earth gives the basic answer. But most of the simplicity was lost when Copernicus eventually found that he had to use many epicycles as well as eccentrics for adjustments between observed positions of planets and predicted positions. These adjustments could not be avoided as long as he used perfect circles and constant speeds for the orbits of all the planets, of which the earth was now one. But to use anything but circles and constant speeds would have been a sacrilege in terms of the doctrine of perfection of the heavens; Copernicus did not consider using anything else.

5. Proximity of Mercury and Venus to the Sun

The Copernican explanation for Mercury's and Venus's always being seen near the sun is simple: The sun is stationary at the center of the world system. Mercury and Venus are the closest planets to the sun, revolving around it as a body of reference rather than around the earth. Mercury and Venus will therefore always be seen near the sun by an observer on the earth or on an outer planet.

Ptolemaic theory as described in Chapter 2 provides for the proximity of Mercury and Venus by placing these planets in epicycles, the centers of which form a line of centers with the moving sun, or by having the planets revolve around the sun as the sun revolves around the fixed earth. It is clear, however, that the Copernican model is simpler in this case, even if the Ptolemaic could predict as well.

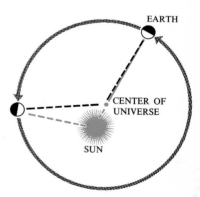

3–5 Like Ptolemy, Copernicus used an eccentric to explain apparent variation in the sun's diameter.

3–6 *Phases of the moon depend upon the relative positions of the sun, earth, and moon.*

6. Varying Size and Brightness of Celestial Objects

The observed diameter and brightness of an object varies according to its distance from the earth. The Copernican explanation for these variations with respect to the planets is that all the planets revolve at different speeds around the sun; their distances from one another and from the earth, therefore, must change. Consequently, the observed brightness of the planets must also vary. The explanation with respect to the sun is that the earth is carried in a perfect circle around the center of the universe. The sun is just off that center (Fig. 3–5). Consequently, an eccentric is involved in which the earth is always at the same distance from the center of the universe but at changed distances from the sun, off-center. The sun therefore varies slightly in diameter as well as in brightness. Slight changes in the diameter of the moon are explainable through the use of an eccentric. The earth is slightly off the geometric center of the moon's orbit. Eccentrics and minor epicycles, already in the Copernican model to explain observations of eastward drift or retrograde motion, are also factors in an explanation of changing distance, diameter, or brightness observed in celestial bodies.

7. Phases of the Moon

The phases of the moon have been described in detail in Chapters 1 and 2. The changing phases of the moon follow the same pattern, whether it be the earth or the sun that is stationary. The phase of the moon depends upon the relative positions of the three bodies, and the explanation is of the same general character in both the Copernican and the Ptolemaic theory. Refer to the detailed Ptolemaic explanation given in Chapter 2 and to Fig. 3–6.

8. Eclipses of the Sun and Moon

Lunar eclipses occur when the moon moves into the earth's shadow, and solar eclipses occur when the earth is in the moon's shadow. In both kinds of eclipses, the sun, earth, and moon form an approximate line of centers. It is therefore immaterial whether this occurs through an earth and moon satellite revolving around a fixed sun or the sun and moon revolving around a fixed earth. The Copernican explanation and prediction of eclipses is basically the same as that of the Ptolemaic model, described in Chapter 2.

9. Seasonal North-South Cycle of the Sun

The observed yearly eastward drift of the sun is not around the celestial equator. As was discussed in Chapters 1 and 2, the ecliptic representing the observed path of the sun in its drift cuts across the celestial equator at two points, called the vernal and autumnal equinoxes. The line of eastward drift extends first to 23½° north and then 23½° south of the celestial equator. With the shifting of the sun's observed position north and south of the celestial equator goes the shifting of the sun's direct rays upon the earth associated with seasons.

In his explanation of seasons, of course, Copernicus believed that the change of the sun's position north and south of the equator in a yearly cycle is only apparent, not actual. The sun is not really moving; the earth is. The axis of the earth is tilted at an angle of 23½° from the perpendicular to the plane of its orbit around the sun and in a fairly fixed direction toward the stars, the North Star specifically (Fig. 3–7).

3–7 Seasons. The earth's axis is inclined at 23½° toward the sun in summer and 23½° away in winter. With the sun's direct rays alternately shifting north and south of the equator, an Arctic Circle observer has 24 hours of daylight on June 22 and 24 hours of darkness on December 22. On the vernal and autumnal equinoxes, there is an equal number of hours of day and night everywhere on the earth.

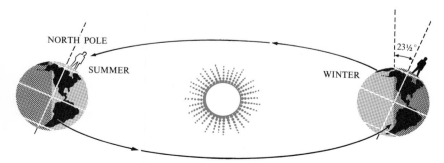

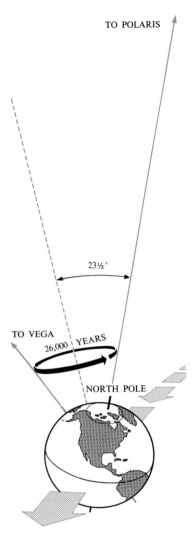

TO POLARIS

23½°

TO VEGA

26,000 YEARS

NORTH POLE

3–8 "Wobble" of the earth. In addition to rotating daily on its axis and revolving yearly around the sun, the earth completes a wobble every 26,000 years. Much like the axis of a top, the earth's axis traces a circle in the heavens between the present polestar and Vega.

As the earth revolves yearly around the sun, the north pole of the earth's axis is inclined toward the sun in summer and away in winter. This results in the direct rays of the sun shifting alternately north and south of the equator. Thus, in Copernican theory seasons result from relative motion between the earth and the sun rather than from absolute motion of the sun. The earth is moving, and the sun appears to move in relative motion. This explanation made acceptance of Copernican theory difficult at a time when even more than today, thinking was in absolute rather than in relative terms.

10. *Precession of the Equinoxes*

Copernicus was well aware that the first days of spring and fall shift completely around the calendar in a cycle of about 26,000 years. (Copernicus actually used the value of 36,000 years estimated by Hipparchus and Ptolemy.) This cycle corresponds to the sun's crossing the celestial equator in the spring and fall less than 1′ of arc farther to the west each year. Copernicus explained this precession of the equinoxes also through a third motion of the earth, his "motion in declination." This motion is roughly analogous to the wobble of a top (Fig. 3–8). A top can rotate around its own axis. At the same time, it can also revolve around a point outside itself. Third, a top can wobble as it rotates and revolves. When the top does so, it is no longer perpendicular to the ground. The axis of the top forms a cone as the upper end of the axis points out a circle on the ceiling, as in Fig. 3–8. Copernicus believed that such a third motion, or "wobble," of the earth explains the slight westward shift of the equinoxes.

Copernicus theorized that the earth's wobble is almost imperceptible because of a period of wobble very slightly less than the period of revolution, 1 year. Today, the precession of the equinoxes is attributed to a wobble of the earth that is almost imperceptible because it involves one cycle for the entire 26,000 years. This means that the North Pole, or axis of the earth, traces one circle in the heavens during the 26,000 years. The stars are so distant that the effect of the earth's revolution on that circle is negligible. In the circle, the axis now happens to be pointing quite closely to our present North Star. In years to come, the axis will point circularly farther and farther away from Polaris until in 13,000 years, it will be directed at Vega before swinging back to its present position.

In this tenth and last observation, the Copernican assumption of a moving earth is able to account for the precession of the equinoxes at least as well as the Ptolemaic assumption of a fixed earth and a rotating stellar sphere. In Ptolemaic theory, the entire sphere of stars partakes in the unknown "wobbly" motion instead of the earth alone.

SCIENTIFIC THEORY AND THE PTOLEMAIC-COPERNICAN ISSUE

So far, we have listed ten basic motions observed in the heavens and described in detail just how these observations of the heavens were explained by two contending theories, the Ptolemaic and the Copernican. If we could project ourselves back to the 16th century without knowledge of what has happened since, and if we were scientifically seeking a model of the universe, which model would we select and why? Such historical projection and analysis can give us an idea of what science is about.

Ideas as well as living things struggle for survival. This fact applies to major ideas within science, as to anything else. Seven criteria have evolved for evaluating a theoretical system in physical science. These criteria are explanation, prediction, flexibility, functionality, simplicity, plausability, and falsifiability. Let us briefly* discuss these criteria and apply them to the Ptolemaic-Copernican issue.

1. *Explanation.* An effective theoretical model systematizes and explains. In other words, it unifies the data gathered by observation into a single system and gives the data coherence and consistency. It structures observation and explains it.

2. *Prediction.* Primarily, this criterion involves future data rather than past or present. A good model anticipates future events accurately and reliably. It is thus able not only to predict but also to be tested by its own predictions.

3. *Flexibility.* A theoretical system must have flexibility. It must have the means within itself for being reconciled with or adjusted to data; it must be modifiable. For example, in the case of the Ptolemaic and original Copernican theories, the geometric devices of eccentrics and epicycles provided such flexibility. Flexibility means being open-ended as well as modifiable. A theoretical system must be open; it must have plumules of growth from the known to the unknown. In modern terms, it must have lines to new research and to its own further development.

4. *Functionality.* Functionality is a vital criterion. A theory thrives on practical application. It becomes entrenched through technologies that it helps establish. Theoretical science and technology reciprocally nourish each other in modern research and development.

5. *Simplicity.* Science strongly emphasizes simplicity. This has been dignified into the principle of parsimony, which in effect states: Other things being the same, the simplest idea is the best. The simplest theory generally is the one that rests on the fewest basic assumptions.

---

*For further description of such criteria, see Gerald J. Holton and D. H. D. Roller, *Foundations of Modern Physical Science*, Addison-Wesley, Reading, Mass., 1958, Ch. 8; and Karl Popper, *Conjectures and Refutations*, Basic Books, New York, 1962.

6. *Plausibility*. Plausibility as a criterion refers to the extent to which a system of ideas fits in with other current systems of thought and experience.

7. *Falsifiability*. Karl Popper in recent years has emphasized a criterion of "falsifiability." With flexibility, a good theory is modifiable, but it should not be endlessly so. There should be a clear basis in experience for rejecting as well as accepting a theory.

The Ptolemaic and Copernican theories during the 16th and early 17th centuries were contending theories that were able to account for observations with equal unity, coherence, and logic if one granted their assumptions. They were also able to predict with about equal accuracy. If you are still in doubt, compare again the Ptolemaic and Copernican explanation of the ten basic observations described earlier in Chapters 1, 2, and 3. Henri Poincaré (1854–1912) generalized that "If a phenomenon is susceptible of one mechanical explanation, it is susceptible of an infinity of others which would account equally well for all features revealed by experience." The word "infinity" is quite strong, but we can agree that for a given period of time, more than one good explanation is possible for the same set of phenomena. If, with Galileo and Newton, we become Copernican, that is a matter of developments in the 17th century. Hindsight is always easier than advance knowledge. Besides, the theory of relativity today holds that a modified Ptolemaic theory is as correct for an earthly observer as Copernican theory is for an astronomer elsewhere in the solar system.

With respect to criterion 3, both systems, as already noted, had great flexibility through their use of eccentrics, epicycles, epicycles upon epicycles, and so forth. Both systems could be adjusted to fit past observations and to predict future ones by using these devices and varying their radii, the value of the constant speeds used, and so on. The flexibility that Copernicus lost by abandoning equants he regained by adopting a moving earth.

The Ptolemaic theory in the Western World was able to stimulate Arabian astronomers, medieval scholastics, and Copernicus to further observation, thought, and application. The Copernican theory led to one of the great intellectual and scientific revolutions of all time and stimulated such great trailblazers as Digges, Bruno, Kepler, Galileo, and Newton. Both theories, therefore, had dynamic, flexible power to lead to further developments.

With respect to functionality, Copernican theory became comparable to Ptolemaic. Shortly after the death of Copernicus, the mathematician Erasmus Reinhold used the added observations and improved numerical values of Copernicus's *Revolutions* to compute new astronomical tables called Prulenic tables. The book and the tables were used in the Gregorian revision of the calendar, but they have not even today totally displaced Ptolemaic tables for navigation.

This reduces the Ptolemaic-Copernican issue pretty much to a matter of plausibility, simplicity, and falsifiability. Plausibility was to the advantage of the Ptolemaic system. Appearances, common sense, Aristotle, philosophy, and religion were against Copernicus. The preface to *Revolutionibus,* written by Copernicus's friend Osiender, introduces the basic idea of the system, a moving earth, as a mathematical simplicity and convenience. Copernicus was most likely unaware of the approach used in the preface; it was written for plausibility and acceptance. Mathematical scheme or not, fear soon arose that this scheme would be interpreted literally, as Digges, Bruno, Kepler, and Galileo did in fairly short order, and that this interpretation would undermine the Bible, the Church, and established thought. Socio-religious repercussions resulted. The Inquisition, the new Protestant Church, and some Jewish communities lined up against it, as well as most astronomers: An earth-centered universe had Aristotle's physics to support it; Copernicus himself had no substitute system of mechanics to explain why the atmosphere moves with the earth, or why the earth does not fly apart, and so on.

Plausibility thus was against Copernicus. A sun-centered universe did not fit in with established ideas of the time. That did not make Copernicus subversive or "wrong." Nor, on the other hand, does it mean that all new, bold ideas have what it takes to survive. Plausibility is a difficult criterion. Who can judge what will be plausible tomorrow?

Since plausibility can change with time and with the development of knowledge and experience, we are left with just the criteria of simplicity and falsifiability. Is Copernicus's theory simpler? We have seen that in principle Copernican theory is simpler: A single earth rotating daily is simpler than having the sun, the planets, and all the stars making daily circles around the earth. A revolving earth eliminates major epicycles from the retrograde motion of the planets. Elimination of equants is also of value for simplicity.

Although seemingly much simpler in principle, the original Copernican system is actually not so simple when worked out in detail. In spite of introducing a moving earth into his scheme, Copernicus had to add ever more and more to the 34 minor epicycles and other circles he used in his early estimates for his system. Otherwise, planets would not show up at the predicted time or place. Copernicus therefore never realized his original hope of the advantage of simplicity in his system. But what if the universe is not a simple one? Then the best theories would not necessarily be the simplest. In either case, the Ptolemaic and Copernican theories would still be about equal contenders.

Neither the Ptolemaic nor the original Copernican theory, however, could measure up to the standard of falsifiability. Each theory could endlessly modify itself with epicycles and eccentrics to correspond to data. True that each system became cumbersome with these geometric devices, but that is the point. No observational test could reject the system; the devices ingeniously prevented that.

Copernicus's *Revolutions* nonetheless quite boldly robbed the earth of its unique status as the center of the universe. This had tremendous psychological, religious, philosophical, and astronomical significance. At least enough to challenge the even bolder spirits of Digges and Bruno and the scientific genius of Kepler, Galileo, and Newton. And enough to spearhead a scientific revolution.

At this point we cannot remain content with a deadlocked Ptolemaic-Copernican issue. Nor is Copernicus's boldness with respect to a moving earth alone sufficient. Copernicus left too many questions unanswered. There were such scientific questions as stellar parallax, an atmosphere moving with the earth, and the earth remaining intact at great speeds. There were also such questions as these: How can a doctrine of perfection of the heavens be reconciled with an imperfect, heavy earth moving around the sun together with perfect, weightless planets? And from where do the necessary forces arise to push the planets around if these bodies are in the same category as the earth?

CHAPTER REVIEW

1. What "commonsense" observations, if any, suggest a moving rather than a stationary earth?

2. Why did Copernicus reject the Ptolemaic model?

3. Describe with a diagram Copernicus's sun-centered model of the universe.

4. Upon what assumptions was the Copernican model based? What assumptions and other features did Copernicus retain from the Ptolemaic world system? Indicate how these assumptions reflect Copernicus's times culturally and scientifically.

5. Explain the following observations through Copernicus's model with the aid of diagrams: (a) succession of day and night, (b) general westward motion of objects in the sky, (c) eastward drift of the sun and moon, (d) retrograde motion of planets, (e) changing diameters of the sun and moon and varying brightness of the planets, (f) constant nearness of Mercury and Venus to the sun, (g) phases of the moon, (h) solar and lunar eclipses, (i) seasons, and (j) precession of the equinoxes.

6. Compare each Copernican explanation in question 5 to the opposing Ptolemaic explanation. What advantages and disadvantages does each model have?

7. How is it possible that two opposing theories, as the Copernican and Ptolemaic, in general explain and predict about equally well the same observations? What are the arguments for and against each theory?

8. List seven criteria for a good theory. Compare the Ptolemaic and

Copernican theories during the 16th century with respect to each of these criteria. If you could project yourself back into the knowledge of those days, which theory would you believe? Why?

9. Aristarchus proposed a sun-centered theory about 18 centuries before Copernicus. Why is sun-centered theory identified as Copernican?

10. How does Copernicus's original model, including circular orbits, epicycles, eccentrics, assumptions, and all, illustrate that science is a human enterprise?

11. What specific prerequisites would you establish in judging whether or not any given human activity may be considered to be science? By these criteria, would you consider psychology, history, or political science to be science?

PROBLEMS

Answer the following questions in accordance with Copernican theory unless otherwise indicated:

1. Why doesn't the sun rise at the same time every morning?

2. Why doesn't the moon rise at the same hour every evening?

3. How would you prove that the moon is not another planet revolving around the sun?

4. If the earth revolved around the sun but did not rotate, how often would the sun rise? How often would the moon rise?

5. If the earth rotated but did not revolve, what would be the effect on seasons? On the eastward drift of the sun? On the heliacal rising of stars? On the basis for 1 year of time? On the 29.5-day period of phases of the moon?

6. With diagrams show why a solar eclipse occurs only during a new moon.

7. Why doesn't a lunar eclipse occur at every full moon?

8. Draw the relative positions of Venus, Jupiter, Saturn, and the sun if the three planets appear on the western horizon shortly after sunset.

9. Suppose Venus, Jupiter, and Saturn all appear just above the western horizon shortly after sunset. Show the relative positions of the three planets and the sun in (a) the celestial sphere (Chapter 1), (b) the Ptolemaic model, and (c) the Copernican model.

10. Draw a sketch to explain parallax of the stars. Why was the inability to find stellar parallax evidence against the Copernican system?

11. Retrograde motion has never been observed for the sun or the moon. (a) How would this be explained by the Ptolemaic theory? (b) How would this be explained by the Copernican theory?

SUGGESTIONS FOR
FURTHER READING

Armitage, Angus, *The World of Copernicus,* Mentor paperback, New York, 1951.

Asimov, Isaac, *The Kingdom of the Sun,* Collier paperback, New York, 1962.

Butterfield, Herbert, *Origins of Modern Science*, Collier paperback, New York, 1962, Ch. 2.

Holton, Gerald J., and D. H. D. Roller, *Foundations of Modern Physical Science*, Addison-Wesley, Reading, Mass., 1958, Chs. 7–8.

Kuhn, Thomas, *The Copernican Revolution,* Vintage paperback, New York, 1959, Ch. 5.

Milton, John, *Paradise Lost,* Book 8.

American Foundation for Continuing Education, *Exploring the Universe,* ed. Louise B. Young, McGraw-Hill, New York, 1963, pp. 99–111.

4   Brahe's Data
and Kepler's Laws

I approve of reasoning if it takes observed fact as its point of depart-
ture, and methodically draws its conclusions from the phenomena.

HIPPOCRATES, 5th century B.C.

BRAHE'S DATA

Let more precision decide! In effect, that characterizes the attitude of
the great Danish astronomer Tycho Brahe (1546–1601) toward the
problem of celestial motions.

At the age of 14, Brahe was greatly impressed by the eclipse of August
21, 1560. It was not the eclipse alone that fascinated him, but the fact
that it had been previously predicted. In succeeding years, a wealthy
uncle sponsored him in the study of law, but he avidly read astronomy
books that he purchased secretly. In November 1572, a new star, or
nova, suddenly appeared. It was this nova's explosion into view that
fired Brahe into a lifetime of astronomical observation. The new star,
almost as bright as Venus, was visible for about 18 months before disappearing. Brahe meanwhile observed all changes in its brilliance, measured angles of its position, and proved to his own satisfaction that the
newcomer was as distant as the fixed stars. What was a newcomer, and
a temporary one at that, doing in a region supposedly as permanent and

*Brahe in his observatory on
the island of Huen. (Pip
Photos, Inc. by Ullstein
Verlag)*

unchanging as the celestial sphere of stars? Then, in 1577, a new comet appeared to set him further aflame. The comet's path was clearly through a number of the impenetrable crystal spheres that supposedly made up the machinery of the heavens. How was this possible?

Enthusiastic as well as able, Brahe by this time (1577) was famous for his astronomical observations and lectures. Frederick II, King of Denmark, placed the Island of Huen, large funds, and a pension at his disposal. On Huen, Brahe built the most efficient observatory yet known, Uraniborg. Most important of all to Brahe were the huge sighting instruments that he had been able to construct in his observatory. (The telescope had not been invented yet.) With a passion for precision, he gave himself the most accurate naked-eye instruments in history. See the photograph of Brahe in his observatory.

For about 21 years at Uraniborg, Brahe pinpointed the positions of about 800 stars. More than that, he traced the positions of the planets entirely through their courses rather than at selected points. He systematically recorded these observations with an unheard-of-accuracy into books of tables later famous as the Rudolphine tables. Copernicus had operated with an accuracy of about 10', or ⅙°, of arc. Brahe's precision was 20 times better, with about 0.5', or ¹⁄₁₂₀°, of arc. He even corrected for light-bending, or refractive, effects of the atmosphere. For Brahe, it was improved instruments and techniques, more precise observation, and systematic plotting of data that would establish the pattern of the universe. His genius was that of infinite patience for systematic observation.

Among other things, he carefully looked for stellar parallax (Fig. 3–2). If the earth revolves, closer stars should be seen shifting yearly against backgrounds of more distant stars. But with the most precise instruments yet, Brahe did not find the parallax he sought. This confirmed his Ptolemaic learnings. Not satisfied, however, with the original Ptolemaic model, Brahe developed a scheme of his own. In his system, known as Tychonic, the planets revolved around the sun—but the sun with all its attendants revolved around a stationary earth (Fig. 4–1). Clearly, Brahe moved up to the Copernican theory—and stopped short: Greater precision revealed no stellar parallax. The earth must be stationary.

In addition to his infinite patience for precision and detail, Brahe also had an independent nature, a fiery temper, and arrogant ways. These acquired for him powerful enemies at Court. When his friend King Frederick died in about 1592, these enemies were able to force him within 5 years from his island, his work, and even his country. Huen ceased to exist as an observatory.

After 2 years of wandering, he was invited by Rudolph II, Emperor of Bohemia, to settle with his instruments in Prague. There he again set up an observatory in a castle and continued his celestial explorations and lectures. In 1601, however, broken in health, he died.

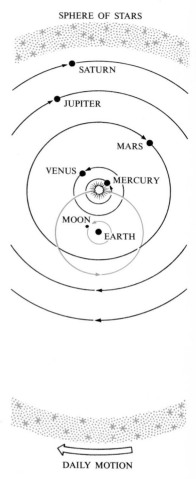

SPHERE OF STARS

DAILY MOTION

4–1 Brahe's model of the world. The earth is stationary at the center of the universe, but the planets revolve around the sun as the sun moves around the earth. Note that the inner planets (Mercury and Venus) revolve counterclockwise and that the outer planets (Mars, Jupiter, and Saturn) revolve clockwise in Brahe's model. Brahe hoped that celestial observations would meet predictions through this scheme.

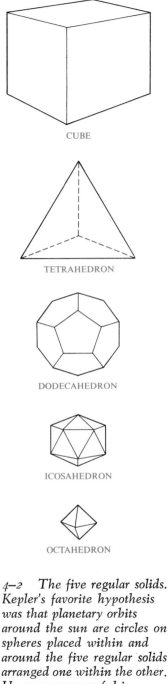

KEPLER:
MATHEMATICAL MYSTIC

A year or so before his death, Brahe hired a young German assistant, Johannes Kepler (1571–1630). As an astronomer, Kepler already had exceptional mathematical ability and imagination. Brahe had recognized this in Kepler's first book in astronomy, *Mysterium Cosmographicum*, published in 1596, and invited Kepler to join him in Prague. Because of serious religious turmoil in his native German province of Styria, Kepler accepted Brahe's invitation. This was fortunate indeed because when Brahe died a year later, his precious data, the largest, most accurate astronomical records up to that time, could not have fallen into better hands.

Genius takes many forms. Kepler, a confirmed Copernican, was a mathematical mystic with great respect for Brahe's data. If Brahe's great talent was that of the observer with infinite patience for acquiring data, Kepler's gift was that of the theoretician with a bold mathematical imagination for persistently, even fanatically, ordering the data.

Kepler was born in Germany on December 27, 1571, of parents of fallen, lesser nobility. From early childhood his personal life was one of persistent sickness, poverty, and frustration. It was in the planets and stars that he found most of his life's consolation.

Quite early, Kepler, like the ancient Pythagoreans, became confident that geometry and numbers are the essence of the universe. As a young lecturer at the University of Graz, he became consumed with the idea of connecting the five regular solids of geometry—the tetrahedron, cube, octahedron, dodecahedron, and icosahedron (Fig. 4–2)—with the orbits of the six known planets. In applying these solids to the solar system, Kepler arranged them in succession one within the other, as described in his work *Mysterium Cosmographicum*. In Kepler's plan, the planetary orbits were circles on spheres placed within and around the geometric solids.

But great men are not always successful in their conceptual schemes, in science or otherwise. No matter how hard Kepler tried, Brahe's meticulous data could not be forced into circles. The geometric solids eventually failed as a model for explaining the size, number, and arrangement of planetary orbits.

Before Brahe died in 1601, Kepler promised him that he would do what he could to test Brahe's own model against the data. At first Kepler faithfully tried to reconcile his colleague's model with the data. But unsuccessful in this, he then tried the original Copernican model. That model would not line up with the data either, except approximately, and with an ever increasing complexity of epicycles, eccentrics, and even equants. Through the use of an eccentric circular orbit, Mars even came within 8' of arc, or ⅛°, of its predicted position. But Kepler rejected the model. He had too much confidence in Brahe's precision to ques-

4–2 The five regular solids. Kepler's favorite hypothesis was that planetary orbits around the sun are circles on spheres placed within and around the five regular solids arranged one within the other. He was unsuccessful in establishing this hypothesis.

tion his data. If circular models did not closely coincide with the data, then away with circles. In that case, the pattern of planetary orbits would have to appear directly from the data itself, much like the pattern that appears when a child traces a line from dot to dot in a pictorial puzzle. For the first time in modern history, conceptual schemes were rejected on the basis of precision of measurement. But Kepler had fanatical faith that when the dots were correctly connected, a mathematically simple universe would appear. Finally, after 17 years of tedious labor, Kepler emerged with his three laws of planetary motion. These laws did simplify the Copernican theory, amazingly so!

KEPLER'S LAWS OF PLANETARY MOTION

Law of the Ellipse

Kepler found that once the planets were freed from circular orbits, their plotted positions formed ellipses. First discovering this with Mars, he was delighted to find the same orbital pattern for other planets. Best of all, the elliptical orbits appeared only when he *assumed* his frame of reference, the earth, to be revolving around the sun, too. Now he needed no celestial spheres, no circular deferents, no epicycles upon epicycles upon epicycles, no further geometric devices. After the elimination of the single assumption of perfection of the heavens, all planetary motions fell into line, the line or pattern of an ellipse if the earth was equated with wanderers in the night sky. All this and more is implied in Kepler's first law of planetary motion: *Every planet moves in an elliptical path with the sun at one focus.*

But just what is an ellipse? A heritage of ancient geometry is the mathematical model of conic sections. Figure 4–3 shows that an ellipse is one of four sections formed by properly cutting a cone. When a circular cone is cut from point *A* at a plane parallel to its base, the cross

4–3 Conic sections.
1. Circle: a section parallel to the cone base.
2. Ellipse: a section not parallel to the base.
3. Parabola: a section parallel to the cone side.
4. Hyperbola: a section beyond the parallel to the side.

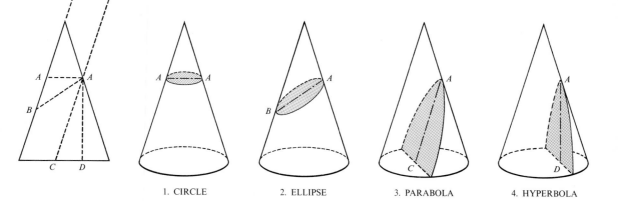

1. CIRCLE   2. ELLIPSE   3. PARABOLA   4. HYPERBOLA

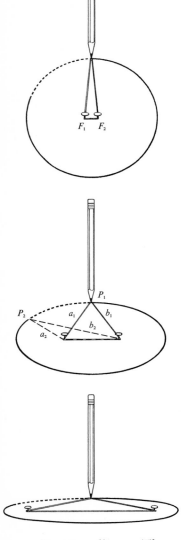

section is a circle. If the cone is cut from *A* at an angle to the base, the new section forms an ellipse.

When a cone is cut parallel to a side, the section forms an open curve known as a *parabola*. Also note that when the section starts from the same point *A* but tilts *(A–D)* beyond the parallel, the open curve formed is a *hyperbola*.

Let us now define an *ellipse* as *the path that a point makes if the sum of its distances from two fixed points (called foci) is always the same*. The ellipse can easily be drawn by attaching a string to two thin nails forced into cardboard and by moving a pencil with the string around it, as shown in Fig. 4–4. No matter where the pencil is, the total length of the string—or total distance of the pencil from the two nails, or foci—remains the same. Any planet, like the pencil, follows an elliptical path because wherever it is in its orbit, the sum of its distances from two fixed points remains the same. And strangely enough, as pointed out in Kepler's law of the ellipse, the sun is at one of the two foci of the various planetary orbits.

As the two foci are placed closer, the ellipse becomes less and less elongated. If the foci were to meet, what form would the ellipse take? Again, note that as the focal points move farther apart, the ellipse becomes more elongated. If the foci were as far apart as possible, what form would the ellipse take? It should be clear that the circle and the straight line can be thought of as special, or limiting, forms of the ellipse. Obviously, astronomers before Kepler, including Copernicus, had been restricting themselves to a limiting form of the ellipse—at a great sacrifice of simplicity.

It follows from Kepler's first law that a planet will be at varying distances from the sun at different positions in its orbit (Fig. 4–5). The point at which a planet is closest to the sun is called *perihelion*. The furthest point is called the *aphelion*. Kepler found that the elliptical orbits of the various planets are only slightly elongated, that is, almost circular. The sun is close in each case to the symmetrical center, and the distances between it and the aphelion and perihelion of each planet are fairly close.

Law of Equal Areas

Although the first law was beautiful in its simplicity, it was insufficient. Alone, it did not provide for the speed of motion of the planets. Accurate observations showed that the speed of a planet varies in its orbit. Is there a regular basis for this variation? If so, what? Without knowledge of how planets change their speeds in elliptical orbits, no reliable predictions could be made of future positions. The ellipse in all its simplicity would not be able to displace the former Ptolemaic or Copernican models. These earlier models were cumbersome, but they at least could make useful predictions of planetary positions by assuming constant speeds.

4–4   *Drawing ellipses. The further apart the thumbtacks (foci F₁ and F₂), the "flatter" the ellipse. When F₁ and F₂ are at the same point, the ellipse is a circle. When F₁ and F₂ are furthest apart, the ellipse becomes a straight line. At whatever point the pencil is, the total length of the string is the same. That is, at any points P₁ and P₂, the two parts of the string have the same total: $a_1 + b_1 = a_2 + b_2$.*

Kepler was confident of the mathematical simplicity and uniformity of nature. He had previously used equal triangles as a mathematical technique in handling areas of circular orbits. He now applied this technique to elliptical orbits. The result was the second law of equal areas, first described with his first law in his book *New Astronomy* (1609). Kepler had started with Brahe's data in 1600. These two laws had taken 9 years to develop.

In his second law, the mathematical formulation is the same for all planets. The law states simply that *an imaginary line drawn from any planet to the sun sweeps over equal areas in equal times.* For this statement to be true, the closer a planet is to the sun, the faster it has to move. In Fig. 4–6, for example, the planet is closer to the sun when it is at point C than when at point A. Let us say that the planet moves from A to B in 30 days. The imaginary line AS sweeps over area ASB during that time. Later, the planet moves from C to D in 30 days. According to Kepler, areas ASB and CSD, swept across by the imaginary lines AS and CS, respectively, are equal. This equality is possible only if the planet moves faster at C than at A, since it moves along the larger arc CD in the same interval of time as along the smaller arc AB.

Even more specifically, if the planet were 5 percent closer at C than at A, Kepler proved mathematically that the planet would move about 5 percent faster at C. Only then would the imaginary line sweep through equal areas CSD and ASB in the same time. And 10 percent closer would mean about 10 percent faster. The speed of a planet at any point in its elliptical orbit increases as its distance from the sun decreases. If, in Fig. 4–6, v_1 and v_2 represent the velocity of a planet at any two points A and C, respectively, and d_1 and d_2 represent the planet's distance to the sun at points A and C, respectively, then with a high degree of accuracy in a nearly circular orbit,

$$v_1 d_1 = v_2 d_2 = \text{a constant } k. \qquad \text{Equation 4–1}$$

Once "perfectly circular" orbits were gone for planets, so was another old assumption, a constant orbital speed v. Constant now instead by Eq. 4–1 (or nearly so) is a product of two entities, the speed v and distance d from the sun for any position of a planet. It also follows that a planet's speed is greatest at perihelion and slowest at aphelion. Kepler had the joy of not only showing a reasonably accurate mathematical relationship between planetary positions and speeds in elliptical orbits, but also finding the relationship confirmed by Brahe's data.

The Harmonic Law

The second law of planetary motion is a simple mathematical pattern of change of motion by a given planet within its own orbit. As such, it enables prediction of the position of a planet at any time. It does not,

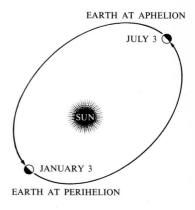

EARTH AT APHELION

JULY 3

SUN

JANUARY 3

EARTH AT PERIHELION

4–5 *The earth is closest to the sun on January 3 and furthest on July 3.*

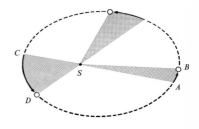

4–6 *Law of equal areas. An imaginary line from any planet to the sun sweeps over equal areas in equal times (area ASB = area CSD).*

however, indicate relationship between motions of different planets one to the other. Kepler's zeal for a basic mathematical unity of the solar system drove him on to seek this larger relationship. For another 9 years he labored.

And then he found what he was after in the form of an equation that joins the sun, earth, and other planets mathematically into an inter-related system of motion apart from the rest of the universe. Let Kepler express his own exaltation at the discovery of his third law of planetary motion, the harmonic law, in his great work *On Celestial Harmonies* (1618):

> It is not eighteen months since I got the first glimpse of light, three months since the dawn, very few days since the unveiled sun, most admirable to gaze upon, burst upon me. Nothing holds me; I will indulge my sacred fury; I will triumph over mankind by the honest confession that I have stolen the golden vases of the Egyptians to build up a tabernacle for my God far away from the confines of Egypt. If you forgive me, I rejoice; if you are angry, I can bear it; the die is cast, the book is written, to be read either now or by posterity, I care not which; it may well wait a century for a reader, as God has waited six thousand years for an observer.

Here, as he first stated it, is Kepler's discovery:

> And so if any one take the period say of the Earth, which is one year, and the period of Saturn, which is thirty years, and extract the cube roots of this ratio and then square the ensuing ratio by squaring the cube roots, he will have as his numerical products the most just ratio of the distances of the Earth and Saturn from the sun. For the cube root of 1 is 1, and the square of it is 1; and the cube root of 30 is greater than 3, and therefore the square of it is greater than 9. And Saturn at its mean distance from the sun is slightly higher than nine times the mean distance of the Earth from the sun.

The law stated simply is this: *The square of the times required by the planets for a complete orbital revolution about the sun are proportional to the cubes of their average distances from the sun.* In algebraic symbols this reads as $T^2 \sim \overline{D}^3$, where T represents the time, or period, of one revolution of a planet. $\overline{D}$ represents the average distance of the planet to the sun.

To really see what so excited Kepler, complete columns 4 and 5 in Table 4–1. Columns 2 and 3 give data on those planets known to Kepler. Column 2 gives the time of revolution in years, and column 3, the average distance of each planet to the sun in astronomical units (au). An astro-nomical unit is the average distance of the earth from the sun, about 93 million miles. To determine the T^2 and $\overline{D}^3$ for each planet, *square* the data of column 2 for column 4, and cube the data of column 3 for column

5. Then compare the values in columns 4 and 5. A generalization appears: $T^2 = \bar{D}^3$. For each planet the time squared of a revolution *equals* the cubed average distance of that planet to the sun when T is expressed in years and $\bar{D}$ in astronomical units.

But if T is in months and $\bar{D}$ in miles or another unit, the following even more general equation holds:

$$T^2 = k\bar{D}^3, \qquad\qquad\qquad \text{Equation 4–2}$$

where k is a constant, the value of which depends on the units used for T and $\bar{D}$.

Table 4–1 | HARMONIC LAW RELATIONSHIPS

1 PLANET	2 TIME OF ONE REVOLUTION T (YR)	3 AVERAGE DISTANCE TO SUN $\bar{D}$ (AU)	4 T^2 ($T \cdot T$)	5 $\bar{D}^3$ ($\bar{D} \cdot \bar{D} \cdot \bar{D}$)
Saturn	29.46	9.54		
Jupiter	11.86	5.20	140.66	140.61
Mars	1.88	1.52		
Earth	1.00	1.00	1.00	1.00
Venus	.62	.72		
Mercury	.24	.39		

When years are used for T and astronomical units are used for $\bar{D}$ in Eq. 4–2, then $k = 1$ and $T^2 = \bar{D}^3$. This was established in the case of the earth, where the period of revolution $T = 1$ year and the average distance to the sun $\bar{D} = 1$ au. That is,

$$T^2 = k\bar{D}^3 \text{ or } k = \frac{T^2}{\bar{D}^3} = \frac{1^2 \text{yr}^2}{1^3 \text{au}^3} = 1 \text{ yr}^2/\text{au}^3.$$

Or for Jupiter, the period of revolution $T = 11.86$ years and the average distance $\bar{D} = 5.20$ au. For Jupiter:

$$T^2 = k\bar{D}^3 \text{ or } k = \frac{T^2}{\bar{D}^3} = \frac{140.66 \text{ yr}^2}{140.61 \text{ au}^3} = 1.000 \text{ yr}^2/\text{au}^3.$$

Kepler's harmonic law unites all planets and satellites into one solar system of motion. Outside this system are stationary stars widely spread in a thick celestial sphere. In a sense, with Kepler, the single, sun-centered world system of Copernicus became separated into a solar family and the surrounding stars. The solar system became an entity of its own.

Determination of Distances to Planets

A further implication of T^2 and $k\overline{D}^3$ is that if the complete period T of revolution of any planet is given by observation, then the average distance $\overline{D}$ of that planet to the sun can be calculated. For example, if a new planet were discovered with a period of revolution T of 84 years, what would be the average distance $\overline{D}$ of that planet to the sun in astronomical units and in miles?

Solution: $T^2 = k \ \overline{D}^3 \ or \ \overline{D}^3 = T^2/k$

$$\overline{D}^3 = \frac{84^2\text{yr}^{2*}}{1 \text{ yr}^2/\text{au}^3} \ = 7{,}056 \text{ au}$$

$$\overline{D} = 19.1 \text{ au.}$$

Since 1 au equals 93 million miles,

$\overline{D} = 19.1 \text{ au} \cdot 93 \text{ million mi/au}$

$\overline{D} = 1{,}776 \text{ million mi.}$

KEPLER'S SOLAR SYSTEM AND THE PRINCIPLE OF PARSIMONY

The work of Kepler highlights the role of assumptions in science and the necessity for constantly examining the assumptions behind *all* that we think or do. Copernicus had kept his own hands tied by the assumptions of uniform and circular motion. Kepler, Pythagorean mystic that he was, also felt deeply about circular orbits. We have seen that he did everything he could with circles, first to make Brahe's scheme work, and then Copernicus's original model. When circles became too cumbersome to suit his aesthetic sense as well as his respect for accuracy, Kepler was willing to abandon the assumption of circles for the assumption of simplicity. With the ellipse, Kepler, in one blow, cut a highly entangled though useful Gordian knot, and the solar system became simple. No

*Units are handled like numbers and cancel out: $84^2\text{yr}^2/1 \text{ yr}^2/\text{au}^3$ becomes $84^2\text{yr}^2/1 \times \text{au}^3/\text{yr}^2$, or 84^2au^3.

cumbersome system of deferents, epicycles, or equants—just elliptical orbits tied together in the simple, unifying, inter-relating equality of ratios:

$$\frac{T_E{}^2}{D_E{}^3} = \frac{T_X{}^2}{D_X{}^3} = \cdots = 1.$$

Significant simplicity indeed! And one that rested on his cherished Copernican assumption that the earth and all the planets move around the sun.

Kepler's laws illustrate the basic scientific principle (really assumption) of parsimony: The simplest theory is the best, other things being the same. To this day, scientists seek the simplest theories to unify and explain what they see. And certainly the simplest is the most convenient. But what if the universe itself is complex and its phenomena are therefore more truthfully portrayed by a complex theory? Should convenience be preferred to truth in that case?

Agreed that Kepler in this elliptical model removed small errors of prediction obtained with Ptolemaic or original Copernican models. Ptolemaic theorists, however, by adding still more epicycles to their already

Kepler explaining his planetary theories to his sponsor, Emperor Rudolph II. (The Bettman Archive, Inc.)

cumbersome model, could have approached even Kepler's accuracy. Even better, what if Kepler had been Ptolemaic and had substituted ellipses or other appropriate forms for circles in Ptolemaic theory? The Ptolemaic model would have been simpler, too.

KEPLER AND MATHEMATICAL HYPOTHESIS TESTING

If any two words describe modern scientific methodology, they are "hypothesis testing." Kepler, together with Galileo and Newton, was an initiator of modern hypothesis testing. Regardless of his strong personal preferences, we have seen that he tested a number of hypotheses on the same problem of planetary orbits: Platonic solids, Brahe's geocentric circles, Copernican circles, the ellipse. In his hands, these ideas became hypotheses that were accepted or rejected by Brahe's data. It was the data that decided. With him, ideas were tested by careful observation; data were not to be forced or "saved" by ideas. For example, if the data of Mars rejected circles and suggested an ellipse, then the ellipse hypothesis had to be tested and retested by data, first for Mars and then for the other planets.

The ideas tested by Kepler in his second and third laws are algebraic. For example, from the equal areas swept over by a planet in the second law, an equation resulted relating quite closely the positions and speeds of a planet: $v_1 d_1 = v_2 d_2 \cdots =$ a constant k for that planet (Eq. 4–1). Observation showed that planetary positions could be predicted from this equation with considerable accuracy. The equation $T^2 = k\overline{D^3}$ (Eq. 4–2) also symbolizes Kepler's harmonic law. With Kepler, equations were displacing epicycles. Algebra for the first time was displacing geometry as a form of law in physical science. Actually, Kepler was operating algebraically without using algebraic symbols as shorthand, as can be seen in Kepler's first statement of his harmonic law, quoted earlier. Kepler, in initiating such a new mathematical form of law, was soon joined by his great contemporary Galileo, operating independently in mechanics. The equation as a form of law came into full bloom in Newton's laws of motion and gravitation, and after that, more and more laws took the form of an equation in the physical sciences.

CHAPTER REVIEW

1. What influence did Brahe's astronomical observations have in establishing our present ideas of the solar system?

2. Draw a sketch of Brahe's world system, and relate the main features of this model to his inability to find stellar parallax.

3. Suppose you were a Ptolemaic astronomer during Brahe's time and you observed the nova of 1572 shine brilliantly for a year or two and then disappear. How would you reconcile this observation with your belief in permanence and consistency in the heavens?

4. What changes did Kepler make in the original Copernican system? Why were these changes important?

5. How did Kepler benefit from Brahe? Compare the talents of these two men.

6. What is an ellipse? Why is Kepler's first law called the law of the ellipse? Why is this law significant?

7. Why is Kepler's second law called the law of equal areas? Why is this law significant?

8. Just what was "harmonized" in Kepler's harmonic law? Why is this law significant?

9. Kepler's law simplified the Copernican system. Would you consider this simplification to be decisive in settling the Ptolemaic-Copernican controversy? Why or why not?

10. Who was the greater innovator, Copernicus or Kepler? Why? Remember that if Kepler benefited from Brahe, Copernicus gained from Aristarchus and other predecessors.

11. What is a scientific law? How does it differ from civil laws? Illustrate.

12. Does scientific procedure generally mean following facts wherever they lead or checking already formed hypotheses against data? Illustrate with the scientific work of Brahe and Kepler.

PROBLEMS

1. The sun's apparent diameter changes slightly during the year. Show by diagrams how this observation was explained by Ptolemy, Copernicus, and Kepler.

2. If a planet is found to increase its speed by 3 percent, what does this indicate about the planet's distance from the sun?

3. Fill in the columns in Table 4–1. Why are the values for the earth the only whole numbers and the only values that exactly match in columns 4 and 5?

4. After its discovery, the planet Uranus was found to have an 84-year period of revolution. What is the distance of Uranus from the sun in astronomical units? In miles?

5. If a new planet were found with a period of revolution of 100 years, what would be the average distance of that planet from the sun?

6. What is the difference between a fact and a scientific law?

7. Give two assumptions, facts, definitions, hypotheses, and theories involved in the development of Kepler's laws, and show how they are involved in the laws.

SUGGESTIONS FOR FURTHER READING

Cohen, I. Bernard, *The Birth of a New Physics,* Anchor paperback, Garden City, N. Y., 1960, Ch. 6.

Koestler, Arthur, *The Sleepwalkers,* Macmillan, New York, 1959.

Koestler, Arthur, *The Watershed,* Anchor paperback, Garden City, N.Y., 1960.

Lodge, Oliver, *Pioneers of Science,* Dover paperback, New York, 1960, Lectures 2–3.

American Foundation for Continuing Education, *Exploring the Universe,* ed. Louise B. Young, McGraw-Hill, New York, 1963.

Holton, Gerald J., and D. H. D. Roller, *Foundations of Modern Science,* Addison-Wesley, Reading, Mass., 1958, Ch. 9.

Omer, Guy C., Jr., et al., *Physical Science: Men and Concepts,* Heath, Boston, 1962, Ch. 8.

5 Galileo's Telescope and the Solar Family

To doubt this system [Ptolemaic] and to seek for another and better one when all men's minds were governed by tradition and authority, and when to doubt was sin—this required a great mind and a high character.

SIR OLIVER LODGE, 1893

PTOLEMY, COPERNICUS, AND GALILEO'S TELESCOPE

Galileo Galilei (1564–1642) was a Copernican colleague of Kepler. Although the two never met, they encouraged each other through correspondence. Galileo was born on February 18, 1564, in Pisa, Italy. The famous Leaning Tower of Pisa is still associated with his name. There is no evidence that Galileo actually dropped balls from the top of the tower in public demonstrations, but the tower has become symbolic of Galileo's work with falling objects and of his Copernican convictions.

Galileo's father, Vincenzio, a descendant of a long line of Florentine nobility, had moved to Pisa to repair family finances. A cultured man and a musical rebel, he and a dedicated group of friends, endeavoring to replace older musical forms with new ones, invented the recitative and other early operatic forms. Galileo, tutored as a boy by his father, benefited early from his father's love of music, books, and mathematics. Like his father, the son could draw artistically and had exceptional literary talent. The son extended an innovating spirit to astronomy and mechanics as well as to the arts.

Vincenzio sent his son at the age of 17 to the University of Pisa to study medicine. But the mathematics of Euclid and Archimedes proved to be of greater fascination to him than the ancient medicine of Aristotle and Galen. In any case, a chandelier swinging back and forth during a sermon in the Cathedral of Pisa led to Galileo's invention of a device to count pulsebeats rather than to his completion of a course in medicine.

The controversial Bruno was burned alive at the stake in 1600 by the Inquisition for Copernican and other religious heresies that he would not recant. At the time Galileo was a Lecturer of Mathematics at the University of Padua. In 1604, another nova spectacularly appeared. Bruno's fate did not prevent Galileo in the freer atmosphere of Padua from lecturing on the Copernican implications of this nova. He remained comparatively quiet as a confirmed Copernican, however, for about another 5 years. Galileo expressed his caution at this time in a letter to Kepler:

> I have written many arguments in support of him [Copernicus] and in refutation of the opposite view—which, however, so far I have not dared to bring into the public light, frightened by the fate of Copernicus himself, our teacher, who, though he acquired immortal fame with some, is yet to an infinite multitude of others (for such is the number of fools) an object of ridicule and derision. I would certainly dare to publish my reflections at once if more people like you existed; as they don't, I shall refrain from doing so.

In 1609, a rumor reached Galileo that a Dutch lens grinder, Lippershey, had devised an instrument with two lenses that brought distant terrestrial objects into closer view. That was all Galileo needed as a clue. Within 24 hours he had constructed the first of several telescopes that he excitedly turned to the skies. For Galileo, the new instrument was an extension of the senses. Through it, the heavens could be observed with a detail never before possible. Direct evidence was at hand to place the Ptolemaic-Copernican issue to a final test. Galileo was hopeful that his colleagues would be willing to observe and to rethink the issue.

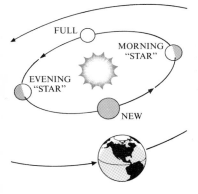

5–1   *Phases of Venus. By Copernican theory, Venus can be on the same side or on the opposite side of the sun as the moving earth. Phases like those of the moon are therefore possible for Venus.*

Galileo's Observations and Conclusions

And observe Galileo certainly did! What that stargazer found he openly reported in his book *The Starry Messenger*, published in 1610. The following are some of the significant observations and inferences in this work:

1. There were mountains, craters, and plains on the moon—much like on the earth. How could the moon be irregular in surface and still be a perfect sphere with a smooth, crystalline face?

2. There were dark spots moving across the face of the sun that apparently rotated around it in about 27 days. What were large spots

doing on a celestial object composed of an unchanging, "incorruptible" substance?

3. There was a bulge around Saturn that prevented perfect sphericity for that body.

An implication of these three observations, for Galileo, was that the above celestial bodies were imperfect in form and earthlike in substance. The earth, therefore, could take a place in space with other objects moving around the sun.

4. Even more important in inference was the sight of four moons revolving around Jupiter. Here, for the first time, was direct evidence of heavenly bodies moving directly around another celestial body instead of directly around the earth. If such objects could move around Jupiter, then why couldn't other objects (planets) revolve directly around the sun?

5. Venus had phases, as predicted by Copernicus. That is, Venus completed a series of phases from new to full to new, like that of the moon. Observed phases for Venus meant that Venus did not shine of its own light, as formerly expected of a perfect heavenly body. Like the earth, Venus shone merely in reflected light. Here again, there was the same standard for the earth as for celestial bodies.

There was also about a 5:1 ratio in the apparent diameters of Venus between its narrow crescent and full phases. This ratio most likely meant that Venus was about five times closer to the earth in its new phase than in its full phase. This could be easily explained with the Copernican model (Fig. 5-1). The ratio was explainable through Ptolemaic epicycles only with great difficulty. But with Venus always between the sun and a stationary earth (Fig. 5-2), the original Ptolemaic model certainly could not explain the nearly full phase seen for Venus. Galileo believed that the phases of Venus were decisive evidence against the Ptolemaic theory.

6. There were myriads of stars in the Milky Way not previously seen. And yet even with Galileo's telescopes of up to 30 power, no star was ever more than a pinpoint of light—nor are they today with incomparably more powerful telescopes. Distances to the stars were therefore much greater than formerly supposed. Immense distances to the stars supported Copernicus's original contention that stellar parallax had not been detected from a revolving earth because stars are too distant.

5-2 Complete phases of Venus were unexplainable by original Ptolemaic theory. Venus was always on an epicycle between the sun and the fixed earth and could never be on a side of the sun opposite to the earth. Only crescent phases were possible for Venus.

Significance of Galileo's Telescope

Galileo's findings scientifically weakened some of the props of an earth-centered system. These findings, however, for reasons given below, were not quite so crucial as he thought:

1. Mountains on the moon, sunspots, and an asymmetrical Saturn seriously undermined the concept of perfection of the heavens, but the earth scientifically could still be the center of a world system without the philosophic-religious assumptions of perfect heavenly bodies, perfect spheres, or perfect circles. That is, Ptolemaic theory could be re-established on other assumptions, just as Copernican theory had been re-established with ellipses by Kepler.

2. The existence of moons revolving around Jupiter does reduce the claim that the earth is the *direct* center of revolution of *all* objects in the universe, but it does not eliminate the possibility that Jupiter itself with its satellites could be revolving around the earth.

3. The Ptolemaic model, as it is customarily understood, is not able to account for the phases of Venus. Ptolemaic theory can get around this by having Mercury and Venus revolving around the sun as the sun revolves around the earth (Heraclides, 4th century B.C.) or by having all planets revolve around the sun as the latter moves around the earth (Brahe, 16th century A.D.). The latter modification can qualitatively explain complete phases seen for planets. Both of the alternatives, however, are admittedly compromises that seriously weaken Ptolemaic theory. Having all planets revolve around the sun as the latter encircles the earth means getting ever further away from the original assumption of the earth as the direct center of all things. If all other planets revolve around the sun, it is but one more step for the earth to do the same. Brahe himself didn't take this last step to Copernican theory because he looked for stellar parallax and couldn't find it. And yet the fact that Brahe's revision of the Ptolemaic model can be used to explain the phases of Venus means that Galileo's telescopic observations were not quite the final blow to an earth-centered system that Galileo thought.

OPPOSITION TO GALILEO

Instruments as extensions of the senses can settle theoretical disputes—if men are receptive to instruments. Galileo's telescopic appeal to the senses came at a time when appeal to authority rather than to direct evidence was still customary among educated men. The senses were still considered to give illusory, transitory details rather than basic, permanent principles and were not to be trusted. Most of Galileo's colleagues therefore ignored his appeal, his observations, and his conclusions.

As an example of this, consider the following argument against the existence of Jupiter's satellites by Francesco Sizzi, an astronomer of Florence:

> There are seven windows in the head, two nostrils, two eyes, two ears, and a mouth; so in the heavens there are two favourable stars,

two unpropitious, two luminaries, and Mercury alone undecided and indifferent. From which and many other similar phenomena of nature, such as the seven metals, etc., which it were tedious to enumerate, we gather that the number of planets is necessarily seven.

Moreover, the satellites are invisible to the naked eye, and therefore can have no influence on the earth, and therefore would be useless, and therefore do not exist.

Besides, the Jews and other ancient nations as well as modern Europeans have adopted the division of the week into seven days, and have named them from the seven planets: now if we increase the number of the planets this whole system falls to the ground.

With respect to such arguments as the above, Galileo quite caustically had the following to say in a letter to Kepler:

We will laugh at the extraordinary stupidity of the crowd, my Kepler. What do you say to the main philosophers of our school, who, with the stubbornness of vipers, never wanted to see the planets, the moon or the telescope although I offered a thousand times to show them the planets and the moon. Really, as some have shut their ears, these have shut their eyes toward the light of truth. This is an awful thing, but it does not astonish me. This sort of person thinks that philosophy is a book like the *Aeneid* or *Odyssey* and that one has not to search for truth in the world of nature, but in the comparisons of texts (to use their own words).

Beyond the boundaries of his own country, the telescope and the *Starry Messenger* won fame for Galileo. And within Italy, the appreciative free Republic of Venice granted him life tenure in his professorship at the University of Padua and doubled his salary. Galileo took heart. Against the advice of friends, he left Padua in 1610, where he had been honored and sheltered for 18 years, to return to Pisa as chief mathematician to the Grand Duke of Tuscany and as head of mathematics at the University of Pisa. In 1611, he was feted in Rome and elected to the new Accademia dei Lincei, one of the earliest scientific societies.

Galileo, an exceptionally able polemicist, was confident that he could convince the highest ranks of the Church that the new astronomy did not contradict religious thought, that the "same Creator was behind both the Bible and Nature." Galileo became more and more open in his Copernicanism. In 1615, he was asked to come to Rome to defend the Copernican position before high Church officials. Galileo had a number of friends in the Church hierarchy. Many cardinals also had an attitude of compromise about the issue. There was, on the other hand, a strong ecclesiastical faction pressuring the Pope and the College of Cardinals for a final, clear-cut decision on the heretical character of Copernicanism. Galileo's persuasive talents and friends proved to be insufficient. The

Congregation of the Index ruled against the Copernican system. Copernicus's *Revolutionibus* was banned and placed on the Index Expurgatorius. No established order easily modifies its patterns of thought. Galileo was officially warned against teaching Copernicanism. He returned home heartsick. For a number of years, Galileo devoted himself to noncontroversial problems in hydrostatics.

When Cardinal Barberini was elected Pope Urban VIII in 1623, Galileo's Copernican heart beat a little faster. The new Pope was a personal friend of Galileo and an enlightened man. Galileo soon discussed with the Pope plans for a book, *Dialogue on Systems of the Universe,* in which each system was to be represented by a spokesman. A third participant in the *Dialogue* would be neutral and open. The Pope acquiesced to an impartial representation of the two points of view. Printed 9 years later, the *Dialogue* sold extensively for 6 months, when suddenly the book was banned. An ecclesiastical faction hostile to Galileo convinced the Church that the *Dialogue* benefited the Copernican cause and that Galileo had circumvented the warning given him in 1616. The *Dialogue* remained on the Index list with Kepler's *Epitome of Copernican Astronomy* and Copernicus's *Revolutionibus* for over 200 years.

Galileo was called to face the Inquisition Court in 1633. Whatever the details of his 3 months' imprisonment, in June 1633, Galileo, on his knees before the Inquisition Court, officially rescinded his belief that the "Sun is the center of the World and that the Earth moves around it."

For the remaining 9 years of his life, Galileo worked quietly under house arrest at his farm on the outskirts of Florence. There, his great accomplishment—perhaps his greatest—was the further development of a new theory of mechanics. This theory was described in his work *Dialogues Concerning Two New Sciences*. A visiting Dutch publisher smuggled the manuscript out of Italy after its completion in 1636. The book was first published in Leyden in 1638.

GALILEO AND ACADEMIC FREEDOM

The following extract from a preface by Einstein to the above *Dialogues* (Drake translation, 1952) is appropriate:

> The *leitmotif* which I recognize in Galileo's work is the passionate fight against any kind of dogma based on authority. Only experience and careful reflection are accepted by him as a criterion of truth. Nowadays it is hard for us to grasp how sinister and revolutionary such an attitude appeared at Galileo's time when merely to doubt the truth of opinions which had no basis but authority was considered a capital crime and punished accordingly. Actually we are by no means so far removed from such a situation even today as many of us would like to flatter ourselves; but in theory, at least, the principle of unbiased

thought has won out and most people are willing to pay lip service to this principle.

The crime in Galileo's case was not in the Ptolemaic convictions maintained by most astronomers and churchmen—for geocentrism could still have been justified even scientifically at the time—but in the ruthless crushing of new ideas. Ideas are not necessarily better because they are new, but the way should be open for honest examination of them for their possibilities. Expanded literacy and progress necessitate that intellectual honesty be an open virtue.

As long as there are men, there will always be polemical struggles of ideas. The level of a civilization is, among other things, the level at which the struggle of ideas can be maintained. Hypotheses must be maintained freely and tested with time.

Galileo's telescope today is a symbol. Pointed as it was to the heavens, the telescope symbolizes an appeal to the senses. Talented men can reason brilliantly in circles for ages; often all that is needed to break the circle is a simple tool. The telescope is such a tool, which Galileo was the first to use in astronomy. In bringing the heavens closer to the earth, he was placing astronomy on a firmer empirical basis. A scientific revolution was about to start. To catch hold of this scientific revolution and to support and extend it to an industrial revolution, a rising middle class would soon make itself felt in Europe. In these revolutions, Galileo's telescope was an early symbol of research and development.

Although today the experimental testing of hypotheses has been established as indispensable to science, intellectual honesty and academic freedom are still live issues everywhere, often even in science. Sir Oliver Lodge in 1893 dramatically exclaimed:

> I have met educated persons who, while they might laugh at men who refused to look through a telescope lest they should learn something they did not like, yet also themselves commit the very same folly.... I am constrained to say this much: Take heed lest some prophet, after having excited your indignation at the follies and bigotry of a bygone generation, does not turn upon you with the sentence, *"Thou art the man!"*

FURTHER EVIDENCES OF A MOVING EARTH

Two centuries after Galileo's death, more powerful telescopes and pendulums provided the final evidences for a moving earth.

Stellar Parallax

Ptolemaic astronomers for ages were insisting that stellar parallax (Fig. 3–2) would be observed if the earth revolves. Brahe, searching for but not finding parallax, stopped short of becoming Copernican, as we have seen. The Copernican explanation that the stars are too distant for observation of parallax appeared defensive and certainly inconclusive. Then, in 1838, the German astronomer F. W. Bessel did find parallax. The stellar shift was slight but unquestionable, and it was followed by other cases; astronomical instruments had finally become powerful enough to detect the yearly shifts of closer stars against backgrounds of distant stars. Men reason brilliantly and mathematically on both sides of a question for thousands of years, and then, by the increased resolving power of a telescope, the entanglement is cut. Men need everything they have and can get—mind, imagination, and sense-extending apparatus—to come to grips with nature.

The Foucault Pendulum

The Foucault pendulum is our best evidence for a *rotating* earth, just as stellar parallax is for a *revolving* earth.

Suspend a weight from a cord directly above a stationary globe, and let the weight swing pendulumlike (Fig. 5–3). The pendulum frame should be attached to the globe. On the globe surface, mark the path along which the pendulum swings. The pendulum's path appears to remain the same during successive swings.

Then slowly rotate the globe under the freely swinging pendulum. Now the pendulum's path over the globe's surface apparently turns through an angle from the original marking. The motion is relative. And the faster the globe underneath is rotated, the greater is the angle through which the path of the pendulum turns. In fact, since the pendulum is

5–3 *Foucault pendulum. A rotating earth daily turns through 360° under a pendulum swinging freely at the North Pole. At the equator, the same pendulum remains constantly swinging at the same angle above a rotating earth.*

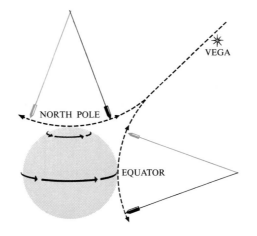

Foucault pendulum demon-
stration. (Culver Pictures,
Inc.)

swinging above the "North Pole" of the rotating globe, its path will turn
through 360° with each rotation of the globe.

Now, imagine the earth to be the globe and a pendulum to be freely
swinging above the earth's surface. If the earth were stationary, the
pendulum's path would keep the same direction indefinitely with respect
to both the earth's surface and the stars. But if the earth is rotating, a
freely swinging pendulum in time would appear to be changing its
direction with respect to the earth's surface, even if not with respect to
the stars. Foucault, the French physicist, had the above idea in mind
when in 1851 he first performed his famous pendulum experiment.
Foucault fixed a wire 200 feet long to a dome of the Pantheon in Paris
and set it in motion. As his pendulum swung, it left new marks in
the sand; the pendulum's path was observed to turn *clockwise*. This
was interpreted as the earth rotating *counterclockwise* under the pendulum, as explained through the globe model above. In the Southern Hemisphere, the apparent deviation of the pendulum's path would be counterclockwise instead of clockwise, as in the Northern Hemisphere. Foucault
pendulums can be found swinging away in planetariums over the face of
the earth today in continuous evidence of the earth's rotation. The
pendulum frame attached to the rotating earth moves with it. But the
pendulum itself is pivoted, and the bob is free to continue swinging in
the same direction toward the stars by *inertia*.* But relative to the ground
rotating under it, the swinging bob changes direction. This change in

*Inertia, the tendency of any object to continue at rest or in motion at constant
speed in a straight line, is discussed in Chapter 8 in the section "Newton's First
Law of Motion."

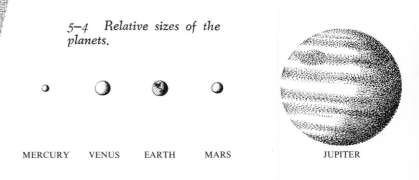

5–4 *Relative sizes of the planets.*

MERCURY   VENUS   EARTH   MARS   JUPITER

direction is a complete circle at the poles, but it gradually decreases with latitude from 360° at the poles to 0° (no change in direction) at the equator.

THE SOLAR SYSTEM AS A UNIT

Brahe's data, Kepler's laws, and Galileo's telescope all contributed to the eventual recognition of the solar family as a unit in the universe. Kepler's laws, based upon Brahe's data, tied the sun and planets together algebraically. Galileo's telescope, while bringing planets and satellites with considerable detail into an immediate common space, left the stars as pinpoints of light from unheard-of distances. Implications were that if the sun was the center of the system, it was the center of a small unit of comparatively few members rather than the center of a world system.

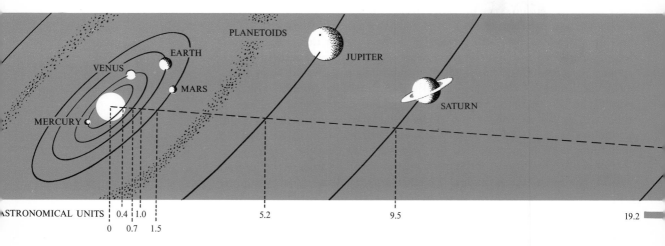

SATURN   URANUS   NEPTUNE   PLUTO

Since Galileo's time, improved telescopes and other instruments have provided a wealth of data about various members of Kepler's solar system. Let us consider some of these data, including those of the planets Uranus, Neptune, and Pluto. The discovery of these planets will be discussed in a later chapter.

Table 5–1, which shows planet characteristics, permits a comparative study of the planets with respect to average distances from the sun, periods of revolution, periods of rotation, inclinations of orbits, mean diameters, masses, surface temperatures, and numbers of satellites.

For comparison, also notice the two scale drawings. The first one (Fig. 5–4) represents the relative sizes of the planets; the second (Fig. 5–5), the relative mean distances from the sun. All planets have their orbits within a relatively few degrees from the plane of the earth's orbit (Fig. 5–6). Could the two scale drawings have been combined into one? Why or why not?

5–5 *Relative mean distances of the planets from the sun.*

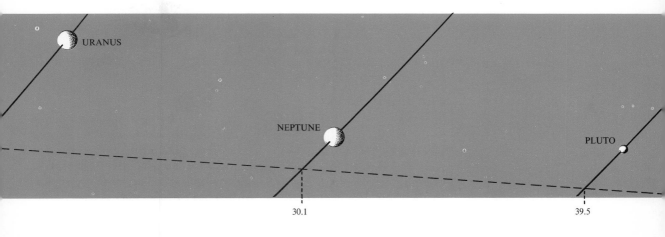

URANUS

NEPTUNE

PLUTO

30.1   39.5

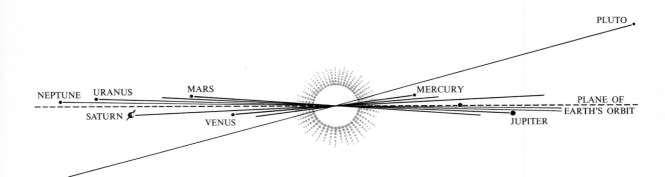

5–6 *Planes of planetary orbits compared to the plane of the earth's orbit. Notice that all planetary orbits are in planes close to that of the earth. Pluto's orbit is inclined farthest from the earth's orbit at an angle of 17° (Table 5–1).*

Over 1 million earths could fit into the sun. How many earths could fit into Jupiter? Notice the solid row of massive outer planets from Jupiter to Neptune, broken by a small, light Pluto at the end.

Consider the construction of a diagram on campus grounds. A given point represents the sun (assumed fixed). Let another point 1 foot away represent the position of Mercury, the planet closest to the sun. The earth will be almost 3 feet away; Jupiter, over 13 feet; and Pluto over 100 feet. Pluto is about 40 times further from the sun than the earth is. No wonder we have difficulty in determining by reflected sunlight whether Pluto has a moon! All planets were thought both to revolve and rotate in a counterclockwise direction except for Uranus, which was thought to have a clockwise rotation. But in 1967, evidence pointed to a clockwise rotation for Venus, too. Which of the planets has the same period for rotation as for revolution? What effect would this have for that planet with respect to length of day or night or distribution of sunlight or temperature range at the surface?

Galileo helped to change ideas through a telescope. Today, more than ever, we are extending our senses through apparatus-laden spacecraft to the moon and planets. And in the process, we are revising our ideas yearly, even monthly. As in Galileo's day, the uncertainties are there, but now at a more precise, complex level.

The Planet Earth

Since the earth is our planet, it is the one to which we compare the others (Tables 4–1 and 5–1). For example, the earth's mean distance from the sun, 93 million miles, is the basis for planetary distances in astronomical units (1 au = 93 million miles). The earth's complete rotation and complete revolution with respect to the stars determine the *sidereal day* and the *sidereal year*, respectively, by which time is measured for the motions of the other planets. The earth's mass is used as a base of 1

Table 5-1 | PLANET CHARACTERISTICS

PLANET	MEAN DISTANCE FROM SUN (MILLIONS OF MILES)	PERIOD OF REVOLUTION (SIDEREAL)	PERIOD OF ROTATION (SIDEREAL)	INCLINATION OF ORBIT (FROM EARTH'S ORBIT)	MEAN DIAMETER (MILES)	MASS (EARTH = 1)	HIGHEST SURFACE TEMPERATURE °F	NUMBER OF SATELLITES
(Sun)			25 days		864,000	330,000	11,000°	9
(Moon)		27.3 days	27.3 days	5.1°	2,160	.012	270°	
Mercury	36	88 days	88 days	7.0°	2,900	.05	770°	0
Venus	67	225 days	243 days	3.4°	7,530	.8	800°	0
Earth	93 (1 au)	365+ days (1 sidereal year*)	24 hr (23 hr, 56 min, or 1 sidereal day†)		7,900	1.00	140°	1
Mars	142	687 days	24.6 hr	1.9°	4,200	.11	80°	2
Jupiter	483	11.9 yr	9.9 hr	1.3°	86,800	318	−220°	12
Saturn	886	29.5 yr	10.6 hr	2.5°	71,500	95	−240°	9
Uranus	1,783	84 yr	10.7 hr	.8°	29,400	15	−300°	5
Neptune	2,794	165 yr	12.7 hr	1.8°	28,000	17	−330°	2
Pluto	3,671	248 yr	6.4 days	17.1°	3,700	.1	−350°	?

*A sidereal year is the period of complete revolution of the earth around the sun with respect to the fixed stars.

†A sidereal day is the period of complete rotation of the earth on its axis with respect to the fixed stars.

for mass comparisons of all major solar system members. And the *plane of the earth's orbit* is a basis for comparing the *inclination of* each *planetary orbit*—that is, the angle that the plane of a planet's orbit makes with that of the earth's orbit (Fig. 5–6).

If we were men on Mars, all the values in Table 4–1 and half the values in Table 5–1 would be different. Mars's properties would be the basis of units and comparisons. Accordingly, the earth's distance from the sun would be somewhat less than 1 au, the earth's period of revolution would be about 6 months (Mars's), the earth's period of rotation would be less than 1 day (Mars's), the earth would be a massive 9 instead of 1. And it would be the earth that has an orbit inclined from Mars at 1.90°. Of course, even to a man on Mars, the earth would still have an axis inclined at 23½° to the plane of its own orbit, would have seasons, would be about 3 percent closer to the sun in the northern winter than in summer, and would show a slight flattening at the poles as evidence of rotation.

Mercury

Mercury, the planet closest to the sun, is also the smallest and the fastest of the planets. Not much larger than our moon, it is actually smaller than two of the satellites of Jupiter. In accordance with Kepler's third law, Mercury completes its orbit around the sun in 88 days. This planet also rotates on its axis every 88 days. With the same periods of rotation and of revolution, virtually the same half of Mercury always faces the sun, and the other half is always turned away. Also, ever near the sun, Mercury is a forbidding planet. The half facing the sun receives about ten times as much heat and light per unit area as the earth. The temperature on that surface is about 770°F—higher than the melting point of lead. The other side, permanently dark, is cold enough to change some of its atmospheric gases to solids. Life as we know it is not possible under such conditions.

Supposedly, Copernicus never saw Mercury. But with difficulty, that planet can be seen by the naked eye as an "evening" or "morning star" when at its greatest distance east or west of the sun. When in transit between the earth and the sun, the planet can be photographed as a small, round, black spot. As would be expected from Copernican theory or from Brahe's model, Mercury shows complete phases like Venus and the moon. Mercury itself has no moon.

In agreement with Kepler's second law, the speed of the planet in its elliptical orbit varies slightly in accordance with its distance from the sun, while its rotation remains constant. This means that its period of revolution is not always exactly equal to its period of rotation. Mercury therefore has a border zone in which the sun rises and sets. But a thin, unprotecting atmosphere results in temperature extremes alternately too high and too low for life in this zone too.

Venus

Venus is second to the moon as the brightest object in the evening sky. Its brilliance is due not only to its proximity to the earth but also to the heavy cloud about 100 miles deep completely enshrouding it and reflecting the sun's light. Because of this permanent cloud, very little is known about the surface of Venus. That planet's period of rotation, however, was estimated at 243 days in 1967, a value that exceeds the 225-day period of revolution. Venus is often referred to as the earth's twin because it is more like the earth than are other planets with respect to size, mass, and an almost circular adjacent orbit. Venus, however, has no moon and is more spherical (according to Mariner V's tracking of radio signals in 1967) than the slightly pear-shaped earth indicated by artificial satellites since 1957.

Any life as we know it on Venus is questionable but still speculative. Probings by the Russian spacecraft Venus IV and the American Mariner V in 1967 showed that the planet's atmosphere is mostly carbon dioxide. And this gas supports plant life. But only small amounts of life-supporting oxygen and water were detected in Venus's atmosphere when the Russian spacecraft made a soft landing on Venus (1967). Three years earlier, *spectral analysis* from the earth reportedly had shown a "considerable amount of water vapor in Venus's atmosphere." At this point, preference probably should be given to the 1967 probe by Venus IV. But the state of knowledge is a fluid one, and more data are needed. A high percentage of carbon dioxide means an atmosphere providing high heat retention—high enough to bring Venus's surface temperature up to about 800°F. This high temperature is hardly conducive to complex forms of life—even if remindful of steaming swamps harboring primitive life on an early earth.

Mars

Mars, the fourth planet from the sun, is reddish in color even to the naked eye—a characteristic suggestive of its namesake, the mythological god of war. Its white polar caps, advancing and receding seasonally, are also famous. With a 24.6-hour day, Mars has about the same period of rotation as the earth. Its position beyond the earth gives it a period of revolution, or year, of 687 days. With the same inclination of its axis as the earth, Mars has four seasons of about 6 months each. The two moons of Mars are both small, 10 miles in diameter at most. Phobos, the inner moon, revolves around Mars three times daily, passing a slower Deimos.

Being further from the sun, Mars receives somewhat less heat and light than the earth. At night there is a considerable loss of the day's heat due to a thin atmosphere. Summer temperatures may range from 80° F at noon to −150° F at night or even to −200° F at the poles.

In terms of temperature, Mars could support life. In fact, of all the planets besides the earth, Mars until recently seemed to have the best possibilities for living things. And there has been the greatest speculation in that regard. Mars's very thin, clear atmosphere had been estimated to have about 0.1 percent of the oxygen and 5 percent of the water vapor that the earth's atmosphere has. The polar caps, as well as occasional clouds, gave promise of an additional small quantity of water. Definite seasonal color changes observed from the earth in some areas of Mars, from red-brown in winter to dark green in spring and summer, suggested some primitive form of plant life.

Earlier in this century, a wave of excitement arose regarding intelligent life on Mars that lasted almost to the present day in the form of flying saucers. First, Schiaparelli, an Italian, and then Lowell, an American, both highly reputable astronomers, reported strange, straight markings on Mars, termed *canali* in Italian. Lowell boldly hypothesized the existence of intelligent beings that dug canals to carry water down from the poles. The observations of Schiaparelli and Lowell may have been optical illusions, because the *canali* have not been observed in recent years. Differences between what we see (data) and what exists (facts) can be real. Or between what we see and how we interpret it. Photographs of Mars taken in 1965 from Mariner IV at altitudes of 7,000 to 10,000 miles above Mars show fairly straight features 100–200 miles long. But the estimated 2- to 7-mile width of these features is too narrow to be canals seen from the earth. The 21 photographs from Mariner IV do show, however, that Mars is more moonlike than earthlike in its vast crater fields and in other surface features. Many of Mars's craters are 30 to 50 miles wide; one crater reaches 300 miles in width! But some surface areas of Mars show much more smoothness than the moon does, because of erosion resulting from at least a thin Martian atmosphere.

Expectations that life exists on Mars were badly shaken, however, by photographs and other data taken in 1969 from Mariners VI and VII at altitudes of only 2,000 miles above Mars. The data gave little evidence for vegetation there, let alone intelligent creatures. Carbon dioxide, necessary for plant life, is the main component of the Martian upper atmosphere. Traces of oxygen are also present. But Mars would need nitrogen as well for even the simplest form of life as we know it—and there is no sign of nitrogen so far. Evidence of thin clouds of ice crystals above Mars's surface does exist, but the famous Martian polar caps seem to be frozen carbon dioxide rather than the frozen water needed. Some *"canali"* regions have turned out to be sequences of dark surface areas, some of which are unrelated and at best aligned by chance. Other *"canali"* are strings of craters, ridges, and other features. And so the pendulum has swung away from high expectation for the existence of living things on Mars. But perhaps final word must await the spacecraft landings planned for Mars in the 1970 s.

Jupiter

Jupiter is the largest of the planets. Thirteen hundred earths could fit into it. Only about 300 times heavier than the earth, it must be composed of much lighter materials, on the average, than the earth is. Galileo saw only the four largest moons of Jupiter. Today, twelve are seen, racing around at different speeds in accordance with Kepler's laws. Jupiter, like Venus, is perpetually enveloped by clouds. Therefore, its surface is not visible. Noticeable markings on these clouds of liquid ammonia and methane afford determination of a short period of rotation, about 10 hours, for Jupiter. This rapid rotation of about 28,000 miles per hour of a point at Jupiter's equator compares to a speed of 1,000 miles per hour of a point at the earth's equator. Such a speed of rotation results in a considerable flattening of Jupiter's poles. There are no water droplets in Jupiter's clouds. There may be an underlying atmosphere of hydrogen and helium. The temperature of observable sections of this huge sphere has been estimated at about $-200°$ F. This forbidding temperature, among other reasons, makes life as we know it unlikely on Jupiter. So does an estimated 8,000-mile-thick atmosphere of ammonia crystals floating in methane and hydrogen gases above a 17,000-mile-deep icy surface. Such descriptions are speculative pending spacecraft probes of this thick, cloudy atmosphere.

Saturn

Saturn is the most beautiful of planets because of its rings—seen by Galileo as bulges of imperfection. These rings, two bright ones and a faint inner one, consist of myriads of minute bodies perhaps 10 miles thick revolving sheetlike around Saturn. Saturn's axis is inclined to the plane of its orbit. Therefore, as this planet slowly and majestically makes its 30-year journey around the sun, we observe the rings in a cycle of angles, from above, edgewise, and below. Only about 10 miles thick at most, these rings disappear twice when edgewise during Saturn's period of revolution unless viewed with the most powerful of telescopes. Recent estimates suggest that the rings may be only inches thick or less!

Saturn, otherwise, is much like Jupiter. It is second to Jupiter in weight and almost as large in diameter. In addition to its three rings, Saturn has nine moons instead of twelve. One of these nine, Titan, is larger than the planet Mercury. Saturn, like Jupiter, has a rapid rotation period of 10 hours and is also considerably flattened at the poles. Saturn further resembles Jupiter in having a surface hidden by banded clouds and an atmosphere of frozen ammonia and methane thousands of miles thick. Further from the sun, Saturn is colder than Jupiter. With temperatures of up to $-250°$ F, Saturn, the outermost planet visible to the naked eye, is probably too cold for living things.

Uranus, Neptune, and Pluto

Uranus, Neptune, and Pluto, the three outermost planets, were unknown before the telescope. Too far from the sun, these three planets, with highest temperatures of about $-300°$ F, $-330°$ F, and $-350°$ F, respectively, are too cold to harbor life.

Uranus was accidentally discovered in 1781 by William Herschel when that great astronomer was systematically surveying the heavens. One of the stars just didn't remain fixed. Although a telescope was used in the discovery, anyone with good eyesight and a knowledge of where to look can discern Uranus with the naked eye. Through a telescope of 20 power, Uranus appears as a small green disc. No permanent surface markings have yet been resolved, but characteristic cloud bands and five satellites have been detected only through the largest telescopes. Uranus is one of the four largest planets, together with Jupiter, Saturn, and Neptune, and it most likely has a thick, cloudy atmosphere with great layers of ammonia crystals and methane gas covering an immense mass of hydrogen underneath.

Neptune, whose existence was predicted in 1846 by Adams and Leverrier, is dull green in color when seen through the telescope. A 2-inch telescope with a magnifying power of 15 diameters can detect it. A 9- or 12-inch telescope brings it in as a disc. Neptune is about 1 billion miles beyond Uranus. This is 11 astronomical units. The sun, Mercury, Venus, and the earth could extend between Uranus and Neptune eleven times! Neptune, in taking 165 years to get around the sun once, moves so slowly with respect to the fixed stars that it remains in each section of the zodiac for 14 years.

Pluto was discovered as recently as 1930 by Clyde Tombaugh at Lowell Observatory, in Arizona. This far-flung member of the solar family broke the string of four large planets just preceding it. Pluto is the smallest of all the planets except for Mercury.

Pluto is the only planet to cross the orbit of another planet, that of Neptune. All planets revolve in orbits that are almost on the same plane as that of the earth. The plane of Pluto's orbit is tilted at an angle of about 17° to that of the earth (Fig. 5–6). This exceptionally large angle of deviation and the planet's small size make the hypothesis that Pluto is an escaped satellite of Neptune plausible.

Any question of a satellite around Pluto itself, of an atmosphere, or a rotation rate for that planet is as yet unanswerable. Because of great distance, small size, recent discovery, and feeble illumination, not very much is yet known about Pluto. With the planet's 248-year period of revolution, 2 more centuries must pass before men will have traced a single journey of Pluto around the sun. However, spacecraft will probably be investigating that planet long before then.

The Moon

Our moon is only one of 31 that we now know about. But on earth, the reflected light from this one has loomed large in survival and in poetic imagination. As if always mindful of us, the moon ever shows the same face. This is possible only because it rotates on its axis in exactly the same time that it revolves around the earth. A slight vibration of its axis shows a little more than half of the moon's surface. This *libration* was first noted by Galileo.

No observable atmosphere or clouds exist on the moon. What appears to be the "man in the moon" is large gray patches against a lighter surface. These 30 or so patches were formerly thought to be seas. Eons ago, these gray areas may have been covered by water or liquid lava. Actually, photographs show that they are plains surrounded by mountain ranges, peaks, valleys, craters, and other rough features. No bodies of water, with characteristic sunlight reflection, have been detected on the moon.

The first men on the moon found a desolate, lifeless place. Without an atmosphere or clouds, there is no wind or water erosion. There is no sound; just eerie silence and strange, stony forms rising grotesquely above flat surfaces. No plants or animals exist to stir anything anywhere. But black, stony meteors noiselessly bombard the surface. And gaping, sprawling craters everywhere reveal their meteoric or even volcanic origins.

All rock samples brought back from the moon to the earth by Apollo 11 (1969) show surface pits highly suggestive of meteoritic impacts. But more strangely, some Apollo 11 samples (as well as lunar rock photographs from earlier spacecraft) also show a roundness and smoothness like terrestrial rocks. Some lunar rocks appear sandblasted, also glassy. How lunar rocks are eroded is unknown, since the moon's surface shows no evidence of water or wind. One hypothesis is that such smooth rock on the moon is formed by meteoritic impact. *Meteorite* craters in Arabia and rocket craters in other desert sands show that smooth, rocklike lumps called "instant rocks" are formed when a high-speed object hits a granular soil.

Most exciting are a number of Apollo 11 moon rocks analyzed to be probably more ancient than any yet found on earth. Measurements show

CHAPTER FIVE

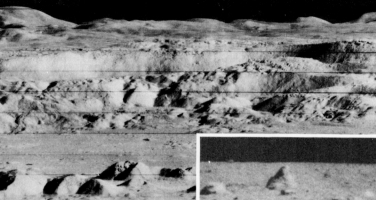

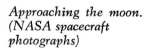

Approaching the moon. (NASA spacecraft photographs)

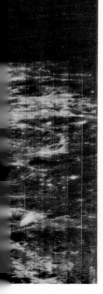

First view of the earth from a spacecraft near the moon. Notice the semblance of a man's face on the crescent earth. (Photograph by NASA's Lunar Orbiter I)

that these lunar rocks may have *crystallized* as long as 4.5 billion years ago. What stories can they tell even about the earth or its origin?

Meteors

Meteors also pepper the earth. Millions of these pieces of iron and stone daily accelerate toward the earth with great speed. Most of these pellets are no larger than a few grains of sand, but some are as large as pebbles and even reach the proportions of rocks weighing tons. Thanks to our atmosphere, very few meteors land. They strike the air with speeds of from 30,000 to 150,000 miles per hour. At such speeds, the heat generated from friction with the air vaporizes most of the meteors to an ash. Observers nearby see the flashes as "shooting stars" or as large fireballs. Six "shooting stars" an hour are ordinarily not too many to count in one evening at a given place. Meteorites (meteors reaching the ground)

Milton looking through Galileo's telescope. (Culver Pictures, Inc.)

generally sink unnoticed into oceans, deserts, mountains and the other uninhabited areas comprising most of the earth's surface. Examined meteorites are generally found to be either iron meteorites, composed mostly of iron with some nickel, or stony meteorites, very similar to ordinary silicate rocks.

Sometimes billions of meteors are observed to travel together in swarms. When these strike the earth's atmosphere, the spectacular results are known as meteor showers. In a famous shower in November 1833, 250,000 meteors were counted from midnight to daylight. Some swarms of meteors have been known to travel in elongated elliptical orbits around the sun. Others burst into view directly after interminable travel through space and time from heaven knows where—we don't know.

Comets

The most awesome spectacle of the skies is the comet. Appearing as flaming torches, brilliant suns, or as huge patches of light with sprouting tails, they have struck terror into the hearts of men for ages. Comets have displayed their fireworks with heads of up to 1 million miles in diameter, long tails trailing for 130 million miles, or six tails extending in a great fan. Stretching even from horizon to zenith, they have been taken by the uninitiated as omens of death and destruction. Such spectacular naked-eye comets appear about once every generation. Some of lesser brilliance can be seen about once a year. With a telescope, comets can be seen in display monthly.

Comets are not only spectacular; some return at regular intervals. Encke's Comet appears in a nearly circular path every 3.3 years. The more commonly known Halley's Comet shows itself in an elongated elliptical path every 76 years.

It is estimated that the famous comet of 1811 will take 3,000 years to return. The orbit of Comet 1864-H extends so far that it should show itself to our descendents in 2 million years. Meanwhile, that comet travels on and on and on. An elongated ellipse is the usual path for a comet that returns, and comets that return are members of our solar system.

If comets do not move in elliptical courses, they follow open hyperbolic or parabolic curves around the sun (see conic-sections diagram [Fig. 4–3] for parabolic and hyperbolic curves). Comets in hyperbolic or parabolic curves do not return. Whatever may be the path of a comet and from wherever it comes, it moves with increased speed toward the sun, makes a hairpin turn quite closely around that body, and swings away.

A comet is first seen as a fuzzy spot that develops a tail as it approaches the sun, the tail pointing away from the sun. We now believe that the head of a comet is a swarm of meteors held together partly with solid ammonia, methane, or ice. Near the sun these cementing materials melt and vaporize. The resulting tail consists of finer particles and gases forced back by a steady stream of charged particles ejected by the sun as a "solar wind," as well as by pressure of the sun's radiant energy. Stars shining through a comet show it to be a discontinuous body. When a comet strikes the earth's atmosphere, a brilliant meteor shower streams through the higher atmosphere, and generally that is all. There is, therefore, little to fear from a comet, even though a large fragment may occasionally get through to the earth's surface. Such a fragment may have formed Arizona's famous meteor crater.

Planetoids

Between the adjacent orbits of Mars and Jupiter, there was thought to be a no-man's-land of 0.3 billion miles—until Ceres, the first *planetoid,* or diminutive planet, was found. Once Ceres was discovered in 1801, a telescopic search was made for more such unknowns. Within 6 years, three more planetoids were found; these, named Pallas, Juno, and Vesta, with Ceres form the Big Four. Since then, about 7,000 smaller planetoids have been reported with minimum diameters of about 1 miles. Estimates are that another 40,000 of these spheroids exist. Except for Ceres, planetoids are too small to be seen with the naked eye. And even Ceres, the largest of them, can be spotted with the unaided eye only at certain times and under the most favorable conditions.

Because these bodies are so small, not much is known about their physical characteristics. But they must be barren; they are too small to hold an atmosphere and any water would have evaporated into space long ago. No wind, water erosion, or soil seems possible. The low temperatures beyond Mars would hardly encourage life.

Quite a bit is known about the motions of some of the planetoids. They follow Kepler's laws, but in elliptical orbits that are generally much more elongated than the orbits of the regular planets. The result is that in some cases, planetoid orbits cross the more circular paths of the planets. In 1937, the planetoid Hermes, little more than a traveling mountain, was photographically picked up by German astronomers as it approached very close to the earth. Perhaps at that time Hitler should have taken heed! He believed in omens.

In conclusion to this chapter, consider the following: If the sun is the center of a small system of comparatively few members, then what keeps that system together? And what keeps the individual members in their orbits? Until such questions are answered, the solar system remains an incomplete hypothesis. In the 17th century, Kepler had the simpler model, but Ptolemaic astronomers still had common sense, the Bible, and Aristotle to explain their system. Kepler had no comparable explana-

Aristotle, Ptolemy and Copernicus discussing cosmology. (Culver Pictures, Inc. photograph of the title page of "Dialogue Concerning the Two Chief World Systems" by Galileo Galilei)

tions for his model. But Galileo was fully aware of this weakness in the Copernican position, and in his *Dialogues Concerning Two New Sciences* met the challenge. He replaced Aristotle's mechanics with a new system, and in the process Galileo established a mathematical, experimental approach to mechanics, for which he has often been called the father of modern science. This new system of mechanics and its quantitative approach to problems of motion are the subjects of the next chapter.

CHAPTER REVIEW

1. Why should Galileo's discovery of Jupiter's four moons necessarily mean that the earth moves around the sun?

2. By a diagram, show why a cycle of moonlike phases is not possible for Venus in the original Ptolemaic system. How does Brahe's earth-centered system (Chapter 4) show that Galileo's discovery of the phases of Venus was not a final blow to earth-centered ideas, as Galileo had thought?

3. List other telescopic discoveries made by Galileo, and evaluate their relative significance as Copernican evidence.

4. How did Kepler's third law and Galileo's observations of the stars help to show that the solar system is a separate unit within the universe?

PART TWO

Force and Motion

6   *Mathematics of Motion*

When you can *measure* what you are speaking about and express it in *numbers,* you know something about it; but when you can not measure it, when you can not express it in numbers, your knowledge is of a meagre and unsatisfactory kind; it may be the beginning of knowledge but you have scarcely, in your thoughts, advanced to the stage of *science.*

LORD KELVIN, 19th century

All science as it grows toward perfection becomes mathematical in its ideas.

A. N. WHITEHEAD, 1911

THE MYSTERY OF GRAVITY

An apple drops from a tree and falls to the ground. Why? We are so accustomed to seeing objects fall that we don't ordinarily think about it. We take falling objects for granted. If a child should ask why things fall, we might answer simply "gravity"—as if a label were an explanation. If pressed further, we might even say that gravity is an invisible force. But this is reasoning in a circle, like a dog chasing its own tail. We see an object fall and talk about a force; to prove the force, we point to the motion of the object. If this mysterious force does exist, what is it? How does it arise? From where? Can its existence be proved? Can something other than a force explain the fall of the apple?

ARISTOTLE AND
WHY THINGS FALL

Five Elements and "Natural Places"

Thinking men speculated about falling objects even before Newton, Galileo, or Aristotle. But Aristotle was among the first to incorporate falling objects into a universal scheme of things. His ideas of gravity were part of his earth-centered scheme of the universe and supported it. There are the heavens and the earth. In between is matter-filled space. Not all substances fall when released; some rise. Burn wood, said Aristotle, and fire, air, and water will move upward; earthy ashes will remain behind. To him, earth, air, water, and fire were four basic elements that in different proportions composed all terrestrial objects. When an object burns, the elements within it are released to seek their own prescribed places in the order of things. The natural place of water is above the earth, air above water, and fire above air. Heavenly bodies are composed of a fifth, ethereal element, quintessence, not to be found below the moon.

Many terrestrial objects are made up mostly of the element earth. The natural place for earthy substances is the center of the universe, where the earth's center is located. When a rock hurtles down from a cliff top, it is seeking its natural center, much like a homing pigeon. Gravity is this downward natural "seeking" of earthy objects for their natural center; it is not a force from the outside. The sphericity of the earth is due to the drawing in of its earthy parts toward their natural place at the center of the universe.

Seas, rivers, and lakes, by their position, show that the natural place of water is just above the earth. Rain falls to its natural place above the earth. Underground springs are seeking their level when they spurt above the ground through a weak point in the earth that traps them. This anthropomorphic upward "seeking" was called *levity*, an upward gravity. Levity and gravity are understandable not in terms of weight but in terms of elements animistically seeking natural places. The following hymn, by Robert Seagrave (1742), is more than a metaphor; it reflects Aristotle's physics:

Rivers to the ocean run
Nor stay in all their course.
Fire ascending, seeks the sun;
Both speed them to their source.

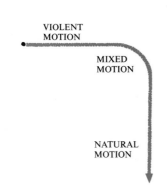

VIOLENT
MOTION

MIXED
MOTION

NATURAL
MOTION

6–1   Aristotle's three types of motion. The horizontally thrown rock travels first solely in "violent" (forced) motion and then entirely in the "natural" motion of gravity. A brief interim of "mixed" motion exists when the violent motion is almost spent and gravity begins to take over.

This simple chemistry of five elements in natural places is the basis of a simple mechanics. Rest is the natural state of affairs for all objects in and around the earth. Everything has an appointed level in accordance with its composition. When an element or object is out of its place, a *natural motion* results when the substance is free to seek its natural level. No outside force is involved. In addition to this natural motion, there is a second type of motion, a *violent motion,* caused by an outside force on an object. Throw a stone and you exert a force to give the stone a violent motion in a horizontal or even upward direction. This forced or violent motion is differentiated from the natural motion of the stone vertically downward. When in violent motion, the stone can continue for a while in its horizontal or upward direction. The reason is that the air displaced in front of the moving stone rushes around it to act as a force behind it. As this process spends itself, the natural motion of gravity takes over. Notice in the diagram representing Aristotelian motion (Fig. 6–1) that there is a very short time of *mixed motion* in which the forced motion is nearly spent and the natural motion is just beginning to take over.

Aristotle's physics is one of common sense. Observation shows that skimming pebbles or moving vehicles quickly come to a stop unless some push or pull is maintained. A constant force seems necessary for a constant velocity on the earth. Further, force and violent motion can be associated as *cause and effect.* That is, no force, no motion (just rest); no cause, no effect. On the other hand, force, a disturbing cause, results in violent motion, the effect.

Aristotle's ideas of motion are thus causal and nonquantitative. They attempt to explain *why* things rest or move rather than describe in any detail *how* things move. Terrestrial objects are at rest in natural places, in natural motion "seeking" their places, or being temporarily forced out of their places only to "seek" them again. The universe is an orderly, geocentric one. These ideas were effective enough to trouble Copernicans with such questions as how can a stone thrown vertically upward land on the same spot from which it was thrown if the earth moves under it? Or how can the earth be the permanent center of gravity toward which heavy objects move and itself be moving around the sun? A new science of mechanics was needed. And when Galileo was under house arrest during the last 9 years of his life, it was to a new science of mechanics that he applied himself.

MATHEMATICAL
DEFINITIONS OF MOTION

We have seen that Brahe's precise observations were highly significant in the development of Kepler's laws. But precise mathematical definitions are highly significant, too. Such brilliant Parisian and Oxford professors in the 14th century as Jean Buridan, Nicholas of Oresme, and William of Occham developed mathematical definitions of *speed* and *acceleration*. Armed with these sharpened tools, Galileo tackled gravity. He further developed principles of acceleration, measured the motion of falling objects, and set laws of falling bodies. A new system of mechanics resulted.

Galileo and these predecessors were mathematical rather than animistic when they classified motion as *uniform* and *nonuniform* instead of "seeking" and "violent." They defined uniform motion as motion in which "the distances traversed . . . during *any* equal intervals of time are themselves equal." Galileo often measured time intervals through pulsebeats. Uniform motion is illustrated by the car in Fig. 6–2 and Table 6–1 that travels 100 ft every 2 sec. Uniform motion is constant motion and is *operationally* defined in terms of distance and time—that is, defined in terms of actual use or process.

Nonuniform motion is motion in which distances covered during equal intervals of time are *not* equal. It is motion that is not constant. In Fig. 6–2 and Table 6–2, during the first 2 sec the gray car travels a distance of 100 ft, but during the next 2 sec, the distance is 120 ft, then 140 ft, then 130 ft, and finally 10 ft in the same time intervals. The motion is nonuniform; it does not involve equal distances in equal times.

Speed: Constant, Instantaneous, and Average

Speed is *distance traveled in a unit of time*, whether it be in miles per hour, feet per second, or meters per second. In this case, emphasis is on the word "unit" rather than on "any interval." In science, reducing things to units is basic. Among other things, units facilitate comparisons. Refer to the diagram of uniform and nonuniform motion (Fig. 6–2). The time interval is given as 2 sec. This interval could have been given as 3 sec, 1 sec, or 0.5 sec and could have been 2 sec in one case and 3 in the other. But the use of 1 sec as a standard has unquestionable advantages. By comparing speeds or distances per second, the motion of all objects can be more easily compared, whether uniform or not.

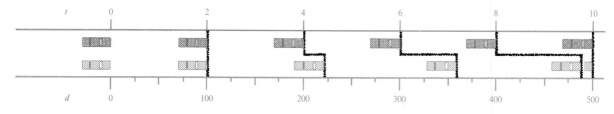

6–2 Uniform versus non-uniform motion. The blue car (Table 6–1), traveling equal distances (100 ft) in equal times (2 sec), moves uniformly. The gray car (Table 6–2), traveling unequal distances in equal times, moves nonuniformly.

Table 6–1 | UNIFORM MOTION

$\triangle t,$ TIME INTERVAL (SEC)	$\triangle d,$ DISTANCE DURING INTERVAL (FT)	$d,$ TOTAL DISTANCE (FT)
0–2	100	100
2–4	100	200
4–6	100	300
6–8	100	400
8–10	100	500

Table 6–2 | NONUNIFORM MOTION

$\triangle t,$ TIME INTERVAL (SEC)	$\triangle d,$ DISTANCE DURING INTERVAL (FT)	$d,$ TOTAL DISTANCE (FT)
0–2	100	100
2–4	120	220
4–6	140	360
6–8	130	490
8–10	10	500

Speed, or velocity,* is not only distance in a unit of time. In another sense, it is a *ratio,* a ratio of distance to time. In algebraic symbols, $v = d/t$, velocity equals the ratio of distance to time. Divide distance covered by time taken and you have speed, whether motion is uniform or nonuniform. When motion is uniform, v is constant. When motion is not uniform, v becomes an *average v,* symbolized as $\bar{v}$. The relationship of velocity, distance, and time is then symbolically expressed as $\bar{v} = d/t$. Symbolic representation of the relationships among changing values or variables, whether they be velocity, distance, and time or anything else,

*In this chapter, "speed" and "velocity" are used synonymously. The difference between these concepts, not significant until Newton, will be discussed in a later chapter.

are *equations*. Galileo was aware of the ratio of distance to time, but he expressed the equation in longhand. He was an expert in geometry but did not know formal algebra. But because he reasoned algebraically, he knew that

if velocity $\quad = \dfrac{\text{distance}}{\text{time}}$

then distance $\quad =$ velocity $\cdot$ time

or time $\qquad = \dfrac{\text{distance}}{\text{velocity}}$

even if he didn't symbolize it as

1. $\bar{v} = \dfrac{d}{t}$

2. $d = \bar{v} \cdot t$

3. $t = \dfrac{d}{\bar{v}} \qquad$ *for uniform motion.* $\hfill$ Equation 6–1

If velocity is equated to a ratio of distance and time, then the units in which it is expressed must be compounded from the ratio. If the distance is in miles and the time in hours, velocity must be in miles per hour. That is, $v = $ miles/hours, or miles per hour. Expressions for speed are familiar from everyday use, but units of other concepts to be discussed will be less confusing if we remember that units are compounded.

In the actual world of events, there are very few cases of objects moving at the same speed for any length of time. A basic problem of motion was, therefore, how to handle nonuniform motion. Specifically, if the speed of an object changes, how can the distance the object travels be related to its time of travel? A first step in answer to this question was to differentiate among *constant* speed, *instantaneous* speed, and *average* speed.

Constant speed is uniform distance covered per unit of time. Constant speed is uniform motion in an established time unit, such as 1 hr or 1 sec. When speed is constant, the speedometer needle is fixed.

Instantaneous speed is a ratio of distance to time at a given instant. For our purposes here, instantaneous speed is the reading that a speedometer gives at any instant of travel. If the motion of a car is not uniform, the instantaneous speed given by the needle reading varies from one moment to another. A reading of 40 mph does not necessarily mean that the vehicle has actually traveled or will travel for 40 mi in 1 hr. The reading of instantaneous through changing speed means that if the speed had not been or would not be changed in 1 hr, 40 mi would be the distance covered. Only for a very short distance, symbolized as $\triangle d$,* and a very short time $\triangle t$, may we say that $v = d/t$, that is, instantaneous

---

*The Greek letter d is $\triangle$, *delta*, and stands for an added amount, or increment, of a changing value such as distance or time.

velocity $v_i = \triangle d / \triangle t$ when motion is not uniform. That is because the ratio of distance to time $\triangle d / \triangle t$ is changing from one instant to the next. When the speed of an object is constantly changing, a most significant achievement, therefore, is to find a single equivalent value of speed for all the varying instantaneous values. That single, simplifying value, of course, is the average speed $(\overline{v})$, already defined as

$$\overline{v} = \frac{\text{total distance}}{\text{total time}} = \frac{d}{t}.$$ Equation 6–1

When velocities increase or decrease uniformly, the average velocity may be found also from the following:

$$\overline{v} = \frac{v_o + v_f}{2},$$ Equation 6–2

where $\overline{v}$ = average velocity

v_o = original velocity

v_f = final velocity.

That is, when velocity increases uniformly, the average speed is one-half the sum of the initial and final speeds.

Acceleration

If not fixed at constant speed, the needle on a speedometer could move evenly and uniformly in a given direction or unevenly and spasmodically. Galileo carefully differentiated between such uniform and nonuniform changes in velocity. According to Galileo, "a body is said to be uniformly accelerated when, starting from rest, it acquires equal increments of velocity during equal time intervals." The concept of acceleration was at the heart of Galileo's study of gravity. It was his mathematical key to the motion of all objects. This concept led to his laws of falling bodies and to Newton's laws of motion and gravitation. Let us explore this concept further.

6–3 Acceleration involves changes of both velocity and time. Cars A and B have equal changes in velocity but in unequal periods of time. The two cars therefore have different accelerations (Eq. 6–3).

Concisely, *acceleration* is the *time rate of change of velocity*. Two factors are involved: change of velocity and the time taken. For example, the speedometer of car *A* in Fig. 6–3 at one instant reads 40 mph, and

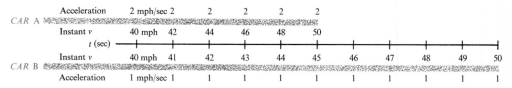

5 sec later, 50 mph. The difference, 10 mph, expresses a change in velocity. This is not sufficient, however. A second car B also changes from 40 to 50 mph, but in 10 rather than 5 sec. The difference in time taken is significant. By the time B's speedometer reads 50 mph, A's speedometer registers only 45 mph. How then are we to compare the two equal changes of speed and still make allowance for the difference in time taken? The answer is to determine the average amount of change of speed *in a unit of time*, that is, in 1 sec.

Car A on an average changed its speed by 2 mph/sec:

$$\frac{(50-40)\ \text{mph}}{5\ \text{sec}} = 2\ \text{mph/sec}.$$

Car B had an average change of

$$\frac{(50-40)\ \text{mph}}{10\ \text{sec}} = 1\ \text{mph/sec}.$$

You can see that the velocity of car A was changing twice as fast as that of car B. The general comparison was made possible by comparing the average amount of change of velocity of each car in the equal time interval of 1 sec. This time rate of change of velocity is acceleration, we repeat, and may be expressed as

$$a = \frac{\text{change in velocity}}{\text{time}} \quad \text{or} \quad \frac{\triangle v}{t}.$$

That is,

$$a^* = \frac{v_f - v_o}{t}, \qquad\qquad \text{Equation 6-3}$$

where
$a =$ acceleration
$v_f =$ final velocity
$v_o =$ original velocity
$t =$ time taken.

When an object accelerates from rest $(v_o = 0)$, then

$$a = \frac{v_f}{t}.$$

That is,

$$\text{acceleration} = \frac{\text{final velocity}}{\text{time}},$$

or

$$v_f = at. \qquad\qquad \text{Equation 6-4}$$

---

*In nonuniform acceleration, the a in the equation is an average acceleration, $\bar{a}$.

Equation 6–4 relates velocity v_f to acceleration a and time t by the definition of acceleration. For example, tripling the time t for a car to accelerate from rest triples the car's velocity v_f.

If the motion of an object increases, the acceleration is positive $(+)$. If the motion of an object decreases, the acceleration is negative $(-)$ and is known as deacceleration or deceleration. To illustrate, if the speed of car A above had changed in 5 sec from 50 mph to 40 mph, its acceleration would be negative, with a value of -2 mph/sec.

$$a = \frac{v_f - v_o}{t} = \frac{(40-50) \text{ mph}}{5 \text{ sec}} = \frac{-10 \text{ mph}}{5 \text{ sec}} = -2 \text{ mph/sec.}$$

Use the definition of acceleration in its algebraic form to show that in the case of car B's speed changing from 50 mph to 40 mph in 10 sec, there would be a deceleration of -1 mph/sec.

Note that in the above examples, we referred to acceleration units as "miles per hour per second." It should be clear that "miles per hour" refers to readings of speed. In the above example, A's speedometer reading dropped from 50 miles per hour to 40 miles per hour. This drop of 10 miles per hour took place in 5 *seconds* and not 5 hours. Therefore, *every second* there was a drop in reading of 2 miles per *hour*. The speed dropped at an average of 2 miles per hour every second. This is expressed as a deceleration of -2 miles per hour per second, or -2 mph/sec.

Suppose speedometer velocities read in feet per second instead of miles per hour. Can you see how acceleration in such a case would be expressed as feet per second every second, or ft/sec/sec?

COMPARISON OF UNITS

CONCEPT	DEFINITION	UNIT (LARGE)	UNIT (SMALL)
Distance	change of position (in motion)	mi	ft
Time	interval between events	hr	sec
Velocity	rate of change of position	mph	ft/sec
Acceleration	rate of change of velocity	mph/sec	ft/sec/sec (or ft/sec^2)

PRINCIPLES OF ACCELERATION

Equation 6–4 relates acceleration, velocity, and time by definition. But how can distance be determined for an object accelerating from rest? An answer lies in combining the definitions of velocity and acceleration symbolized in Equations 6–1, 6–2, and 6–4. This algebraic combination is as follows:

1. Remember that $d = \bar{v}t$.

   Distance = average velocity · time (Eq. 6–1).

2. And that $\bar{v} = \dfrac{v_o + v_f}{2}$.

   Average velocity = ½ the sum of the initial and final velocities.

3. Or $\bar{v} = \dfrac{v_f}{2}$.

   Average velocity = ½ the final velocity when $v_o = 0$.

4. Then $d = \left(\dfrac{v_f}{2}\right)t$.

   Substituting $v_f/2$ for average velocity $\bar{v}$ in line 1.

5. But $v_f = at$.

   Final velocity = acceleration · time (Eq. 6–4).

6. Therefore, $d = \left(\dfrac{at}{2}\right)t$.

   Substituting at for v_f in line 4.

   Or $d = \frac{1}{2}at^2$.

   Equation 6–5

Equation 6–5 is a principle of acceleration that relates distance traveled d to acceleration a and time interval t.

It can be similarly shown by a proper substitution with $v_f = at$ and $d = \frac{1}{2}at^2$ that

$$v_f^2 = 2ad. \qquad\qquad \text{Equation 6–6}$$

(Hint: If $v_f = at$, $t = v_f/a$, and $t^2 = v_f^2/a^2$. Then v_f^2/a^2 can be substituted for t^2 in Equation 6–5.)

Equation 6–6 is a principle of acceleration that relates final velocity v_f to acceleration a and distance traveled d.

Equations 6–4, 6–5, and 6–6* can be expressed in words as follows:

Principle 1. With constant acceleration, speed acquired from rest is directly proportional to time. Example: With constant acceleration from rest, a car travels ten times as fast after 10 sec as after 1 sec.

Principle 2. With constant acceleration, distance traveled from rest is proportional to the square of the time. Example: With constant acceleration from rest, a car travels *100* times as far in 10 sec as in 1 sec.

Principle 3. With constant acceleration, speed from rest is proportional to the square root of the distance traveled. Example: The ratio of the velocities of two cars A and B traveling at 75 mph and 25 mph is, of course, 3:1, but the stopping distance of the two cars at those speeds is 9:1 (see example 4 below).

*Objects may accelerate from initial speeds as well as from rest. See Appendix D for adaptations of Eqs. 6–4 to 6–6 that allow for such initial speeds.

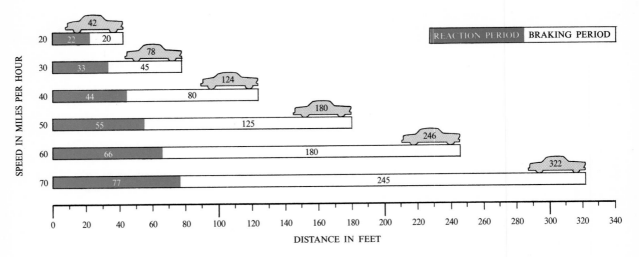

SPEED IN MILES PER HOUR

DISTANCE IN FEET

6–4 Stopping-distance graph. A small increase in speed means a relatively large increase in stopping distance. Notice that a stopping distance must be allowed for reaction as well as for braking

The graph in Fig. 6–4 illustrates Principle 3. Notice how small increases in speed mean comparatively large increases in stopping distances.

By using the values given in the columns for speed v and for braking distance d in Equation 6–6, the negative acceleration a expected of brakes can be determined. Also notice in the table that much additional distance is lost in reaction time. With increasing speed, both the reaction distance and the braking distance mount as threats in an emergency.

The following examples illustrate these relationships in more detail.

Example 1 (Principle 1). How long does it take a car to reach 60 mph when uniformly accelerating from rest at 5 mph/sec?

Solution: Eq. 6–4

Given: $v_f = 60$ mph

$$a = \frac{5 \text{ mph}}{\text{sec}}$$

$$v_f = at$$

To find t: 60 mph $= \dfrac{5 \text{ mph}}{\text{sec}} (t)$

$$t = 12 \text{ sec.}$$

Example 2 (Principle 2). How many feet does a car travel from rest when it accelerates at 5 mph/sec for 10 sec?

Solution: Eq. 6–5

Given: $a = 5$ mph/sec $= 7.3$ ft/sec/sec $= 7.3$ ft/sec²

   $t = 10$ sec

To find d: $d = \frac{1}{2}at^2$

   $d = \frac{1}{2}\dfrac{7.3 \text{ ft } (100 \text{ sec}^2)}{\text{sec}^2}$ (Note that units cancel out like numbers.)

   $d = 365$ ft.

Example 3 (Principle 3). A man driving an auto at 60 mph sees a child 300 ft ahead. If his brakes can give him a negative acceleration of -17 ft/sec/sec, can he stop his car without hitting the child? Reaction distance at that speed is about 65 ft (see Fig. 6–4).

Solution: Eq. 6–6

Given: $v_o = 60$ mph $= 88$ ft/sec

   $v_f = 0$

   $a = -17$ ft/sec/sec

To find d: The distance required for stopping from an initial velocity v_o of 60 mph would be equal to that starting from rest and accelerating to 60 mph.

Therefore, $v^2 = 2ad_1$

   $88^2 = 2(17)d_1$

   $34d_1 = 7{,}744$

braking distance $d_1 = 228$ ft (approx.)

reaction distance $d_2 = 65$ ft (average)

total distance $d = 293$ ft (approx.).

The driver barely stops short of hitting the child 300 ft ahead.

Example 4 (Principle 3). What is the relationship in the braking distances between a car moving 75 mph and one moving 25 mph?

Solution: Eq. 6–6

Given: $v_1 = 75$ mph

   $v_2 = 25$ mph

To find $\dfrac{d_1}{d_2}$: $v_1^2 = 2ad_1$ or 75^2 (mph)² $= 2ad_1$

   $v_2^2 = 2ad_2$ or 25^2 (mph)² $= 2ad_2$

$$\frac{v_1^2}{v_2^2} = \frac{2ad_1}{2ad_2} \quad \text{or} \quad \frac{5,625 \ (\text{mph})^2}{625 \ (\text{mph})^2} = \frac{d_1}{d_2}$$

$$\frac{d_1}{d^2} = \frac{9}{1}.$$

That is, the ratio of stopping distances is 9:1 if the ratio of speeds is 3:1. The car in example 3 required 228 ft (ignoring reaction distance) to stop at 60 mph. At 30 mph, or half the velocity, only one-fourth of that distance, or 57 ft, would be the braking distance.

VISUALIZING MOTION THROUGH GRAPHS

The Graph as a Coordinate System

In the first chapter we saw that early in the science of astronomy, men projected *coordinate systems* upon the heavens to identify the positions of objects and to describe their motions. Thanks to René Descartes (1596–1650), the French contemporary of Galileo who founded analytical geometry, we have a general system for identifying positions of objects moving anywhere. This Cartesian coordinate system has two main axes, referred to as the x axis and y axis, as shown in Fig. 6–5 with Table 6–3. Instead of distances being measured north and south or east and west of these lines, they are measured in equally spaced units above ($+$) and below ($-$) the x-axis and in units to the right ($+$) and left ($-$) of the y-axis. The position of any point P plotted above or below the x-axis is called the y coordinate of point P; the position of P to the right or left of the y-axis is called the x coordinate of that point. In Fig. 6–5, point P has an x coordinate of $+6$ units and a y coordinate of $+8$ units. In this case the coordinates are said to be (6,8). The x coordinate is generally given first. The coordinates of point Q in the figure are (8,10), and of point R are $(-4,-6)$. See if you can plot the following points: $(6,-8)$, $(-6,8)$, $(-6,-8)$, $(8,-10)$, and $(-4,6)$. Review your algebra if you are unable to plot these points. Modern civilization abounds with Cartesian coordinate systems in the form of statistical graphs, street plans, topographical maps, and the like.

A graph is a coordinate system in which one variable, such as time, is plotted against another variable, such as velocity or distance. The changing values of time, for example, could be indicated along the x-axis, and the values of velocity or of distance along the y-axis. In the motion of any object, a value of velocity exists for each value of time. Points can be plotted on a graph from the corresponding values of time and velocity. Connecting the points on the graph gives lines or curves characteristic of graphs.

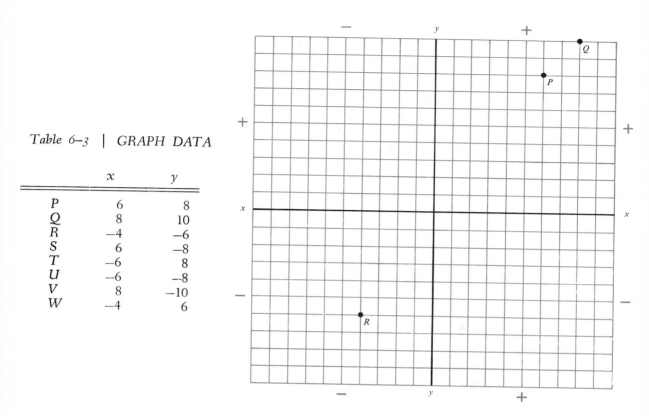

Table 6-3 | GRAPH DATA

	x	y
P	6	8
Q	8	10
R	-4	-6
S	6	-8
T	-6	8
U	-6	-8
V	8	-10
W	-4	6

6-5   Plotting a graph. A graph shows relationship between variable quantities (x and y in Table 6-3).

Tables and Graphs

Tables provide the most systematic arrangement of data, and graphs, through their lines or curves, enable us to visualize relationships in the data. In Tables 6-4 to 6-6, you will find data for an object that supposedly moved for 5 sec with uniform speed, then with uniform acceleration, and finally with nonuniform acceleration. All three tables have data systematized for time, instantaneous velocity, and acceleration. The three associated graphs (Figs. 6-6 to 6-8) depict the relationship between instantaneous velocity and time for the object moving in the three ways described in the tables. In each graph, the line joins points plotted from the time and velocity data given in the tables.

Some spaces in the tables under velocity, acceleration, and distance have intentionally been left blank. There has been previous discussion in this chapter regarding the $d = \bar{v} \cdot t$ and $v_f = a \cdot t$ which relate distance, velocity, acceleration, and time in uniform and accelerated motions. From that discussion, see if you can fill in the blank spaces.

Table 6-4 | UNIFORM VELOCITY

t (SEC)	v (FT/SEC)	a (FT/SEC²)
1	50	0
2	50	0
3		0
4	50	0
5		0

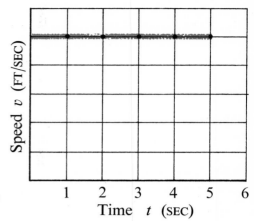

6–6   Velocity plotted against time at no acceleration.

Table 6-5 | UNIFORM ACCELERATION

t (SEC)	v (FT/SEC)	a (FT/SEC²)
1	10	10
2	20	10
3		10
4	40	
5	50	10

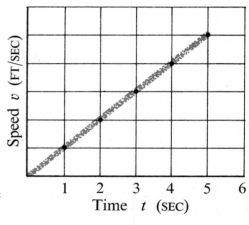

6–7   Velocity plotted against time at uniform acceleration.

Table 6-6 | NONUNIFORM ACCELERATION

t (SEC)	v (FT/SEC)	a (FT/SEC²)
1	10	10
2	20	6
3	26	14
4	40	0
5	40	0

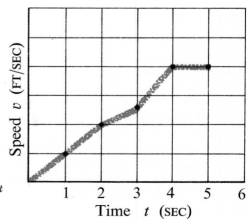

6–8   Velocity plotted against time at nonuniform acceleration.

The graph for uniform velocity (Fig. 6–6) shows a straight horizontal line. Does velocity change with time in uniform motion? Why or why not? How does the horizontal line show this?

Direct Proportions

Notice the diagonal in the relationship between velocity and time in the graph for uniform acceleration (Fig 6–7). Does the line show velocity to increase as length of time increases? If so, does velocity increase exactly to the extent that time does? Prove or disprove your answer by (1) determining the value of the velocity on the graph for any time value, then (2) checking to see if the value is doubled when the time is doubled, and (3) tripled when the time is tripled. *If two variables,* such as velocity and time, *exactly increase or decrease together,* they are said to be in *direct proportion.* Are velocity and time in direct proportion to each other in the graph? How could you show whether they are or not through the table? How could you show whether they are or not through the equation $v_f = a \cdot t$?

Inverse Proportions

Quantities can be in *inverse proportion* as well as direct proportion. When *one quantity decreases as another increases,* the two quantities are in *inverse* proportion. *Double* the average velocity for a 400-mi trip, and the time is reduced to *one-half.* *Triple* the average velocity for the same trip and the time becomes *one-third.* In this case, the average velocity is in inverse proportion to the time. Can you explain this example of inverse proportion through the equation $d = \bar{v} \cdot t$?

Interpolations

In the tables above, data are given at the end of each second of motion. If we wanted to find out from the second graph what the velocity would be 2.5 sec after the uniform acceleration started, the answer of 25 ft/sec would be an *interpolation.* Interpolations involve information not given directly by data but arrived at by mathematical reasoning between direct points of information. Interpolations are based on the assumption that the line or curve drawn between any two points of information would not change if more data were added there from actual observation. In this case, the assumption would be that the accelerated motion during the third second is consistently uniform in accordance with the equation $v = at$.

Extrapolations

In the tables above, data are given for only 5 sec of motion. If a prediction of what the speed would be after a sixth second were desired from the second graph, the diagonal line could be extended with a light or dotted line, and a reading could be taken from the proper point. A reading of this kind on a line or curve extended beyond the data given is called an *extrapolation*. Extrapolations are always based on the assumption that the line or curve would not change if extended by more data beyond the given limits. In this case, the assumption would be that the motion after the fifth second would remain uniform acceleration in accordance with the equation $v = at$.

Interpret the meaning of the zigzag line with respect to speed-time relationships in the graph for nonuniform acceleration (Fig. 6–8). Are speed and time always in direct proportion to each other in this case? If not, are there any sections in the graph in which speed and time are in direct proportion? Explain.

Now, using the completed data for distances from the tables, draw graphs for uniform speed and for uniform acceleration with distance, replacing speed along the *y*-axes and keeping time still along the *x*-axes. In each case, first establish the points on the graph from the table, and then connect the points for the seemingly best-fitting line or curve. In which case(s), if any, do you obtain unbroken lines? Broken lines? Curved lines? Are there cases of direct proportion between distance and time? How is direct proportion between distance and time determined? How is direct proportion recognized in a graph? In an equation?

Galileo approached falling objects mathematically to test gravity. This chapter presented the mathematical details necessary to give Galileo's accomplishments meaning.

CHAPTER REVIEW

1. Just what is gravity? Why do things fall?
2. How did Aristotle explain gravity?
3. Aristotle's cosmology and mechanics assumed five elements, natural order, and natural places. Show how Aristotle's mechanics supported Ptolemaic theory against Copernican.
4. Copernicus transferred the sun to the center of the universe. What system of ideas did Copernicus have for explaining what keeps the earth "in the heavens" revolving around the sun?

5. How does change in speed lead to separate concepts of instantaneous, average, and constant speed? Illustrate the differences among these three concepts of speed.

6. How does change in speed lead to the concept of acceleration? Illustrate.

7. Give a mathematical definition of speed. Of acceleration. Why are these mathematical definitions important?

8. What relationships exist among values of speed, acceleration, distance, and time? Illustrate. Why are these relationships important?

9. Show how graphs visually depict relationships among values of speed, acceleration, distance, and time.

10. Illustrate interpolation and extrapolation on a graph. What assumptions exist in interpolation and extrapolation?

11. Are the relationships among speed, acceleration, distance, and time true by definition, by experience, by both, or by what? Differentiate between a statement's being "true by definition" and "true by experience." Illustrate.

12. Why could this chapter have been called "Mathematizing Motion"?

13. Do you agree with Lord Kelvin's statement heading this chapter? Why?

PROBLEMS

1. How long does it take sunlight traveling with a speed of 186,000 mi/sec to reach the earth? To reach Pluto?

2. How far does a car traveling at a constant speed of 30 mph go in 20 sec?

3. A plane travels 385 air mi in 50 min. What is the average velocity of the plane? At the same average velocity, how long would a plane take to travel from Chicago to San Francisco (about 1,850 air mi)?

4. How far does a car go that uniformly accelerates from rest to 60 mph in 20 sec?

5. Why is it incorrect to refer to acceleration units as miles per hour instead of miles per hour per second? Or as feet per second instead of feet per second per second? Change 5 mph/sec to feet per second per second.

6. A car starting from rest reaches a speed of 45 mph in 15 sec. At the same acceleration, how much more time is needed to reach a speed of 75 mph?

7. A car decelerates from 60 mph to a stop in 4 sec. What is the average deceleration of the car? How far does the car go during the 4 sec?

8. Show that with constant acceleration from rest (for example, 5 ft/sec/sec), a car travels ten times as fast in 10 sec as in 1 sec.

9. Show that with constant acceleration from rest (for example, 5 ft/sec/sec), a car travels 100 times as far in 10 sec as in 1 sec.

10. In Table 6–1 compare the braking distance of a car traveling at 60 mph to that of one traveling at 30 mph. Is this ratio in accord with Equation 6–6? Compare the reaction distances in the two cases.

11. By using a value in the column in Table 6–1 for speed v and a corresponding value from the column for braking distance d, determine the negative acceleration a to be expected of brakes.

12. A driver in an auto speeding at 80 mph sees several cattle across the highway 500 ft ahead. With a braking acceleration of −15 ft/sec, can he stop his car without hitting the cattle? Allow 90 feet as a reaction distance at that speed.

13. What does it mean to say that when distance equals velocity times time $(d = vt)$, d is *directly proportional* to t $(d \propto t)$?

14. What is meant by the statement that distance is proportional to time squared $(d \propto t^2)$?

15. What is meant by the statement that velocity is *inversely proportional* to time $(v \propto 1/t)$? Illustrate.

16. Why do any two values in direct proportion, as $d \propto t$, give a straight-line graph? Illustrate.

17. Why do two quantities in inverse proportion, as $v \propto 1/t$, always give a straight-line graph? Illustrate with a graph.

18. How can you tell the difference between an inverse proportion and a direct proportion on a graph? Illustrate.

19. Draw a continuous curve or graph of (a) velocity versus braking distances from Table 6–1, (b) velocity versus reaction distance from Table 6–1, and (c) velocity versus total distance from Table 6–1.

SUGGESTIONS FOR
FURTHER READING

Cohen, I. Bernard, *The Birth of a New Physics,* Anchor paperback, Garden City, N.Y., 1960, Ch. 2.

Taylor, Lloyd W., *Physics, the Pioneer Science,* Vol. 1, Dover, New York, 1941, Chs. 1–2.

White, Harvey, *Modern College Physics,* Van Nostrand, New York, 1962, Chs. 3–4.

Holton, Gerald J., and D. H. D. Roller, *Foundations of Modern Physical Science*, Addison-Wesley, Reading, Mass., 1958, Ch. 1.

Cheronis, Nicholas D., et al., *Study of the Physical World*, Houghton Mifflin, Boston, 1958, Ch. 11.

7   *Testing Gravity*

> When Galileo rolled balls down an inclined plane, a new light burst upon investigators of Nature.
>
> IMMANUEL KANT, 18th century

The "new light" recognized by the physicist and philosopher Immanuel Kant was the dawn of a new mathematical approach to the universe now known as theoretical physics. Let us look further into the significance of Kant's words.

WHICH FALLS FASTER?

If a 100-pound boulder and a 1-pound rock were dropped at the same instant from the top of a cliff, which would hit the ground first? About how much sooner? And why? How would you answer these questions?

Aristotle's answer was that "bodies fall faster in proportion to their weight." That is, a 100-pound object should fall 100 times faster than a 1-pound object. Or, in Aristotelian words, "An iron ball of one hundred pounds falling from a height of one hundred cubits reaches the ground before a one pound ball has fallen a single cubit." The commonsense reasoning was that to the extent the heavier object has extra weight, it is impelled to move faster. Snowflakes and feathers can be observed to settle to the ground at a fairly constant speed; raindrops, at a higher speed. Heavier objects than these fall faster because they are heavier.

Galileo questioned Aristotle's position and maintained that all objects, regardless of weight, would fall equally fast in a vacuum. Resistance of the air on wide surfaces holds back the feather and snowflake that in a vacuum would fall as fast as a coin or cannonball. Aristotle, claiming that "nature abhors a vacuum," did not think in terms of a vacuum. Galileo visualized a vacuum as an ideal, free-fall situation, without air resistance, and thereby equated the fall of objects. He backed up his reasoning in several ways. One of them was to show through another simple thought experiment that two identical bricks would fall together whether separated or sides touching (Fig. 7–1). Whether two bricks are touching to form one long brick or slightly separated to remain two, their downward velocity should remain the same; that is, objects of different weights should fall equally fast. More precisely, the velocity of a falling body should be independent of its weight.

That heavy objects would fall much faster than light ones seemed so self-evident to Aristotle and most of his followers that they felt it unnecessary to test the principle by actually dropping rocks. Records show, however, that John Philoponus, in the 6th century, did experiment with objects of different weights and found that they fell with almost equal speeds through the air. There is a story that Galileo dropped objects of different weights, sizes, and materials from the Leaning Tower of Pisa. Whether or not he really did is unknown, but the story has become a symbol of his experimental approach to nature. In any case, in his *Dialogues Concerning Two New Sciences*, there is some evidence that he dropped objects from high places somewhere. Salviati, who represents Galileo in the *Dialogues*, does claim that "you find on making the experiment [with a 100-lb ball and a 1-lb ball] that the larger outstrips the smaller by two finger breadths." Then a little later, another character, Sargredo, exclaims, "But I, Simplicio, who have made the test, can assure you that a cannon ball weighing one or two hundred pounds, or even more, will not reach the ground by as much as a span ahead of a musket ball weighing only half a pound, provided both are dropped from a height of 200 cubits [about 300 ft]." Galileo explained that the slight difference in time between the two balls was due to air resistance. He claimed that with actual free fall in a vacuum, any two iron balls would hit the ground at the same time. Since then, this claim has been substantiated many times. Even a feather and a coin dropped together in a long vacuum tube arrive together at the bottom of the tube.

Actually, "free fall" as a concept involves an ideal situation in which objects can fall without any air resistance or friction* whatever. In actual life, even the best of vacuum tubes contains minute amounts of air or other gases. But Galileo's approach was to set up an ideal situation for the basic principle that all objects fall equally fast regardless of

Which falls faster? (The Bettmann Archive, Inc.)

---

*Friction is defined as forces that resist motion between surfaces in contact.

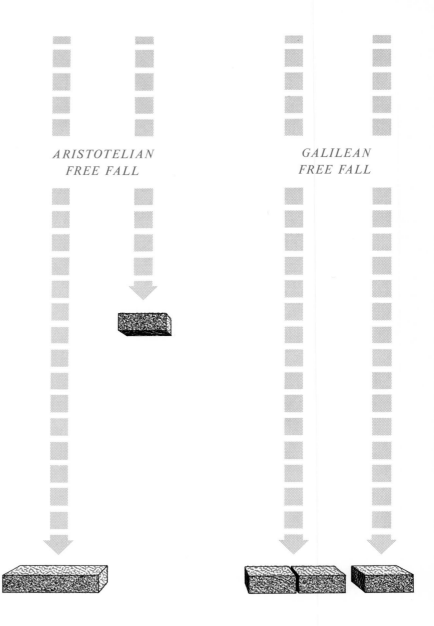

*7–1   Aristotle versus Galileo
on free fall. Aristotle reasoned
that the larger brick should
fall faster because of its
greater weight. Galileo held
that halves of the large brick
would fall at the same rate
whether joined or separated.*

weight and then to make allowances for the air resistance and friction
that exist in actual life. This "free fall" became an idealized conceptual
model through which to understand small differences actually found in
the speeds of falling objects. Beginning with Galileo, idealized thought
experiments became established practice in probing nature.

GALILEO AND
HOW THINGS FALL

Thought experiments with falling objects in idealized situations gave Galileo his idea that weight does not influence the velocity of a freely falling object. But he did not stop there. In taking a new look at falling objects, he was interested in "mathematizing" and measuring their motion. The question was, How was this to be done? How was the fall or the motion of an object to be reduced to numbers, so that more could be understood about gravity and about motion in general? Galileo's quantitative approach to nature here is quite well expressed by the quotation from Lord Kelvin that heads Chapter 6. Today we would say that Galileo was operational and mathematical. First of all, he believed that in understanding gravity, emphasis should be upon *how* things fall rather than *why* things fall. *How* is an appeal to observation; *why*, to speculation. He believed that it is premature to speculate about the *why* before knowing more about the *how*. He therefore experimentally observed specific falling objects, but more than that, he systematically used mathematics as a tool, language, and logic; he used it to measure, define, and describe what he saw.

GRAVITY AS
UNIFORM ACCELERATION

A Hypothetical Case of Free Fall

Like Galileo, we start with a hypothetical case of free fall. A stone is dropped from a high cliff. If we were watching the stone, we would probably agree that its speed increases as it descends. Is the acceleration uniform or not? How could we find out? One way would be to ask ourselves *how* the stone would fall *if* it did fall with uniform acceleration and then to determine whether it actually does fall that way. At least, that is the way Galileo approached the problem.

Table 7–1 illustrates how a stone would fall from rest at an assumed uniform acceleration of 10 ft/sec/sec.* The values in columns 1–2 (Table 7–1) may be considered as hypothetical data in an idealized thought experiment. Columns 3–10 represent reasoning from the data. And generalizations may be found in the bottom row.

Column 1 indicates the equal time intervals in seconds, and column 2, the equal velocity increments $\triangle v$ of 10 ft/sec *gained each second*. To be

*The actual value eventually determined for g, the acceleration of gravity, will be given later in this chapter.

specific in our thought experiment, we will assume the arbitrary value of 10 ft/sec/sec for a uniform acceleration of gravity, symbolized as g and shown in column 2. Column 3 represents the buildup of instantaneous speed (v_f) that an imaginary speedometer on the stone would show second by second as equal increments of speed are added. Fill in the spaces left blank in the first three columns.

Column 4 illustrates another basic definition Galileo used to analyze motion: average velocity $\bar{v}$. The average velocity applies in each case to the total fall of the stone to the end of the given second. For the first 4 sec, for example, our uniformly accelerating stone should have the following average velocity: Since the stone falls from rest $(v_o = 0)$,

$$\bar{v} = \frac{v_o + v_i}{2} = \frac{0 + 40 \text{ ft}}{2 \text{ sec}} = 20 \text{ ft/sec } (v_i \text{ from column 3}).$$

Why does each value for average velocity $\bar{v}$ in column 4 always equal one-half the corresponding instantaneous velocity v_i in column 3?

Column 5 indicates the total distance of fall d at the end of each second. Any value in column 5 can be obtained through the definition $\bar{v} = d/t$ or $d = \bar{v} \cdot t$ (Eq. 6–1). For example, after 4 sec:

$$d = \bar{v} \cdot t = 20 \text{ ft/sec} \cdot 4 \text{ sec}^* = 80 \text{ ft } (\bar{v} \text{ from column 4}).$$

Each value in column 6 represents a ratio of distances. The total distance d the stone has fallen after each second is compared to the 5 ft fallen after the first second $(d_1 = 5 \text{ ft})$. For example, after the third second, the ratio of distances $d:d_1$ is 45:5 (from column 5) or 9:1 (column 6). Surprisingly enough, consecutive values in column 6, without exception, turn out to be squares of 1, 2, 3 . . . continuously. For example, the first value is 1, or 1^2, the second value is 4, or 2^2, the third value is 9, or 3^2, and so on. You fill in the fourth value. As shown in column 7, each of these squares is *identical in amount* to the corresponding square of the time of fall! For example, after 6 sec the time squared (t^2) is 6^2, or 36 (column 7). That is also the value in column 6. There are no exceptions in the equalities between the two columns.

*Hypothetical Equations
in Assumed Free Fall g*

Remember that our hypothetical case of a falling stone is a thought experiment of a sort. The stone is an imagined stone, not one actually falling. The first five columns were built up through arithmetic reasoning

*Remember that units cancel out like numbers.

Table 7-1 | HYPOTHETICAL FREE FALL FROM REST
(ASSUMED ACCELERATION = 10 FT/SEC²)

1	2	3	4	5	6	7	8	9	10
		VELOCITY (FT/SEC)		DISTANCE OF FALL (FT)					
	Δv	v_f IN-STANTANEOUS	$\bar{v}$		$d:d_1$	t^2		v_f^2	
TIME t (SEC)	GAINED DURING EACH SEC	NEOUS AFTER EACH SECOND	AVERAGE VELOCITY TO GIVEN INSTANT	d TOTAL	RATIO	TIME SQUARED	$5t^2$	VELOCITY SQUARED	$20d$
1	10	10	5	5	$d_1 = 1$ (or 1^2)	1	5	100	100
2	10	20	10	20	4 (or 2^2)	4	20	400	400
3	10	30		45	9 (or 3^2)		45		900
4		40	20	80		16	80	1,600	1,600
5	10		25		25 (or 5^2)		125	2,500	
6				180	36 (or 6^2)	36		3,600	3,600

Generalizations

If a = 10 ft/sec² $v_f = 10t$ $d = \bar{v}t$ $\bar{v} = v_i/2$ $d = 5t^2$ col. 6 values = col. 7 values $v_f^2 = 20d$

  $= at$ $= \frac{1}{2}at^2$ $= 2ad$

If a = g $v_f = gt$ $d = \frac{1}{2}gt^2$ $v_f^2 = 2gd$ or $2gh$

from definitions of velocity. Assumed in the reasoning is a constant acceleration of 10 ft/sec/sec for the stone. In columns 6 and 7 and in the remaining columns, we can see one of the beauties of mathematical thought experiments and of tabular organization, too: Through them hidden equations often can be discovered for probing nature by actual experimental test.

Column 8 represents $5t^2$, or 5 times the time squared. But notice that all the values for $5t^2$ in column 8 are identical to the values for total distance d in column 5. For example, after the fourth second, the square of the time t^2 is 4^2, or 16, and 5 times the 4^2 is 80, as found in column 8. The same value of 80 is also found in column 5 for the total distance of the stone's fall after 4 sec. These equal values down both columns show a new relationship between total distance and time of fall:

$$d = 5t^2.$$

That is, knowledge of time of fall would give the distance of fall if gravity has a known uniform acceleration. A stopwatch and a stone could give the height of a cliff! Galileo was the first to recognize the direct proportion between distance of fall d and time squared t_1.

Column 9 denotes v_f^2, and column 10, $20d$. These two columns are also unique in having identical values. This means that if our hypothetical stone falls with uniform acceleration, the instantaneous velocity squared of the stone at any point of its fall equals 20 times the total distance fallen to that point. That is,

$$v_f^2 = 20d \text{ or } v_f^2 = 20h,$$

where h, height of fall, is used for d.

Test your understanding of Table 7–1 by filling in the various spaces and rows that have been left blank.

Our entire free-fall table is an arithmetic buildup to general equations. So far, our analysis of the table has been quite specific. Now, notice the equations in the row of generalizations under the free-fall columns. These equations are significant because they serve the following functions:

    1. Generalize the particulars in the columns above them.
    2. Emphasize the relationships among time, distance, velocity, and acceleration.
    3. Provide mathematical hypotheses of gravity for experimental testing.

For example, notice the relationships of columns 1, 2, and 3. For all intervals of time, column 3 values = column 2 values · column 1 values. This is indicated as a generalization, or equation, under column 3:

$$v_f = 10t.$$

Column 5 values = column 8 values, as previously observed. This is indicated under column 8:

$$d = 5t^2.$$

The equality between column 9 values and column 10 values has also been previously noted. The equality is indicated under both columns:

$$v_f^2 = 20d \text{ (or } 20h\text{)}.$$

In these equations under columns 3, 8, and 9–10, there are coefficients 10, 5, and 20, respectively. Notice that

10 = the assumed value for g, the uniform acceleration of gravity

5 = the assumed value for $\frac{1}{2} g$

20 = the assumed value for $2g$.

Substituting g for the numbers in the above equations, we obtain

$$v_f = gt \qquad\qquad \text{Equation 7–1}$$
$$d = \tfrac{1}{2} gt^2 \qquad\qquad \text{Equation 7–2}$$
$$v_f^2 = 2gh. \qquad\qquad \text{Equation 7–3}$$

These equations are shown in Table 7–1 (bottom row) to be special cases of

$$v_f = at \qquad\qquad \text{Equation 6–4}$$
$$d = \tfrac{1}{2} at^2 \qquad\qquad \text{Equation 6–5}$$
$$\text{and} \quad v_f^2 = 2ad. \qquad\qquad \text{Equation 6–6}$$

In Equations 7–1, 7–2, and 7–3, a value of 10 ft/sec/sec is assumed for the acceleration of gravity g. Equations 7–4, 7–5, and 7–6 are versions of Equations 7–1, 7–2, and 7–3 for whatever constant value g may be found to have.*

If an object falls toward the earth with uniform acceleration, *then* Eqs. 7–4 to 7–6 describe how the stone falls. Our hypothetical case of a falling stone has involved us in a type of reasoning that may be called *if . . ., then . . . .* Our reasoning ran as follows: *If* a stone falls with uniform acceleration g, *then* the equations

---

*An actual value of g = 32 ft/sec/sec has been determined, as described in a later section.

$$v_f = gt$$
$$d = \tfrac{1}{2}gt^2$$
$$\text{and} \quad v_f^2 = 2gh$$

describe the fall of that stone. But we remain with the *if* as an assumption or hypothesis to be tested. Nature—that is, gravity—does not have to conform to the man-made mathematical pattern of uniform acceleration. However, the effect of gravity can be tested; *if* objects actually fall with uniform acceleration, *then* experimental measurements will show them to fall in accordance with the above equations. *If* objects actually do *not* uniformly accelerate, *then* experimental measurements will *not* be in line with the above equations. The determining experimental measurements are our next concern.

MATHEMATICAL HYPOTHESES AND TESTING FREE FALL

Natural processes do not necessarily conform to our patterns of thought. It is one thing for Galileo to have spelled out an idea of uniform acceleration, and it may be another for objects to fall with uniform acceleration.

For Galileo, the point was to put his idea to a test. As he expressed it: "But as to whether this acceleration is that which one meets in nature in the case of falling bodies . . . this would be the proper moment to introduce one of those experiments—and there are many of them—which [test] in several ways the conclusions reached."

Experiments are a way of asking questions of nature. Galileo tested gravity and set a research pattern that is typical of science even today. In this pattern, mathematical equations are used to predict events that can be checked experimentally. If the experimental results are as predicted, the equation is considered a good working hypothesis for further investigation. If not, the equation is abandoned, and a new hypothesis is sought. Let us consider Galileo's inclined-plane experiments to gain more insight into the nature of both gravity and modern science.

Direct Testing of Free Fall

Galileo's hypothesis was that objects fall with a uniform acceleration *g*, as already described. That is,

$$g = \frac{v_f - v_o}{t},$$

as already mathematically defined, and

$$g = \frac{v_f}{t}$$

when an object falls from rest ($v_o = 0$).

The constant v_f/t was illustrated in Table 7–1. Recall that column 3 represents the instantaneous velocity v_f, and column 1, values of the time t in which an object falls. We found that at *all points of fall,* the ratio of

$$\frac{\text{any column 3 value}}{\text{corresponding column 1 value}} \quad \text{or} \quad \frac{v_f}{t}$$

is always the same. A direct test of gravity as uniform acceleration would therefore be possible if velocity and time readings could be made at different positions of an object in actual fall. If any ratio of v_f/t always gives the same numerical value, that is, remains constant as illustrated, the object for which the data were collected must have fallen with uniform acceleration.

Unfortunately, freely falling objects move so rapidly that even today it is difficult to measure their velocities directly. Falling objects just do not come with built-in speedometers. Galileo had a water clock and his pulse for time, but even with these timing devices, how could he have determined the velocity of an object at different points of its fall or when it hit the ground?

Indirect Testing of Free Fall

While measurement of the velocity of freely falling objects is not feasible, measurement of the total distance of fall is. But is it possible to substitute distance for velocity in testing for uniform acceleration of gravity? After all, velocity, not distance, is in the mathematical definition of uniform acceleration,

$$g = \frac{v_f}{t}.$$

The answer can be found by again referring to the free-fall table. We previously noted that each value in column 8 is five times the corresponding value in column 7; the total distance of fall after each second, in each case, is five times the time squared.

At all points of fall,

$$d = 5t^2$$

or $\quad \dfrac{d}{t^2} = 5.$

From this relationship, we conclude that an object falls with constant acceleration if d/t^2 is the same value at all points of fall. Basically, all that is needed to decide about constant acceleration in free fall is a measuring rod to determine distance and a watch to determine time. Over 3 centuries ago, Galileo came to this conclusion by similar reasoning with Euclidean geometry.

Inclined-Plane Experiments

The mathematical hypothesis and the experimental plan   To determine whether d/t^2 is constant for freely falling objects, Galileo decided to "dilute" gravity and thereby increase the time of fall. He believed that gravity is a force causing a ball to roll down a hill as well as to fall freely in space. Instead of dropping objects through the air, he therefore decided to let a brass ball roll down an inclined plane at different angles. His rationale was as follows:

1. The difference in time of descent between a freely falling and a rolling ball is really in its acceleration. If the plane is horizontal, the ball will not move down; the acceleration is zero. With a small angle between the inclined plane and a tabletop, the ball will develop speed slowly; the acceleration downward is small. The greater the angle between the inclined plane and the table, the faster the ball increases its speed, that is, the greater is the downward acceleration. Finally when the inclined plane approaches the vertical, the acceleration approaches the maximum free-fall value of g.

2. Free fall, to Galileo, was a special case, a maximum limiting case, of the inclined plane. This would be particularly true under ideal circumstances in which "a perfectly smooth ball" rolls down a "perfectly smooth" inclined plane. Thus, the effect of the inclined plane at different angles is to "dilute," or reduce, the effect of gravity.

3. The important inference is that if a ball has uniform acceleration when rolling down an inclined plane, it has uniform acceleration when falling freely.

4. Therefore, tests for the uniform acceleration of a body rolling downhill are, by extrapolation, tests for free fall.

Experimental procedures and results   At this point, let Salviati in the *Dialogues* describe for Galileo the actual experimental details and results:

We took a piece of wooden scantling, about 12 cubits long, half a cubit wide, and three finger breadths thick. In its top edge we cut a straight channel a little more than one finger in breadth; this groove was made smooth by lining it with parchment, polished as smooth as possible, to facilitate the rolling in it of a smooth and very round ball made of hardest bronze. Having placed the scantling in a sloping position by raising one end some one or two cubits above the other, we let the ball roll down the channel, noting, in a manner presently to be described, the time required for the descent. We repeated this experiment more than once in order to be sure of the time of descent and found that the deviation between two observations never exceeded one-tenth of a pulsebeat. Having performed this operation until assured of its reliability, we now let the ball roll down only one-quarter of the length of the channel; and having measured the time of its descent, we found it to be precisely one-half of the former. Next we tried other distances, comparing the time for the whole length with that of the half, or for three-fourths, or indeed for any fraction. In such experiments, repeated a full hundred times, we always found that the distances traversed were to each other as the squares of the times, and this was true for *any* inclination of the . . . channel along which we rolled the ball.

Figure 7–2 illustrates the results described above by Galileo in letting a ball roll down an inclined plane. Notice that the total distances from the starting position have the relationship of $1:4:9:16:25$, or $1^2:2^2:3^2:4^2:5^2$, at the end of the first, second, third, fourth, and fifth seconds. This relationship between distance and time holds regardless of the angle between the plane and the horizontal. Do these results compare with the relationship between total distance and time predicted in columns 6 and 7 in Table 7–1 for the freely falling stone? If so, Galileo's actual results match his predicted results, and his mathematical hypothesis of a uniform acceleration of gravity is verified at least tentatively.

Also notice that Galileo in his description is idealizing his results. Here, as in free fall, he is reporting his results as if he had operated in a vacuum with a perfectly smooth ball on a perfectly smooth inclined plane.

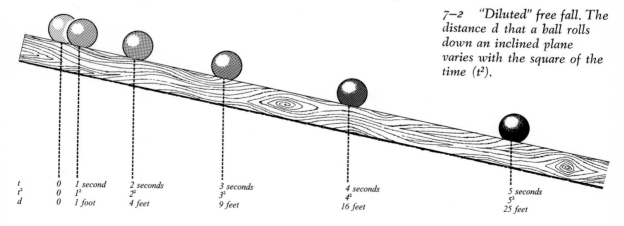

7–2 *"Diluted" free fall. The distance d that a ball rolls down an inclined plane varies with the square of the time (t²).*

t	0	1 second	2 seconds	3 seconds	4 seconds	5 seconds
t^2	0	1^2	2^2	3^2	4^2	5^2
d	0	1 foot	4 feet	9 feet	16 feet	25 feet

Analysis of Galileo's hypothesis testing   Galileo's procedures in his famous inclined-plane experiments can be summarized as follows:

1. Galileo posed the question of whether objects fall with uniform acceleration.
2. He sought an answer by *assuming the hypothesis* that they do fall that way.
3. He mathematically deduced from his definition of uniform acceleration a *constant ratio* between the distance of fall and the time squared (d/t^2) ob objects affected by gravity.
4. He tested his hypothesis of uniform acceleration through experiments in which balls were rolled down inclined planes in a way that permitted measurements of distance and time (Fig. 7–2).
5. He repeated the experiments at different angles of the inclined plane.
6. He accepted his hypothesis that objects fall with uniform acceleration when the measured ratio of distance and time squared is a constant as predicted for any angle of the inclined plane.

Galileo's conclusion and logic   Galileo's inclined-plane experiments illustrate that science proceeds not only inductively from observation to ideas but also deductively from ideas to observations. Galileo first formed his hypothesis of a uniform acceleration g for gravity, and then he tested it by taking distance and time measurements of a ball rolling downhill. He was proceeding from an idea to evidence.

Further, Galileo used deductive logic when he concluded a constant acceleration in free fall from a constant acceleration down an inclined plane. The following compares Galileo's reasoning to a syllogism first formalized as deductive logic by Aristotle:

ARISTOTLE'S SYLLOGISM		GALILEO'S DEDUCTIVE LOGIC
1. All men are mortal.	*Major premise*	$d/t^2 =$ a constant for any angle θ of the plane.
2. Socrates is a man.	*Minor premise*	Free fall is a special case of angle $\theta = 90°$.
3. Therefore, Socrates is mortal.	*Conclusion*	Therefore, d/t^2 or $g =$ a constant for free fall.

Can you see any fallacies in the statements comprising Galileo's deductive logic?

Hint 1: Is *free fall* simply a special case of rolling at a 90° angle? Would not *sliding* become a factor by the time the plane angle equals 90°?

Hint 2: Galileo used a 12-cubit, or 18-ft, inclined plane in his experiments. On what basis did he assume that there is uniform acceleration of gravity beyond 18 ft?

A Pendulum Experiment

Galileo used pendulums as well as inclined planes to study gravity. He described one such investigation with a pendulum (Fig. 7–3). If the pendulum bob at one end of the cord is released from rest at point A, the bob will swing down to B and rise back up to the same vertical height (h) at C if pivot friction and air resistance are removed. Then, as Galileo pointed out, if a nail obstruction is placed under the support at D so as to be hit by the cord, the bob will rise to the original height at C^1 even though through a shorter arc BC^1. Then, in reverse, whether swinging back from C or C^1, the bob in a frictionless situation will swing down and back up to its original position at A. Whether *from* C or C^1, the bob has the same return velocity at the bottom of its swing at B.

If you try the above experiment, you will find with Galileo that pendulum friction can be so small that even without ideal conditions, the bob will return very close to the original height at A. From such observations, Galileo concluded that only the vertical distance h above a surface determines the speed v at the surface and that any downhill curve or slope would give the same speed as a vertical drop. Galileo's experimental conclusion may be summarized as $v^2 = 2gh$ (Equation 7–3) as in Table 7–1, bottom of columns 9 and 10.

But how would Galileo's idea about downhill slopes apply to inclined planes? In Fig. 7–4, points A, B, and C are all at the same altitude. A ball may roll from A, B, or C and arrive at O with the same speed. As Galileo expressed it: "The speeds acquired by one and the same body

7–3 *Different downhill curves or slopes give a falling object the same speed. Whether swinging back from point C or C', the pendulum bob attains a speed at point B that enables it to rise to its original altitude h.*

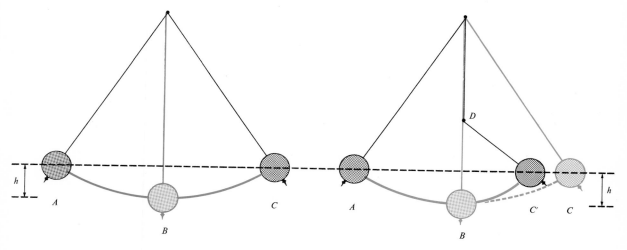

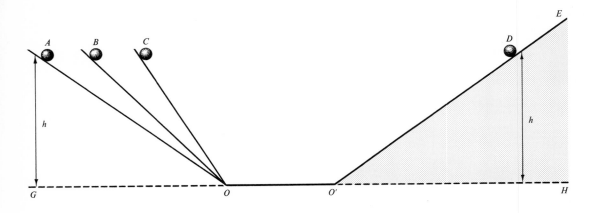

7–4   Galileo: "The speeds acquired by one and the same body moving down planes of different inclinations are equal when heights of those planes are equal." Whether starting from point A, B, or C, the ball rolls up to point D (if friction is negligible).

moving down planes of different inclinations are equal when the heights of those planes are equal."

Once at point O, how high up the plank O^1E will the ball roll? Like a pendulum bob, whatever the rolling ball gains in speed down one plane $(AO, BO,$ or $CO)$ with gravitational acceleration, it should lose rolling up the plane O^1E with gravitational deceleration. Since the velocity gained or lost depends upon height only, the point D at which the ball comes to a stop should be at a height equal to that of the point A, B, or C, from where the ball started to roll. The reverse, as with a pendulum, would also be true. If the ball is released at point D on plane EO^1, then the ball eventually will roll back up to the same height h, whether by OC, OB, or OA.

LAWS OF FALLING BODIES

Galileo's instruments may have been crude by today's standards, and his assumptions many, but his experiments completely convinced him that objects would fall with uniform acceleration in a vacuum. This hypothesis of a uniform acceleration of gravity has been verified in countless precise experiments since Galileo's time.

Once it became established that objects do fall with uniform acceleration, the three free-fall equations at the bottom of Table 7–1 passed from the stage of mathematical hypotheses to scientific laws. They are mathematical relationships that apply to the world of things. As laws, they precisely describe relationships among distance, time, velocity, and acceleration of fall and precisely predict these quantities, if proper allowances are made for air resistance and friction.

Since these equations already have been given considerable attention, we will just list them here again as laws of falling bodies.

For freely falling bodies starting from rest:

$$v_f = gt.$$

Equation 7-1

$$d = \tfrac{1}{2} gt.$$

Equation 7-2

$$v_f^2 = 2gh.$$

Equation 7-3

For freely falling bodies starting with an initial velocity v_o:
See Eqs. A–1 to A–3 in Appendix D.

We have seen that the acceleration of gravity g is just a special case of uniform acceleration a. Whatever relationships exist among distance, velocity, acceleration, and time in the laws of falling bodies exist for any situation in which an acceleration is constant $(a = k)$. The laws of falling bodies are converted into more general laws of acceleration by substitution of the general symbol a for g in the free-fall equations. For objects that accelerate from rest, the acceleration laws then take the form of Eqs. 6–4 to 6–6. For objects that accelerate from an initial velocity v_o, the acceleration laws take the form of Eqs. A–4 to A–6 in Appendix D.

A PENDULUM LAW
AND THE VALUE OF g

We have seen how Galileo developed laws of falling bodies without knowing the numerical value of the acceleration of gravity g. To illustrate how Galileo did this, we even assumed in Table 7–1 a tentative value for g of 10 ft/sec². It was 22 years after Galileo's death that the great Dutch physicist Christian Huygens (1629-1695) reported a definite value of 9.8 m*/sec², or 32 ft/sec², for g. Huygens determined this value by swinging a pendulum and applying the following equation, now called the *law of the simple pendulum*:

$$T = 2\pi \sqrt{\frac{l}{g}}$$

Equation 7-4

or

$$g = \frac{4\pi^2 l}{T^2},$$

where T = period of one swing to and fro

l = length of pendulum

g = acceleration of gravity.

*The metric system of units in general use except in English-speaking countries will be considered in Chapter 8.

Notice from Eq. 7–4 that a relationship exists only among T, l, and g in the swing of a simple pendulum. Galileo had not worked out the above equation, but he was the first to recognize the following:

1. The length of arc, the material, and the weight have no bearing on the period of swing of a simple pendulum. For example, a pendulum does not take more time in a longer arc as might be expected, because a greater speed at the center of its swing compensates for the greater distance.

2. The period T is in direct proportion to the square root of the pendulum's length, that is, $T \propto \sqrt{l}$.

3. Gravity is not just an acceleration to be identified with the swing of a pendulum but a force or agency that causes this swing. By Huygens's time, the acceleration effects of a force of gravity could be mathematically and experimentally shown, as represented by g in Eq. 7–4.

Determine the value of g for yourself. The procedure is simple:

1. Suspend a cord with a small weight tied to the lower end as a bob.

2. Measure the length l of your simple pendulum from the pivot point to the center of the weight.

3. Swing the pendulum and observe the total time for a number of swings. The average period of a swing to and fro (T_{av}) will be the time for all swings divided by the number of complete swings to and fro. That is,

$$T_{av} = \frac{\text{total time}}{N}.$$

4. Use your values of T_{av} and l in Eq. 7–4 and solve for g. How close to 32 ft/sec^2 do you get?

5. If you repeat steps 2 and 3 five or ten times and average your values of l and of T_{av}, your g should be closer. Why?

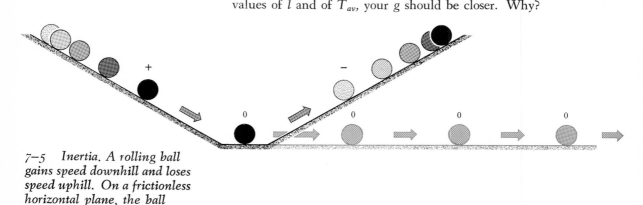

7–5   *Inertia. A rolling ball gains speed downhill and loses speed uphill. On a frictionless horizontal plane, the ball should roll on endlessly at constant velocity (Galileo).*

THOUGHT EXPERIMENTS
AND A CONCEPT OF INERTIA

Let us conclude with several more of Galileo's significant thought experiments. When the ball in Fig. 7–5 rolls down the inclined plane on the left, it gains speed, as indicated by the + sign. In rolling up the inclined plane on the right, the ball loses speed, as shown by the − sign. The ball has positive acceleration downward and negative acceleration upward. If the ball and the horizontal surface between the two planes are perfectly smooth, the acceleration sign would be neither a + nor a − but a zero. The speed would neither increase nor decrease but would remain constant. This has great significance, said Galileo. If the frictionless horizontal plane were indefinitely extended, the ball would continue to roll on indefinitely without any force acting upon it. The inference was revolutionary. Under frictionless conditions, the ball would be in permanent natural motion. Motion in a straight line at constant speed is just as much a natural state of affairs as rest, reasoned Galileo. In fact, rest is just a special case of motion in which speed equals zero $(v = 0)$. Objects ordinarily slow down because friction slows them down. The smoother the ice on a pond, the less the friction force, and the further a smooth pebble skids. Understand motion through the idealized frictionless situation, and then make allowances for the friction that does exist in actual situations. In such a way, idealized thought experiments can give greater understanding of nature. In any case, in this thought experiment by Galileo, we first see the modern concept of inertia, the concept that once any object is moving, it will continue on at constant velocity unless an unbalanced force acts upon it.

In the light of the above, consider another of Galileo's thought experiments (Fig. 7–6). If a stone is dropped from the top of the mast of a ship at rest, no one is surprised if the stone lands at the base of the mast. But what if the ship is moving at 20 mph when the stone falls? Will the stone still land at the base of the mast, or will it land behind the base? Whether the ship is at rest or in motion, said Galileo, the stone will still land at the base of the mast (Fig. 7–6). Before the stone was dropped, it was traveling horizontally at 20 mph along with the ship. Even though the stone is separated from the ship when it falls, the stone is still traveling at 20 mph by inertia, like the ball rolling along the horizontal plane. By inertia, the stone, even while falling, moves along horizontally with the ship until it hits the deck at the base of the mast.

Now, let the earth be the ship and the top of a cliff be the mast. If a stone is dropped from the top of the cliff, the stone, by inertia, should hit the ground at the base of the cliff whether the earth under it is moving or not. The stone was on the moving earth (ship) before dropped and separated. Similarly, a stone thrown vertically upward eventually lands on the same place from which it was thrown, even if the earth

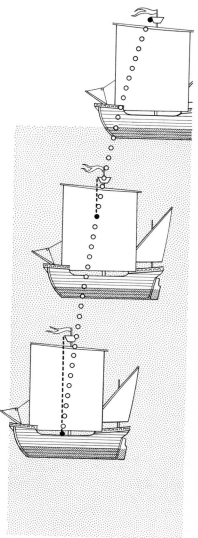

7–6 By inertia, the stone falling from the mast retains its original horizontal velocity. The stone therefore travels along horizontally with the ship until striking the deck at the base of the mast. The path of the stone appears to be a straight (dashed) line on the ship but a parabola from the shore.

under it moves. The stone was on the earth before being thrown and, by inertia, persists in the same horizontal motion. Thus, with two qualitative thought experiments, involving no actual measurements, Galileo escaped from the restrictions of Aristotelian thought.

PROJECTILE MOTION AND FALLING TARGETS

Suppose that a stone is thrown horizontally from a cliff top at the same instant another stone is merely dropped. Which stone would hit the ground first? Aristotle's answer was that the dropped stone would arrive first. The "violent" motion prevails at first for the horizontally thrown stone. Only as this motion wears off does gravity take over. Meanwhile, the stone that was dropped has been on its way down.

Galileo maintained that both stones would hit the ground at the same time if air resistance is ignored. To be sure, one stone has a horizontal motion at constant speed, but this stone also has a vertical motion of fall the instant it is thrown. And the vertical part of this stone's motion is the same as the motion of the dropped stone, as shown by the cannonballs in Fig. 7–7. The two stones therefore strike the surface at the same time, although at two different places. Figure 7–7 also shows that the horizontal motion and the free fall together give the stone a parabolic path—the same parabolic curve of Pythagorean conic sections (Fig. 4–3). Mathematics in nature indeed!

At this point Galileo would probably refer us back to his thought experiment of the stone falling from the mast of a moving ship (Fig. 7–6). To a sailor who releases a stone from the top of the mast, the stone falls at a vertical. Only gravity would seem to be acting. To an observer on shore, the path of the same stone is a parabola, not a straight line. The motion of the ship is superimposed on the fall of the stone. Notice the relativity of motion: A straight-line path for the sailor on the moving

7–7 Regardless of their different horizontal speeds, the cannonballs reach the ground in equal time. Free fall is independent of horizontal motion.

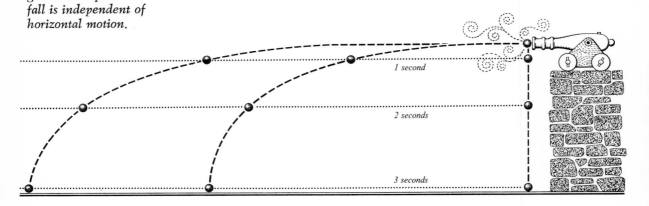

1 second

2 seconds

3 seconds

ship is a parabolic curve for the observer on shore. A single event from two frames of reference becomes two different observations.

But whether seen in a straight line or in a parabolic curve, the stone hits the deck for both observers. A vertical motion of free fall is there for both, whether seen combined with horizontal motion or not. Further, for Galileo, the stones on the cliff could have been projectiles launched horizontally at any altitude. And if, for example, balls are fired from a cannon (Fig. 7–7), regardless of the different initial forward speeds, "all the balls in all the shots made horizontally remain in the air an equal time." Galileo generalized this idea as a principle of independence of projectile motion velocities. According to this principle, projectile motion can be resolved into two independent components, a vertical and a horizontal. The horizontal motion remains constant if air resistance is ignored, and the vertical acceleration occurs regardless of the horizontal motion.

For example, in the shooting of the arrow in Fig. 7–8, the path of the arrow is a parabola. This path is a composite of the uniform horizontal motion that the arrow would have if there were no gravity and of the free fall motion that the arrow would have if it were dropped rather than fired. The arrow, of course, in approaching the tree, falls as fast as the apple and therefore hits the apple.

Test your understanding of Galileo's principle by answering the following questions:

Suppose a pilot wishes to drop a package from a plane moving 100 mph horizontally at 1,600 ft to a marooned party on a tiny, rocky island.

1. Should the pilot drop the package when he is directly overhead or before? Why?

2. If before, how much so in terms of time? In terms of distance? (Hint: Remember that the height of the plane is related to the time of fall through $d = \frac{1}{2}gt^2$. Drawing a diagram may also help.)

7–8   If the apple drops the instant the expert archer releases his arrow, the arrow hits the falling apple. The arrow and apple fall equally far in the same time interval.

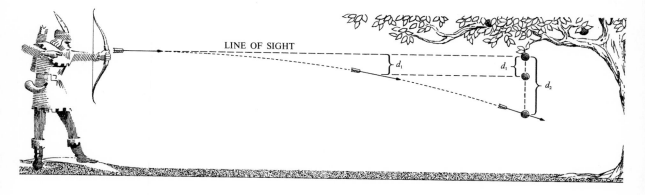

LINE OF SIGHT

LAW OF
INDEPENDENCE
OF VELOCITIES

Centuries of experimental evidence supporting Galileo's hypothesis about projectiles have made his principle into a *law of independence of velocities*. In physical science, principles constantly supported by observational evidence tend to become laws. The law of independence of velocities, like the principle, states that projectile motion combines free-fall acceleration with uniform horizontal motion if air resistance is ignored. The vertical acceleration remains independent of any uniform horizontal motion. Air resistance slows down horizontal as well as vertical motion, but does not otherwise affect their independence. We shall see that in Galileo's independence of horizontal and vertical velocities, there is the germ of Newton's highly significant concept of vectors and a significant clue to understanding what keeps planets and satellites in orbit.

GALILEO AND THE
FOUNDATIONS OF MECHANICS

Galileo developed mathematical principles of motion and tested gravity with them. In the process, there arose a new approach to physics referred to as mechanics, a new body of knowledge, and a new method of inquiry. Galileo's new mechanics, in support of the Copernican system, included:

1. A concept and assumption of inertia.
2. Precise mathematical vocabulary for motion.
3. Mathematical principles of acceleration.
4. New concepts of an acceleration and force of gravity in which the acceleration of falling objects is an effect of a gravity force.
5. A principle of independence of inertial velocity and gravitational acceleration in projectile motion.

The new knowledge included discoveries of:

1. Laws of falling bodies.
2. Other laws of acceleration.
3. Laws of the pendulum.
4. The law of independence of velocities.

The new method of inquiry may be referred to as mathematical hypothesis testing. Thought experiments and/or former experience lead to a tentative mathematical hypothesis. The hypothesis is used to predict measurable events. Controlled experiments are then set up to check the predictions. Galileo's experimental appeal was to both the mind and the senses. He used mathematics as a language and a logic that permitted measurement and evidence. Galileo was delighted to find that again and again the universe showed itself to be mathematical. Gravity could be described and tested mathematically—with success. Galileo's mathematical experimentalism characterizes science today. Chapters 6 and 7 contained the mathematical and experimental details necessary to give his work meaning.

CHAPTER REVIEW

1. Which falls faster, a 10-lb or a 1-lb rock? Much faster? Why?

2. Compare Galileo's answers to question 1 to Aristotle's answers. What did Galileo assume about gravity? What did Aristotle assume?

3. A coin falls much faster than a feather in air, but both fall equally fast in a vacuum. What bearing does this observation have upon the gravitational problem of "which falls faster"?

4. What is meant by a uniform acceleration of gravity?

5. Describe Galileo's inclined-plane experiments verifying that the acceleration of gravity is uniform. How could Galileo expect conclusions obtained from rolling a ball "downhill" to apply to a freely falling ball?

6. Why may Galileo's approach to the nature of gravity be called a "how" approach rather than a "why" approach?

7. How do Galileo's inclined-plane experiments illustrate modern hypothesis testing?

8. Show how Galileo used observations with both a pendulum and inclined planes to conclude that only the original altitude of a falling object determines the object's speed at the surface and that any downhill curve or slope gives the same speed as a vertical drop.

9. Equations 7–1 to 7–3 symbolically represent Galilean laws of acceleration. Show how each law relates the distance, time, velocity, and acceleration of a falling object. Show how these three equations indicate a common uniform acceleration of gravity for all objects.

10. How can the uniform acceleration of gravity g be determined by swinging a simple pendulum?

11. How can the height of a building be determined by a stopwatch?

12. How can a stone thrown vertically upward land on the same spot from which it was thrown if the earth moves?

13. What does "inertia" mean? How does Galileo's thought experiment of a stone dropped from a mast on a moving ship illustrate inertia? How does this thought experiment support Copernican theory?

14. How does inertia show itself in the motion of a projectile?

0 FT/SEC

1. Fill in the vacant spaces in Table 7–1. On what basis is each value in column 2 the same, whereas the values in column 3 increase by 10 ft/sec and in column 4 by 5 ft/sec?

2. Replace the hypothetical value of 10 ft/sec added each second* in Table 7–1, column 2, with the actual free-fall value of 32 ft/sec/sec. Then rework the entire table with the corrected value, including the bottom row of generalizations.

3. Identify each of the following columns in your corrected Table 7–1 (problem 2) with specific laws of falling bodies (Eqs. 7–1 to 7–3): (a) column 3, (b) columns 5 and 8 together, and (c) columns 9 and 10 together.

4. A stone starting from rest is dropped from a high building ($g = 32$ ft/sec²). (a) What is the stone's speed *after* the first second? (b) What is the *average* speed *during* the first second? (c) How far does the stone fall during the first second? (d) What is the stone's speed after the third second? (e) What is the average speed during the first 3 sec? (f) How far does the stone drop during the first 3 sec?

5. A stone merely dropped from a bridge takes 4 sec to hit the ground. With what speed does the stone land? What is the average speed of the stone? How high is the bridge?

6. A stone merely dropped from a cliff takes 5 sec to hit the ground. How high is the cliff?

7. The Empire State Building is 1,400 ft high. How long will a stone dropped from the top take to reach the ground? What will be the stone's speed at the ground? What minimum vertical speed is needed to throw a ball to the top of the Empire State Building? (The ball's acceleration upward, −32 ft/sec/sec, would be opposite and equal to its acceleration downward, 32 ft/sec/sec.)

8. A ball thrown vertically upward returns to the ground in 6 sec (Fig. 7–9). How high did the ball go? If the ball returns with the same speed it was thrown, what is that speed?

9. Starting from rest a person skis down a slope with an acceleration of 5 ft/sec: (a) What is the skier's speed after the third second? After the fourth second? (b) What is his average speed during the fourth second? (c) What is his average speed for the first 4 sec? (d) How far does he go in 4 sec? (e) How far does he go in 5 sec?

10. Two identical marbles released from the same point roll down planks unequal in length. Which marble, if any, hits the ground with

7–9 *The ball returns in 6 sec. How high did it go? How fast was it thrown? (See problem 8.)*

*The numerical value of 10 used hypothetically with ft/sec/sec in Table 7–1 is actually appropriate for the metric system (see Chapter 8), in which $g = 9.8$ m/sec/sec.

a greater speed? Why? (Ignore friction, but remember the Galilean laws of acceleration.)

11. Will a simple pendulum increase its period of swing if released from a higher position? Why?

12. How much does increasing the length of a simple pendulum from 1 ft to 4 ft change its period of swing?

13. Should a pilot drop a package when just above a marooned party or before? Why?

14. A ball is released from a cliff at the same instant that another is horizontally hurled from the same position at 100 ft/sec. Which ball, if any, will hit the ground first? Why? (Ignore air resistance.)

15. Should a monkey in a tree drop to the ground the instant a gun aimed at it is fired? Why?

SUGGESTIONS FOR FURTHER READING

Cohen, I. Bernard, *The Birth of a New Physics*, Anchor paperback, Garden City, N.Y., 1960, Ch. 5.

Priestley, Herbert, *Introductory Physics*, Allyn and Bacon, Boston, 1958, Ch. 4.

White, Harvey, *Modern College Physics*, Van Nostrand, New York, 1962, Ch. 5.

Holton, Gerald J., and D. H. D. Roller, *Foundations of Modern Physical Science*, Addison-Wesley, Reading, Mass., 1958, Chs. 2–3.

Lemon, Harvey B., *From Galileo to the Nuclear Age*, Univ. Chicago Press, Chicago, 1949, Chs. 1 and 3–6.

Beveridge, W. I. B., *Art of Scientific Investigation*, Vintage paperback, New York, 1957.

Galilei, Galileo, *Dialogues Concerning Two New Sciences*, tr. Henry Crew and Alfonso De Salvio, Dover paperback, New York, 1952, First, Third and Fourth Days.

Schneer, Cecil, *Search for Order*, Harper, New York, 1960, Ch. 4.

Butterfield, Herbert, *Origins of Modern Science*, Collier paperback, New York, 1962, Ch. 5.

Omer, Guy C., Jr., et al., *Physical Science: Men and Concepts*, Heath, Boston, 1962, Chs. 11–14.

8   *Laws of Motion*

If I have seen farther ... it is because I have stood on the shoulders of giants.

ISAAC NEWTON, 1687

Galileo and Kepler were the giants upon whose shoulders Newton stood. He started with Galileo's laws of falling bodies and Kepler's laws of planetary motion and ended with a theory of gravitation that unlocked the universe. Newton's key was the concept of force. He mathematically related force to acceleration, to circular motion, to Kepler's laws, and to a universal gravitation. And when he was through, the cosmos seemed like a huge machine grinding away as relentlessly as fate. Newton's mechanistic universe is spelled out in Chapters 8 and 9.

BIOGRAPHICAL SKETCH OF NEWTON

Isaac Newton was born in 1642, the year of Galileo's death, on a farm in Lincolnshire, England. His mother, widowed early, hoped that her only son would grow up to run their small farm. But the young Newton had little inclination for farming. Sundials and water clocks were more appealing than horses and plows. Newton's uncle influenced his mother to send him to Cambridge University. There a new world of mathematics, astronomy, and optics opened up for him under the guidance of the eminent Professor Isaac Barrow.

The Great Plague decimating London closed Cambridge during 1665 and 1666. Newton retired to the comparative safety of the family farm. It was during the quiet of these 18 months that the shy, reticent Newton with ingenious insight developed differential and integral calculus, formulated a new theory of color, established his famous laws of motion, and "mechanized" the universe in one of the great scientific breakthroughs of all time. His *Principia*, or *Mathematical Principles of Natural Philosophy*, finally published in 1687, dominated physics and astronomy for 250 years, and his *Opticks*, published in 1704, is still a model of scientific hypothesis testing.

Newton returned to Cambridge as a graduate Fellow in 1667 and 2 years later became professor of mathematics when Barrow retired. At 30, Newton became a Fellow in the British Royal Society, the highest of scientific honors.

The remarkable creativity of Newton's twenties subsided in his thirties. *The Royal Society Transactions of 1672* contains a description by Newton of his new reflecting telescope. After that, the oversensitive Newton, disturbed by controversies with such eminent colleagues as Hooke, Huygens, and Leibnitz, seems to have lost enthusiasm for scientific investigation. It was only at the insistence of Newton's friend Halley that *Principia* was finally published.

In any case, Newton was elected a member of Parliament by the university in 1688. Eight years later, he entered into permanent government service as Warden of the Mint, and in 1699 he became Master of the Mint, a position which he held for the rest of his life. Although he served as president of the Royal Society from 1703 to 1727, his own investigations during those years were primarily theological rather than scientific. His early scientific achievements, meanwhile, had made him famous throughout Europe. A scientific and industrial revolution was catching hold in England. Textile manufacturing was increasing, trade was expanding, cities were growing, and scientific communication was becoming international through scientific societies and their journals. When Isaac Newton died in 1727, he was buried in Westminster Abbey, internationally recognized and honored.

FORCE AND MOTION

Force is not a new concept. Men early identified force as push or pull that tends to move stationary objects. Then Aristotle emphasized that force is needed not only to move stationary objects but also to keep them moving. Without a sustaining force, a skimming stone slows to a stop.

If planets and stars move ceaselessly, it is because celestial spheres carry them; and behind the celestial spheres is an Unmoved Mover.

That all motion would cease without forces Galileo disputed. He claimed that objects at the earth's surface tend to move at constant velocity without forces. Refer back to Galileo's inclined-plane thought experiment (Fig. 7–5). Once the ball rolls down to the horizontal, it can be expected to roll along the horizontal indefinitely at constant speed if all friction is removed. Horizontally rolling balls or skimming stones ordinarily slow down only because friction forces resist motion. Remove friction, said Galileo, and objects once moving continue along endlessly. No force is necessary to keep them moving—only to stop them. This tendency for an object to continue in horizontal motion at constant speed without a force—or to remain at rest if at rest—we recall, Galileo called inertia.

NEWTON'S FIRST LAW: MOTION WITHOUT FORCE

Newton's first law of motion, often called the *law of inertia*, states that *every body continues in its state of rest or of constant speed in a straight line unless acted upon by an unbalanced force.* In this statement, Newton is accepting Galileo's concept of inertia. But he is also extending it. By emphasizing "every body," Newton is boldly applying the concept of inertia to the whole universe. Whether it be a ball, a stone, or a meteor, any object moves at constant speed in a straight line not only on earth but anywhere in space unless a net force acts upon it. In Newton's first law, inertia is dynamic, universal, and revolutionary. Motion, not rest, is the natural state of affairs. Rest is a special case of inertial speed, $v = 0$. A parked car has an inertial speed of zero and tends to remain at that speed.

NEWTON'S SECOND LAW: FORCE AND ACCELERATION

The first law involves motion without force. No force, no acceleration—just rest or constant speed in a straight line. Newton's second law, however, provides for motion with force. As Newton expressed it, "Change of motion is proportional to the motive force impressed, and is made in the direction of the right [straight] line in which that force is impressed." Clearly, *force is associated not with constant speed but with changing speed or acceleration.* To Newton, force is a cause of acceleration. Wherever an object is accelerating, a force is acting. A force may be assumed to act on a falling object, even if an arm cannot be seen stretching up from the earth to pull the object downward. Let one of today's rockets "coast" at constant speed in a straight line far out in space. If one of its engines is ignited, the rocket will accelerate (or decelerate). The applied force of the engine results in acceleration for the rocket.

Newton's second law, the law of acceleration, may also be expressed as follows: *The acceleration of a body of given mass is proportional to the applied force and is in the direction of the force.* Clearly, this law does more than associate an accelerated mass and a force. It relates them on a precise, quantitative basis. In the symbolic language of algebra, the law may be expressed as

$$F \propto a$$

where F symbolizes *force* upon

   m, a given *mass*,

   a symbolizes *acceleration*, and

   $\propto$ means is *proportional to*.

From $F \propto a$, we can deduce or reason to Eq. 8–1 as follows:

1. Doubling F doubles a,
   tripling F triples a, ... That is,
   $$F \propto a \text{ implies } \frac{F}{a} = \frac{2F}{2a} = \frac{3F}{3a} \ldots.$$

F		a
If a 10-lb force gives a mass m an acceleration of	5	ft/sec²,
then a 20-lb force will give the mass m an acceleration of	10	ft/sec²,
and a 30-lb force will give the mass m an acceleration of	15	ft/sec²,
or a 5-lb force will give the mass m an acceleration of	2.5	ft/sec².

2. In the above illustrations of $F \propto a$, the applied forces were always on the same body of mass m. What if forces are applied to different objects or masses? It is reasonable to suppose that a 2-t vehicle should require *twice* as much force to give it the same acceleration as a 1-t car. That is, accelerating force F should be proportional to mass m, or

$$F \propto m.$$

That is, doubling m implies doubling F to produce the same acceleration; tripling m implies tripling F to produce the same acceleration ...

$$F \propto m \text{ implies } \frac{F}{m} = \frac{2F}{2m} = \frac{3F}{3m} = \cdots = \text{ a constant } a.$$

If a   50-lb force gives a   500-lb piano an acceleration of 3.2 ft/sec²,
then a 100-lb force should give a 1,000-lb piano an acceleration of 3.2 ft/sec²,
and a 150-lb force should give a 1,500-lb piano an acceleration of 3.2 ft/sec²,
or a   25-lb force should give a   250-lb piano an acceleration of 3.2 ft/sec².

3. If $F \propto m$ and $F \propto a$, then the two proportions may be combined into one statement,

$$F \propto ma,$$

force is proportional to both mass and acceleration.

4. A skillful definition of a unit for force changes the statement that $F \propto ma$ into one of the most significant equations in history:

$$F = ma.$$ Equation 8–1

The equation states that an accelerating force equals the product of the mass and acceleration of the object acted upon by the force. Table 8–1 illustrates three definitions of force that make Eq. 8–1 an equality. For example, a *newton*—named after Newton—is defined in the mks* system as *that force which gives a 1-kilogram mass an acceleration of 1 meter per second per second.* By definition, $1 = 1 \cdot 1$: 1 newton $= 1$ kg mass $\cdot$ 1 m/sec². For the equation $F = ma$ to be correct in the mks system, the units of force should be in newtons, mass in kilograms, and acceleration in meters per second per second. For example, a force F of 450 newtons is needed to give a piano 150 kg in mass m an acceleration a of 3 m/sec². That is,

$$F = ma$$

$$F = 150 \text{ kg} \cdot 3 \text{ m/sec}^2 = 450 \text{ kg m/sec}^2 = 450 \text{ newtons.}$$

Or, a *poundal*† in the English fps‡ system *is* defined as *that force which gives a 1-pound mass an acceleration of 1 foot per second per second.* Again by definition, a force of 1 poundal $= 1$-lb mass $\cdot$ 1 ft/sec². For the equation $F = ma$ to be correct in the English system, the unit of force must be in poundals, the mass in pounds, and the acceleration in feet per second per second. An accelerating force of 6,400 poundals gives a car 3,200 lb in mass an acceleration of 2 ft/sec². If $F = ma$, then $m = F/a$. That is, force is directly proportional

---

*mks is the abbreviation of the meter-kilogram-second system of units.
†A poundal is 1/32 of a pound, or 1/2 an ounce.
‡fps is the abbreviation of the foot-pound-second system of units.

Table 8–1 | *UNITS FOR NEWTON'S SECOND LAW (EQ. 8–1)*

SYSTEM	FORCE	=	MASS	×	ACCELERATION
fps (English)	poundals		pounds		ft/sec^2
cgs (metric)	dynes		grams		cm/sec^2
mrs (metric)	newtons		kilograms		m/sec^2

to both mass and acceleration, but mass and acceleration are inversely proportional to each other. For example, suppose a 450-newton force is applied to each of two pianos, one with a small mass m of 150 kg and another with a large mass M of 450 kg. If the small mass m has a relatively large acceleration A of 3 m/sec^2, the large mass M will have a small acceleration a of 1 m/sec^2. That is, $m \cdot A = M \cdot a$. Increasing the mass (1 to 3) from 150 kg to 450 kg decreases the acceleration (3 to 1) from 3 m/sec^2 to 1 m/sec^2.

Force and Inertial Mass

Newton's first and second laws are among the most important laws in physics. The second law establishes mathematical relationships among force, mass, and acceleration in a universe of motion. But even more basic than this, the two laws together establish precise working definitions of terms that they relate: force, inertia, and mass. Acceleration had been mathematically defined before Newton. Inertia with Galileo and Newton became the tendency of an object to maintain a constant speed in a straight line or to remain at rest. Force became that which when applied to an object tends to make it change its velocity. If inertia means maintaining the status quo of uniform motion or rest, a force means changing the status quo. An object accelerating anywhere indicates a force.

So much for force. But what is mass? Mass, loosely associated with the quantity of matter in an object, has become identified with inertia in the first and second laws of motion.* The extent to which a piano has inertia—that is, resists having its speed or direction changed by a force—is the extent to which the piano has mass. The mass of the piano can therefore be measured by the inertia of the piano. This principle of mass measurement is symbolized by $m = F/a$. The more force that must be applied to the piano to give it a particular acceleration a (for example, 3 ft/sec^2), the more resistance to change of motion—and there-

---

*Actually, these two laws are one law. The first law is a special case of $F = ma$ in which F and a are zero and in which all that is left in the equation is the mass representing the object either at rest or at constant speed in a straight line.

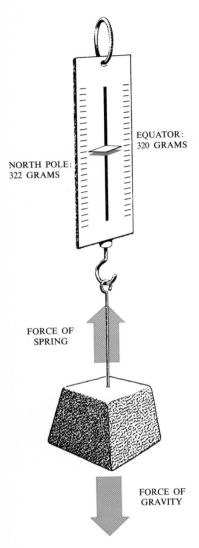

NORTH POLE:
322 GRAMS

EQUATOR:
320 GRAMS

FORCE OF
SPRING

FORCE OF
GRAVITY

8–1 *The weight of any-thing is an external force of gravity acting upon it. This force varies somewhat from the equator to the poles.*

fore the more mass m—the piano has. Mass defined in this way is known as *inertial mass* to distinguish it from *gravitational mass* (discussed in a later chapter).

Clearly, inertial mass as well as force is mathematically defined through Newton's second law in a circular process. Force is known through mass, and mass, through force. Force is determined by a mass being accelerated; and the larger the mass at a given acceleration, the larger the force ($F = ma$). Mass, on the other hand, is determined through a force applied to give it acceleration; and the larger the force necessary for a given acceleration, the larger the mass ($m = F/a$). This circular logic of defining force through mass and mass through force is a weakness that left the way open for a later development of physics based on the concept of *field* rather than *force*.

Gravity as a Force: Weight versus Mass

Weight is a force of gravity that acts on a mass tending to give it a free fall acceleration g. Your weight, unlike your mass, is not a property of yourself, but an external force that tends to pull you to the center of the earth. In the process, you are kept on the earth just as are the atmosphere and the birds.

Weight as a force of gravity may be explained as follows through Newton's second law, $F = ma$: If an object with mass m falls with an acceleration of gravity g, there must be an accelerating gravitational force F_g acting upon it. The gravitational force, mass, and acceleration then have the relationship $F_g = mg$. The amount of this pull of gravity is illustrated by an object hanging from a spring scale (Fig. 8–1). The greater the force of gravity on the suspended object, the greater is the deformation of the spring. But the spring scale has always been considered to give a reading of weight. Therefore, F_g and the weight W of an object are the same.

In general,
$F = ma.$

In particular,
$F_g = mg.$

If W and F_g are the same, then
$W = mg.$

Equation 8–2

Thus, weight W is a force of gravity that acts on a mass m to give it a gravitational acceleration g. Notice, in accordance with Equation 8–2 and Table 8–1, that a weight of 320 poundals—that is, 10 lb—will give a 10-lb mass an acceleration of 32 ft/sec².

Weight has been found to vary at different locations on the earth's surface. A spring scale, for example, shows a larger reading for the same mass at the North Pole than at the equator. Weight as a gravitational force is therefore a relative quantity. It depends upon three factors emphasized by Newton in his law of universal gravitation, discussed in the next chapter. And by $F = ma$, or $W = mg$, as the weight W of an object increases when moved from equator to pole, free-fall acceleration g changes in direct proportion. Your weight W, from the equator to a pole, increases by about ½ of 1 percent, and so does your acceleration g in falling freely.

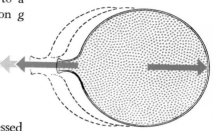

NEWTON'S THIRD LAW: ACTION AND REACTION

8–2   Action and reaction. Air escaping with force from the open end of a balloon permits an opposite and equal force at the other end to send the balloon forward.

Forces always occur in pairs. This idea, uniquely Newton's, was expressed as follows in his third law of action and reaction: "To every action there is always opposed an equal reaction; or the mutual actions of two bodies upon each other are always equal, and directed to contrary parts." Expressed briefly, Newton's third law states: *Every force involves an opposite and equal reacting force.* In other words, wherever one object is found exerting a force upon another, the second object will be found exerting an equal and opposite force back upon the first object. Algebraically, $F_1 = -F_2$, and the forces of action and reaction do not act upon the same object but upon the two objects that are interacting. A few illustrations follow:

Step out of a rowboat onto a dock. The boat moves backward as you move forward. Your foot and the boat are interacting objects. The *backward force* of your foot *upon the boat* is matched by the *equal forward force* of the boat *on your foot.*

In walking, you press each foot against the ground to exert a *backward force upon the ground.* This is accompanied by an *equal forward force upon your foot* by the ground as you move forward. Now the ground and foot are the interacting objects exerting opposite and equal forces. If "terra firma" (the solid earth) is perfectly smooth ice, you are unable to exert a force on it, and it on you. You therefore slip and fall; you are unable to walk.

The hot gas leaving a jet plane in one direction is accompanied by the plane moving in the opposite direction—action and reaction. As in the balloon (Fig. 8–2), air escaping at one end reduces the forces on that end to give an imbalance that causes the object to move in an opposite direction.

When a cannonball zooms forward, the cannon lurches backward. On wheels, the cannon would roll backward when fired (Fig. 8–3). But the body of the cannon is so much more massive than that of the cannonball that it does not move back so far in a given time t—that is, acquire the speed of the cannonball. This statement may be algebraically expressed as

$$M \cdot v = -m \cdot V,$$ Equation 8–3

where M = mass of cannon

m = smaller mass of cannonball

v = smaller acquired velocity of cannon

V = larger acquired velocity of cannonball.

For example, a cannon with a 7,500-lb mass M fires a comparatively small shell 50 lb in mass m. If the shell has a large forward velocity V of 3,000 ft/sec, the cannon has a correspondingly small backward velocity v. This is shown as follows:

$$Mv = -mV \quad \text{or}$$

$$v = \frac{-mV}{M}$$

$$v = \frac{-50 \; \cancel{lb}^*}{7,500 \; \cancel{lb}} \cdot 3,000 \; \text{ft/sec}$$

$$v = -20 \; \text{ft/sec}.$$

The $-$ sign before the "20 ft/sec" indicates that the small velocity of the cannon is opposite in direction to the large velocity of the cannonball.

*Remember that unit designations cancel out like numbers.

8–3 Action and reaction. The forward momentum $(m \cdot V)$ of the cannonball equals a backward momentum $(M \cdot v)$ of the cannon $(m \cdot V = M \cdot v)$.

Newton's third law, symbolized simply as $F_1 = -F_2$, leads to Equation 8–3 as follows:

1. $$F_1 = -F_2.$$ (Newton's third law)

2. $$F_1 = m_1a_1 \text{ and } F_2 = m_2a_2.$$ (Newton's second law)

3. Therefore, $m_1a_1 = -m_2a_2.$ (substitutions for F_1 and F_2 in 1)

4. And $\dfrac{m_1v_1}{t_1} = \dfrac{-m_2v_2}{t_2}.$ (by definition, $a_1 = \dfrac{v_1}{t_1}$, etc.)

5. $$m_1v_1 = -m_2v_2.$$ (cancellation of ts, since $t_1 = t_2$)

The product of the mass m and velocity v of any object is known as *momentum mv.* We may therefore say that the forward momentum m_1v_1 of a bullet equals the backward momentum of a gun $-m_2v_2$. Clearly, the concept momentum is a mathematical one derived from Newton's laws of force and motion.

In summary, Newton's third law is significant for not only its assumption of forces existing in pairs everywhere but also its emphasis on objects interacting one upon another. This recognition of interaction in turn led to one of the basic laws in physics, the law of conservation of momentum, discussed further in Chapter 10.

VELOCITY VERSUS SPEED

Before Newton, speed and velocity meant the same thing. With the second law, these two concepts became significantly different. When a meteor curves away from a straight-line path, it is indicating that a force is acting upon it. This is so even if the meteor is traveling at constant speed. Change of direction is as significant as change of speed with respect to the presence of force or acceleration. The definition of *velocity* as *distance per unit of time, or speed, in a given direction* emphasizes the importance of direction in the motion of an object. A velocity of 30 mph due north must be determined by both a speedometer and a compass, whereas a speed of 30 mph can be determined by a speedometer alone.

Constant speed, therefore, does not necessarily mean constant velocity. In Chapter 6, speed was described as constant when equal distances are traveled in equal times. This description is valid regardless of whether the motion is in a straight line or not. Speedometers do not determine direction. For velocity to be constant, not only must equal distances be covered in equal times, but the direction must remain the same. A car traveling uniformly at 60 mph on a circular track is moving at constant speed but not at constant velocity. The car is changing direction continuously and therefore is accelerating in direction. Constant speed in a circle, therefore, is termed *uniform circular motion*. Uniform motion in a straight line does not require force; it can be inertial. However, to maintain uniform circular motion, a constant force is required, and the acceleration is constant.

VECTORS: 3 MILES PLUS 4 MILES MAY EQUAL 5 MILES

A quantity like speed, in which direction is not considered, is known as a *scalar quantity* or a scalar. Volume and mass are other Newtonian illustrations of scalar quantities. A quantity like velocity, which involves direction as well as magnitude, is called a vector quantity or a *vector*. Force, weight, and acceleration are also vectors. The direction in which a force is applied determines the direction in which the object accelerates. Weight is a case of a gravitational force from the earth acting upon an object that tends to accelerate the object toward the center of the earth.

In the case of scalar quantities, where only magnitude counts, 3 + 4 = 7 in accordance with ordinary arithmetic; in the case of vectors, *where direction counts too*, 3 + 4 may equal 5 of a given unit. Suppose a hiker walks 3 mi due east from point *A* to *B*, and then due north 4 mi from *B* to *C*, as in Fig. 8–4. If direction does not matter, as with scalars, the man has walked a total of 7 mi. Actually, the man is 5 mi from his starting point, even though he walked 7 mi. Addition that considers direction is known as vector addition and may be handled through a scale drawing. In Fig. 8–4, let 1 in. = 2 mi. The 3 mi from *A* to *B* is represented by an arrow 1.5 in. long pointing eastward; the 4 mi from *B* to *C*, by an arrow 2 in. long pointing northward. The arrow pointing from *A* to *C* represents the resultant distance of the man from his starting point. The *AC* measurement is 2.5 in., or 5 mi. The Pythagorean theorem of geometry gives the same results as the above scale-drawing method. This theorem states that the square of the hypotenuse of a right triangle equals the sum of the squares of the two sides. That is,

$$\overline{AC}{}^2 = \overline{AB}{}^2 + \overline{BC}{}^2$$

$$\overline{AC}{}^2 = 3^2 \text{ mi}^2 + 4^2 \text{ mi}^2$$

$$\overline{AC}{}^2 = 9 \text{ mi}^2 + 16 \text{ mi}^2 = 25 \text{ mi}^2$$

$$\overline{AC} = 5 \text{ mi.}$$

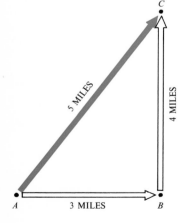

8–4 Vectors: 3 mi + 4 mi = 5 mi. (Direction counts!)

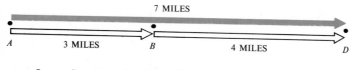

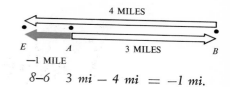

8–5 *3 mi + 4 mi = 7 mi.*

8–6 *3 mi − 4 mi = −1 mi.*

The above scale drawing can also be used to illustrate the following vector addition of velocities. Suppose a man paddles a canoe 3 mph due east across a stream while a current carries him 4 mph due north. The resultant velocity of the man is 5 mph measured at an angle of 53° from his intended direction.

Let us return to the hiker. Suppose that after walking 3 mi due east from point *A* to point *B*, the hiker continues due east for another 4 mi. His resultant distance from *A* is 7 mi, as in Fig. 8–5.

On the other hand, if at the point *B*, the hiker reverses his direction for 4 mi, his displacement is −1 mi, or 1 mi to the *west* of point *A*, the starting point (Fig. 8–6).

In summary, quantities involving directions, whether they be distances, velocities, forces, or other vectors, may be added through the following "head-to-tail" procedure:

1. From a suitable starting point, draw an arrow to scale representing the magnitude and direction of the first vector, *AB*.

2. From the "head" of the first arrow, draw to scale an arrow to represent the magnitude and direction of the second vector. If there are further vectors, draw a representative arrow for each in succession from the "head" of the preceding line, *CD, DE, . . .* etc.

3. Connect the starting point and end point with an arrow *AX* directed *away* from the starting point. The length of the last arrow represents the magnitude of the resultant vector to the given scale; the direction of this arrow gives the direction of the resultant.

In Fig. 8–7, in which direction will the rock go, and with how much force? It is clear from the scale drawing that a resultant force, or vector, generally differs in direction from any of its component forces.

CENTRIPETAL AND CENTRIFUGAL FORCES

Force became identified with uniform circular motion through Newton's second law. This should be clear from the distinction between constant speed and constant velocity in a previous section. To Newton, a force is required to cause any object (1) to change its motion from constant speed in a straight line to constant speed in a circle and (2) to keep an object, such as the moon, moving in a circle. As stated earlier, any object moving in a circle must have a force acting upon it.

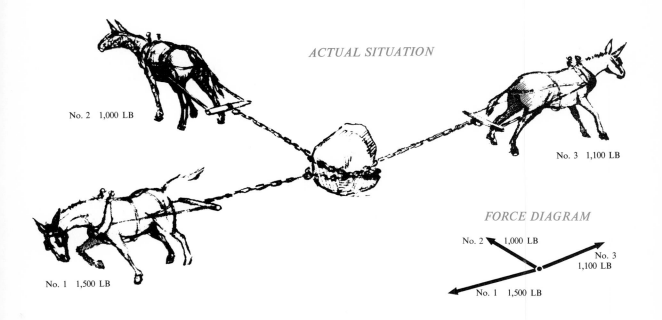

ACTUAL SITUATION

No. 2   1,000 LB

No. 3   1,100 LB

No. 1   1,500 LB

FORCE DIAGRAM

No. 2   1,000 LB

No. 3
1,100 LB

No. 1   1,500 LB

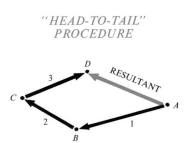

"HEAD-TO-TAIL"
PROCEDURE

RESULTANT

*8–7   In which direction will
the rock go? Forces on the
rock are drawn to scale in the
force diagram and then
arranged "head-to-tail"
beneath. The resultant force
on the rock is the arrow AD
connecting the starting and
end points in the "head-to-
tail" procedure. The length
of AD represents the amount
of the resultant force, and the
direction of AD is the direction in which the rock goes.*

A stone moves in a horizontal circle when appropriately twirled by hand
from a string (Fig. 8–8). The tension of the string tends to pull the stone
toward the center of the circle at any point of the stone's orbit. Such a
force toward the center of a circle is called a *centripetal* ("center-seeking")
force. If the string is released and no longer exerts a force upon the stone,
the stone moves off inertially in a straight line. The original circular
motion of the stone clearly is a resultant of its inertial velocity and its
centripetal velocity.

But Newton's third law of action and reaction applies to circular motion
as well as to linear motion. Newton's law predicts that a centripetal, or
"center-seeking," force on one object is accompanied by an opposite and
equal *centrifugal*, or "center-fleeing," *force* on another object (Fig. 8–8).
If the string pulls inward on the stone, the stone pulls outward on the
string. Try whirling a stone around on a string. You will then become
aware of an outward tug of the string on your hand as the stone pulls
outward on the string. The outward pull of the stone on the string is
the centrifugal force predicted by Newton's third law.

On further thought, however, it is because the circling stone tends
to go off in a straight line that it pulls outward on the string. Centrifugal
force, therefore, is identified with inertia. Another illustration is the
passenger in a car rounding a curve who feels himself pushed outward
against the side of the turning car. Actually, by inertia his body tends
to continue on in a straight line while the car turns. Similarly, through
inertia, people in an amusement park are forced away from the center of
a rapidly rotating disk. On a spinning earth, a rotating-disk experience
would result for all of us if it were not for the centripetal force of gravity.

UNIFORM CIRCULAR
MOTION AND ACCELERATION

If centripetal and reacting centrifugal forces exist in uniform circular motion, by Newton's second law acceleration must also exist. But how can there be acceleration if speed does not change in uniform circular motion? The answer, of course, is that speed does not change but direction does. And thanks to Newton's concept of vectors, already discussed, change in direction means change in velocity and therefore acceleration. Such directional changes in velocity can be quantitatively determined through use of vector addition.

For example, suppose the circle in Fig. 8–9A represents the path of a stone whirled counterclockwise on a string (Fig. 8–9B). The string gives the stone a centripetal force and an acceleration toward the center of the circle. Assign the stone any constant speed v. At point P_1 on the circle, the stone has a velocity represented by the tangent vector v_1 drawn from the point. The tangent arrow indicates the direction that the stone would go if released at point P_1; the length of the tangent is drawn to scale to represent the speed. At point P_2, the stone has a velocity represented by the tangent vector v_2. The directions of tangent vectors v_1 and v_2 differ, but the lengths of the tangents are the same, since the speed of the stone does not change. To obtain the difference $\triangle v$ between the velocities v_1 and v_2, the tangent vectors are redrawn just below circle O so as to start from the same point Q. $\triangle v$ is the line drawn between the two arrow points; it represents the change in velocity. The quantitative value of $\triangle v$ can be determined by measuring the length of the line to scale. The direction of $\triangle v$ can be seen to be parallel to the line to the center of the circle from a point midway between P_1 and P_2 on the circle. That $\triangle v$ is directed toward the center of the circle is to be expected, since $\triangle v$ and an associated centripetal acceleration result from the centripetal force of the string on the stone.

By consideration of the angles involved at O and Q in Figs. 8–9A and 8–9B, it is possible to show geometrically that

since $\triangle v = at$

and arc $P_1P_2 = vt$

$$\frac{vt}{r} = \frac{at}{v}$$

and $a = \dfrac{v^2}{r}$, Equation 8–4

where a = centripetal acceleration

t = time from P_1 to P_2

r = radius of circle, or string length

FORCE ON STONE

FORCE ON STRING

8–8 *Inertia tends to send the stone off in a straight line, and the string to pull the stone toward the center. A circular path results. The inertial tendency of the stone results in its outward pull on the string.*

v = uniform circular speed of stone.

This means that in uniform circular motion the amount of an object's acceleration a toward the circle center is directly proportional to the speed squared v^2 of revolution and inversely proportional to the radius r of the circle.

The amount of the centripetal force on the stone or on any object in uniform circular motion can be determined by substituting v_2/r (from Eq. 8–4) in

$$F = ma$$

or

$$F = \frac{mv^2}{r},$$

Equation 8–5

where F = centripetal force

a = centripetal acceleration

m = mass of the object

v = uniform circular speed

r = radius of circle.

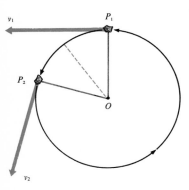

8–9A *The stone changes in velocity without changing in speed.*

In accordance with Eq. 8–5, centripetal or centrifugal force F is directly proportional to the mass m of an object and to its speed squared v^2, and inversely proportional to the radius r of the circle of curvature. Equation 8–5 is used for expressing centrifugal as well as centripetal forces, since these are opposite and equal forces in any given case. The centrifugal force on the string is opposite and equal to the centripetal force on the stone.

To illustrate, a stone of 100 g is whirled on a string of 1 m with a uniform speed of 50 cm/sec. (1) What is the centripetal force in dynes that acts on the stone? (2) What centrifugal force acts on the string?

Solution: From Eq. 8–5

$$\text{I.} \quad F = \frac{mv^2}{r} = \frac{100 \text{ g} \cdot (50 \text{ cm/sec})^2}{100 \text{ cm}}$$

$$F = 2{,}500 \text{ g} \frac{\text{cm}}{\text{sec}^2} = 2{,}500 \text{ dynes.}$$

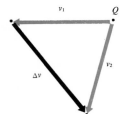

8–9B *The stone's change in velocity $\triangle v$, or acceleration, is toward the center of the circle.*

2. Since the centripetal and centrifugal forces are opposite and equal, the centrifugal force on the string is also 2,500 dynes.

High speed around curves is dangerous for a car because centrifugal force F on a car varies directly according to the speed *squared* (v^2). And sharp curves on a highway are particularly dangerous at high speeds. A sharp curve means a small radius of curvature r. According to the centrifugal force equation, the smaller the radius of curvature r, the greater is the centrifugal force F on the car.

As we shall see, Newton successfully extended his concept of accelerating force to the universe, and the equation $F = ma$ became a law. From Newton on, laws in the physical sciences more and more took the form of equations. Mathematical physics at least, was here to stay. And as Einstein expressed it:

Physics really began with the invention of mass, force, and an inertial system. These concepts are all free systems. They led to the formulation of the mechanical points of view.... Science is compelled to invent ideas corresponding to the reality of our world.... Science is not just a collection of laws, a catalogue of unrelated facts. It is a creation of the human mind, with its freely invented ideas and concepts.

CHAPTER REVIEW

1. Discuss the significance of "straight lines" and "constant speeds" in Newton's first two laws of motion.

2. How do we know when we have a straight line if a succession of horizontal meter sticks forms a circle around the earth?

3. Why is Newton's first law called the law of inertia? What does "inertia" mean?

4. Define and illustrate a force according to Newton's second law.

5. What is the difference between Newton's definition and the more common definition of force as push or pull? Why may Newton's definition be called both "operational" and mathematical?

6. What meaning, advantages, and limitations does Newton's concept of mass have in the second law? How are matter, mass, and inertia inter-related?

7. Illustrate the difference between the mass and the volume of an object.

8. Why is Newton's second law called a law of acceleration? Illustrate how Newton's law of inertia is a special case of his law of acceleration.

9. Is it true by Newton's second law that wherever an object accelerates, a force is acting, seen or unseen? If so, is there not an assumption present that *only* forces can accelerate objects? Could there be another unseen or unknown entity in nature that causes objects to accelerate?

10. Differentiate between gravity as force and as acceleration by Newton's second law.

11. What is the difference between the mass and the weight of an object?

12. By Newton's second law, show how your weight is a force of gravity acting upon you rather than something entirely native to you.

13. Illustrate Newton's third law. If, by the law, every force is accompanied by another opposite and equal force, why do the two forces not cancel each other out leaving no force or acceleration?

14. Discuss an assumption of each law of motion.

15. What is a vector? Explain how "3 mi plus 4 mi may equal 5 mi."

16. Illustrate the difference between speed and velocity. Why is this difference in terms important in understanding linear motion? In understanding circular motion?

17. Illustrate force as a vector in linear motion. In circular motion.

18. Discuss and illustrate centripetal and centrifugal forces as applications of Newton's concept of force (second law) to circular motion. Discuss these forces as applications of the third law to circular motion.

19. How is it possible for a stone whirled around on a string to tug *radially* on your hand, and yet to move off *at a tangent* when you release the string?

20. Review this chapter by tracing the Newtonian system building that relates forces to all moving objects.

21. Discuss to what extent Galileo deserves credit for the Newtonian laws and concepts discussed in this chapter. Be specific.

PROBLEMS

1. Can a body be in motion if no forces are acting upon it? Explain.

2. In which direction do you tend to fall when standing in a bus that starts suddenly? That stops suddenly?

3. Explain by Newton's first law why smooth cardboard can be quickly jerked from under a glass of water without spilling the water. Why must this be done quickly?

4. (a) If a force of 48 newtons gives an object an acceleration of 6 m/sec², what is the mass of the object in kg? (b) What force in newtons is required to give another object twice as heavy half the same acceleration?

5. If a 64-lb force gives a 64-lb mass an acceleration of 32 ft/sec², what force in pounds gives the same mass an acceleration of 1 ft/sec²? What force in poundals?

6. (a) What force in poundals gives a 160-lb mass an acceleration of 1 ft/sec²? What force in pounds? (b) What force in poundals is necessary to give a 160-lb mass an acceleration of 32 ft/sec²? What force in pounds?

7. (a) A man standing on a platform scale in a stationary elevator

weighs 160 lb. If the cable snaps, what is the reading on the scale as the elevator freely falls? (b) If the elevator, under control, accelerates downward at 3.2 ft/sec², what is the scale reading? (c) If the elevator accelerates upward at 32 ft/sec², what is the scale reading? (d) What is the scale reading if the elevator accelerates upward at 3.2 ft/sec²?

8. (a) A parked car 1,500 kg in mass is given an accelerating force of 3,000 newtons. What is the car's acceleration? (b) What is the car's velocity in meters per second after 20 sec? (c) What distance does the car cover in 20 sec?

9. How could you "prove" that a piano exerts an opposite and equal force against you when you lean against it?

10. What minimum forces act on a parked car? If forces are acting, why is the car stationary?

11. In a tug-of-war between two equally strong boys, why can a fixed post replace one of the boys?

12. A small sailboat is stationary in a dead calm. Could a battery-powered fan in the boat be used to move the boat? Explain.

13. (a) A man weighing 75 kg leaps to the shore from a rowboat weighing 150 kg. If the man moves forward at a speed of 6 km/hr, how fast does the boat move backward? (b) What is the momentum of the boat? The momentum of the man?

14. In a tug-of-war on smooth ground, team 1 pulls against team 2 with a force of 100 kg weight. Team 1 members have a total mass of 400 kg, and team 2, 300 kg. Ignoring friction, (a) with what force must team 2 pull in order to remain stationary? (b) If team 2 pulls with a force of only 80 kg weight, what is the net accelerating force? (c) What is the acceleration in part (b)? (Note that both teams comprise one system of motion and mass.) (d) Starting from rest, what is the velocity of the system in part (b) after 3 sec? (e) What is the momentum of each team after 3 sec?

15. Which of the following illustrate *constant velocity?* (a) A stone at the end of a cord is whirled in a circle at a constant speed of 1 m/sec. (b) A truck climbs a steep hill, its speed decreasing from 60 mph at the bottom to 20 mph at the top. (c) A car turns a corner at a constant speed of 35 mph. (d) A car climbs a long, straight hill at a constant speed of 40 mph.

16. A man walks 8 mi south and then 6 mi west. How far is he from his starting point in miles?

17. A boy swims at a 4 km/hr velocity across a river that has a current of 3 km/hr. At the end of a half hour, the boy reaches the other side. (a) How far downstream is he in kilometers? (b) How wide is the river? (c) How far is the swimmer from his starting point?

18. A plane moving at a speed of 300 mph due north meets a wind blowing from the west at a speed of 50 mph. Show by a scale drawing what the new speed and direction of the plane is.

19. (a) Is the centrifugal force due to rotation of the earth the same everywhere on earth? Explain. (b) Why does centrifugal force not pull you off the earth?

20. (a) What is the speed in miles per hour of the earth's rotation at the equator? (Use 4,000 mi for the earth's radius.) (b) What is the centrifugal force upon a 160-lb person at the equator?

21. The earth revolves around the sun at a speed of 19 mph. (a) What is the resulting centrifugal force upon you? (b) Why are you not pulled off of the earth by centrifugal forces of rotation and revolution?

SUGGESTIONS FOR FURTHER READING

Taylor, Lloyd W., *Physics, the Pioneer Science,* Dover paperback, New York, 1959, Chs. 9–11.

Cheronis, Nicholas D., et al., *Study of the Physical World,* Houghton Mifflin, Boston, 1958, Ch. 12.

Lemon, Harvey B., *From Galileo to the Nuclear Age,* Univ. Chicago Press, Chicago, 1949, Chs. 2 and 7.

Holton, Gerald J., and D. H. D. Roller, *Foundations of Modern Physical Science,* Addison-Wesley, Reading, Mass., 1959, Ch. 4.

White, Harvey, *Modern College Physics,* Van Nostrand, New York, 1962, Chs. 2 and 6.

Schneer, Cecil, *The Wonderful Machine,* Harper, New York, 1960, Ch. 7.

Lodge, Oliver, *Pioneers of Science,* Dover paperback, New York, 1960, Lecture 7.

Omer, Guy C., Jr., et al., *Physical Science: Men and Concepts,* Heath, Boston, 1962, Chs. 15–16 and 18.

Hall, A. R., *The Scientific Revolution,* Beacon paperback, Boston, 1956, Chs. 1–4.

Campbell, Norman, *What Is Science?* Dover paperback, New York, 1952.

9 Gravitation
and a Mechanical Universe

Ah, but a man's reach should exceed his grasp, Or what's a heaven for?

ROBERT BROWNING, 1855

And the same year (1666) I began to think of gravity extending to ye Orb of the Moon .... I deduced that the forces which keep the planets in their Orbits must be reciprocally as the squares of their distances from the centers about which they revolve; and thereby compared the force requisite to keep the Moon in her Orb with the force of gravity at the surface of the earth, and found them [to] answer pretty nearly.

ISAAC NEWTON, 1687

WHAT HOLDS THE
SOLAR SYSTEM TOGETHER?

It started back in 1666, the year that the Black Plague kept Newton at home on the farm. The story goes that an apple falling from a nearby tree caused him to raise questions about the moon. Does the earth's gravity extend to the moon? If so, why hadn't the moon ages ago fallen to the earth like a monstrous apple? Do the same laws of motion that apply to rolling balls or falling apples apply to celestial objects, too? If so, what holds the solar system together?

173

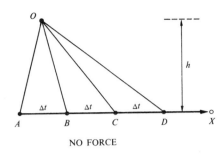

NO FORCE

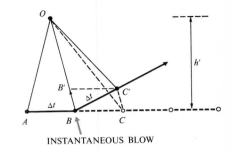

INSTANTANEOUS BLOW

9–1   No force and equal areas. An object moves with constant velocity along line AX. Another line from a central point O to the moving object sweeps over equal areas in equal times (△AOB = △BOC = ···).

9–2   An instantaneous force and equal areas. A sharp blow toward O at point B sends the object toward C' instead of C. Equal areas still exist (△AOB = △BOC') in equal units of time.

Systematic answers to such questions comprise much of Newton's *Principia.* The law of universal gravitation that emerged is one of the greatest syntheses in all science. Newton's thinking in the development of this law is classic in scientific research and deserves our consideration. *Principia* is a formal presentation of Newton's ideas 21 years after he developed them. We therefore cannot be sure of the sequence of his ideas as they actually occurred. Human insights and thought processes are complex. Often a flash of insight occurs first, and then logic and evidence are built up to support the insight. In any case, the sequence that follows in Newton's scientific investigation of gravity is arranged for continuity and clarity.

HYPOTHESIS OF GRAVITATIONAL FORCE

The falling apple hits the ground; if the moon "falls," it falls perpetually—it never reaches the earth. In considering this difference, Newton recognized that before falling, an apple is at rest; the moon is not. As a clue, recall that Newton had the concept of inertia. If the same laws of nature hold for the heavens as for the earth, then by inertia, the moon—or any planet, for that matter—should move out of its orbit at a tangent. Why doesn't it? Is it not reasonable to suppose that gravity extending as a force to the moon prevents the moon from moving off at a tangent—much as a string acts on a whirling stone (Fig. 8–8)? Through analogies, a scientific hypothesis may be born. The moon replaces the stone; the earth, the hand; and gravity, the string. As in all analogies, however, there are differences between objects compared. The string, extending visibly between the stone and the hand, clearly pulls inward upon the stone. In the case of the moon, there is no material connection between

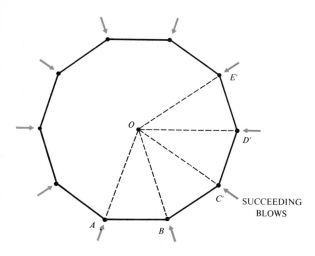

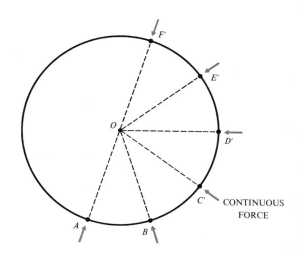

it and the earth. The distance between the two bodies is almost 0.25 million mi. How could a force be acting across such a distance? Newton's answer was simply that by analogy, the moon acts *as if* there were such a gravity force upon it across space—like that upon the apple when it leaves the tree!

Central Forces and Equal Areas

But Newton did not rest upon analogy alone. Through his concept of vectors, he geometrically proved* that (1) any object moving at a constant speed in a straight line would travel in a circle *if* a central force continuously acted upon it, and (2) the object under this force would travel in accordance with Kepler's law of equal areas. Newton's geometric reasoning is shown in Figs. 9–1 to 9–4.

Figure 9–1 represents the law of equal areas for an object moving at constant velocity along line AX. No force is acting. The object travels equal distances AB, BC, CD, and so on during equal time intervals indicated as $\triangle t$. (The $\triangle$ before a symbol, you recall, means a small quantity of that symbol. In this case, $\triangle t$ is a small interval of time.) Point O is anywhere outside of the line of motion. If lines are drawn from point O to A, O to B, O to C, and so on, it can be shown that a line from point O to the moving object sweeps over equal areas in equal times:

1. The area of any triangle is half of its base times its altitude.
2. Triangles AOB, BOC, COD, and so forth have equal bases, AB, BC, CD, and so forth, and the same altitude, h.

9–3 *A repeated force and equal areas. Further regular sharp blows toward O are made at points D′, E′ . . . . The path of the object forms a regular polygon. Now* $\triangle AOB = \triangle BOC$ $= \triangle C'OD' = \cdots$ *in equal time intervals.*

9–4 *Continuous force and equal areas. A continuous force toward central point O instead of repeated blows gives the object a circular path.*

*At a later point in this chapter, *mathematical proof* will be differentiated from *scientific evidence.*

3. Therefore, the areas of the triangles *AOB, BOC,* and *COD,* swept over as the object moves from *A* to *B* to *C* to *D,* are equal.

Suppose that the above object, when at point *B,* is given a single blow toward point *O.* Figure 9–2 represents the law of equal areas, still applying under the new condition of a force applied for an instant toward the center *O.* As a result of the instantaneous force of the blow at *B,* in the time interval $\triangle t$, the object arrives at point *C′* instead of at point *C.* If the object had been stationary when struck, its displacement—that is, its distance and direction—during $\triangle t$ would have been *BB′.* The actual displacement *BC′* of the object is the resultant, or vector sum, of the original displacement *BC* without the blow and of the displacement *BB¹,* which would have taken place if the object had been at rest when struck. That is, its actual motion *BC′* is a combination of its two component motions, *BC* and *BB′.* (Review the "head-to-tail" procedures for vector addition in Chapter 8.)

It can be shown as follows that triangle *AOB* and triangle *BOC¹* in Fig. 9–2 are equal in area:

1. Triangle *AOB* and triangle *BOC* are equal in area, as shown above (Fig. 9–1).
2. *CC′* is parallel to *BB′* by construction.
3. Triangle *BOC* and triangle *BOC′* have the same base *OB.*
4. Triangle *BOC* and triangle *BOC′* have equal altitudes *h* and *h′,* since parallel lines are everywhere equidistant.
5. Triangle *BOC* and triangle *BOC′* are equal in area, since they both have the same value for ½ base · altitude.
6. Therefore, triangle *AOB* and triangle BOC′ are equal in area, since both equal the area of triangle *BOC.*

In this way, the law of equal areas is seen to hold in the case of a single blow at point *B* toward point *O.*

Now, suppose that after point *B,* the same object is struck at regular intervals with instantaneous blows of equal force toward the center *O* (Fig. 9–3). *C′, D′, E′,* and so on represent the points where these equal, instantaneous blows are struck. At each of these points, the same vector addition applies in succession, as at point *B* in Fig. 9–2. Figure 9–3 shows the resulting positions of the points *C′, D′, E′,* and so on; their symmetry around the center *O;* and their equal distances from the center *O.* Clearly, the triangles indicated, *AOB, BOC′, C′OD′,* and so forth, are equal in area, and the line from the center *O* to the moving body sweeps over equal areas in equal time intervals.

Finally, suppose that the above object at constant speed is subjected to a *continuous* force of constant magnitude toward point *O* instead of a regularly repeated blow toward the same center. The path of the object will take the form of a circle, as in Fig. 9–4. The equal arcs *AB, BC′,*

C'D', and so on represent the equal distances traveled by the objects in equal time intervals. And since all radii of a circle are equal, the areas *AOB, BOC', C'OD'*, and so on, swept over in equal times by the line from the center *O* to the moving body, are equal. This conclusion, based on a continuously acting centripetal force, is in accordance with Kepler's law of equal areas. It can be seen that as the time interval for regularly repeated blows would become ever smaller in Fig. 9–3, the path of the object would approach ever more closely to the circle resulting from a continuously acting force in Fig. 9–4.

As a last step toward identifying Kepler's law of equal areas with centripetal forces, Newton proved through calculus that the orbit of an object would be an ellipse if the object were subjected to a continuous force directed toward one of the foci of the ellipse. Remember that a circle is but a special case of an ellipse in which the two foci are at the same point (Fig. 4–4). His calculus proof, however, is beyond our scope here.

But mathematical evidence does not constitute scientific proof. In the world of actual planetary or satellite motion, for example, there may be unknown factors other than central forces that could account for elliptical orbits of planets or the law of equal areas. Aristotelian astronomers did not require central forces for celestial motion. They had celestial spheres. Nor does Einstein's theory of relativity today require central forces in astronomy. Einstein replaced gravitational forces at a distance with space-time fields.

To Newton, however, in the 17th century, the concept of gravitational force at a distance was the key to the understanding of motion and of the universe. And he set about looking for further mathematical proofs and scientific evidence for gravitational forces acting at a distance.

Gravitation across Space:
An Inverse Square Law

A central deflecting force may keep the moon in an elliptical orbit, but how could Newton establish this force to be the earth's gravity? Or how could he establish a similar gravitational force from the sun to keep the planets in orbit? Newton's first steps in answering these questions was to seek some relationship between the amount of a gravitational force and the distance through which it acts. It would certainly seem that a force of gravity would weaken with distance, but how much so was the question. The following delineates what Newton found and how he found it:

1. Consider a planet to complete a circle of radius *r* in time *T*.

2. The speed v of the planet is the circumference $C = 2\pi r$ divided by the period, or time of one revolution T. That is,

$$v = \frac{2\pi r}{T}.$$

Equation 9–1

3. Now substitute the above expression for v in the centripetal force equation of Chapter 8,

$$F = \frac{mv^2}{r}.$$

Equation 8–5

Or $\quad F = \frac{m}{r} \frac{4\pi^2 r^2}{T^2} = \frac{4\pi^2 mr}{T^2}.$

Equation 9–2

4. But by Kepler's third law of planetary motion,

$$T^2 = kr^3.$$

5. This time, substitute kr^3 for T^2 in Eq. 9–2 to obtain:

$$F = \frac{4\pi^2 mr}{T^2} = \frac{4\pi^2 mr}{kr^3} = \frac{4\pi^2 m}{kr^2}.$$

6. Since $4\pi^2$, m, and k are all constants:

$$\frac{4\pi^2 m}{k} = k',$$

where k' is a new constant.

7. Now substitute k' for $\frac{4\pi^2 m}{k}$ in step 5:

$$F = \frac{k'm}{r^2},$$

Equation 9–3

where $m =$ the planet's mass, and r the planet's orbital radius.

Equation 9–3 is Newton's famous inverse square relationship. This principle states that a gravitational force F from the sun upon a planet is inversely proportional to the square of the orbital radius r^2 of that planet. (The mass m of a planet is assumed to remain constant.) The greater the distance squared of the planet, the less the force of gravity.

By Newton's third law, a gravitational force from the sun to the earth means an opposite and equal gravity force back to the sun from the earth. And the sun is further than the moon from our planet. If the principle of inverse squares applies to the moon in its orbit, then the earth's gravity therefore theoretically extends not merely to the moon but to infinity. Place as large a number in the denominator of Eq. 9–3 as you wish; there will always be a value for the earth's force of gravity. Only if the moon were at an infinite distance would the earth's force of gravity become zero. Similarly, a central gravitational force of the sun would reach the furthermost planet and beyond.

We can further illustrate the inverse square relationship with your own weight. In Chapter 8, we identified your weight with the earth's gravitational force upon your body. Through calculus, Newton also proved that a gravitational force may be considered to be operating from the center of mass of one object to that of another. The earth's gravity, accordingly, acts upon you from a center approximately 4,000 mi below the earth's surface.

Let us say that your weight is 160 lb (or 5,120 poundals). This means that a gravity force of 160 lb is acting upon you across a distance of 4,000 mi from the earth's center. In accordance with the inverse square principle, your weight should decrease as you ascend above the earth (Fig. 9–5). For example, your weight at a distance of 4,000 mi above the earth's surface can be predicted as follows:

1. The force F acting on you at the surface, 4,000 mi from the earth's center, is

$$F = \frac{k'm}{r^2}.$$ Equation 9–3

2. The force F' acting on you 4,000 mi above the earth's surface, or 8,000 mi ($2 \cdot 4,000$ mi) from the earth's center, is

$$F' = \frac{k'm}{(2r)^2} = \frac{k'm}{4r^2}.$$

3. The ratio of the forces acting on you at the two different positions indicated is

$$\frac{F'}{F} = \frac{k'm/4r^2}{k'm/r^2} = \frac{1}{4}.$$

4. Substituting your weight of 160 lb at the earth's surface for F,

$$\frac{F'}{160} = \frac{1}{4}$$

$$4F' = 160 \text{ lb}$$

$$F' = 40 \text{ lb}.$$

That is, your weight at a point 4,000 mi above the earth's surface is 40 lb.

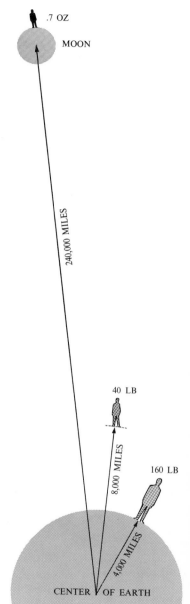

9–5 *Weight decreases by an inverse square with distance from the earth's center (Table 9–1).*

Suppose now that you were about 240,000 mi from the earth's center, the moon's distance away (Fig. 9–5). Following the above example, can you show that your weight at the distance of the moon would be 1/3,600 of what it is at the earth's surface? (That is, 1/3,600 of 160 lb, or about 0.7 oz!)

Table 9–1 illustrates more completely the inverse square relationship between weight and distance from the earth's center.

Table 9–1 | *INVERSE SQUARE RELATIONSHIP*

DISTANCE FROM EARTH'S CENTER		INVERSE SQUARES	YOUR WEIGHT	
MI			LB	OZ
4,000	$(1 \cdot 4,000)$	$\frac{1}{1^2} = \frac{1}{1}$	$1 \cdot 160 \text{ lb} = 160$	
8,000	$(2 \cdot 4,000)$	$\frac{1}{2^2} = \frac{1}{4}$	$\frac{1}{4} \cdot 160 \text{ lb} = 40$	
12,000	$(3 \cdot 4,000)$	$\frac{1}{3^2} = \frac{1}{9}$	$\frac{1}{9} \cdot 160 \text{ lb} = 17$	12
16,000	$(4 \cdot 4,000)$	$\frac{1}{4^2} = \frac{1}{16}$	$\frac{1}{16} \cdot 160 \text{ lb} = 10$	
32,000	$(8 \cdot 4,000)$	$\frac{1}{8^2} = \frac{1}{64}$	$\frac{1}{64} \cdot 160 \text{ lb} = 2$	8
240,000	$(60 \cdot 4,000)$	$\frac{1}{60^2} = \frac{1}{3,600}$	$\frac{1}{3,600} \cdot 160 \text{ lb} = 0$	0.7
∞		$\frac{1}{\infty^2} = 0$	$0 \cdot 160 \text{ lb} = 0$	0.0

Clearly, *if* Newton's inverse square relationship holds, you would still have some earthly weight as far away as the moon. Only at an infinite distance from the earth does the earth's gravitational force cease acting upon you.

GRAVITATION TESTED: THE MOON'S DAILY FALL TOWARD THE EARTH

Mathematical reasoning often leads to brilliant hypotheses about the world but does not constitute scientific evidence. For that, hypotheses must be tested. How was "inverse squares" to be tested? Newton's answer was simply this: "Use the moon!" Test the inverse square relationship through the moon's motion. First, *predict from inverse squares* how much the moon *should* fall daily; then *calculate from data* of the moon's motion how much the moon *does* fall daily. *If the predicted value closely approximates the observed value,* scientific evidence exists for an "inverse squares" extension of gravity to the moon.

But how could the moon be falling to earth? The moon's path obviously is around the earth and not directly toward it. Consider Galileo's analysis of projectile motion (Fig. 7–7). By application of Galileo's principle of independence of velocities to the moon, the moon, by inertia, tends to move off at a tangent at any point in its orbit. This motion at a tangent is similar to the inertial horizontal velocity of the cannonball in projectile motion. And just as there is a vertical fall of the cannonball independent of its horizontal motion, so there is also a gravitational free fall of the moon toward the earth independent of its inertial motion. The moon's actual orbit is a resultant of its two independent velocities, just as the parabolic curve of the cannonball is a resultant of its two velocities. The moon, therefore, is like a projectile circling around the earth but never landing because of the curvature of the earth. It is as if the earth bends back. This idea, highly fruitful with modern artificial satellites, was first recognized by Newton in his famous mountain illustration (Fig. 9–6). Let us quote from Newton's *Principia*, Part 3:

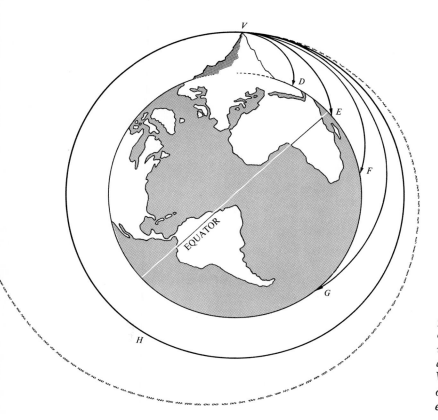

9–6 *A projectile fired with enough speed from a high mountaintop could become an artificial satellite (Newton). With still more speed, an object may escape from the earth.*

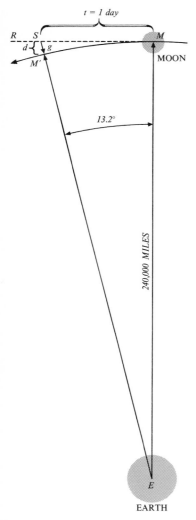

9–7   *Predicted fall of the moon toward the earth: 6,300 mi per day. The moon, by inertia, moves 13.2° in 1 day from point M to point S. But independently, the earth's gravity g pulls the moon the distance d from S to M'. The distance d can be predicted by $d = \frac{1}{2}gt^2$ with $g = .107$ in./sec² at the moon's distance from the earth.*

That by means of centripetal forces the planets may be retained in certain orbits, we may easily understand, if we consider the motions of projectiles; for a stone that is projected is by the pressure of its own weight forced out of the rectilinear path, which by the initial projection alone it should have pursued, and made to describe a curved line in the air, and through that crooked way is at last brought down to the ground; and the greater the velocity is with which it is projected, the farther it goes before it falls to the earth. We may therefore suppose the velocity to be so increased that it would describe an arc of 1, 2, 5, 10, 100, 1,000 miles before it arrived at the earth, till at last, exceeding the limits of the earth, it should pass into space without touching it. Let *AFB* [see photograph of Newton's drawing] represent the surface of the earth, *C* its center, *VD, VE, VF,* the curved lines which a body would describe, if projected in an horizontal direction from the top of a high mountain successively with more and more velocity; and, because the celestial motions are scarcely retarded by the little or no resistance of the spaces in which they are performed, to keep up the parity of cases, let us suppose either that there is no air about the earth, or at least that it is endowed with little or no power of resisting; and for the same reason that the body projected with a lesser velocity describes the lesser arc *VD,* and with a greater velocity of the greater arc *VE,* and, augmenting the velocity, it goes farther and farther to *F* and *G,* if the velocity was still more and more augmented, it would reach at last quite beyond the circumference of the earth, and return to the mountain from which it was projected . . . .

But if we now imagine bodies to be projected in the directions of lines parallel to the horizon from greater heights, as of 5, 10, 100, 1,000 or more miles, or rather as many semidiameters of the earth, these bodies, according to their different velocity, and the different force of gravity in different heights, will describe arcs [like the moon] either concentric with the earth, or variously eccentric, and go on revolving through the heavens in those orbits just as the planets do in their orbits.

Predicted Value of the Moon's Fall from the Inverse Square Hypothesis

At the earth's surface, objects in free fall move downward with an acceleration g of 32 ft/sec². If the inverse square relationship applies to the moon, that body should fall toward the earth with an acceleration g of 1/3,600 · 32 ft/sec², or 0.107 in./sec² (Fig. 9–7). That is, if the earth's gravitational force at 240,000 mi is reduced to 1/3,600 of its surface value at 240,000 mi, so would its gravitational acceleration. Using Galileo's law of falling bodies, $d = \frac{1}{2}gt^2$ and the above value of g = 0.107 in./sec², the distance of fall d is 0.054 in. in 1 sec, 16 ft in 1 min, or *about 6,300 mi in 1 day.*

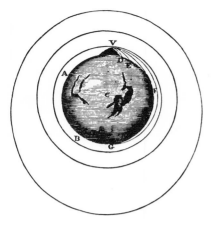

A replica of Newton's illustration in "Principia" explaining satellite motion through projectile motion.

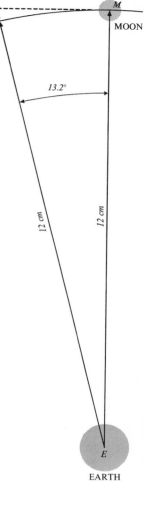

Observed Value of the Moon's Fall

Figure 9–8 is drawn to scale from knowledge based on observations of the moon's motions in its nearly circular orbit. The point M represents the position of the moon at any given instant. The line EM is the average distance of 240,000 mi from the earth's center to that of the moon. MR is the straight-line path of the moon without a gravitational force from the earth. The moon moves through the arc MM' during a period of 1 day. The angle MEM' is indicated as 13.2°, since the moon completes one revolution in 27.3 days and 360°/27.3 equals 13.2°. Since the scale of the drawing is 20,000 mi to 1 cm, the radii EM and EM' are approximated at 12 cm. The line SM' represents the daily fall of the moon from a straight-line path. This line can be directly measured at about 30 mm, or 3 cm, for an answer of about 6,000 mi.

Comparison of the Predicted to the Observed Value of the Moon's Daily Fall

Our above theoretical prediction of approximately 6,300 mi for the moon's daily fall compares to about 6,000 mi for the observed fall. Similarly, when Newton found that his predicted values reasonably matched his observed values, he concluded that the force that pulls the apple to the earth is the same that keeps the moon in its orbit—a universal force of gravity.

Newton's Gravitational Inferences

Newton further concluded that a gravitational force of the sun holds the planets in orbit just as the earth's gravity holds the moon. Each planet

9–8 Observed fall of the moon: About 6,000 mi per day. By scale-drawing measurement, the observed fall of the moon SM' is about .3 cm, compared to 12 cm representing the 240,000-mi distance to the moon. Three-tenths of 1 cm represent 6,000 mi.

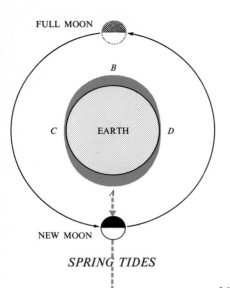

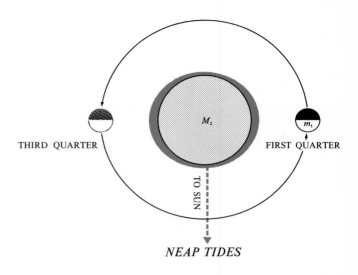

SPRING TIDES

NEAP TIDES

would move off in a straight line by inertia if it were not for the sun and its central gravitational force. The moon, through "inverse squares," is therefore a connecting link between gravity on the earth and the gravitational pull of the sun on the planets. Gravitation explains Kepler's laws; a follow-through of Galileo's new system of mechanics, it explains how the earth can be a planet moving around the sun. Gravitational forces between the sun and planets and between planets and moons tie them all together into one mechanical system dominated by the sun. Newton had given his answer to the question "What holds the solar system together?"

TIDES AND GRAVITATION

But gravitation should work both ways: Every action has an opposite and equal reaction. If the earth attracts the moon across space, then the moon must also attract the earth (Fig. 9–9). As evidence for an opposite and equal force of the moon on the earth, Newton pointed to the tides. Tides are the periodic rise and fall of a water level, particularly noticed along ocean shores. For example, a high tide at a given place on one day will be repeated there the next day—but about 51 min later. This lag of 51 min corresponds to the daily 51-min lag in the rising and setting of the moon. Figure 9–9 illustrates how the moon's gravitational pull causes tides. By an inverse square force, the water is pulled up from the earth on the side A facing the moon. But at point B on the far side, the water is subject to less pull than the earth's center beneath and therefore tends to remain behind as a tide. Tides are thus high at areas A and B and low at C and D. But since the earth rotates daily, the pull of the moon results in two noticeably high and two low tides in 24 hr and 51 min.

9–9   Spring and neap tides. Tides result from the gravitational pull of the moon and sun on the earth. Very high (spring) tides result at new and full moon when solar tides coincide with lunar tides. Much lowered (neap) tides result when solar tides are out of step with lunar.

As could also be predicted through gravitation, the sun also produces its own tides. *Spring*, or very high, tides result twice monthly when solar tides coincide with lunar tides (at new and full moon), and *neap*, or very low, tides when the solar tide is out of step with the lunar (at the first and third quarters). That is, at new and full moon (spring tides), the sun reinforces the moon's high tide and further lowers the moon's low tide. A week later, at first or third quarter (neap tides), the sun lowers the moon's high tide and heightens the moon's low tide. About 70 percent of tidal effects are due to the moon and 30 percent to the sun.

Refer back to Fig. 9–9. The gravitational force F_E of the earth on the moon by Newton's second law should be proportional to the mass of the moon m_1 ($F_E \propto m_1$). Similarly, the back gravitational force F_m of the moon on the earth should be proportional to the larger mass M_2 of the earth ($F_m \propto M_2$). Since the earth and moon are in mutual attraction with $F_E = -F_m$, Newton concluded that both the above proportions could be combined into a common F_{grav} in which

$$F_{grav} \propto m_1 M_2. \qquad\qquad \text{Equation 9–4}$$

But

$$F_{grav} = \frac{k'm}{r^2} \ \ \text{(by Eq. 9–3).}$$

Combining Eqs. 9–3 and 9–4, Newton found that

$$F_{grav} = G\,\frac{Mm}{r^2}. \qquad\qquad \text{Equation 9–5}$$

Notice that GM in Equation 9–5 replaces k^1 in Equation 9–3. That is, the earth's mass M is algebraically factored out of k^1 to leave a new gravitational constant G.

Gravitational attraction between the earth and the moon in Equation 9–5 is mutual and depends only on their masses and common distance. More specifically, this force of gravitation is in direct proportion to each of the masses and inversely proportional to the square of the distance between them. The G is a constant of proportionality later designated as a universal gravitational constant.

NEWTON'S LAW OF UNIVERSAL GRAVITATION

But Newton did not limit gravitation to the earth and to the moon. Or to the sun and the planets. He extended gravitation to all objects. The mutual gravitational force between the earth and the moon depends in part on their masses, that is, on the quantity of matter within them. Therefore, gravitation applies to all matter. Whether stars or grains of sand, all objects share a mutual gravitational attraction. A world gravity structures the universe and makes it one. Newton's crowning achievement, the *law of universal gravitation*, states simply that

> *Every body in the universe attracts every other with a force directly proportional to the product of their masses and inversely proportional to the square of the distance between their centers.*

Shape, hardness, color, chemical composition—nothing matters in the universal gravitation of objects—only quantity of mass and distance!

To summarize, in answer to the question "What holds the solar system together?" Newton extended Galileo's laws of falling bodies and his own laws of motion to the moon and planets; and he applied his (and Huygens's) concept of centripetal force to these bodies in orbit. Then with the aid of Kepler's laws, he came up with universal gravitational forces between the sun and planets and between planets and moons that ties them all together into one mechanical system dominated by the sun. And the forces are mechanical and universal; their effects are measurable and can be treated mathematically. Newton had "stood on the shoulders of giants and seen further."

CAVENDISH'S *G* EXPERIMENT AND WEIGHING THE EARTH

Determining G

If mutual gravitational forces exist among all objects, then why do not dishes on a table ordinarily gravitate toward each other like magnets? It is certainly reasonable to expect some evidence of gravitational attraction in everyday objects around us if gravity is universal. And yet experimental evidence for mutual attraction of ordinary objects was not found until about a century after *Principia*. In 1798 Henry Cavendish (1731–1810), the eccentric genius after whom England's most renowned research laboratory is named, reported that he had measured gravitational forces among experimental objects of known mass. For his experiment, Cavendish had improved upon a torsion balance devised by a friend, Rev. John Michell. The torsion balance technique essentially was one of suspending from a very thin wire a long, narrow rod with a small sphere m_1 and m_2 at each end and then of bringing a pair of massive spheres M_1 and M_2 toward the suspended spheres (Fig. 9–10).

As the large spheres approached close to the small ones, gravitational attraction was detected by the measurable twist of the vertical suspension:

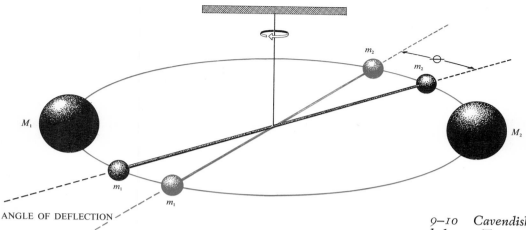

ANGLE OF DEFLECTION

The rod moved through the angle of deflection θ. Known external forces were then applied to balance, thereby indicating the amount of the gravitational forces causing the twist.

Further, with the gravitational forces now known, as well as the values of all four masses and the distances between them, Cavendish was able to compute the value of the constant of universal gravitation G in Newton's famous gravitation equation, $F_{grav} = G\ Mm/r^2$. Modern refinements in the torsion balance give a value of

$$G = .0000000667, \quad \text{or} \quad 6.67 \times 10^{-8*}$$

if the masses are in grams, the distance in centimeters, and force in dynes. Essentially this means that if two masses of 1 g each were placed 1 cm apart, they would exert a force of 0.0000000667 dynes upon each other. Certainly not much of a force against friction! No wonder objects are not ordinarily observed to gravitate toward each other.

A number of years later, Von Jolly, a German scientist, reinforced Cavendish's evidence for universal gravitation. He used an equal arms-balance in an ingeniously simple technique (Fig. 9–11). A spherical flask filled with 5 kg of mercury at S was counterbalanced by weights in pan P. When Von Jolly placed a lead sphere of 5,775.2 kg at a distance of 56.86 cm—from center to center—below the mercury, the equilibrium of the

9–10 Cavendish's torsion balance. Two small lead spheres are horizontally attracted toward two massive ones placed close by. The motion twists the vertical wire suspension. The amount of gravitational force causing the twist corresponds to the angle of deflection of the horizontal rod and is determined by balancing out this force against known external forces.

*This power form of expression for small and for large numbers is described in Appendix B.

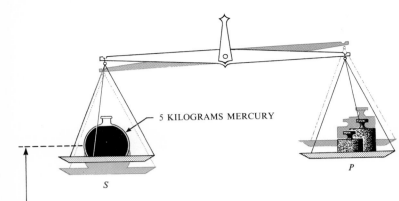

5 KILOGRAMS MERCURY

S

P

56.86 cm

5775.2 kg

balance was definitely disturbed: The mercury moved downward toward the lead in gravitational attraction.

When Von Jolly then added 0.589 mg of weight to pan P, the scale balanced again: The added weight of 0.589 mg offset the gravitational force of the lead. Clearly, the gravitational force F_{grav} between the lead and the mercury was 0.589 mg. Here again was gravitational attraction directly measured between objects on an everyday scale.

Can you apply the law of gravitation $F_{grav} = G\ Mm/r^2$ to Von Jolly's above data to determine the value of the constant of universal gravitation G that he obtained? (Von Jolly's value of 6.465×10^{-8} cm^3/g sec^2 is comparable to the current value already given.)

Why would G in the gravitation law be *the same for any two objects anywhere*, even though the gravitational force F changes as objects and their relative distances are changed?

Weighing the Earth

Once Cavendish had determined the value of the constant G, calculation of the earth's weight was simple. More correctly, calculation of the earth's mass M_e was simple through Newton's $F = G\ M_e m/r^2$. (The "weight" of any object refers to the gravitational force of the earth on that object; the concept "weight" cannot be applied to the earth itself as a mutual force of itself acting on itself!)

For calculating the earth's mass, consider a 1 g mass of chalk m_c. At the earth's surface, the 1 g mass of chalk has a weight of 1 g force, or 980 dynes. That means the earth attracts a 1 g mass m at its surface with a force F of 1 g. The radius of the earth, or distance d from the center of the chalk to the earth's center, is 4,000 mi. Therefore, the earth's mass M_e may be determined through Newton's equation of gravitational force as follows:

Given: $F = 1$ g $= 980$ dynes

To find: M_e

$m_c = 1$ g

$d_e = 4,000$ mi $= 6.37 \times 10^8$/cm or 637,000,000 cm

$G = 6.67 \times \dfrac{10^{-8} \text{ cm}^3}{\text{g sec}^2}$ or $0.0000000667 \dfrac{\text{cm}^3}{\text{g sec}^2}$.

Solution: $F_{\text{grav}} = \dfrac{G\, M_e m_c}{d^2}$

or

$$M_e = \dfrac{F_{\text{grav}}\, d^2}{G\, m_c} = \dfrac{(980)\ (637000000)^2}{(0.0000000667)\ (1)}$$

$$= 6 \times 10^{27} \text{ g (6 followed by 27 zeros)}$$

$$= 66 \times 10^{20} \text{ t (66 followed by 20 zeros).}$$

And once Cavendish had determined the mass of the earth, determining the masses of other solar system members was possible through Newton's and Kepler's laws. Table 5–1 compares the masses and diameters of the sun, moon, and planets to those of the earth.

PREDICTING AND DISCOVERING NEW PLANETS

Newton's gravitational force equation provided tentative relationships between assumed gravitational forces, masses, and distances of objects; it was originally a mathematical hypothesis. The equation was subjected to observational test. Newton's successful moon-fall predictions and the experiments of Cavendish and Von Jolly solidly supported the gravitational force equation. The equation apparently could be applied to the universe. Gravitation as a tentative hypothesis of mutual forces acting upon objects across space had enough specific evidence to be generalized into a theory. But perhaps it was when the equation led to the discovery of unknown planets that it reached the status of a law of the universe. The testing for universal gravitation began with the moon, proceeded earthward to ocean tides and man-made lead spheres, and then reached outward to space beyond the furthermost known planets.

In 1610, Galileo reported discovering four moons of Jupiter through a telescope. But it wasn't until 1781 that telescopes in the hands of William Herschel were powerful enough for the discovery of another planet. For years Sir William had been systematically re-examining the heavens with his prized 10-ft telescope and adding to his fame as a great English astronomer through his discoveries of new stars, comets, and nebulae.

Henry Cavendish. (Brown Bros. photograph)

Then, one night another new object of unusual appearance showed itself. When on many successive evenings this irregular speck of light changed its position among the stars but did not disappear, excitement mounted; here was not another comet but a new planet! Uranus had been silently orbiting unknown to man until discovered by talent and chance.

Through a few observations and Kepler's laws, an expected elliptical orbit of 84 years was plotted for Uranus. All went well for about 40 years; the observed positions of the new "wanderer" conformed to the expected orbit. Then things began to go wrong. More and more, Uranus was departing from its prescribed path. Since due allowances had been made for gravitational pulls of other known planets, the answer to the discrepancies did not lie there. Some suggested that perhaps Newton's law of gravitation was failing for large distances.

But independently, two young mathematicians were intrigued by another possibility: Perhaps another unknown planet beyond Uranus was pulling the latter out of orbit; perhaps Uranus was approaching an opposition with a new planet. If so, instead of being limited or discredited,

complete cycle of 26,000 years accounts for the slow shift of seasons. In Newton's system, gravitational forces are causes; observations, effects.

Even more, the Newtonian mechanics broke the deadlock of a simple observational relativism. In Chapters 1–3, we saw that the same celestial observations can be used as evidence by either the Ptolemaic or the Copernican theory. For example, the sun is observed to move across the sky, daily drifting behind the stars. This can be explained by either the sun moving around the earth or the earth rotating and revolving around the sun. In either case, the result is the same. As long as there is relative motion between the earth and the sun, *to an observer on earth,* the sun appears to be moving around the earth. And yet, to make relativistic matters worse, *from the sun,* the earth would appear to be moving around the sun; *from the moon,* the earth would appear to be moving in a monthly cycle relative to the stars. All seems to depend upon the observer's frame of reference. But Newtonian mechanics provided an answer to the relativistic dilemma: Actually, the smaller mass must move around the larger mass. The sun and the earth have equal and opposite gravitational forces upon each other to pull each other around a common center of mass— that is, the center of mass of the earth and the sun as a system. But the sun has 330,000 times the mass of the earth and therefore 1/330,000 the acceleration of the earth. The resulting effect upon the sun is therefore negligible. Moreover, the common center of mass is quite close to the sun's center. The earth, therefore, moving around the common center of mass, moves around the sun. For the same reasons, the moon moves around the earth. Since the moon has only 1/81 of the earth's mass, the center of mass of these two as a system is near the earth's center. The moon, therefore, in moving around a common center of mass close to the earth's center, moves around the earth. If one accepts Newton's laws of motion and gravitation, one accepts the above explanations—and the Copernican system. The Royal Society of London gave its acceptance quite early.

Soon telescopes and the new physics not only displaced the earth but also the sun from the center of the universe. Galileo had found far more pinpoints of light in the Milky Way than men had ever dreamed of, let alone seen. Newton's friend Halley, for whom Halley's Comet is named, found the solar system to be moving relative to the stars. William Herschel in 1803 observed "double stars" revolving around each other. These "double star" revolutions were explainable by gravitation. Before long, the sun became merely one star among billions in a galaxy. This galaxy, the Milky Way, is also held together by gravitation. More than that, the sun was placed not at the center of the Milky Way, but about 30,000 light-years off-center. The Milky Way, with a diameter of about 100,000 light-years and a thickness of about 15,000 light-years is lens-shaped, very much like its neighbor galaxy, Andromeda (Fig. 9–12). The sun and its planets revolve around the galactic center at a speed of about 150 mi/sec to complete one revolution in approximately 250 million years. But even

9–12　*The galaxy Andromeda, similar to our galaxy, the Milky Way. (Photograph from the Mount Wilson and Palomar Observatories)*

our galaxy is not at the center of the universe; from recent observations, it is just one of billions of galaxies moving away from one another in an apparently expanding universe.

No wonder medieval thinkers feared for their Ptolemaic universe! But let us be careful that we do not appear medieval to men of the future. We, too, have an infinitely long way to go in knowledge, apparatus, and perspective.

EQUATIONS "EXPLAIN" AND PREDICT EVENTS

To explain and predict events in an uncertain world around them, men have always developed large conceptual schemes, whether in ancient mythology, Aristotle's concentric spheres, the Ptolemaic systems, Copernicus's sun-centered circles, or Kepler's elliptical orbits. Before Newton, conceptual systems, or models, of the world were geometric models. Even Copernicus had used geometric space relationships of deferents, epicycles, and eccentrics to make celestial predictions. Kepler and Galileo set precedents for algebraic expression of laws, but with Newton, equations became an established form of hypotheses-to-be-tested and of physical laws. Equations as mathematical models were found to describe and predict events more concisely and adequately than other models. Geometric models alone became insufficient.

Newton's law of gravitation is, of course, an equation. Gravitational forces at a distance may not exist, but Newton set up his equation on the assumption that they do. Forces are assumed to exist between any two masses by virtue of their being matter. If two masses and the distance between them can be observed and measured, the assumed force can be calculated although it is unseen ($F = G \ Mm/r^2$). From an animistic "homing instinct" of heavy objects for the center of the universe, Aristotle's gravity became, through Galileo, a local phenomenon of free fall on the moving planet earth. Now with Newton, gravity is a universal force represented by an equation. The equation is a mathematical description of observed relationships between material objects everywhere. As an equation, gravity had a transition in status from hypothesis to theory and law. Gravity was a hypothesis when Newton assumed it to be a particular force acting from the earth upon the moon. As a hypothesis, it was a specific assumption to be tested with little or no previous evidence. Gravity was again specific, tentative, and limited enough to be a hypothesis when Newton used the concept to explain tides. In this case, gravity was a specific reactive force of the moon on the earth. And again, gravity was a hypothesis when Cavendish experimentally sought a "horizontal" gravitational attraction between metal spheres.

Gravity achieved the scope and relative certainty of a theory when it was tested successfully as an ad hoc hypothesis of forces acting at a distance in a variety of situations as above. The fall of the moon, ocean tides, and orbital fall of planets, when verified, were individual successes of the gravity hypothesis. Specific pairs of objects were involved in each case. The evidence could be generalized, even extrapolated, to consider gravity as a force existing not just between the earth and the moon, the moon and the earth, the sun and Mars, but between any two objects in the solar system or even in the universe. Accordingly, both a hypothesis and a theory are proposed explanations of events involving assumptions—for example, mechanical forces acting at a distance—but a theory generally involves more evidence, certainty, and scope than a hypothesis. A theory generally includes several hypotheses.

Theories as explanations can be qualitative. Ocean tides, a falling apple, or a slight horizontal motion of Cavendish's small spheres toward larger ones can be qualitatively explained by the general theory of universal gravitational forces acting through distances: No numbers need to be used. Laws as equations have been defined as *mathematical relationships among measurable characteristics repeatedly verified.* Newton's theory of universal gravitation became a law after the theory successfully took the mathematical form of an equation. Through mathematical logic and inverse squares, the theory was expressed in the quantitative relationships of an equation. As an equation, the theory still assumes universal forces acting at a distance, but it relates these unseen forces to measurable masses and distances. That is, the equation not only explains observed universal motion through gravitational forces but accurately predicts unknown future events through such assumed forces. The dramatic prediction and discovery of Neptune illustrate the point. Once the gravitational equation was solidly supported by evidence, it became a law.

Physical laws became universal with Newton. They must apply consistently and repeatedly everywhere—or else be qualified, modified, or replaced. Basic differences among hypotheses, theories, and laws, therefore, can be understood as differences in degree of certainty as well as in scope.

As we have seen, Kepler's laws had direct origins in Brahe's data. They were empirical laws. In comparison, Newton's law of gravitation developed in part from Kepler's laws and not directly from data. If Kepler's laws mathematically described *how* planets revolve, Newton's law took a long step toward explaining *why* they revolve.

FORCES AND MOTION: A MECHANICAL VIEW OF NATURE

Newton's laws of motion as well as gravitation are equations. These equations became components of a unified complex of even more scope than a theory or law: the conceptual model of a mechanical universe. In this model, the universe appears like a huge machine grinding away as relentlessly as fate under Newtonian forces. It was the success of these four laws in astronomy that led to their extension to all nature, the huge and the minute, in an all-encompassing mechanical view, the view that the universe can be understood primarily from concepts and laws of mechanics. This view was first expressed by Newton as follows:

> I wish I could derive all [phenomena] of nature by some kind of reasoning from mechanical principles: for I have many reasons to suspect that they [phenomena] all depend upon certain forces by which the particles of bodies are either mutually attracted . . . or are repelled and recede from each other.

Or, again, from the preface of *Principia*:

> The whole burden of philosophy [of nature] seems to consist in this—from the phenomena of motions to investigate the forces of nature and then from these forces to demonstrate the other phenomena.

The universe became as deterministic as fate in the following famous words (1802) of the French mathematician Laplace:

An intelligence knowing, at a given instant of time, all forces acting in nature, as well as the momentary positions of all things of which the universe consists, would be able to comprehend the motions of the largest bodies of the world and those of the smallest atoms in a simple formula, provided it were sufficiently powerful to subject all data to analysis; to it, nothing would be uncertain, both future and past would be present before its eyes.

In a mechanical view, all matter—and eventually energy, too—becomes composed of moving particles in interaction under universal forces. Everything is reduced to mathematical relationships among forces, matter, and motion in absolute space and time. And the forces are from within matter itself. Even space is like a huge container in which all objects mechanically move about. The relentless determinism of a mechanistic universe is well represented in planetarium apparatus that projects with precision the appearance of the skies 2,000 years backward or 3,000 years forward. Know all causes, and effects are guaranteed.

SYNTHESIS IN SCIENCE

A great synthesizer takes the various pieces of a puzzle and fits them with penetrating insight into a common pattern—but many or most of the pieces have been shaped by other men. The pieces of Newton's puzzle were provided in previous chapters; this chapter was concerned with the patterning.

Newton was well aware of having related the work of Kepler, Galileo, Huygens, Descartes, and others; this was reflected in his reference to "standing on the shoulders of giants." But the pattern he came up with is one of the crowning intellectual achievements of all time. It dominated physics until the turn of this century—about 250 years—and still serves well an appropriate realm in modern physics. Its mechanistic world view has been one of the great challenges in the history of ideas and technologically has changed the face of the earth.

Newton's synthesis, like all conceptual systems, represents, among other things, a search for order, unity, and simplicity. How else can a big idea unify a complex of observations, concepts, theories, and laws? Newton's synthesis also represents a search for natural causes, or at least a further step in the search. Newton's mechanical universe replaced celestial spheres with universal forces arising from within all objects themselves, whether in the heavens or on the earth. Forces acting at a distance displaced the animal-like "seeking" of objects for natural places.

Unseen forces may be a projection of man's mathematical mind upon the universe; even Newton stated that things act "as if" the forces are there. But certainly these forces were more impersonal than objects "seeking" places. In any case, forces were natural causes, and observations, effects. Unseen, impersonal forces explained elliptical orbits.

To celestial observations as old as man, Newton's gravitational forces linked concepts of inertia, principles of acceleration, laws of falling bodies and of projectile motion, laws of planetary motion, general laws of motion, and a concept of vectors, as well as centripetal and centrifugal force equations. Accompanying these were a host of assumptions, definitions, hypotheses, concepts, theories, principles, experiments, applications, and implications. Men of many nationalities through the centuries were represented, as they are in all science and culture. In search of unity, Newton's mind and imagination related falling objects and celestial motions in a new, all-embracing order. To see likeness in unlikeness, to recognize similarity in the fall of an apple and the motion of the moon, is truly a uniqueness of the probing human mind and imagination. As A. N. Whitehead so aptly expressed it:

> The progress of Science consists in observing interconnections and in showing with a patient ingenuity that the events of this ever-shifting world are but examples of a few general relations, called laws. To see what is general in what is particular, and what is permanent in what is transitory, is the aim of scientific thought.

And in the process--to use Carnap's eloquent words—"The symbols and equations of the physicist bear the same relation to the actual world of phenomena as the written words of a melody do to the audible tones of the song itself."

CHAPTER REVIEW

1. How far does gravity extend? How do we know?

2. What keeps the moon in orbit?

3. Why is the difference in meaning between speed and velocity important in understanding what keeps the moon in orbit?

4. How did Newton use Kepler's second and third laws in developing his law of gravitation?

5. In what sense does the moon daily fall toward the earth?

6. How did Newton use the moon's daily fall toward the earth as a test for his law of gravitation?

7. How do Galileo's ideas of projectile motion enter into Newton's test of the moon's fall?

8. Which Galilean law of falling bodies did Newton use in his gravitational test of the moon? How did he use the law?

9. Why do not stationary objects around us move toward each other through gravitation?

10. What assumptions exist in Newton's law of gravitation?

11. (a) Explain tides as evidence of the law of gravitation. As evidence of Newton's law of motion. (b) How do spring and neap tides further confirm tides as evidences for gravitation?

12. Discuss Cavendish's *G* experiment as evidence for gravitation.

13. Why were the discoveries of the new planets Neptune and Pluto evidence for gravitation?

14. Explain and illustrate the difference between mass and weight. Why are your weight and mass the same in value at the earth's surface but different above the surface?

15. By Newton's law of gravitation, show how your weight is basically an interaction between you and the earth rather than an independent property of yourself. Upon what three main factors does your weight depend?

16. How can the mass of the earth be determined with a stone, a spring scale, and Newton's law of gravitation?

17. According to Kepler's second law, the earth is slowest in its orbit when furthest from the sun. How is this explained by Newton's law of gravitation?

18. Give a gravitational analogy between a planet's change in orbital velocity and the swing of a pendulum. (Diagrams may help.)

19. If, according to Newton, every action has an opposite and equal reaction, why doesn't the earth fall "up" to meet a rocket halfway as the rocket falls "down" to the earth?

20. If Newton's law of gravitation is a synthesis of Kepler's laws of planetary motion, Galileo's laws of falling bodies, Galileo's ideas of projectile motion, and Newton's (and Galileo's) laws of motion, why is so much credit given to Newton for that law?

21. How does Newton's law of universal gravitation answer the following Ptolemaic questions? (a) Why is the atmosphere not left behind if the earth rotates? (b) How can the earth be a center of gravity and still be moving around the sun? (c) Why would not the earth be shattered by its own fast rotation (over 1,000 mph at the equator)?

22. Why are Newton's laws considered decisive in rejecting earth-centered models of the universe?

23. (a) What is a mechanical view of the universe? How did Newton's laws of motion and universal gravitation lead to a mechanical view? (b) How did the concept of vectors lead to a mechanical view?

24. Trace gravity as an idea from Aristotle to Galileo to Newton.

25. Explain the law of gravitation as a "mathematical relationship among measurable characteristics repeatedly verified."

26. Use materials of this chapter on gravity to illustrate the following: an assumption, a definition, an observation, a hypothesis, a theory, a law, and a conceptual model. Point out relationships and differences among these terms.

27. Which of Newton's procedures in his investigation of gravity were hypothesis forming and which were hypothesis testing?

28. Where did imagination arise in Newton's problem solving?

PROBLEMS

1. Explain through Newton's law of gravitation why your weight at the equator is less than at the poles.

2. By the inverse square law of gravitation, if you decrease the distance between two objects from 3 m to 1 m, the force between them would be how many times greater?

3. Is the sun's gravitational pull on the earth constant? Why?

4. If the earth were four times as far from the sun, the gravitational force of the sun on the earth would be how many times smaller?

5. Explain why there are two high tides daily rather than one.

6. If the earth had twice its present radius and double its present mass, a girl now weighing 50 kg would have what weight?

7. What is the weight 8,000 mi from the earth's surface of a man whose weight on the earth is 180 lb?

8. What would your weight be 4,000 mi above the earth's surface? 12,000 mi above the surface? 240,000 mi above the surface?

9. An artificial satellite weighing 360 kg on the earth is in orbit around the earth at 8,000 mi above the surface. (a) With what force, if any, is the satellite pulled toward the earth? What keeps the satellite in orbit? (b) How much acceleration, if any, does the satellite have toward the earth? Why?

10. (a) If a spaceship weighs 1,000 lb on earth, how much does it weigh on the moon if the acceleration of gravity on the moon is 5 ft/sec? (b) What gravitational force in pounds does the earth still exert on the spaceship when the ship is on the moon?

11. The moon is 240,000 mi from the earth and has a mass of about $\frac{1}{80}$ of the earth's mass. At what position on a line of centers between these two bodies would a spaceship have no weight?

12. Using the law of gravitation and the comparative mass and radius of the moon (Table 5–1), show that gravitational force and acceleration on the moon are about $\frac{1}{6}$ of those on the earth.

13. A man with a 100-kg weight on earth has what weight on the moon? On Jupiter? On Mars? (See Table 5–1 for necessary radii and mass data.)

14. Using Table 5–1 as a model and an acceleration of gravity on the moon of 5 ft/sec, work out a table of free fall on the moon.

15. A stone dropped from a cliff on the moon falls with an acceleration of 5 ft/sec/sec. (a) How fast will the stone be moving 2 sec after it is dropped? (b) What is the *average* speed during the *second* second? (c) How high is the cliff if the stone falls for 10 sec?

16. On the moon you could throw a ball to a much higher altitude than on the earth. Why? Ignoring air resistance, would a ball thrown vertically upward on the moon at 100 ft/sec come down with a greater speed than it would on the earth? Why?

17. (a) Could you leap higher on Jupiter than on the earth? Why? (b) Would a rock thrown upward on Jupiter at a speed of 50 kg/sec return to the surface at the same speed? (Ignore air resistance.)

18. The gravitation force F between two objects changes with the masses of the objects and the distance between them. Why would G in the gravitation law be the same for any two objects anywhere?

19. What is *wrong* with the following argument? (a) A large rock of mass m_r falls with acceleration g and gravitational forces $m_r g$ toward the earth. (b) By Newton's third law $(F = -F)$, the earth should be approaching the rock with acceleration $-g$ and gravitational force $-M_e g$. (c) That is, $m_r g = -(M_e g)$, or $m_r = M_e$. (d) Therefore, all rocks have the same mass as the earth.

SUGGESTIONS FOR FURTHER READING

Taylor, Lloyd W., *Physics, the Pioneer Science,* Dover paperback, New York, 1959, Ch. 13.

Holton, Gerald J., and D. H. D. Roller, *Foundations of Modern Physical Science,* Addison-Wesley, Reading, Mass., 1959, Chs. 11 and 13–15.

Cheronis, Nicholas D., et al., *Study of the Physical World,* Houghton Mifflin, Boston, 1958, Ch. 14.

Bronowski, Jacob, *The Common Sense of Science,* Vintage paperback, New York, 1953, Chs. 1–4.

Conant, James, *Science and Common Sense,* Yale Univ. Press paperback, New Haven, Conn., 1962, Chs. 1–3.

Klein, Morris, *Mathematics in Western Culture,* Oxford Univ. Press, New York, 1953, Chs. 14 and 16.

Schneer, Cecil, *The Search for Order,* Harper, New York, 1960, Chs. 7–8.

Hall, A. R., *The Scientific Revolution,* Beacon paperback, Boston, 1956.

Cohen, I. Bernard, *Birth of a New Physics,* Anchor paperback, Garden City, N.Y., 1960, Ch. 7.

Cohen, I. Bernard, "Isaac Newton," *Scientific American,* 193:6 (December 1955), 73–80.

Editors of *Scientific American, Lives in Science,* Simon and Schuster paperback, New York, 1957, Ch. 1.

Butterfield, Herbert, *Origins of Modern Science,* Collier paperback, New York, 1962, Chs. 5, 8, and 10.

PART THREE

Energy and
Its Transformations

10   Mechanical Energy

The whole burden of [natural] philosophy seems to consist in this—from the phenomena of motions to investigate the forces of nature and then from these forces to demonstrate the other phenomena.

PREFACE TO NEWTON'S Principia, 1687

FROM FORCE TO ENERGY: EXTENSION OF THE MECHANICAL VIEW

Ours is an amazing age of energy transformations. Electric generators, motors, engines, machines, and other transformation devices are changing the face of the earth. Through them, steel mills, skyscrapers, and freeways replace prairies and wilderness; planes challenge the birds for their skies; and rockets even now boldly investigate interplanetary space—all with tremendous effects upon the ways men live and think.

But what is energy, and how did modern energy transformations result from Newton's concept of force? We have seen astronomy give birth to classical mechanics, but once the youngster was born, it grew lustily. From the mathematical concept of force emerged dynamic concepts of momentum, work, energy, and power—and with them, the law of conservation of energy, one of the most potent postulates of modern science. The law stating simply that *the total energy of the universe or of any isolated system within it is constant* projects an equals sign ($=$) into the universe. A given quantity of light (and heat) may appear in a room with the flick of a switch, but an *equal* amount of electrical energy disappears. The amount of (electrical) energy before *equals* the amount of (light and heat) energy afterward. In accordance with the conservation principle, the light is not created; the electricity is not destroyed; one is merely transformed into the other by a "switch." Energy itself as an entity is permanent and constant; it merely changes form.

QUANTITY OF MOTION: MOMENTUM VERSUS "LIVING FORCE"

The conservation principle behind our high-powered civilization had simple theoretical beginnings. The ancient Roman poet Lucretius (1st century B.C.) in a flight of scientific as well as poetic imagination wrote in his masterpiece, *The Nature of the Universe:* "Nothing can be created out of nothing.... Nature resolves everything into its component atoms and never reduces anything to nothing." Also, atoms all move. "Driven along in an incessant but variable movement, some of them bounce far apart after a collision, while others recoil only a short distance from the impact." Lucretius, fired by the bold atomic scheme of Leucippus, is expressing a principle of conservation of matter. The atoms that make up matter are neither created nor destroyed. Matter changes form as its component atoms move.

But matter itself moves, even as did Leucippus's atoms. And many centuries later it was inconceivable to Descartes that there shouldn't be something about motion itself that is conserved—that is, neither created nor destroyed but merely transformed. Mathematician that he was, he called that something a "quantity of motion," which he defined as the product of mass and velocity ($m \cdot v$). If a person is to be hit by a moving object, let it be by one that is light in mass and slow in motion! When hit, a person becomes aware that an increased mass as well as an increased velocity means increased force of impact. That is, $F/2F = mv/(2m)v$ (doubling the mass m doubles the force F); and $F/2F = mv/m(2v)$ (doubling the velocity v doubles the force F).

Pull back a simple pendulum (Fig. 10–7). When released, the bob accelerates until reaching its lowest point B, and then it continues on upward to point C. Specifically, what keeps the bob swinging against gravity from B to C? "Violent motion," Aristotle would have said. "Impetus" was John Buridan's word (14th century). "Inertia," said Galileo. "Quantity of motion," said Descartes, seconded by Newton. *"Vis viva,"* a "living force" [of motion], claimed Leibnitz, another contemporary of Newton. A slight impact on one side of a balance overcomes a large weight on the other side. "Therefore, the living force of motion," said Leibnitz, "is to be differentiated from the static or dead force of weight." The height of fall h is a factor in the speed v of a pendulum bob in accordance with $v^2 = 2gh$, a law of falling bodies. Therefore, the "living force" that keeps the pendulum swinging depends not on the mass and velocity, but on the mass and velocity *squared*. If one is struck by a pendulum bob, its "living force" of mass times velocity squared can be felt on impact, argued Leibnitz. *Double* the speed with which a freely falling rock hits soft earth, and the rock will have *four* times the "living force" and will sink four times as far into the ground. That is, $F/4F = mv^2/m(2v)^2$.

Who was right, Descartes or Leibnitz? Is force of impact to be associated with mv or mv^2? Why? What light can Newton's second law, $F = ma$, throw on the question?

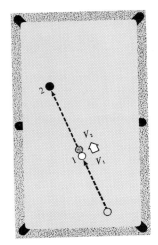

10–1   Conservation of momentum. The momentum lost by the billiard stopped "dead" is gained by the ball hit.

LAW OF CONSERVATION OF MOMENTUM

Suppose a large meteor hits a spaceship. The meteor exerts a force F upon the ship and changes its velocity from v_1 to v_2.

According to Newton's second law: $F = ma = m(v_2-v_1)/t = (mv_2-mv_1)/t$. The mv_2 or the mv_1 is Descartes's "quantity of motion," now called momentum. All moving objects have a mass m, a velocity v, and therefore a momentum mv.

Before being hit, the spaceship had a mass m, a velocity v_1, and therefore a constant momentum mv_1. After being hit, the ship changes velocity from v_1 to v_2, and momentum from mv_1 to mv_2. The difference in velocity, $\triangle v_2 - v_1$, means a difference in momentum, $\triangle mv = mv_2 - mv_1$.

If a meteor exerts a force upon a rocket when striking it, the rocket exerts a force back upon the meteor (Newton's third law). If $F_1 = -F_2$, then $\triangle m_1v_1 = -\triangle m_2v_2$ (Chapter 8), or $\triangle M_1 = -\triangle M_2$. That is, the *momentum gained* by one object equals the *momentum lost* by the other. Generalized, we have the *law of conservation of momentum: The total momentum of an isolated system is constant* (that is, never increases or decreases). Or, as Newton expressed it, "the quantity of motion [total momentum] is not changed by the action of bodies among themselves." A gain of momentum by the rocket is canceled by a loss of momentum of the meteor striking it.

A billiard ball often may be observed to stop "dead" when hitting a stationary one (Fig. 10–1). In accordance with the law of conservation of momentum, the second ball will then be observed to continue on with the same momentum ($\triangle m_2v_2$) that the first ball lost ($-\triangle m_1v_1$). Momentum was neither gained nor lost—just transferred.

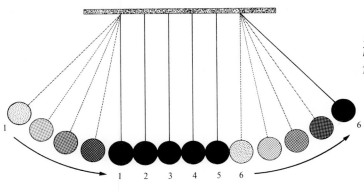

Figure 10–2 further illustrates the conservation law. Ball 1 is pulled back and dropped. An instant after ball 1 strikes ball 2, ball 6 at the other end swings out a distance about equal to that traveled by ball 1. Since balls 2, 3, 4, and 5 remain at rest in their original row, clearly ball 1 and ball 6 have exchanged velocities and momentums. If balls 1 and 2 are pulled back and dropped together, on impact balls 5 and 6 will fly out together for distances equal to those of 2 and 1, respectively. Again, conservation of momentum is observed. Similarly, if the first three balls are raised and released together, the last three at impact will fly out together in paths symmetrical to the first three.

FORCE VERSUS IMPULSE

We have seen in the case of the spaceship hit by a meteor that

$$F = ma$$

or

$$F = \frac{m \triangle v}{t} \text{ or } \frac{\triangle mv}{t}.$$

That is, a force F impressed upon an object (the spaceship), causes an increase (or decrease) $\triangle mv$ in momentum per unit of time. The greater the force F, the greater the change in momentum $\triangle mv$ per second. But

$$F = \frac{\triangle mv}{t}$$

may be algebraically changed to

$$Ft = \triangle mv.$$

The *Ft* equated to the change in momentum $\triangle mv$ represents not the force of the meteor's impact but a product of force and time. The "force" that Descartes associated with "quantity of motion" *mv* was therefore a "compound" term of *force multiplied by time (Ft)*, now called *impulse*. Through mathematical precision, scientific ideas are clarified and new ideas emerge.

FORCE AND WORK

It takes force to lift a box against gravity, move a piano against friction, wind a watch against a spring, or accelerate a car. In each case a force is applied *against* a resistance of some kind, whether gravity, friction, elasticity, or inertia.

And in each case the force is applied to an object through a distance. The box is lifted; the piano, moved; the watch, wound; the car, accelerated—all in space. The distance through which the force is applied is as important as the force itself. As a 100-lb force lifts a 100-lb box through 1 ft, 2 ft, 3 ft, or *x* ft, something is added to each foot of the way. Obviously, the something added is not force; the 100-lb weight remains the same. What is added equally each foot of the way is something compounded of force and distance, or *work*. Precisely defined, work is *force times distance in the direction of the force*. Symbolically,

$$\text{work} = Fs. \hspace{4cm} \text{Equation 10–1}$$

Three main types of work are work against gravity, work against friction, and work for acceleration. Let us look into each type in detail.

Work against Gravity

To lift is to work against gravity. The lifting force is opposite and equal to the weight (gravity force) and is therefore vertical to the earth's surface. To lift a 5-lb weight to a 1-ft height, the work $(F \cdot s) = 5$ lb $\cdot$ 1 ft $= 5$ ft-lb. To a 2-ft height, the work $= 5$ lb $\cdot$ 2 ft $= 10$ ft-lb. To a 3-ft height, the work $= 15$ ft-lb. Five ft-lb of work is added for each foot that the weight is lifted. Doubling the height doubles the work done, tripling the height triples the work, and so on.

Now compare the work done to the two weights in Fig. 10–3:

1-lb wt: work $= Fs = 1$ lb $\cdot$ 5 ft $= 5$ ft-lb

5-lb wt: work $= Fs = 5$ lb $\cdot$ 1 ft $= 5$ ft-lb.

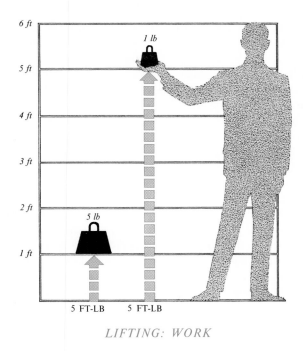

LIFTING: WORK   HOLDING: NO WORK

Leibnitz claimed that a 1-lb weight dropped from 5 ft would have the same "living force," or mv^2, upon striking the ground as a 5-lb weight dropped from 1 ft. Clearly, if we use the concept of work instead of "living force," Leibnitz is correct. There is as much work involved in lifting a 1-lb object through 5 ft as in lifting a 5-lb object 1 ft. Distance is as important as force in the concept of work.

The unit for work expressed as foot-pounds above seems strange only until one remembers that pounds were multiplied by feet. That the unit for work is expressed as foot-pounds rather than pound-feet is merely a matter of convention. When force is in dynes and distance in centimeters (cgs system), the unit for work is the *dyne-centimeter, or erg* (Table 10–1). When force is in newtons and distance in meters (mks system), the unit for work is the *newton-meter, or joule*, in honor of James Joule, the famous English scientist.

10–3 Work = force · distance. Lifting 5 lb through 1 ft is the same amount of work as lifting 1 lb through 5 ft.

10–4 Just holding an object involves force but not work. Why?

Table 10–1 | UNITS OF WORK

SYSTEM	FORCE	DISTANCE	WORK
British	lb	ft	ft-lb
cgs	dyne	cm	erg (dyne-cm)
mks	newton	m	joule (newton-m)

It is possible to exert a large force and still do no work (Fig. 10–4). Since work = $F \cdot s$, a force of 1,000 lb and a distance of 0 results in work = $1,000 \cdot 0 = 0$ ft-lb. You may strain like a Samson to lift a 1,000-lb weight or crumble a wall, but unless either moves, your work is zero. Similarly, a man merely holding a 100-lb sack of cement is exerting a 100-lb force, but he is not working. A force must actually move an object against a resistance for work to exist. Work always involves force, but force does not always result in work.

Clearly, the concept of work is a mathematically precise definition that arose out of complexities in the concept of force. Mathematics serves science well.

In running up a stairway, you are lifting yourself against gravity. The stairway in Fig. 10–5 is 12 ft high, 16 ft across, and 20 ft along a diagonal. If your weight is 160 lb, the work you do against gravity in lifting yourself to the top of the stairs is this: Work = $F \cdot s = 160 \cdot 12 = 1,920$ ft-lb. Only the height, and not the horizontal or diagonal measurements of the stairway, counts as distance against gravity. The horizontal part of your motion is against friction, not gravity. (Air resistance is also friction.)

10–5   In work against gravity, only vertical distance counts.

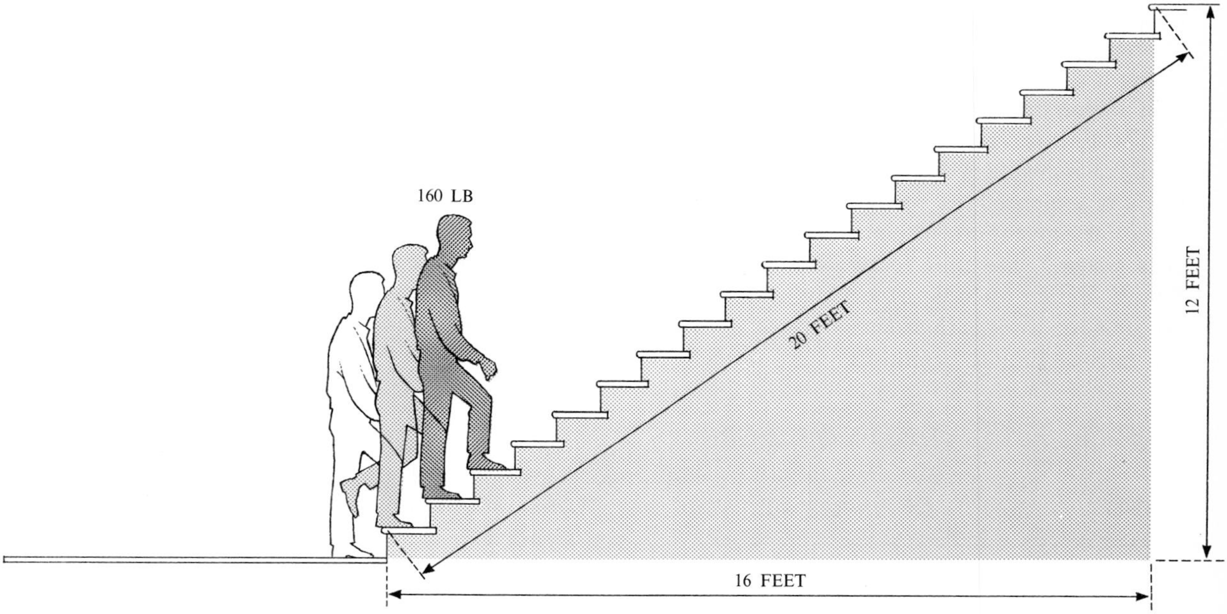

160 LB

20 FEET

12 FEET

16 FEET

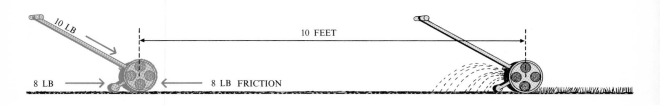

Work against Friction

Friction is defined as resistance to the relative motion between surfaces in contact. This resistance involves an interlocking of minute irregularities on surfaces in contact, adhesion between surfaces, or depression of softer objects by harder ones. Friction between solid objects is either sliding or rolling. Since friction acts as a force that opposes motion in any direction, it requires at least an opposite and equal force to be overcome. A force of 10 lb on a box is necessary to keep it moving against 10 lb of friction force at the floor.

In calculating work, only that component of a force counts that is in the direction of an object's motion. For example, in Fig. 10–6, only the horizontal component of the force applied at the diagonal is effective in moving the mower against the friction forces. At a given angle, a force of 10 lb on the handle may mean an effective horizontal force of 8 lb in the direction of motion. In this case, the work across 10 ft of lawn would be

work = Fs = 8 lb × 10 ft = 80 ft-lb.

Starting friction is greater than moving friction. That is, the force required to start moving an object against friction is greater than that required to keep it moving.

The engine of a car at constant velocity on a highway exerts a forward force to overcome such opposing friction forces as between the wheels and pavement, air resistance at car surfaces, and so on. Without friction, the wheels of the car, once moving, could roll on indefinitely with the engine off. The engine's work against friction equals its forward thrust (force) against all friction forces times the distance moved.

Work for Acceleration

Work for acceleration is essentially work against inertia. Inertia is the tendency of an object to maintain a constant velocity. To overcome that tendency and to increase or decrease the speed of an object or change its direction requires force and work.

To keep a car moving at constant velocity, a forward force is needed to balance opposing friction forces. To increase the speed of the car, the engine must supply an additional accelerating force. When a driver removes his foot from the gas pedal, friction at the wheels acts as a slow braking, or decelerating, force. To decrease the speed of a car quickly, brakes provide an additional force of deceleration. To change the direction of the car around a curve, a turning force is needed at the steering wheel.

The use of a speed-increasing, braking, or turning force for a distance involves work. Work for acceleration equals the accelerating force times the distance through which the acceleration (or deceleration) takes place (Fs).

WORK AND ENERGY

But again, what is energy? How is it to be identified? Light, sound, electricity, fuel, and food are forms of energy. What do they have in common? These questions are difficult, but from the concept of work we obtain the concept of *energy as ability to do work.* Whenever we have anything that can exert force through distance, we have energy. Oil runs locomotives; electricity operates motors; gasoline runs cars; food powers us. And since forces and distances can be measured, energy, the entity behind work, can be measured, too.

Kinetic Energy

Leibnitz's concept of "living force" not only gave birth to the concepts of work and energy, but in the process it also directly related these two concepts. And if "living force" was the mother, mathematics was the father.

Work is involved in lifting an object; it is also present in the fall of an object. Gravity is the force F that accelerates the mass m of a falling object through a distance of fall s (work $= F \cdot s$). And one thing is certain: The greater the distance s through which a rock falls, the greater the velocity squared v^2 of the rock as it hits the ground ($v^2 = 2gs$ from the law of falling bodies). We now have an F, s, m, and v^2 in a free fall, or accelerated, situation. By Newton's second law, work Fs can be *equated* to Leibnitz's "quantity of motion" mv^2 by placing a coefficient of ½ before mv^2. That is, $Fs = \frac{1}{2}mv^2$ is algebraically provable as follows:

Since $\quad F = ma = mg \quad$ (Newton's second law)

$\qquad Fs = mgs \qquad$ (multiplying both sides by s)

and since $v^2 = 2gs \qquad$ (law of falling bodies)

$\qquad$ or $\dfrac{v^2}{2g} = s \qquad$ (dividing through by $2g$)

$\qquad Fs = \dfrac{mgv^2}{2g} \qquad$ (substituting for the second s in line 2)

$\qquad$ or $Fs = \frac{1}{2}mv^2. \qquad$ (cancellation of gs) $\qquad$ Equation 10–2

The physicist Thomas Young in 1807 proposed the term "energy" for mv^2; G. G. Coriolus placed the $\frac{1}{2}$ in front of the mv^2 for reasons mathematically understandable from Equation 10–2; and Lord Kelvin first labeled the term $\frac{1}{2}mv^2$ as *kinetic energy* or *energy of motion*. Symbolically,

$$KE = \tfrac{1}{2}mv^2. \qquad\qquad\qquad \text{Equation 10–3}$$

Since Fs represents work and $\frac{1}{2}mv^2$ represents energy of motion, Equation 10–2 implies that energy of motion ($\frac{1}{2}mv^2$) equals the work done (Fs) to an object to accelerate it from rest. This equation thus applies to objects in any motion, not only in free fall. Any moving object can do an amount of work equal to the work supposedly done to it to accelerate it from rest. In elastic collisions, for example, moving objects do work upon objects they strike. A falling rock can force its way into the ground. The kinetic energy of the rock at impact is $\frac{1}{2}mv^2$. If the rock has fallen far, the v^2 and kinetic energy are great. If the ground is hard, the necessary force F to penetrate into the ground against friction is large, and the distance s into the ground may be small. If the ground is soft, the resistance F of the ground is smaller and the penetration deeper. But whatever force is necessary, the kinetic energy of the rock will be equal to the work on the ground; that is, $\frac{1}{2}mv^2 = Fs$. In the same way, the kinetic energy of a fast-moving bullet may be spent in penetrating a thick block of wood. In soft wood, the necessary force is small and the distance large (fS); with hard wood, the force is large and the distance small (Fs).

Practical use of the work made possible from falling objects is illustrated by a pile driver. A pile is a heavy beam driven into the ground to a great depth to support a building or other large construction. The pile driver forces the pile into the ground by repeatedly raising a heavy weight (ram) to a given height from where the ram is dropped onto the beam. The kinetic energy of the ram forces the beam further into the ground with each impact. In the process, the kinetic energy is transformed into heat.

For appropriate units in Eq. 10–3, see Table 10–2.

Table 10–2 | KINETIC ENERGY UNITS

KE	m	v
Ft-poundals	lb	ft/sec
Ft-lb	slugs* (1 slug = 32 lb)	ft/sec
Ergs	g	cm/sec
Joules	kg	m/sec

For example, the kinetic energy of a 3,200-lb car traveling at 30 mph (44 ft/sec) would be:

$$KE = \tfrac{1}{2}mv^{2}{}^{*} = \tfrac{1}{2}\,\frac{W^{*}}{g}\,v^{2} = \tfrac{1}{2} \cdot \frac{3{,}200\ \text{lb}}{32\ \text{ft/sec}^{2}} \cdot 44^{2}\ \text{ft}^{2}/\text{sec}^{2}$$
$$= 96{,}000\ \text{ft-lb.}$$

Because velocity v is squared in Eq. 10–3,

doubling the v to 60 mph gives *four times* the KE (4 · 96,800 ft-lb);
tripling the v to 90 mph gives *nine times* the KE (9 · 96,800 ft-lb).

Obviously, because velocity is squared, a car in an accident is an engine of destruction in which velocity is a more important factor than mass.

The concept $\tfrac{1}{2}mv^{2}$, one of the most significant in classical physics, is clearly mathematical in origin. As energy, $\tfrac{1}{2}mv^{2}$ represents something physically unseen: We multiply the mass of an object by its velocity squared and call $\tfrac{1}{2}$ the product "kinetic energy." Through Newton's laws we equate this mathematical term to that of work and find that the equality explains and predicts events in the physical world. The concept of energy of motion, like that of momentum, emerged from the problem of quantity of motion and eventually led to a most powerful principle for "calling the world to order," the law of conservation of energy.

The controversy between Leibnitz and Descartes over whether force was to be identified with mass times velocity or mass times velocity squared was clearly a semantical one. Descartes and Leibnitz were using the term "force" with different meanings. With Descartes, force acted through *time* ($Ft = mv$); with Leibnitz, force acted through *space* ($Fs = \tfrac{1}{2}mv^{2}$). Once this became clear, there was no controversy. Descartes's mass times velocity became the concept of momentum, and Leibnitz's mass times velocity squared led to the concept of energy, particularly kinetic energy.

*The mass of an object in *slugs* is obtained by dividing the weight W of the object by the acceleration of gravity g, 32 ft/sec².

Potential Energy

Work is involved in the acceleration or fall of an object. But work requires energy. From where does the free-fall energy come? The clue is in the position of the object above the ground; an object is assumed to have an *energy of position,* called *gravitational potential energy,* by virtue of being above the earth. The reasoning is that for an object to have altitude, work previously had to be done to lift it. The amount of work Fs in lifting an object against gravity equals the weight W of the object times its altitude h. The energy used in lifting an object is considered to have become transformed by work into energy of position. Energy of position is thus a potential energy accrued from previous work. Potential energy is realized as energy of motion when an object is released. Gravitational potential energy thus becomes a link between the energy required to lift an object and the free-fall kinetic energy of an object; as a concept, potential energy was invented for the linkage.

An object at height h is said to have a potential energy equal to the work Fs used to raise it to its position. That is, potential energy $PE = Fs$. Since the lifting force F must equal the weight W of an object (and $h = s$), symbolically,

PE	$=$	Fs	$=$	Wh
in ft-lb				lb · ft
g-cm				g · cm
joules				kg · m

The gravitational potential energy of an object thus equals the product of its weight and altitude. The greater the weight and altitude of an object, the more the work required to lift it to its position, and the greater its potential energy. Consequently, an object loses potential energy constantly as it falls (height h decreases), but meanwhile it gains energy of motion (velocity v increases). Whether or not the energy of motion that the falling object gains is as much as the potential energy that it loses will be discussed in the section on the conservation of mechanical energy.

Potential energy may be expressed in foot-pounds, gram-centimeters, and joules (kg-m), depending upon what units are used for weight and altitude. In Fig. 10–3, it took 5 ft-lb of work either to lift the 1-lb weight through 5 ft or to lift the 5-lb weight 1 ft. Each weight gained in potential energy the 5 ft-lb of energy lost by the person doing the work of lifting. The weights are at different altitudes, but with equal amounts of work previously applied to them, they have equal potential energies, since the products of their weights and altitudes are equal ($PE = W \cdot h$; 1 lb · 5 ft = 5 ft-lb; and 5 lb · 1 ft = 5 ft-lb).

There are other forms of potential energy besides gravitational. Bent springs have potential energies that slowly move watch hands. Drawn bows have potential energies that send arrows flying. Such potential energies are due to elastic deformations rather than to elevation. They are mechanical although not gravitational energies.

Other potential energies besides mechanical include magnetic, electrical, chemical, and thermal. Potential energies in magnetic or electric fields are revealed by the motions of compass needles or electrically charged particles inserted within these fields, respectively. A stick of dynamite has a chemical potential energy that becomes apparent when a match is applied. A coiled rattlesnake or a crouched tiger has formidable potential energy. Water vapor shows thermal potential energy by giving off considerable heat without losing temperature when condensing into liquid water.

POWER

Time sooner or later becomes a factor in our ideas as in our lives; time enters into concepts of work.

Suppose that you weigh 160 lb. Whether you run up a stairway 12 ft high in 6 sec or walk up in 16 sec, the work done is the same:

$$\text{Work} = F \cdot s = W \cdot h = 160 \text{ lb} \cdot 12 \text{ ft} = 1,920 \text{ ft-lb (Fig. 10–5)}.$$

You have lifted yourself 12 ft against gravity in either case. But you lift yourself faster when you run up than when you walk up. This time factor in work is taken care of by the concept of *power*, defined as *work done per unit of time* or *time rate of doing work*. That is,

$$P = \frac{\text{work}}{\text{time}} = \frac{Fs}{t}. \qquad \text{Equation 10–4}$$

Let us compare the power in running to the power in walking in the above illustration:

$$\text{Running:} \quad P = \frac{W \cdot h}{t_1} = \frac{160 \text{ lb} \cdot 12 \text{ ft}}{6 \text{ sec}} = 320 \text{ ft-lb/sec}$$

$$\text{Walking:} \quad P = \frac{W \cdot h}{t_2} = \frac{160 \text{ lb} \cdot 12 \text{ ft}}{16 \text{ sec}} = 120 \text{ ft-lb/sec}.$$

The power running was 2.67 times your power walking:

$$\frac{320 \text{ ft-lb/sec}}{120 \text{ ft-lb/sec}} = 2.67.$$

The term "horsepower" has been common in English-speaking countries ever since James Watt introduced it. The *horsepower* is a *unit of power equal to 550 ft-lb of work per second,* or 33,000 ft-lb/min. The horsepower was Watt's estimate of the amount of work a horse can do in a unit of time. But the horse must have been a giant, because this is considerably more power than an average horse has!

At 120 ft-lb of work per second, your power would be 120/550, or 0.22 hp. At 50 ft-lb of work per second, your horsepower would be 50/550, or 0.09. (0.1 hp is considered good for sustained human output.) A 100-hp motor can lift 100 times 550 ft-lb/sec, or 55,000 ft-lb/sec. It can lift 550 lb through 100 ft in 1 sec or 1,000 lb through 55 ft in 1 sec. This work may be against gravity, friction, inertia, or combinations of these.

The metric unit of power is the *watt.* Mechanically, a watt is a unit of power equal to 1 joule/sec (10^7 ergs/sec, or 10^7 dyne-cm/sec), or 1 newton-m/sec. A kilowatt is 1,000 watts. And 746 watts $=$ 1 hp. Since we are accustomed to the watt as an electrical rather than a mechanical unit of power and to the kilowatt-hour as an electrical unit of work, we shall discuss these terms more fully later.

TRANSFORMATIONS
OF MECHANICAL
ENERGY: THE PENDULUM

Potential energy may be transformed into kinetic energy and kinetic energy into potential energy. There is no better example than a simple pendulum. At a high point *A* of its swing (Fig. 10–7), the pendulum for an instant

10–7   A simple pendulum well illustrates mechanical energy transformations. At point A the pendulum's energy is all potential. At point B its energy is all kinetic. As the pendulum swings from A to B, more of its energy transforms from potential to kinetic. What energy transformation occurs in the pendulum's swing from B to C?

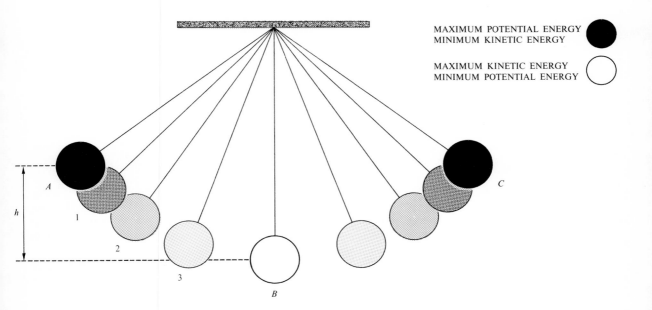

MAXIMUM POTENTIAL ENERGY
MINIMUM KINETIC ENERGY

MAXIMUM KINETIC ENERGY
MINIMUM POTENTIAL ENERGY

has no speed and therefore no energy of motion. At that point, its gravitational energy of position is maximum, and all its energy is potential.

From points A to B, the potential energy steadily diminishes from maximum to zero with loss of altitude. And the kinetic energy constantly increases from zero to maximum with gain of speed. But the total potential energy lost down to any point equals the total kinetic energy gained to that point if friction is ignored. Stated otherwise, the *sum* of the potential and kinetic energies is always the same, whether the bob is at point A, 1, 2, 3, or B. That is,

$$PE_{max} = PE_1 + KE_1 = PE_2 + KE_2 = \cdots = KE_{max} = \text{a constant.}$$
Equation 10–5

At the low point B of the swing, the potential energy of the pendulum as a system is zero, and the speed and kinetic energy of the bob are maximum. All the potential energy at point A has been transformed into energy of motion.

But the pendulum does not remain at low point B. Its maximum energy of motion carries it up against gravity. As it ascends, its speed and kinetic energy decrease, and its potential energy increases. At high point C all its kinetic energy has been transformed back into potential energy, and the

total *PE* gained = total *KE* lost $\qquad\qquad$ Equation 10–6

$\qquad$ or $W \cdot h = \frac{1}{2}mv^2$ (by definition)

$\qquad\quad$ or $mgh = \frac{1}{2}mv^2$ (since $W = mg$)

$\qquad\quad$ or $2gh = v^2$ (law of falling bodies again! [Eq. 7–3]).

At point C the process is continued, and the pendulum continues swinging from C to B to A to B to C indefinitely in repeated transformations from potential energy to kinetic to potential....

CONSERVATION OF MECHANICAL ENERGY

The above discussion may be generalized into a principle of conservation of mechanical energy stating that *in an isolated mechanical system, the total energy remains constant*. Specifically, the two types of mechanical energy, kinetic and potential, *are neither created nor destroyed;* one is merely transformed into the other, with the total of the two energies remaining constant.

Let us return to the falling rock example for further illustration of this conservation principle (Table 10–3).

Table 10–3 | CONSERVATION OF MECHANICAL ENERGY

W (LB)	h (FT)	W · h = PE (FT-LB)	F · s = KE (FT-LB)	PE + KE (FT-LB)
2	5	2 · 5 = 10	2 · 0 = 0	10
2	4	2 · 4 = 8	2 · 1 = 2	10
2	3	2 · 3 = 6	2 · 2 = 4	10
2	2	2 · 2 = 4	2 · 3 = 6	10
2	1	2 · 1 = 2	2 · 4 = 8	10
2	0	2 · 0 = 0	2 · 5 = 10	10

In the table, the PE and KE are calculated at five positions of the falling 2-lb rock. Notice that *the KE in column 3 increases by the same amount (2 ft-lb) that the PE decreases in column 2.* Consequently, the total energy KE + PE in column 3 is the same (10 ft-lb) throughout the fall of the rock (air resistance is ignored). In the fall of the rock, potential energy was not destroyed; it was transformed in the work for acceleration (F · s) into kinetic energy of the rock. When the rock hits the ground, its kinetic energy is not destroyed but transformed by work into heat of friction, as in the case of the pile driver.

Conservation of mechanical energy is also closely approximated in the elliptical orbit of a planet or satellite. Points P (perihelion) and A (aphelion) in the earth's orbit (Fig. 4–5) are analogous to the low and high points in the swing of a pendulum (Fig. 10–7). When the earth is closest to the sun at point P, the earth has a low potential energy, a maximum velocity (Kepler's second law), and a maximum kinetic energy $\frac{1}{2}mv^2$. Through its kinetic energy, the earth then moves away from the sun. In moving away, it is working against the gravitational force of the sun; velocity and kinetic energy are therefore reduced as distance from the sun and potential energy are increased. When the earth is furthest from the sun at point A, it has its maximum potential energy and minimum kinetic energy. At "high" point A, the earth is pulled back toward the sun. Work is done for acceleration; potential energy decreases, and kinetic energy increases. At point B, the cycle starts again.

Perpetual Motion and Energy Conservation

In the above illustrations, the swinging pendulum and the orbiting earth were treated as isolated systems. To be really isolated, a system must not be subject to any external forces; no outside energy should enter and no inside energy should leave. Actually, there is no such thing as an isolated system. Such a system is an ideal to be approached but not fully achieved. A swinging pendulum as a system must be pivoted, and a pivot means friction. The pendulum swings in ever smaller arcs to a stop: Kinetic and potential energies are slowly reduced in work against friction and air resistance. The heat of friction that replaces the energies of motion and position is dissipated into the surroundings and lost from the system.

Perpetual-motion machines have been the ideal of inventors for centuries. A perpetual-motion machine as an isolated system hopefully would operate indefinitely without further supply of fuel or energy. But friction forces and resulting heat losses slow down all machines and require fuel for continued operation.

Even planets, solar systems, or galaxies are not isolated, self-sufficient systems. Planets move in a space that is not a perfect vacuum. Not only slight frictional forces but also gravitational forces from other celestial bodies act upon planets in orbit. The solar system is subject to forces of the larger system, the Milky Way, of which it is a part; the Milky Way is but one galaxy in a universal interacting system of galaxies. Perhaps the closest thing to perpetual motion we know is the universe itself: Everything within it is in motion; as a unit it is supposedly expanding; in terms of energy it is self-sufficient.

But even the universe is considered to be "running down." According to the concept of energy dissipation, the more complex forms of energy—including living forms—gradually dissipate into energy in its simplest form: heat. Concepts of energy conservation and energy dissipation truly extend the mechanical view. The concept of dissipation of energy, known as the second law of thermodynamics, will be more fully discussed in Chapter 13.

CHAPTER REVIEW

1. Show how the concepts in each of the following pairs are related and how they are different. Illustrate in each case: (a) force and work, (b) work and energy, (c) force and energy, (d) force and impulse, (e) work and power, (f) energy and power, and (g) force and power.

2. Why are the four concepts emphasized in question 1 important?

3. (a) Show how the concepts of work, impulse, energy, and power emerged from Newton's concept of force. (b) How does the emergence of these concepts reflect the development of a mechanical view of nature?

4. (a) What are two main forces against which work is done? (b) Describe work for acceleration as a third main type of work. Illustrate.

5. Show how the individual concepts within each of the following pairs are related and how they are different. Illustrate in each case:

(a) velocity and momentum, (b) velocity and kinetic energy, and (c) momentum and kinetic energy.

6. Why are the three concepts in question 4 important?

7. (a) Show how the concepts of speed, velocity, momentum, and kinetic energy resulted from efforts to measure motion. (b) How does the emergence of these concepts reflect the development of a mechanical view of nature?

8. Relate the individual concepts within each of the following pairs, and illustrate the relationship: (a) force and acceleration, (b) work and kinetic energy, and (c) impulse and momentum.

9. Use a swinging pendulum to define, illustrate, and relate kinetic and potential energy.

10. What is meant by transformation of energy? By conservation of energy?

11. (a) Use a swinging pendulum to explain the law of conservation of mechanical energy. (b) Give two or three other illustrations of this law. (c) Why is this law important?

12. (a) What is conservation of momentum? Why is it called a law? (b) Illustrate the law of conservation of momentum. Why is this law important?

13. How is the law of conservation of momentum related to Newton's third law?

14. (a) Explain perpetual motion. (b) How does perpetual motion seem to follow from the law of conservation of mechanical energy? Illustrate with a swinging pendulum or with another example. (c) Why is perpetual motion impossible to achieve?

PROBLEMS

1. How much work can an 8-lb bowling ball traveling 30 ft/sec do?

2. (a) A 10-lb weight falls 10 ft upon a post. How much work does it do in driving the post into the ground? (b) If the same weight falls 20 ft upon the post, how much work does it do on the post? (c) What is the ratio of distances fallen between parts (b) and (a)? What is the ratio of amounts of work done? Why are the two ratios the same?

3. How much work does a man do in holding a box weighing 50 kg at a position 1 m above the ground? Why?

4. Against what three things does a truck do work when accelerating up a hill?

5. Which has more potential energy, a 10-lb weight 20 ft above the ground or a 20-lb weight 8 ft high?

6. (a) How much work in joules is done in lifting a sack of potatoes

30 kg in mass to a shelf 2 m high? (b) What is the potential energy in joules of the potatoes? (c) If the sack of potatoes falls to the floor from the shelf, with what momentum in kilogram-meters per second does it hit the floor? (d) With what kinetic energy in joules does the sack of potatoes hit the floor? (e) What becomes of this kinetic energy when the potatoes come to rest on the floor?

7. A boy throws a baseball weighing 5 oz vertically with a speed of 64 ft/sec. (a) What is the potential energy of the ball at the top of its flight? (b) What is the kinetic energy of the ball when it hits the ground? (c) What is the momentum of the ball when it hits the ground?

8. A pump can remove 300 lb of water per second from a mine 500 ft deep. What is the horsepower of the pump?

9. A boy 40 kg in mass runs up a stairway 4 m high in 10 sec. (a) What is the boy's force on the stairs in newtons? (b) What is the boy's work in joules against gravity? (c) What energy in joules does the boy expend? (d) What is the boy's power in joules per second?

10. A man walks up a flight of stairs in 12 sec and then runs up in 5 sec. Compare (a) the force, (b) the work, and (c) the power involved in both cases.

11. A car 4,000 lb in mass climbs to the top of a 200-ft hill in 40 sec. (a) What is its work in foot-pounds against gravity? (b) What is the power involved in foot-pounds per second? In horsepower? (c) What potential energy in foot-pounds does the car gain? (d) What velocity in feet per second would the car attain if its brakes failed and it coasted freely downhill from the top? Ignore friction.

12. (a) The earth travels fastest when nearest the sun. Show by pendulum analogy that this observation is consistent with the law of conservation of mechanical energy. (b) Is the law of conservation of momentum involved? Why?

13. In moving around the sun, which has the most kinetic energy: the earth, Venus, or Jupiter? Which has the least kinetic energy?

SUGGESTIONS FOR FURTHER READING

Taylor, Lloyd W., *Physics, the Pioneer Science,* Dover paperback, New York, 1959, Chs. 16–17.

Holton, Gerald J., and D. H. D. Roller, *Foundations of Modern Physical Science,* Addison-Wesley, Reading, Mass., 1959, Ch. 17.

Priestley, Herbert, *Introductory Physics,* Allyn and Bacon, Boston, 1958, Ch. 5.

Cheronis, Nicholas D., et al., *Study of the Physical World,* Houghton
Mifflin, Boston, 1958, Ch. 18.

Omer, Guy C., Jr., et al., *Physical Science: Men and Concepts,* Heath,
Boston, 1962, Ch. 17.

11 Heat Phenomena and the Caloric Theory

Science is compelled to invent ideas corresponding to the reality of our world.... Science is not just a collection of laws, a catalogue of unrelated facts. It is a creation of the human mind with its freely invented ideas and concepts.

ALBERT EINSTEIN, 1938

HEAT: MATTER OR ENERGY?

What is heat? Something from the sun, a fire, or a lamp warms us. Without that something we would not exist. But it is easier to talk about heat and to use it than to define it.

On the one hand, heat may be associated with energy. Heat of friction replaces the mechanical energy of a pendulum as the pendulum swings to a stop. Heat also replaces the kinetic energy of a pile driver when the ram drops upon an object. It is logical to *assume* that if mechanical energy disappears, the heat replacing it is also energy.

Or again various forms of work result in energy: Work against gravity results in potential energy, and work for (positive) acceleration adds kinetic energy. Work against friction results in heat. Heat, therefore, should be a form of energy, too.

On the other hand, heat seems like an invisible substance: Touch a hot pan and something seems to enter your hand. What is that something? A prune absorbs water and swells; an iron bar absorbs heat and expands. Can it be that heat is an unseen fluid that expands objects absorbing it? Or contracts objects emitting it? If air can be an invisible penetrating substance, why not heat, too?

That leaves us with this question: Is heat matter or energy? And how is the question to be resolved?

To the great Scottish chemist Joseph Black (1728–1799), heat was matter. This matter was a special fluid called caloric by Antoine Lavoisier (1743–1794), supposedly consisting of minute invisible particles that enter and leave other substances. Black developed his concept of heat fluid in a lifetime of experiment, reflection, and teaching at the Universities of Glasgow and Edinburgh. His work founded a new science of thermodynamics (heat dynamics). Like Galileo in mechanics before him, Black emphasized a mathematical approach. He used thermometers and developed calorimeters for measurement. Starting with a general concept of thermal equilibrium, he experimentally established a law of conservation of heat and a method of mixtures that could predict universal results. His caloric theory of heat unified and explained his results. Black's caloric theory was later displaced by the kinetic molecular theory, just as the big ideas of science today will probably be displaced by more adequate ones tomorrow. Meanwhile, in his time, Black called the world of heat to order from an undeveloped, haphazard state. He was a truly great experimental and theoretical scientist.

FIRST THE PHENOMENA

Let us take a leaf from Black and proceed directly to phenomena of nature in our attempts to understand nature. What was the character of heat phenomena that Black had to unify and explain? The phenomena and the caloric explanations are considered in succeeding sections under such headings as heat transfer, expansion due to heat, thermometry, heat versus temperature, method of mixtures, and change of state.

HEAT TRANSFER

Whatever heat is, it travels, whether directly through space from the sun or carried by air and water currents. In fact, it reaches us in three ways: by *conduction, convection, and radiation.*

Conduction is *transfer from one part of a medium to another without visible motion of the medium.* Touch the handle of a silver spoon that is in hot tea, and you soon become aware that silver is a good conductor of heat. Metals are generally good conductors. Such nonmetals as glass, wood, paper, and asbestos are poor conductors or good insulators. Metals vary in their conductivity. In Fig. 11–1, the hollow pipe is heated by

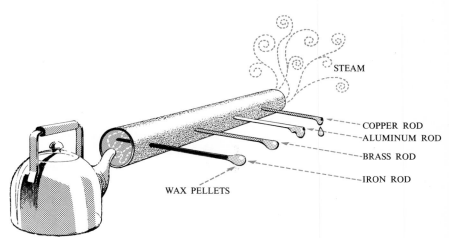

11–1 *Heat transfer by conduction. The wax pellets at the ends of the metal rods melt in the following order: copper, aluminum, brass, and iron rods. Metals in general are good heat conductors, but they vary in their speed of conduction.*

STEAM

COPPER ROD
ALUMINUM ROD
BRASS ROD
IRON ROD

WAX PELLETS

steam. As heat passes through the parallel solid rods, the wax pellets drop off in accordance with the conductivity of the particular metals. Clearly, iron, brass, aluminum, and copper may be ranked as good conductors of heat in increasing order. *At the same room temperature,* a tile floor feels colder than a wool rug to bare feet: With better conductivity than the rug, the tile absorbs heat from the feet faster than the rug.

Liquids are generally poor conductors, and gases are poorer still. In Fig. 11–2, a flame is applied to the top of the test tube which is filled with water. The water just above the flame can boil, while the ice held below remains unmelted. Obviously, water is a poor conductor of heat. Woolen clothing contains many small pockets of air that tend to keep the body warm. The air acts as insulation that tends to keep body heat in.

Convection is *the transfer of heat from one part of a fluid to another by flow of the fluid from the hotter parts to the colder.* Liquids and gases, as fluids, move and are therefore excellent carriers of heat. When a liquid or gas is unevenly heated, warmer parts of the fluid expand and rise because of buoyancy as cooler parts sink. A convection current results. For example, hot air rises above a fire and is displaced by cooler air moving in along the floor (Fig. 11–3). If a window is opened, cold air enters at the bottom and warm air leaves at the top in a convection current. Hot winds (or cold wintry blasts) are ancient experiences of man, and so are warm or cold water currents that bring or remove heat.

Men have also long been aware of solar radiation. In this case, *the heat transfer is through a vacuum;* the sun and the earth have neither a conducting nor a circulating medium connecting them. The three forms of heat transfer may be illustrated by a potbelly stove. If one end of a poker is within the hot coals, placing a hand on the other end of the poker gives heat by conduction. Hands placed above the stove receive heat by convection. Hands in front of the stove receive heat mostly by radiation, through spaces between air molecules; air is a poor conductor.

11–2 *Water is a poor conductor of heat. The ice cube remains unmelted as water boils above the flame.*

Heat transfer was easily explained by the caloric theory: Heat is an invisible fluid gained or lost by objects. The fluid consists of minute caloric particles. Hot objects have a higher concentration of these particles than cool objects. These particles tend to repel each other and therefore move from areas of greater caloric concentration to those of less concentration—that is, from warmer objects to cooler ones. Therefore, when a hand touches a hot poker, the heat particles move from the poker to the hand. The hand gains heat particles that the poker loses. The hand becomes warmer; the poker, cooler. Different substances vary in their abilities to attract and to admit heat particles; therefore, some substances are good conductors, and some are fair, and some are poor.

In the above illustration of the tile and the rug, the tile attracts heat particles faster than the rug does. The feet lose heat particles faster to the tile than to the rug, and so they feel cooler on the tile. If we place our hands in a current of warm air, heat particles transfer to our hands and they feel warmer. Caloric particles radiated from the sun through space are also absorbed by objects, which then become warmer. Caloric theory could simply and clearly explain heat transfer.

EXPANSION DUE TO HEAT

Objects generally expand or contract with heat transfer. They expand when heated and contract when cooled. Railroad tracks are laid with gaps between rails to allow for expansion due to heat. These gaps can be seen to be appreciable in cold weather and slight in very hot weather. Different substances do not expand equally when heated. If a thin brass strip is welded to an iron strip of the same size, the brass expands much more than the iron and bends back the iron (Fig. 11–4). A thermostat is such a compound bar that bends to make or break an electrical circuit as the temperature falls or rises.

Mercury in a thermometer clearly expands when exposed to body heat. In general, liquids expand more than solids, and gases more than liquids. The explosive possibilities of confined gases are well known.

Water is one of the very few exceptions to expansion of materials when heated and their contraction when cooled. Water expands when *cooled* from 4°C (or 39°F) to the freezing point, and when *freezing* at 0°C (or 32°F). A hollow cast-iron ball filled with water and left out to freeze will be split open by the expansive force of the freezing water. Ice contracts when melting and continues to contract as liquid water up to 4°C. After 4°C, water expands when heated like other substances.

Change in size of objects when heated or cooled was easily explained by Black's caloric theory. A heated object gains caloric particles and therefore occupies more space (expands). A cooling object loses caloric particles and therefore occupies less space (contracts). The extent to

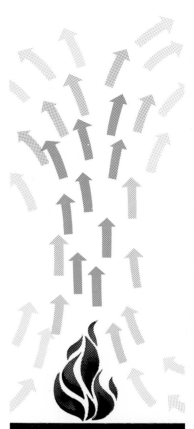

11–3 Convection currents. Hot air above the flame is displaced by cooler air moving in along the floor. The resulting convection currents transfer heat.

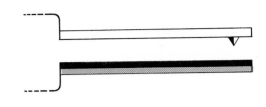

11–4 Metals expand un-
equally when heated. A
thermostat consists of two
metal bars welded together,
one of which bends back the
other when heated to make or
break an electric circuit.

which any substance gains or loses heat particles determines the extent
to which the substance expands or contracts. But the strange behavior of
freezing water or type metal was baffling to caloric and later theories.

THERMOMETRY

Man has long depended upon his senses for an idea of the warmth or
coldness of surrounding objects. But senses alone cannot be trusted for
temperature. Place your right hand in cold water and your left in hot
water for a brief time. Then place both hands into lukewarm water. Even
though both hands are in the *same* water, the water will feel cool to your
left hand and warm to your right.

In searching for something more dependable and precise than sensory
impressions for measuring temperature, Galileo invented the ancestor of
the modern thermometer (Fig. 11–5). His air thermometer was based
on the expansion of air when heated. A bulb of air was extended into a
container of water by a long, narrow stem. With air in the tube, water
rose to a given level. As the air in the bulb acquired heat, it expanded,
forcing the water down. When cooled, the air contracted, permitting the
water to rise. Readings of the relative temperatures of objects in contact
with the bulb were taken through an arbitrary scale along the stem.
Galileo did not know about barometric pressure and did not realize that
external air pressure acting on the water in the container also caused
changes in the height of the water. The effects of changing air pressure
were eventually eliminated in thermometers by sealing mercury, alcohol,
or other such temperature indicators in glass.

By the 18th century, thermometers were accurate instruments; in the
hands of Joseph Black, they became powerful research tools. Contributing
to the effectiveness of these instruments had been the calibration of
standard thermometer scales by G. D. Fahrenheit (1668–1736) and Anders
Celsius (1701–1744), German and Swedish physicists, respectively.

Calibration of a mercury thermometer (Fig. 11–6) includes (1) establishing two fixed points, (2) giving these points number values, and (3)
dividing the distance between the two fixed points with equal unit

intervals called degrees. The illustration provides a comparison of present-day Celsius and Fahrenheit thermometer scales. In both cases, the two fixed points are the freezing and boiling points of water. But the Celsius values of 0° and 100° for the freezing and boiling points appear simpler than the 32° and 212° Fahrenheit values for the *same* points. How did these particular values arise? In the Fahrenheit scale (1724), the scale was first marked in and then the freezing and boiling points of water were determined. The values turned out to be our present 32° and 212°F. Celsius in 1742 reversed the process. He first arbitrarily set the freezing and boiling points of water as 0° and 100°, and then he marked in the rest of his scale. These Celsius values for the freezing and boiling points of water were well chosen, since they afforded the simplicity of 100 equal intervals or Celsius degrees between these two points, as compared to 180 Fahrenheit intervals or degrees. Specifically, if

$$100°C \quad range = 180°F \; range \; (Fig. \; 11-6)$$

$$1°C \; change = \frac{9}{5}°F \; change$$

or 5°C change = 9°F change.

Obviously, the Celsius degree is a larger unit; the ratio is 5°C:9°F. That is, a 5°C change is equivalent to a 9°F change; 10°C change to 18°F; 15°C change to 27°F, and so on.

For interconversion between the two scales, apply the above 5:9 ratio to Fig. 11–6. For example, to change a 30°C reading to a Fahrenheit reading:

1. 5°C change = 9°F change
   30°C change = 54°F change (6 5s°C correspond to 6 9s°F).
   (6x5)   (6x9)
2. But the Fahrenheit freezing point of water is 32° (and not 0°).
3. Therefore, the 54°F change is 54° above the freezing point of water (32°F); 54° above freezing brings the Fahrenheit reading to 54° + 32° = 86°F.
4. That is, the 30°C reading corresponds to an 86°F reading (Fig. 11–6).

Equation 11–1 below is a "shorthand," symbolic representation of the above interconversion process and problem:

$$F = \frac{9}{5} C + 32 \qquad \text{Equation 11-1}$$

$$= \frac{9}{5} \cdot 30 + 32$$

$$= 54 + 32$$

$$F = 86°.$$

11–5 Galileo's air thermometer. Air in the tube expanded when heated, forcing the water down and giving a rough measure of temperature changes. Galileo was unaware of barometric pressure also affecting the water level in the tube.

Note that the 9:5 ratio of Fahrenheit to Celsius degrees discussed above and the 32° difference in the allowance for the Fahrenheit freezing point of water are both provided for in the equation.

To convert Fahrenheit readings to Celsius, the following equation is simpler than Eq. 11–1:

$$C = \frac{5}{9} (F - 32).$$
Equation 11–2

HEAT VERSUS TEMPERATURE

In spite of thermometer scales, considerable confusion existed in Joseph Black's day between concepts of temperature and heat. What is temperature? How is it different from heat? A full kettle of water at 200°F is at the same temperature as a glass of water at 200°F, but certainly the kettle contains more water and therefore more heat than the glass (Fig. 11–7). Temperatures may be equal if amounts of heat are not. Obviously, temperature and heat are related but not synonymous. Confusing heat with temperature is, in Black's own words, "confounding the quantity of heat in different bodies with its general strength or intensity, though it is plain that these are two different things, and should always be distinguished." Black was the first to emphasize that *temperature is intensity of heat*. In terms of the "fluid" theory, heat would be the total amount of caloric within a body, but temperature would be the concentration of caloric. Like ink, a given amount of caloric in a glass of water would certainly be more concentrated than the same amount of caloric distributed in a kettle of water. The caloric concentration would show itself in the form of a higher temperature reading; the ink by depth of color.

Thermometers, however, do not measure the total amount of caloric,

11–6   Celsius versus Fahrenheit temperature scales. The temperature of melting ice (0° C or 32° F) and of boiling water (100° C or 212° F) determines two basic fixed points on each scale. The Celsius range of degrees is 100° and the Fahrenheit is 180°, for a ratio of 5:9. With a 32° allowance for the different values of the melting point of ice, Eqs. 11–1 and 11–2 permit conversions between the two thermometer scales.

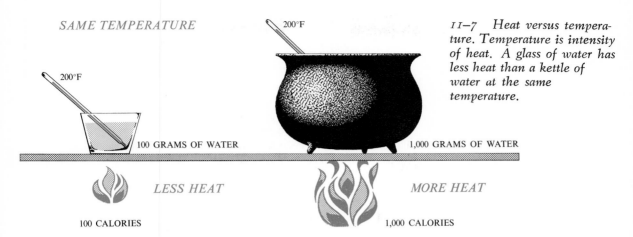

200°F

200°F

100 GRAMS OF WATER

1,000 GRAMS OF WATER

*11–7   Heat versus tempera-
ture. Temperature is intensity
of heat. A glass of water has
less heat than a kettle of
water at the same
temperature.*

LESS HEAT

MORE HEAT

100 CALORIES

1,000 CALORIES

or heat. In the above illustration, the thermometer gave a reading of
200°F whether in a glass or kettle of water; it did not give the heat
content. For measuring amounts of heat rather than intensity of heat,
another type of apparatus is necessary, the calorimeter (Fig. 11–8),
described later. And if temperature is measured in degrees, then heat is
to be measured in other units, calories or Btu's.

How is amount of heat to be measured? To measure, one first must
have units of measurement. Water exists almost everywhere as a standard
of comparison for other things. *A particular amount of heat is necessary
for raising 1 g of water 1°C*—for example, from 14°C to 15°C. This
amount today is called a *calorie*. Since 1 g is a small amount of water,
the calorie is a small unit of heat. In dietetics, therefore, the large Calorie—
note the capital letter "C"— is used. One Cal = 1,000 cal (or 1 kcal).

In the British system, 1 lb of water and 1°F are used. *A British thermal
unit (1 Btu) is the amount of heat required to raise 1 lb of water 1°F.*

Given that 1 lb = 454 g and 1°F = 5/9°C in range, see if you can
prove that

1 Btu = 252.2 cal.

SPECIFIC HEAT

Joseph Black was concerned with showing how temperature and heat
are related, as well as how they differ. The above definition of a calorie
(or of a Btu) clarifies this relationship. A particular amount of heat has to
be added to a given amount of water to raise its temperature—"caloric
concentration"—by 1°C (or 1°F).

But because 1 cal of heat is required to raise 1 g of water 1°C does
not mean that 1 cal of heat will do exactly the same thing for other
substances. Black experimentally observed that

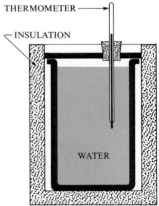

THERMOMETER

INSULATION

WATER

*11–8   A calorimeter is an
insulated container that
primarily measures heat
exchanges among substances.*

the same quantity of matter of heat has more effect in heating quicksilver (i.e., mercury) than in heating an equal measure of water, and therefore, that a smaller quantity of it is sufficient for increasing the sensible heat of quicksilver by the same number of degrees . . . . Quicksilver, therefore, has less *capacity* for the matter of heat than water has; it requires a *smaller* quantity of it to raise its temperature by the same number of degrees . . . .

We must, therefore, conclude that different bodies although they be of the same size, or even of the same weight, when they are reduced to the same temperature of degree of heat . . . may contain very different quantities of the matter of heat.

Black's concept of a different "capacity of heat" for different substances led to highly fruitful tables of *specific heats* (Table 11–1). In today's terms the specific heat of a substance *is the ratio of the amount of heat required to raise the temperature of a given mass of a substance through a given range to the heat required to raise an equal mass of water through the same range.* Note that all other substances in Table 11–1, including ice and steam, have smaller specific heats than liquid water. Water has the greatest specific heat of all ordinary substances. It takes about nine times as much heat to raise 1 lb of water 1° as to raise 1 lb of iron 1° and about 30 times as much heat for water as for mercury or lead.

Black's concept of specific heat capacity brilliantly illustrates the development of invaluable new concepts from the clarification of old. He distinguished between temperature and heat, operationally defined the latter, and ended with specific heat, among other accomplishments.

Table 11–1 | SPECIFIC HEATS*

SUBSTANCE	SPECIFIC HEAT	SUBSTANCE	SPECIFIC HEAT
Water	1.00	Glass	.20
Ice	.50	Iron	.11
Steam	.48	Lead	.031
Air	.24	Mercury	.033
Alcohol (ethyl)	.58	Silver	.056
Aluminum	.22	Soil (dry)	.20
Copper	.093	Tin	.055

*Specific heats are primarily ratios in comparison to water, base 1.00. They therefore have the same numerical values in both the metric and the British system of measurement. The specific heat capacity of water is 1 cal/g °C, 1 kcal/kg °C, or 1 Btu/lb °F.

Application of
Specific Heat to Heat Calculations

How many kilocalories (Calories) of heat would we need to raise 5 kg of water from 20°C to 30°C?

    1. By definition, every kilogram of water absorbs 1 kcal of heat for every 1°C rise in temperature.

    2. Therefore, 5 kg of water would require 5 kcal of heat for *every 1°C rise in temperature.*

    3. But a 10°C rise in temperature is required (from 20°C to 30°C). Therefore, 5 kg of water would require $5 \cdot 10 = 50$ kcal of heat to increase 10°C in temperature. The above type of calculation was generalized by Black as follows:

Heat gained or lost = weight · temperature change · specific heat capacity

$$\triangle H \qquad\qquad = \quad W \quad \cdot \qquad \triangle t \qquad\qquad \cdot \quad c.$$

In the above case:

$$\triangle H = W \cdot \triangle t \cdot c$$

$$= 5\,\text{kg} \cdot 10°\text{C} \cdot 1 \; \frac{\text{kcal}}{\text{kg} \; °\text{C}}$$

$$\triangle H = 50 \text{ kcal.}$$

    Let us now calculate the amount of heat required to raise the temperature of 5 kg of iron from 20°C to 30°C. (Note that the specific heat c of iron is 0.11.)

Given: $W = 5$ kg

        $\triangle t = 30°\text{C} - 20°\text{C} = 10°\text{C}$

        $c = .11$ kcal/kg °C

To find $\triangle H$: $\triangle H = W \cdot \triangle t \cdot c$

$$= 5 \text{ kg} \cdot 10°\text{C} \cdot .11 \; \frac{\text{kcal}}{\text{kg}°\text{C}}$$

$$\triangle H = 5.5 \text{ kcal absorbed by the iron.}$$

    Since iron has a specific heat of 0.11 (about 1:9), we expect iron to require only about 1/9 as much heat as the same weight of water in a 10°C temperature rise. (Compare the 5.5 kcal required for iron to the 50 kcal required for water in the previous problem.)

BLACK'S METHOD
OF MIXTURES AND
CONSERVATION OF HEAT

If two substances at different temperatures are mixed, heat will flow from the substance with the higher temperature to the one with the lower temperature until the temperature of both is the same. Mix hot and cold water. The hot water will lose heat and the cold will gain heat until both bodies have the same temperature. This concept of thermal equilibrium was first given quantitative precision by Black. The heat "fluid" emitted by the hot water is absorbed by the cold water. That is, *heat lost by body A equals heat gained by body B* (if complete insulation from surroundings is assumed). Five kg of water at 0°C mixed with 5 kg of water at 90°C settles at 45°C. The cold water gains heat to a midpoint temperature of 45°C, and the hot water loses heat to 45°C, since the amounts of originally hot and cold water are equal.

However, 10 kg of hot water at 90°C and 5 kg of cold water at 0°C should settle at a point higher than 45°C. In this case there is twice as much hot water as cold; therefore, an equilibrium temperature (60°C) is expected closer to the original hot water temperature (90°C) than the cold water temperature (0°C). The heat lost by the hot water equals the heat gained by the cold and the 10 kg of hot water drops less than the 5 kg of cold water rises. That is,

Given: $Wh = 10$ kg

$\quad\quad\quad W_c = 5$ kg

$\quad\quad\quad T_h = 90°$ C

$\quad\quad\quad T_c = 0°$ C

$\quad\quad\quad c = 1$ kcal/kg °C (specific heat capacity of water)

To find: equilibrium temperature T_e

Solution: *Heat lost* by hot water $=$ *heat gained* by cold water

$$W_h \cdot \triangle T_h \cdot c = W_c \cdot \triangle T_c \cdot c$$

$$10 \text{ kg} \cdot (90°C - T_e) \cdot 1 \text{ kcal/kg °C} = 5 \text{ kg} \cdot (T_e - 0) \cdot 1 \text{ kcal/kg °C}$$

$$900°C - 10 \, T_e = 5 \, T_e$$

$$-15 \, T_e = -900°C$$

$$T_e = 60°C.$$

The equilibrium temperature of the mixture is 60°C.

Let us now place a 5-kg iron bar (instead of cold water) at 0°C into 10 kg of hot water at 90°C. Would the two "bodies" also settle at a common temperature of 60°C as above? Since iron has a low specific heat (0.11) compared to the specific heat of water (1.0), iron should rise to a higher temperature than the same weight of water. Black's "method of mixtures" predicts a rise in temperature by the iron bar and a drop to the same temperature by the hot water. This new equilibrium temperature is calculated below:

Given: $W_1 = 10$ kg

$W_2 = 5$ kg

$T_1 = 90°C$

$T_2 = 0°C$

$c_1 = 1.0$ kcal/kg °C

$c_2 = .11$ kcal/kg °C

To find: equilibrium temperature T_e

Solution: *Heat lost* by hot water = *heat gained* by cold iron bar

$$W_1 \cdot \triangle t_1 \cdot c_1 = W_2 \cdot \triangle t_2 \cdot c_2$$

$$10 \text{ kg} \cdot (90°C - T_e) \cdot 1 \frac{\text{kcal}}{\text{kg °C}} = 5 \text{ kg} (T_e - 0) \cdot .11 \frac{\text{kcal}}{\text{kg °C}}$$

$$900°C - 10T_e = .55 T_e$$

$$T_e = 85.3°C.$$

Black's "heat fluid" principle of heat gained equals heat lost illustrated above is essentially *a principle of conservation of heat.* Black's "heat fluid" can be neither created nor destroyed. In heat transfer the fluid merely redistributes itself from hotter to cooler objects until thermal equilibrium is reached. The amount of heat supplied or withdrawn is proportional to the mass of the object and to the change of temperature ($H \propto m \triangle t$). Or $H = cm \triangle t$, where c is a specific heat constant that varies from one substance to another. And $c_1 m_1 \triangle t_1 = H$ (transferred) $= c_2 m_2 \triangle t_2$. Today we say that *in an isolated system, heat is neither created nor destroyed but merely redistributed from areas of higher to areas of lower temperature.*

Beginning with Black, insulated containers called calorimeters (Fig. 11–8) were developed to minimize heat transfer to (or from) surroundings during heat exchange experiments. Calorimeters can absorb most heat ordinarily lost to (or gained from) surroundings. Since the weight and specific heat of a calorimeter can be determined, the calorimeter can be included as part of the heat exchange process. The heat conservation principle then takes the following more accurate experimental form:

Heat lost by hotter substance(s) = heat gained by cooler substance(s)

+ heat gained (or lost) by calorimeter.

Through this more accurate form of the heat exchange principle, specific heats and heat capacities of different bodies could be more precisely determined, together with other heat exchange information. The following four steps illustrate the use of the calorimeter in determining the specific heat of a substance X.

1. A measured mass of cold water is placed in a calorimeter of known mass and specific heat. The cold water and calorimeter will be at the same observed temperature.
2. A measured mass of substance X is heated to a known temperature.
3. The hot substance is placed within the cold water. After constant stirring, the final common temperature of the mixture is noted.
4. The known quantities of mass, temperature change, and specific heat are substituted in the heat exchange equation, and the unknown specific heat of substance X is calculated.

Black's highly significant method of mixtures obviously required previous concepts of thermal equilibrium, differentiation between temperature and heat, and a new concept of specific heat capacity. Precision of terms went hand in hand with the development of scientific research and ideas.

CHANGE OF STATE

Matter is found in three states: solid, liquid, and gaseous. A solid (ice) keeps its volume and shape. A liquid (tap water) keeps its volume but changes shape according to its container. A gas (steam) changes both volume and shape.

Substances change their state from solids to liquids to gases by absorbing heat, and from gases to liquids to solids by emitting heat. Everyone has observed ice melt into a liquid or liquid water boil away into vapor when heated. In the opposite process, water vapor in the air condenses into drops of liquid on ice-cold lemonade pitchers, or liquid water freezes in refrigerators. In these cases water loses heat to cooler surroundings. The pitcher is cooler than the water vapor in the air; the refrigerator is lower in temperature than the liquid water placed within it. The pitcher and the refrigerator absorb heat from the water. The water vapor condenses in one case and freezes in the other.

Latent Heat: Melting and Freezing

Black said, "we may consider all . . . liquids as solids melted by heat" and all gases as liquids vaporized by heat. However, Black also observed through careful experiments that most substances freeze or melt at a definite temperature characteristic of that substance. These particular temperatures became known as *freezing points* or *melting points*. Add heat to ice, and it will remain solid until 0°C. At that point, with added heat, the ice becomes liquid. If we cool liquid water at any temperature, the water remains liquid until it reaches 0°C. At that point, if cooled further, it becomes ice. The freezing point and the melting point are the same. Black also noticed that certain substances such as glass, wax, and butter, are exceptions to a fixed melting and freezing point. Glass is at a lower temperature when it begins to liquefy than when it completes the process.

But even more than this, Black observed that a mixture of ice and water holds a 0°C temperature until all the ice is melted. That is, even when heat is applied, the temperature of the water does not increase. During the ice-melting process heat does not raise temperature as expected. Why? "This heat," answered Black, "must be added in order to give the form of a liquid; and I affirm that this large addition of heat is the principal and most immediate cause of the liquefaction induced."

"On the other hand," continues Black, "when we freeze a liquid, a very large quantity of heat comes out of it while it assumes a solid form . . . and the temperature of the body as measured by a thermometer is not diminished . . . and it appears that a solid state cannot be induced without a large quantity of heat."

Place a pitcher of ice and water at 32°F in a refrigerator also at 32°F, and neither the ice will melt nor the water freeze. Remove the pitcher from the refrigerator into the warm room, and the ice will melt. But a thermometer in *the ice-water mixture remains steadily at 32°F until all the ice is melted*. The heat of the room was used for changing ice into water without a change in temperature.

Once Black noticed that large amounts of heat are absorbed by objects just for melting at constant temperature or are given out by objects freezing, he worked diligently with his method of mixtures to determine exactly how much heat is involved in such processes. Such heat of liquids is known as "hidden" or *latent heat of fusion* because the presence of these heats is not generally given away by any temperature change of the objects when melting or freezing. Latent heat, therefore, is identified with the *change of state* of an object, as differentiated from specific heat, identified with the *change of temperature*.

For example, how much heat is needed just to melt 1 kg of ice? The method of mixtures answers the problem as follows. Place 1 kg of ice at 0°C into 1.5 kg of hot water at 70°C, and stir thoroughly until all the ice is melted by the hot water. Suppose that at this point you find that the equilibrium temperature is 10°C. Neglect the heat absorbed by the container.

Solution: Let x = number of kilocalories needed to melt 1 kg of ice

10 = number of kilocalories need to raise the melted ice from 0°C to 10°C

$1.5\ (70 - 10)$ = number of kilocalories given out by the water in cooling.

Heat units taken in by ice = heat units given out by water

$$x \text{ kcal} + 10 \text{ kcal} = 1.5\ (70 - 10) \text{ kcal}$$

$$x = 80 \text{ kcal}.$$

That is, 80 kcal of heat are required to melt 1 kg of ice. The heat of fusion of water is 80 kcal/kg.

Table 11–2 contains the latent heats of fusion determined for a number of common substances. Notice that the heat of fusion of water, 80 kcal/kg, is considerably greater than the other substances given except lithium. It takes about 30 times as much heat to melt 1 kg of ice as it does to melt 1 kg of mercury in solid form. This also means that when water freezes, it gives off 30 times as much heat as liquid mercury does when it becomes solid.

Table 11–2 | *MELTING POINTS AND HEATS OF FUSION*

SUBSTANCE	MELTING POINT (°C)	HEAT OF FUSION (KCAL/KG)	SUBSTANCE	MELTING POINT (°C)	HEAT OF FUSION (KCAL/KG)
Water	0	80	Mercury	−39	2.8
Alcohol (ethyl)	−114	25	Nitrogen	−210	6.1
Lead	327	5.9	Oxygen	−219	3.3
Lithium	186	160	Zinc	420	24

A solid (ice, for example) absorbs a characteristic amount of heat to melt. When solidifying, the liquid returns the same amount of latent heat to its surroundings.

Table 11-3 | *BOILING POINTS AND HEATS OF VAPORIZATION*

SUBSTANCE	BOILING POINT (°C)	HEAT OF VAPORIZATION (KCAL/KG)	SUBSTANCE	BOILING POINT (°C)	HEAT OF VAPORIZATION (KCAL/KG)
Water	100	540	Mercury	357	71
Alcohol (ethyl)	78	204	Nitrogen	−196	48
Lead	1,525	175	Oxygen	−183	51
Lithium	1,336	511	Zinc	918	475

Latent Heat: Boiling and Condensation

But Black did not stop with phenomena of melting and freezing. He also investigated boiling as a transition of liquids to gases. If there is a "hidden" heat of fusion, why not also a "hidden" heat of vaporization? If ice or other solids "hide" heat absorbed in melting from thermometer detection, perhaps liquids also "hide" heat absorbed in boiling. If a latent heat is characteristic of melting, it should also be characteristic of boiling.

In his experimental investigations of boiling, Black found that

1. The liquid gradually warms and at last attains that temperature which it cannot pass without assuming the form of vapor. In these circumstances, we always observe that the water [or other liquid] is thrown into violent agitation which we call *boiling*.

2. *However long and violently we boil* a liquid, we cannot make it the least hotter than when it began to boil. The thermometer always points at the same degree, namely the vaporific point of that liquid . . . often called its *boiling point*.

3. I can easily show, in the same manner as in the case of liquefaction, that a very large quantity of heat is necessary for the production of vapor . . . [and that the heat] enters into the vapor gradually while it is forming without making the vapor hotter.

4. In the reverse process of a vapor condensing back into a liquid, the very same large quantity of heat comes out of it into the colder surrounding matter by which it is condensed.

In this way Black initiated a concept of *heat of vaporization*, defined as *the quantity of heat required to vaporize a unit mass of liquid without a change of temperature*. With his calorimeters he also initiated techniques for determining the heat of vaporization of different substances. Table 11-3 lists the particular heats of vaporization of a number of substances experimentally determined. These findings make it clear that substances vary in the amount of heat required for boiling. Notice here again that water, with its heat of vaporization of 540 kcal/kg, needs much more heat for boiling than other ordinary substances. By the same token, water returns much more heat to its surroundings when condensing from a vapor to a liquid.

When water vapor condenses into clouds or fog, it releases considerable heat into the surrounding atmosphere. The considerable heat of vaporization of water as compared to its specific heat and even heat of fusion is clearly seen in Fig. 11–9, a graph representing the change of ice to steam as constant heat is applied.

Suppose that we take 1 lb of ice at −40°C and change it to steam at 120°C by steadily applying 80 kcal of heat per minute. With a negligible heat loss to surroundings, the following data are observed for each step of the process:

STEP	TIME (MIN)	HEAT APPLIED (KCAL)
1. Heating the 1 kg of ice from −40°C to 0°C	.25	20
2. Melting the ice at 0°C	1.00	80
3. Raising the temperature of water to 100°C	1.25	100
4. Boiling the water at 100°C	6.75	540
5. Raising the temperature of steam to 120°C	.13	10
Total	9.38	750

Notice that 540 kcal of heat out of the total 750 kcal are used to change the water into steam in step 4. Remember that the specific heat capacities of ice, water, and steam are only 0.5, 1.0, and 0.5 heat units, respectively, as compared to the 540 units needed for boiling water and the 80 units required for melting ice. The comparisons are clear in Fig. 11–9 in terms of time taken for each step in the process.

Black's caloric theory also successfully explained the latent heats he observed. Since heat particles were a substance, they could combine "chemically" with other particles. At the freezing point, heat particles united with ice (or other solids) to form a new substance, liquid water (or other liquids). At the boiling point, heat particles united with liquid water (or other liquids) to form a new substance, a vapor. Ice shows different properties from water, and water different properties from vapor.

In short, heat particles are matter. In a change of state, heat particles *combine* with their host substances to form new substances. When combined, heat particles cannot increase the temperature of substances. To increase the temperature of host substances absorbing them, heat particles must accumulate *uncombined* in spaces within. In this way, Black successfully explained latent heat.

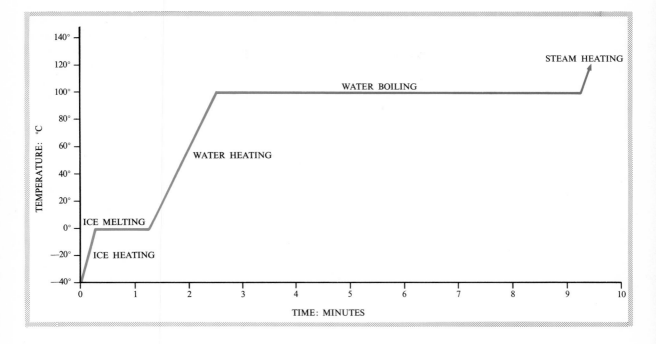

11–9 Heat required to change ice at −40° C to steam at 120° C. (Negligible heat loss to surroundings is assumed.) Note that most of the heat needed is to change water to steam at the same temperature (100° C) rather than to raise the temperature of ice, water, and steam through 160° C.

SUCCESS OF
THE CALORIC THEORY

In short, the fluid theory of heat was a successful one. Black's caloric particles explained most of the heat phenomena of interest at the time. When these material particles were pictured to repel each other and to be attracted to other substances, they provided a conceptual scheme that could explain heat transfer. In particular, they could explain why heat flowed from areas of higher concentration (temperature) to areas of lower concentration until equilibrium was reached. The fluid theory of heat also unified and explained such phenomena as thermal expansion of objects and change of state. The theory explained differences between temperature and heat and led to new concepts of heat capacity, latent heat, and heat conservation.

The caloric theory not only explained, but it enabled prediction: It led to the calorimeter, and the calorimeter became a powerful tool of heat measurement and prediction. If heat is a material fluid, then heat can be conserved; Black based his method of mixtures on the conservation principle that heat is not gained or lost but is transferred from one object to another. The calorimeter insulated the heat; and the heat capacities of different objects within could be measured, or their equilibrium temperatures could be predicted.

As we shall see, the caloric theory developed weaknesses. But let us remember that no great innovator in science or any area of human experience has ever given a conceptual model that is final. Black organized observations; introduced new quantitative concepts and techniques; developed theories that unified, explained, and predicted; and stimulated other creative men to further ideas, techniques, and methods. What pioneer could do more?

CHAPTER REVIEW

1. What is heat? Why can it not be defined as that which always increases the temperature of a body to which it is added?

2. What observations from mechanical work suggest that heat is energy?

3. What observations early suggested that heat consists of minute particles of matter?

4. Compare and illustrate the three methods of heat transfer.

5. Does a thermometer measure heat? Explain.

6. (a) What is the difference between *heat* and *temperature*? Illustrate. (b) How are heat and temperature related?

7. (a) A gallon jug and a pint of water are at the same temperature. Do they contain equal amounts of heat? Why? (b) Is it possible for the two containers of water to be at different temperatures and yet contain the same amount of heat? Explain.

8. Which is more convenient, the Fahrenheit or the Celsius scale? Why? Relate your answer to the way the two scales were originally calibrated.

9. If a Celsius degree equals 9/5 of a Fahrenheit degree, why is this not the ratio between corresponding readings on the two temperature scales?

10. (a) Define "calorie," "kilocalorie," "Calorie," and "Btu." (b) Why are the definitions of those units called operational definitions? (c) What numerical relationships do these heat units have to one another?

11. What is the "specific heat" of a substance? Illustrate.

12. Why does the specific heat of a substance have the same value in the British and the metric system?

13. (a) Explain and illustrate the differences in the concepts of specific heat, heat of fusion, and heat of vaporization. (b) How are these different "heats" related? (c) Why are these concepts important?

14. What is the caloric theory of heat? What are its assumptions?

15. How does the caloric theory explain each of the following phenomena or concepts? (a) Transfer of heat by conduction. (b) Heat transfer by convection currents. (c) Heat by radiation. (d) Temperature. (e) Differences in the specific heats of substances. (f) Change of

state. (g) Latent heat of fusion. (h) Latent heat of vaporization. (i) Conservation of heat.

16. (a) Explain and illustrate Joseph Black's method of mixtures. (b) Show how Black's method of mixtures relates to a law of conservation of heat.

17. Why is Black considered to have laid the foundations for a science of heat? Specifically what was scientific about Black's efforts and accomplishments?

18. How could Black have been so productive while operating with a caloric theory that successors the next century discarded?

PROBLEMS

1. Explain the following phenomena: (a) Metals make the best frying pans. (b) A piece of iron feels colder than a piece of wood at the same temperature. (c) For good ventilation, windows should be open at the top and bottom. (d) A hot air duct from a furnace generally terminates in a lower rather than an upper section of a wall. (e) Ice floats. (f) Fans have a cooling effect. (g) Water keeps cool in porous canvas bags. (h) Large bodies of water moderate the climate of surrounding areas. (i) Radiators in hot-water heating systems are generally longer than in steam heating systems.

2. Does a radiator heat a room primarily by radiation? Explain.

3. Why does not increasing the size of a gas flame under a pan of boiling water cook an egg faster?

4. Why does a cube of ice at 32°F more effectively cool lemonade that the same weight of cold water at 32°F?

5. (a) Why would a closed glass container full of freezing water burst? (b) Would the same thing happen if the container were full of freezing alcohol? Why?

6. Change the following to Celsius readings: room temperature, 68°F; body temperature, 98.6°F; and liquid air, −310°F.

7. What temperature is the same on the Celsius and Fahrenheit scales?

8. (a) Change the temperature scale in Fig. 11–9 from Celsius to corresponding Fahrenheit readings. (b) Does this change in scale require adjustments in the graph curve itself? Why?

9. The *specific heat capacity* of water is 1 cal/g °C, 1 kcal/kg °C, or 1 Btu/lb °F. (a) What does "specific heat capacity" mean? (b) Show that 1 cal/g °C is equivalent to 1 kcal/kg °C. (c) Show that 1 cal/g °C is equivalent to 1 Btu/lb °F.

10. (a) How much heat is needed to melt 1 lb of ice? 1 g of ice? 1 kg of ice? (b) How much heat is needed to vaporize 1 lb of water? 1 g of water? 1 kg of water?

11. Compare the amount of heat (Btu's) needed to raise the temperature of 1 lb of ice from 31°F to 32°F to the amount of heat needed: (a) To change the ice to 1 lb of water at 32°F. (b) To raise the 1 lb of water from 32°F to 33°F. (c) To change the water to 1 lb of steam at 212°F.

12. In Table 11–2 change (a) the melting points of water, mercury, and zinc to the corresponding Fahrenheit temperatures and (b) the heats of fusion to Btu's per pound.

13. In Table 11–3 change (a) the boiling point temperatures of water, alcohol, and oxygen to the corresponding Fahrenheit temperatures and (b) the heats of fusion to Btu's per pound.

In problems 14–20, assume that heat losses to the containers and outside surroundings are negligible unless otherwise indicated.

14. What temperature results if 100 g of ice at 0°C are placed in 100 g of water at 60°C?

15. What temperature results if 100 g of water at 0°C are mixed with 250 g of water at 60°C?

16. How much heat is needed to change 10 lb of ice at 10°F to steam at 222°F?

17. How much heat is emitted by each 1,000 lb of water vapor in the air condensing into fog or cloud droplets?

18. (a) How much ice will a 5-lb bar of iron at 200°C melt? (See specific heats in Table 11–1.) (b) What is the equilibrium temperature for the iron and the ice water?

19. What temperature results from mixing 500 g of water at 0°C with steam at 100°C?

20. A glass container (see Table 11–1 for the specific heat of glass) weighing 100 g contains 500 g of water and 500 g of ice, all at 0°C. If 20 g of steam at 100°C are placed into the container, what is the equilibrium temperature? Take into consideration the heat absorbed by the container.

SUGGESTIONS FOR FURTHER READING

Priestly, Herbert, *Introductory Physics*, Allyn and Bacon, Boston, 1958, Chs. 10–14.

Conant, James, ed., *Harvard Case Histories in Experimental Science*, Vol. 1, Harvard Univ. Press, Cambridge, Mass., 1957, Case 3, pp. 119–155.

Holton, Gerald J., and D. H. D. Roller, *Foundations of Modern Physical Science,* Addison-Wesley, Reading, Mass., 1959, Ch. 19, pp. 119–155.

Taylor, Lloyd W., *Physics, the Pioneer Science,* Vol. 1, Dover paperback, New York, 1959, Chs. 19–21.

White, Harvey, *Modern College Physics,* Van Nostrand, New York, 1953, Chs. 29–30.

Lemon, Harvey B., *From Galileo to the Nuclear Age,* Univ. Chicago Press, Chicago, 1949, Chs. 14–17.

12   *Conservation of Energy*

Nothing comes from nothing, and nothing can become nothing.

DEMOCRITUS, 5th century B.C.

Because of its practical use, and for its own intrinsic interest, the principle of conservation of energy may be regarded as one of the great achievements of the human mind.

WILLIAM DAMPIER, 1929

HEAT OF FRICTION
AND ENERGY OF MOTION

Every successful theory in time exposes a weakness leading to its own decline. Heat of friction was the Achilles' heel of the caloric theory. Rub two blocks of wood together, and the surfaces become warmer. Why? From where does this heat of friction come? The calorists theorized that heat fluid is squeezed out from the interior of the blocks. That is, caloric is neither created nor destroyed; it is merely forced to the surface by friction.

"No," challenged Count Rumford (1753–1814) as he supervised the boring of cannon. "No," corroborated Sir Humphrey Davy (1778–1829), rubbing two pieces of ice together. "No," speculated ship's surgeon Julius

Robert Mayer (1814–1878), observing venous blood color in different climates. And "No," argued James Prescott Joule (1818–1889) as his paddles vigorously stirred water in calorimeters. All these men claimed evidence that heat of friction is heat produced by motion, that heat is a form of motion (energy)—not a form of matter.

Count Rumford's
Cannon-Boring Experiments:
From Mechanical Motion to Heat

Count Rumford was actually Benjamin Thompson, a Massachusetts colonist who remained loyal to England. He was knighted by George III for his services during the American Revolution and was later made a Count by the Duke of Bavaria for serving as Inspector General of Bavarian Artillery and Minister of War. Astute observations of heat phenomena, particularly in the manufacture of Bavarian cannon, made Rumford famous in the history of science. He was exceedingly impressed by the exceptional amounts of heat emitted in the boring of cannon: "Being engaged lately in superintending the boring of cannon, I was struck with the very considerable degree of heat that a brass gun acquires in a short time in being bored, and with the still higher temperatures (much higher than that of boiling water, as I found by experiment) of the metallic chips separated from it by the borer." To measure heat given off, he encased 2.5 gal of water around a cannon. To the amazement of spectators, the water came to a boil and continued to boil as long as the boring continued. There was no limit to the heat given off. How could there be so much caloric in a substance? Squeeze a sponge hard enough or long enough, and no moisture remains. As Rumford saw it, the endless heat was due to the motion of the borer—in fact, to the work of the two horses turning a capstan to operate the borer (Fig. 12–1). Heat was not a substance squeezed out of brass but a motion (energy) imparted to it by outside work. In Rumford's words, "It is hardly necessary to add that anything which an insulated body or system of bodies can continue to furnish without limitation cannot possibly be a material substance; and it appears to me extremely difficult, if not quite impossible, to form any distinct idea of anything capable of being excited and communicated except it be *motion*."

Rumford was also aware of great quantities of latent heat given up by water turning to ice. Water contains latent heat that it emits when changing to ice. If heat is a substance, water should weigh less when frozen than when liquid; heat substance is gone. In a series of careful experiments, Rumford showed that there is no observable change in the weight of water on freezing. Rumford further observed: "The weight of gold is neither augmented nor lessened by one-millionth part upon

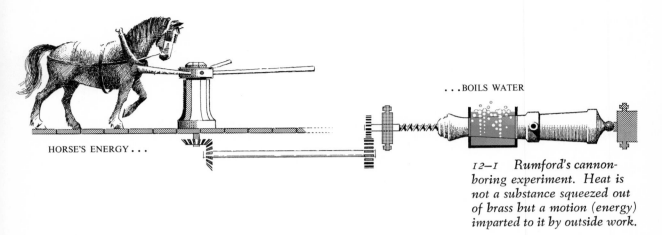

HORSE'S ENERGY . . .

. . . BOILS WATER

12–1   Rumford's cannon-boring experiment. Heat is not a substance squeezed out of brass but a motion (energy) imparted to it by outside work.

being heated from the point of freezing water to that of a bright red heat. I think we may safely conclude that all attempts to discover any effect of heat upon the apparent weight of bodies will be fruitless." Supporters of caloric theory could claim, however, that heat is a weightless substance (much like the ether assumed in space as a medium for light waves). Or calorists could claim that the weight of heat is imperceptibly small, much as is claimed today regarding the neutrino, an atomic subparticle.

Davy's Ice Experiment

Sir Humphrey Davy (1778–1829), a protégé of Rumford at the newly formed British Royal Institute, was one of the great chemists of his time. Among his famous experiments was one in which two blocks of ice were rubbed together and almost entirely converted to water through friction. The entire apparatus and surroundings were kept at the freezing point; no heat entered. But from where did the ice obtain heat for melting? From within itself? If the rubbed surfaces of the ice blocks were melted by caloric "squeezed out" from within itself, the interiors would have become even colder and therefore would not have melted. To Davy, the heat for melting the ice could have come only from the motion (that is, energy) of the apparatus rubbing the ice blocks together.

But in spite of such experiments, the caloric theory remained strong for another half century. The caloric theory could still solve most of its problems, and the "motion" theory of heat was still too vague. Successful physical theories do not easily succumb to brilliant new ideas lacking precise, numerical detail.

Joule's Paddle Wheel Experiments: The Mechanical Equivalent of Heat

It was with the experiments of James Joule (1818–1889) that the matter theory of heat was eclipsed. Joule's paddle wheel experiment is famous. Joule revolved a brass paddle wheel in water (Fig. 12–2) to find a quantitative relationship between mechanical energy and heat. The mechanical energy was determined through the work done by two falling lead weights operating the paddle (work = weight · distance fallen). The paddle churned the water, warming it. The temperature rise of the water was measured by a sensitive thermometer, and great pains were taken to minimize heat loss. Knowing both the amount of water and its temperature rise, Joule could calculate the amount of heat generated.

In repeated tests, Joule found that more work generated more heat. In fact, the amount of heat gained was predictable from the amount of work done. This can be seen in the following relationships between mechanical work and heat:

Heat gain = work done

    1 Btu = 778 ft-lb

or 1 cal = 4.19 $\times$ 10⁷ ergs

          = 4.19 joules (named after Joule)

or 1 kcal = 427 kg-m.

To illustrate: A 77.8-lb weight falling 10 ft (work = 77.8 lb · 10 ft = 778 ft-lb) should generate 1 Btu of heat in water (that is, enough heat to warm 1 lb of water 1°F).

  Work done = heat gain

77.8 lb · 10 ft = 1 Btu

      778 ft-lb = 1 Btu.

A 778-lb rock falling 10 ft to the ground should generate 10 Btu of heat in the ground.

7,780 ft-lb = 10 Btu.

The above constants 778, 4.19, and 427 are current conversion factors between units of heat and units of work and are close to Joule's original values. These conversion factors are called the *mechanical equivalents of heat* and are symbolized by *J* in honor of Joule.

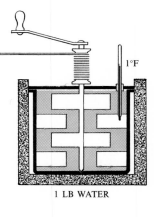

1°F

1 LB WATER

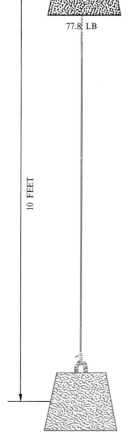

77.8 LB

10 FEET

12–2   Joule's paddle wheel experiment. Falling weights raised the temperature of water by turning paddles. The heat gained corresponded to the mechanical work done. Thus, heat has a mechanical equivalent.

Joule's mechanical equivalent of heat (J) may be generalized as follows:

$$J = \frac{\text{mechanical work done } (W)}{\text{heat gained } (H)} = \frac{778 \text{ ft-lb}}{\text{Btu}} \quad \text{or} \quad \frac{\text{joules}}{\text{cal}}.$$

The above equation may be interpreted as follows: No matter how much mechanical work (W) is done or heat (H) gained, the *ratio W/H* of work done to heat gained remains the same *constant* value J, 778 ft-lb/Btu, or 4.19 joules/cal.

Joule performed his heat of friction experiments repeatedly for 35 years (1843–1878). It was his persistent retesting for the reliability of his conversion factor (J) that made Joule's work decisive in the overthrow of the caloric theory. That heat is energy rather than matter seemed settled—at least until Einstein. If mechanical energy and heat are interconvertible with mathematical exactness, how can heat not be a form of energy?

THE STEAM ENGINE: FROM HEAT TO MECHANICAL ENERGY

If mechanical energy is transformed into heat, why shouldn't heat be transformed into mechanical energy? The steam engine is an answer to this question.

The ancient Chinese invented gunpowder and used it in rockets. Europeans of the Middle Ages used the powder to propel musket shot and cannonballs. Actually, a gun is an engine that converts the heat and expansive force of an explosion into mechanical motion.

At the beginning of the 18th century, the British coal industry was in danger. Water was flooding the mines. In 1705, Newcomen helped save the industry with pumps powered by the first engine of commercial importance. But the Newcomen atmospheric engine was very crude and required an excessive amount of fuel for the work it did. The engine was driven by atmospheric pressure; steam, used incidentally within it, actually did no pushing. In 1763, James Watt was repairing a Newcomen engine when he recognized the epoch-making possibilities of using the pushing power of steam. With counsel from Joseph Black on the latent heat of steam, Watt developed the first true steam engine. In so doing, he made possible the Industrial Revolution, which changed the character of civilization and the face of the globe. Watt steam engines concentrated large amounts of power in individual plants. Factories and mass production techniques crowded out independent artisans as large cities replaced small towns and villages. Railroads and steamboats shrank the globe. Modern technology was born; steam was doing mechanical work. Not only did Joule's paddle wheels heat water, but sufficiently heated water turned wheels (Fig. 12–3). Not only was motion (mechanical energy) transformed into heat, but heat was transformed into motion.

LAW OF
CONSERVATION OF ENERGY

The Law and Its Meaning

The law of conservation of energy warrants more attention here. Simply and sweepingly, the law states: *The energy of the universe is constant.* Implied are that (1) energy exists in various forms—mechanical energy,

12–3 The steam engine transforms heat (of steam) into mechanical energy (of a flywheel and shaft) to run locomotives and other devices.

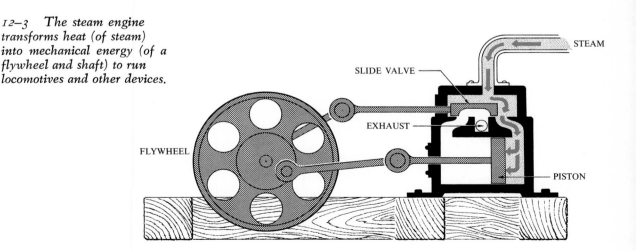

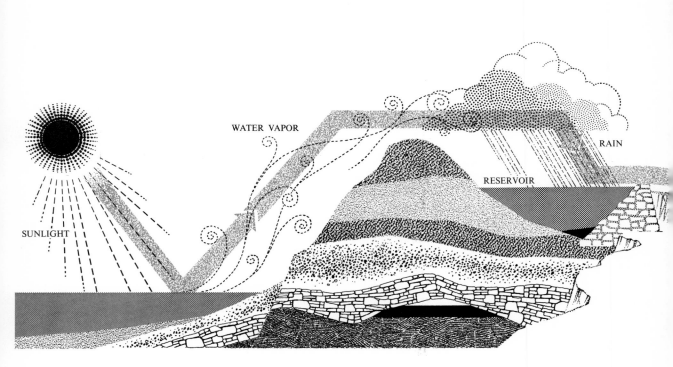

WATER VAPOR

RAIN

RESERVOIR

SUNLIGHT

*12–4 From sunlight to
electric light. Like "the house
that Jack built," the heat
energy of the sun evaporates
water that condenses as cloud
droplets, that fall as rain, that
is stored in reservoirs, that falls
on waterwheels, that operate
generators, that supply electric
energy, that is transformed
into light. Energy is neither
created nor destroyed—only
transformed. Devices
merely assist in energy
transformations.*

heat, light, sound, electricity, magnetism, or chemical energy; (2) energy
changes from one form to another; and (3) each form changes in amount,
but the total amount of all forms remains the same. That is, although
changing in form, energy is basically indestructible and interconvertible.
Identity exists in diversity. Although form and details change, total energy is constant: it always equals itself; something in the universe is
dependable.

Mechanical energy changing to heat is but one illustration of energy
transformation. To state that 778 ft-lb = 1 Btu is to refer to the *same
energy* changing from a mechanical form expressed in foot-pounds to
a heat form in Btu's. The "=" sign indicates equality by identity. And
if this same energy takes still other forms, the equality still holds by the
same token of identity.

Five ft-lb of work are involved in lifting a 1-lb melon 5 ft. If you
lift the melon, you supply 5 ft-lb of energy by muscular activity. Your
muscular activity depends upon chemical energies and heat within body
cells, which in turn depend on food energy and on oxygen supply. And
food has its origins in the sun: Plants depend on sunlight and animals
feed on plants and other animals. Coal and oil are fossil fuels that represent plants and animals of distant geologic ages. When we burn coal or
oil, we are using long-stored but converted sunshine.

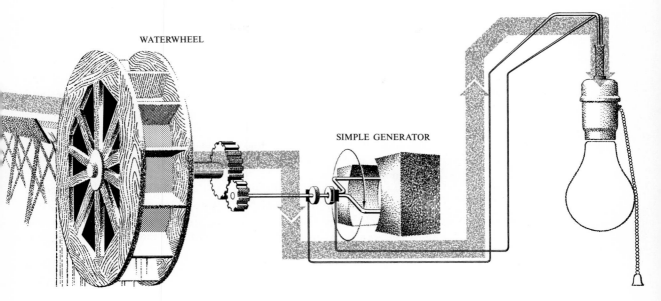

WATERWHEEL

SIMPLE GENERATOR

When we flick on a light switch, we are also using solar heat—but as energy that has made many changes between the sun and the lamp. Light is transformed from electrical energy; electrical energy, from relative motion between coils of wire and magnetic fields; motion of coils or magnets, from rotating waterwheels; rotating waterwheels, from falling water; falling water, from ground water or ocean water evaporated by the sun (Fig. 12–4). Energy can do useful work as it transforms.

Development of the Law

By Joule's time, conservation of energy as a broad principle was in the air. Limited aspects of it had been worked out. Newton's law of action and reaction led to conservation of momentum (Chapters 9 and 10). Huygens proposed a conservation of kinetic energy (mv^2 then) for elastic (billiard ball) collisions. Work concepts and swinging pendulums led to a principle of conservation of mechanical energy—and also to efforts toward perpetual-motion machines (Chapter 10). Black took seven-league steps with his conservation of heat principle (Chapter 11). Experiments by Rumford and Davy pointed to heat as a form of energy and Joule established a quantitative connection between mechanical energy and heat through persistent, precise techniques (Chapter 11). While Joule's paddle wheels were transforming mechanical motion into heat, steam engines were transforming heat into mechanical motion. And simple electric circuits were already transforming electricity into heat.

Mayer's Synthesis

What remained was for someone with enough insight, interest, and imagination to put the pieces together and present the whole picture. This the German physician Julius R. Mayer (1814–1878) did, later reinforced by the technical language, mathematical rigor, and pointed applications of his countryman Hermann von Helmholtz (1821–1894), the famous biophysicist.

Mayer in 1840 was a young ship's doctor when he noticed that venous blood from patients in equatorial waters was a deeper red than that from patients back home. This launched him into speculations about connections between body heat and chemical reactions, and from there to interconvertibility of all energies of nature.

The physicist Mach relates an incident during a visit of Mayer to the physicist Von Jolly. In answer to Mayer's ideas about energy transformation, Von Jolly said: "But if what you say is true, then water should be warmed by merely shaking it." Mayer quickly left. Von Jolly forgot the incident until several weeks later, when Mayer rushed back into the room and excitedly exclaimed, "And so it is!" Mayer had made a connection between mechanical energy and heat.

Mayer's friend Rumelin, Rector of the University of Tubingen, reports that Mayer, walking along a road with him one day, had this to say about four "steaming horses" pulling a passing carriage:

> The heating of the horses, the increased oxidation of the food they have consumed, the frictional heat which the moving wheels have left in blue stripes along the road, the consumption of grease at the axles—these are not mere incidents; but the motion of the horses and their mechanical work transform themselves into these heat effects, and indeed in accordance with a *fixed quantitative relation* [author's italics] to find and to formulate which, he regarded as his most important task, although he had no longer any doubt about the correctness of the principle.

Mayer also became impressed by Gay-Lussac's forgotten experiment of 1807 involving the effect of heat on gases and the work done by them. Gay-Lussac had found that when gases were allowed to expand freely *in a vacuum,* they hardly dropped in temperature. But when the same gases expanded *against a surrounding medium,* such as air, the expanding gases showed a considerable temperature drop (Fig. 12–5). Mayer's

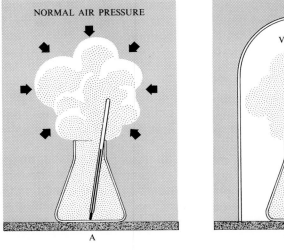

NORMAL AIR PRESSURE

VACUUM

A

B

12–5 Expanding gases do work and lose energy. In 12–5A the gas expands against air pressure and loses heat as shown by a drop in temperature. By comparison, in 12–5B the gas expanding in a vacuum has no resisting air pressure against which to work. The thermometer shows no drop in temperature or loss of heat.

interpretation was that heat from the gas is converted into the work of pushing aside the opposing medium.

And so in 1842, a year before Joule began his experiments, Mayer independently postulated a mechanical equivalent of heat. Then, while Joule focused on precision, Mayer extended the transformation idea to all known energies, often in hazy fashion.

Said Mayer:

> In numberless cases, we see motion cease without having caused another motion or the lifting of a weight; but a force [energy] once in existence cannot be annihilated, it can only change its form: and the question therefore arises, What other forms is force, which we have become acquainted with as falling force [*PE*] and motion [*KE*], capable of assuming? Experience alone can lead us to a conclusion.

Before he was through, Mayer attributed the origin of heat, fuel, mechanical energy, and most other energies on earth to the sun. The relationship of food to human activity and the significance of coal as "concentrated" sunshine were only two examples. He pointed out a conversion of mechanical work into electrical energy: He used the electrophorus, a simple electrical device, to illustrate the conversion of mechanical energy into electrical energy. (To separate the oppositely charged disks required more work than just to lift an uncharged disk. The extra mechanical energy showed itself as electrical energy accumulated in Leyden jar condensers.) From Pouillet's measurements, Mayer calculated that the annual amount of solar heat could melt a "glacier" 100 ft thick completely encasing the earth. Current estimates are about 175 ft. This amount of heat is about 40,000 times as much as all living creatures need, including the billion or more mechanical horsepower used by man.

Mayer went so far in his conservation of energy calculations as to conclude that as burning coal, the sun could keep up its temperature for only 4,600 years. This was not too far from chemical estimates in the 1920s. Mayer was born too soon for atomic energy. But that did not keep him from stating that with its radiation loss, the sun had an equivalent mass loss. According to Mayer's figures, 200 billion tons of meteors per minute rain down upon the huge sun to balance out the radiation loss. Therefore, the sun does not lose mass or temperature. An imagination indeed that replaces radiation loss with a mass equivalent—and all in the name of conservation of energy!

When Mayer attempted to publicize his ideas, he almost martyred himself. He was considered a physician dabbling in physics. His language was archaic, his ideas lacked experimental and mathematical rigor, and his impatience at opposition was alienating. Seriously disturbed by professional ridicule, Mayer, still a young man, broke down. Fortunately, he survived a suicide attempt, but he never completely regained his mental balance. His scientific creativity was finished. Thanks, however, to the efforts of Helmholtz and English physicist John Tyndall, Mayer did receive belated recognition at the end of his life.

Helmholtz had what Mayer lacked in technical language, mathematical logic, and experimental know-how. The former, independently of Mayer and Joule, also worked his own way to a broad principle of conservation of energy. Thoroughly mechanistic, Helmholtz emphasized that heat, light, sound, electricity, and so forth are all forms of motion (that is, mechanical energy) and are therefore branches of mechanics. In fact, all nature and science is to be understood in terms of Newton's laws. He therefore reduced all phenomena to motions of mass-points and then applied mathematical expressions of potential energy and kinetic energy in fields of mechanics, heat, electricity, magnetism, physical chemistry, and astronomy. His mathematical conservation laws within various fields could be tested, and together they formed one large conservation law in terms of mechanics. Unknowingly, he had given a mathematical structure to Mayer's ideas. And once he became aware of Mayer's contributions previous to his, Helmholtz, exhibiting rare professional chivalry, devoted himself to publicizing Mayer's contributions reinforced by his own.

Significance of the Conservation Law

The significance of various conservation principles forming the general law of conservation of energy has been discussed as these principles were introduced (Chapters 10–12). Let us at this point add that the general law of conservation of energy is one of the great syntheses of all time, comparable to those of Ptolemy and Newton. Through it, the various areas of science were placed on a common foundation of energy in the extension of a mechanical view. Certainly modern physics and technology could hardly exist without the "=" of the conservation law.

The law reveals the international character of science: Men of different countries and different times contributed to its development. Often, men of different nations working at almost the same time but independently from more or less common knowledge on common scientific problems made similar discoveries. Originating among ancient Greek atomists, the conservation idea includes on the roster of its development: In Italy, Lucretius and Galileo. In England, Newton, Huygens, Watt, Davy, Joule, Faraday—for chemical, electrical, magnetic, and optical inter-relationships —and Tyndall for his classic work, *Heat as a Mode of Motion,* 1862. In Switzerland, Bernoulli for anticipating by a century a kinetic model of gases (1738). In Russia, Mikhail V. Lomonosov (1711–1765), who anticipated not only kinetic theory and conservation of energy, but also differentiated between atoms and molecules and emphasized conservation of matter. In America, Franklin for conservation of electrical charge and Joseph Henry for electric, magnetic, and mechanical relationships. In Germany, Leibnitz, Mayer, Helmholtz, and Einstein. In France, Descartes, Lavoisier, Laplace, and Sadi Carnot (1796–1832), the last for his independent anticipation of energy theory, calculations of mechanical equivalent of heat, and ideal heat-engine cycles. And in Denmark, the engineer Colding, who independently formulated the conservation of energy principle.

To return to Dampier's words: "Because of its practical use, and for its own intrinsic interest, the principle of conservation of energy may be regarded as one of the great achievements of the human mind." Perhaps Dampier's statement should conclude, "of many human minds."

CHAPTER REVIEW

1. Trace the heat from your electric stove to origins in the sun.

2. Trace the kinetic energy of a moving car to origins in the sun.

3. Can you think of any form of energy on earth that does not originate in the sun?

4. How do you interpret the meaning of Democritus's words "Nothing comes from nothing, and nothing can become nothing"?

5. State the law of conservation of energy. What is the difference between *transformations* of energy and *conservation* of energy? Why is this difference significant?

6. In what sense does the conservation law project an equals sign into the universe?

7. Discuss assumptions of the conservation law.

8. Why was the boiling of the water in Rumford's cannon-boring demonstrations significant?

9. (a) Specifically how were Rumford's experimental results evidence against the caloric theory? (b) Were Rumford's findings primarily evidence for energy transformations or for conservation? Explain.

10. Why should melting ice by rubbing two pieces together, as Davy did, be significant?

11. Were Davy's findings evidence for energy transformations or conservation? Explain.

12. Describe Joule's paddle wheel experiments. What features of Rumford's and Davy's experiments existed in Joule's experiments? How did Joule's quantitative approach represent a significant step forward in the development of the conservation law?

13. How was Watt's invention of the steam engine evidence for transformations of energy? How was this evidence different than that of Rumford, Davy, and Joule?

14. Discuss Mayer's contributions to the conservation law. Why may they be considered to be synthesizing contributions?

15. What points of significance does the energy conservation law have that were not raised in previous questions?

PROBLEMS

1. How many kilocalories are required to lift a 25-kg child to a 1-m height 100 times?

2. A 20-lb weight falls 100 ft into 200 lb of water. (a) How much heat in Btu's does the water gain? (Assume no heat loss.) (b) What is the temperature rise in Fahrenheit degrees of the water?

3. A 20-kg weight falls 100 m into 200 kg of water. (a) How much heat in kilocalories does the water gain? (Assume no heat loss.) (b) What is the temperature rise in Celsius degrees of the water?

4. Twenty kg of force are needed to move a 25-kg box along a hall. (a) What work is done to move the weight 10 m down the hall? (b) How much heat of friction in kilocalories does the floor gain?

5. A given grade of coal yields 14,000 Btu/lb. Assuming that all the fuel energy is transformed into mechanical energy, how much mechanical work could be done?

6. How much food in kilocalories must a man eat to compensate for lifting a total of 1 t of bricks 20 ft?

7. A man eats 3,000 kcal of food. What is the mechanical work equivalent in joules of that energy intake? In foot-pounds?

8. A block of ice stops a 4-oz bullet traveling 1,500 ft/sec. How much ice is melted?

9. A waterfall is 100 m high. How much warmer is the water at the bottom than at the top? (Hint: The temperature difference is the same regardless of the amount of water considered.)

SUGGESTIONS FOR
FURTHER READING

Taylor, Lloyd W., *Physics, the Pioneer Science*, Vol. 1, Dover paperback, New York, 1959, Ch. 22.

Holton, Gerald J., and D. H. D. Roller, *Foundations of Modern Physical Science*, Addison-Wesley, Reading, Mass., 1959, Ch. 20.

Brown, S. C., *Count Rumford, Physicist Extraordinary*, Doubleday paperback, Garden City, N.Y., 1962.

Conant, James, ed., *Harvard Case Histories in Experimental Science*, Vol. 1, Harvard Univ. Press, Cambridge, Mass., 1957, Case 3, pp. 155–214.

Mott-Smith, Morton, *The Concept of Energy Simply Explained*, Dover paperback, New York, 1964.

Chalmers, T. W., *Historic Researches*, Morgan, London, 1949, Ch. 2.

Berry, A. J., *From Classical to Modern Chemistry*, Cambridge Univ. Press, New York, 1954, Ch. 2.

Tyndall, John, *Heat as a Mode of Motion*, Appleton-Century-Crofts, New York, and Dover paperback, New York, 1958.

Schneer, Cecil, *The Search for Order*, Harper, New York, 1960, Ch. 11.

13 Kinetic Molecular Theory —A Mechanical Model of Heat

In the kinetic theory of matter and in all its importance, we see the realization of the general philosophical program: to reduce the explanation of all phenomena to the interaction between particles of matter.

ALBERT EINSTEIN AND LEOPOLD INFELD, 1939

MOLECULES IN MOTION: AN EXTENSION OF THE MECHANICAL VIEW

We have discussed heat of friction as energy of motion but the question "Energy of motion of *what?*" still remains. As a pendulum swings to a stop, its mechanical energy transforms into heat. What motion, if any, replaces that of the pendulum? The great Russian chemist Mikhail Lomonosov (1711–1765) answered these two questions in 1745 before the Russian Academy of Sciences when he said, "Bodies can move in two ways—total motion, when the whole body uninterruptedly changes its place with the particles remaining immovable in relation to each other, and internal motion, which is the movement of the infinitely small particles of the body."

The swinging of the pendulum is slowly replaced by added molecular motions of the surrounding air. Lomonosov continued, "All the changes occurring in nature follow the law that what is lost by one body is gained by another.... A body that moves by its force [energy] another body will itself lose as much force [energy] as it communicates to the one it moves." The pendulum, by its energy, moves air particles and loses as much energy as it gives to the air particles (conservation of energy).

Leucippus and Democritus (5th century B.C.) taught that matter is composed of atoms and that heat is to be understood in terms of the motions of atoms. As Lucretius expressed it for them: "All nature then, as it exists by itself, is founded on two things: there are *atoms* and there is void in which these atoms are placed and through which they *move* about...." If all matter is made up of atoms and all atoms are in motion—as they were for ancient atomists—then a heated iron rod expands because an increased motion of its atoms increases the space occupied by them.

Then, 21 centuries later, we find the trail of the atomists again:

17th century: Galileo, Descartes, Bacon, Boyle, and Gassendi all referred to the heat of an object in terms of the motions of particles that compose it.

1704, Newton: Heat consists in a minute vibratory motion of the particles of bodies.

1706, John Locke: Heat is a very brisk agitation of the insensible parts of the object which produces in us the sensation from which we denominate the object hot; so what in our sensation is heat, in the object is nothing but motion.

1738, Daniel Bernoulli: It is admitted that heat may be considered as an increasing internal motion of the particles.

1745, Mikhail Lomonosov, as quoted above.

1780, Lavoisier and Laplace: Heat is the *vis viva* [the mv^2] resulting from the insensible movements of the *molecules* of a body.

Clearly, Lavoisier and Laplace mathematically pinpointed heat as what we call energy of motion ($\frac{1}{2}mv^2$) of molecules. And the *molecule* conveniently is defined as *the smallest particle characteristic of a substance*. The kinetic energy concept of mechanics was thus extended to the unsettled area of heat; unseen moving molecules explained heat phenomena. Accordingly, speeds of surrounding air molecules increase as arcs of a swinging pendulum decrease: The kinetic energy lost by the pendulum is gained by air molecules (and pivot particles, too). The concept $KE = \frac{1}{2}mv^2$ is extended into microscopic and submicroscopic realms. What more beautiful example is there to illustrate the take-over of one field of investigation (heat) by the successful concepts of another field (mechanics)? Or to illustrate attempts to understand the unknown through the known?

TORRICELLI'S AIR PRESSURE EXPERIMENTS

Caloric theory was eclipsed not only by its weakness in explaining heat of friction but also by mounting interest in gases.

Pumps were important in mines. Galileo had been asked why suction pumps could not raise water higher than 34 ft. Galileo did not have the correct answer, but his student Torricelli did. We live under an ocean of air, and Torricelli was the first to realize the significance of that in terms of *air pressure*. Air is not very dense, but Torricelli believed that the hundreds of miles of it above us have enough weight to exert significant pressure at the earth's surface. But 34 ft was as high as air pressure could support water, a much denser* substance (Fig. 13–1). And Torricelli in 1643 attempted to prove his point by "balancing" a column of mercury by air pressure. Knowing that mercury is even heavier than water, Torricelli completely filled a glass tube—about 40 in. long and sealed at one end—with mercury. Then, careful not to allow air into the tube, he inverted the tube into an open dish of mercury and in the process invented his famous barometer. The level of the mercury fell to about 30 in. (or 76 cm) above the mercury in the dish, leaving a vacuum in the tube above the mercury. Torricelli knew that mercury is 13.6 times as dense as water. If air pressure "balances" water to a height of 34 ft, air pressure should support mercury to a height of 2.5 ft (34 ft/13.6 = 2.5 ft). Torricelli's observed results matched his predicted results beautifully. What is more, Torricelli's mercury device, a barometer, could measure air pressure changes. As air pressure rises or falls, so does the mercury column.

By definition, *pressure is force per unit area* (lb/in.² or g/cm²). Since a mercury column 30 in. (or 76 cm) high above 1 sq in. of surface weighs about 14.7 lb, so should a "balancing" column of air extending to the top of the atmosphere. The air pressure is therefore 14.7 lb/ sq in. at sea level.

Torricelli further hypothesized that if air pressure supports 30 in. of mercury at sea level, then the height of the mercury column should decrease as one climbs a mountain: The column of air "balancing," or supporting, the mercury is reduced as one ascends. The famous French scientist Pascal sent an assistant mountain climbing to test Torricelli's hypothesis. The results were positive: As the altitude increased, the height of the mercury column decreased. Use of barometers for air pressure measurement had begun, and experimentation with air was facilitated.

*The *density* of a substance is its *mass per unit volume*. For example, mercury has a density of 13.6 g/cm³; water, 1 g/cm³; and air, 0.00129 g/cm³ at 0°C and standard (sea level) pressure.

13–1 Large barometer constructed by Pascal at Rouen for measuring air pressure. (The Bettmann Archive, Inc.)

BOYLE'S LAW
AND AIR PRESSURE

Robert Boyle (1627–1691) was fascinated by what he called the "spring of the air." That air is compressible anyone knows who has ever pressed down on a bicycle pump with the outlet plugged up. The air trapped at the bottom of the cylinder occupies ever less space as the piston is lowered. But with a decrease in the volume of the air, the air pressure increases sharply, and the trapped air will not permit the piston to touch bottom. (Try it!)

Boyle was interested in knowing more about air pressure. He used a J-tube into which he poured mercury (Fig. 13–2). Air was trapped in the closed short arm. When the mercury was at the same height in both arms of the tube, the air pressure (P_1) in the closed arm "balanced" the outside air pressure (P_1) on the mercury surface in the open arm. The more mercury that Boyle poured into the tube, the higher the mercury rose in the short arm, and the less was the volume (V_2) of the trapped air. When the original volume (V_1) of the trapped air was reduced to half ($V_1/2$), Boyle found that the pressure of the trapped air doubled (to $2P_1$); with the volume reduced to a third ($V_1/3$), the pressure tripled (to $3P_1$), and so forth. (The pressure of the trapped air can be calculated by a "balancing" principle: The inside air pressure "balances" the outside air pressure algebraically added to the pressure of mercury between the open-arm and closed-arm levels.) Boyle concluded that *at constant temperature, "the volume of a mass of gas varies inversely with its pressure."*

This conclusion is symbolized as

$$V \propto \frac{1}{P} \text{ or } VP = \text{a constant } k.$$

That is, $\dfrac{V_1}{V_2} = \dfrac{P_2}{P_1}$,

where $V_1 =$ the original volume at pressure P_1

$V_2 =$ the new volume at new pressure P_2,

or

$$P_1V_1 = P_2V_2. \qquad \text{Equation } 13\text{-}1$$

Equation 13–1, experimentally confirmed countless times, is now known as Boyle's law. Independently, about 25 years later than Boyle, the French scientist Edme Mariotte formulated the same law.

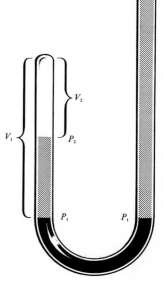

13–2 Boyle's law: $P_1V_1 = P_2V_2$. At constant temperature the volume of a gas varies inversely with its pressure. V_1 is an original volume of air trapped by mercury in the closed arm of a J-tube at ordinary air pressure P_1. When more mercury is poured into the open arm of the tube, the mercury rises (see shaded sections), so that V_2 is the reduced volume of the trapped air under the proportionately greater pressure P_2.

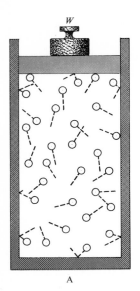

13–3A Bernoulli's kinetic model of gases. Gas particles chaotically dash about, colliding ceaselessly with one another and container walls.

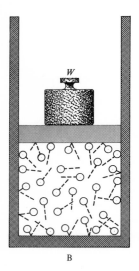

13–3B An increased weight moves the piston down until the total weight is balanced by the upward force of the bombarding gas particles. The larger the outside pressure, the smaller the volume of a gas (Boyle's law).

BOYLE'S "SPRING OF THE AIR" HYPOTHESIS

An empirical law—that is, one based directly on data relationships—needs explanation. To explain his findings (Eq. 13–1), Boyle proposed a unique "spring of the air" gas model, atomistic but static in character: Gases are composed of rows of springlike corpuscles in contact. Gases are highly compressible because their component corpuscles are highly compressible.

Boyle's "spring of the air" did not advance beyond a hypothesis. Gases, unlike solids or liquids, are known to expand indefinitely in all directions. The springlike corpuscles could not explain the observed characteristic of gases to increase in size indefinitely. Any spring reaches an elastic limit and snaps. Upholders of the "spring of the air" hypothesis therefore assumed that beyond a certain distance, corpuscles repel each other. The necessity for such an assumption led Boyle and others to consider kinetic models of gases as alternatives in which particles were in violent motion. Meanwhile, Boyle's "spring of the air" served its purpose. It drew attention to corpuscles. And even if corpuscles of matter could not be seen, men reasoned on the assumption that they exist, saw how predictions worked out, and then modified or changed ideas accordingly. And drawing attention leads to progress.

BERNOULLI'S KINETIC MODEL

Daniel Bernoulli in 1738, a century before Joule, Mayer, and Helmholtz, developed a kinetic model of gases that related mechanical energy and heat quantitatively. In Bernoulli's model (Fig. 13–3A), the "corpuscles" were not only unattached and minute, but in violent, random motion. Countless even in small vessels, the gas particles dashed about without end, unpredictably colliding with one another and the walls of the containers. Bernoulli identified gas pressure with this ceaseless bombardment of container walls by gas particles. Billions of repeated individual sharp blows have the effect of a sustained force on an area of a container. And pressure is force per unit area—inches squared, centimeters squared, and so forth.

In Bernoulli's model (Fig. 13–3B), the weight W forces the piston down. As the descending piston crowds the fast-moving gas particles into a smaller space, more particles hit the piston at any instant. The weighted piston moves down until the upward force of the particles is large enough to balance it. The heavier the weight on the piston, the further the piston descends before a balance is reached. That is, the larger the outside pressure, the smaller the gas volume. When a gas is forced into a smaller volume, more of its particles strike a square centimeter (or square inch) each second, and the pressure that the gas exerts increases. Conversely, when a gas expands into a larger volume, fewer of its particles strike a unit area each second, and its pressure decreases. Reducing outside pressure permits a gas to expand and decrease its own pressure.

In this way Bernoulli used moving molecules to relate gas pressure to volume and explained Boyle's law. In Boyle's J-tube (Fig. 13–2), the mercury in the closed arm, pistonlike, trapped air. Additional mercury poured into the open end acted as additional weight, crowding air particles into a smaller volume.

Bernoulli also associated heat with the agitated motion of the molecules by stating that an increase in heat corresponds to an increase in the particles' speed. Bernoulli did not pursue this point further, but we can see that an increase in the particles' speed (Fig. 13–3) on the piston forces the piston up, giving the gas more volume. This new relationship between the temperature T and volume V of a gas, independently discovered by Jacques Charles and Joseph Gay-Lussac early in the next century, will be discussed in a later section.

Bernoulli's dynamic model and its ability to explain order through disorder, to explain physical laws through chance motions of particles, was ignored for a century. The new model did not appear plausible enough in the framework of current ideas; its insights were too much in advance of the times.

KINETIC EVIDENCE:
BROWNIAN MOTION

In 1827, botanist Robert Brown had evidence for Bernoulli's kinetic model and did not know it. Observing small pollen particles suspended in water, Brown was mystified by their agitated, chaotic motions. The particles unceasingly zigzagged about without apparent rhyme or reason (Fig. 13–4) like bees around a disturbed beehive. But pollen particles are not disturbed bees; Brown was unable to explain what he saw. "Chance favors the prepared mind," but no mind is prepared in all areas. Brown was not prepared for a particle theory of matter or for random motions of such particles.

It was not until 1879 that William Ramsay theorized that Brownian motion is due to collisions of the comparatively large suspended pollen particles with water molecules. And with a given pollen particle bombarded on all sides by much smaller water molecules at various speeds, there is no way to predict which way the pollen particle will move at any instant. The unceasing agitation of pollen reflects the irregular, haphazard motions of water molecules.

Cigarette smoke illuminated and examined under a microscope also reveals individual smoke particles in the same agitated motions as Brown's

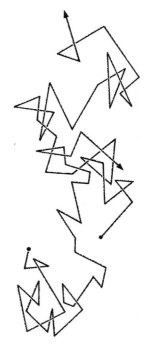

13–4 Brownian motion. Agitated, chaotic motions of pollen particles suspended in water support kinetic molecular theory. Such agitated pollen particles were first observed by botanist Robert Brown (1773–1858).

pollen particles. Surrounding air molecules do to larger suspended smoke particles what water molecules do to pollen particles. A parallel and a conclusion are clear: If the kinetic model holds for gases (air molecules around smoke or dust), it also holds for liquids (water molecules around suspended pollen). In that case, the kinetic model should apply to solids, too. A substance in solid form (ice) should have the same components as in liquid form (tap water) even if the components are closer together and reduced in motion.

In this extension of the kinetic model from fluids (gases and liquids) to solids, we again see the nature of scientific reasoning: inductive-deductive leaps (Chapter 4) from what is observed to what is unknown. The process is "inductive" because from observed gases and liquids, a kinetic molecular model is generalized for all matter; "deductive" because the generalization is then applied to solids as unknowns. Evidence of its rightful application to the unknown then becomes necessary, and the more evidence, the better. But whatever the process, the kinetic model of gases extended into a kinetic model of *matter,* and the latter began to serve as a kinetic model of *heat.*

KINETIC
MOLECULAR ASSUMPTIONS

The kinetic molecular model of heat, like all other big ideas in science, is a complex of inter-related assumptions, observations, concepts, definitions, laws, hypotheses, and theories (as defined in early chapters). No conceptual system, however, is stronger than its underlying assumptions. In this section we will therefore confine ourselves to basic assumptions of the kinetic molecular model.

The first four assumptions below apply to *all* molecules; the last three to *gas* molecules. Gases are more uniform in behavior than are liquids and solids, and they afford insights into all matter and heat. Emphasis on gases is therefore warranted.

1. *Matter is composed of molecules* If we could cut a half of a sliver of wood into half, cut half of that half, and then half of succeeding halves trillions of times, would we eventually get to a unit, the molecule, that could no longer be "cut" and still be wood? That is, is matter composed of ultimate particles? Or is matter continuous, so that at least mathematically, one could take ½ of ½ of ½ of ½ ... of an object indefinitely? No matter how often one would divide a sliver, would there always be a half left to take another half of and still have wood? If so, matter has no primary units, no molecules (or atoms) as "building blocks." This issue of matter being particle or continuous in nature is an old one. Kinetic theory assumes that matter is composed of molecules or other noncon-

tinuous particles. And as seen in Bernoulli's explanation of Boyle's law, gas molecules would need to be minute, numerous, and fast.

Recent evidence shows that 1 cu cm of a gas at normal pressure and temperature contains about 25,000,000,000,000,000,000 molecules (or about 2.5×10^{19}). Suppose these molecules were magnified to the size of grains of sand. A container 1 mi deep, wide, and high would not be large enough to hold all these molecules. You could not count them if you spent the rest of your life doing so. Yet we are referring merely to molecules ordinarily in just 1 cu cm of gas.

2. Molecules are in constant motion   Brownian motion has already been cited as evidence for random motion of liquid and gas molecules. You can easily observe random effects of air molecules upon motions of dust particles illuminated by a movie projector.

Molecules of oxygen or nitrogen in air at 0°C are now estimated to travel at an average speed of about 0.3 mi/sec. Hydrogen molecules, lightest and fastest of all, travel at an average speed of about 1 mi/sec. At such speeds, collisions are continual and chaotic. Vast numbers of molecules collide and ricochet in all directions. No one can predict in which direction a given molecule will go or precisely how fast it will go.

With continual collisions, a gas molecule travels with different speeds at different times. Some are faster than average; others are slower; and some are even at rest at an instant of collision. The majority, however, have speeds within a fairly narrow range.

3. Newtonian laws apply to molecules   The minuteness of molecules or their high speeds would not make them exceptions to Newtonian laws. Molecules, like visible objects, have inertia, change their velocities, exert forces, have kinetic and potential energies, and do work. Kinetic theory extends Newtonian physics to molecules.

4. Molecules collide without friction   Unlike larger objects, however, molecules collide without friction. Like "ideal" billiard balls, molecular collisions are perfectly elastic. Otherwise, friction would soon bring molecules to a stop, and heat would not exist. Everything would be dead cold!

Besides, heat due to friction between objects is explained in terms of increased energies of component molecules. Molecules themselves cannot be objects containing the molecules that explain heat. To assume molecular friction would be like Gertrude Stein's definition of a rose: "A rose is a rose is a rose . . . ." Poetically but not scientifically, we can define an object without relating it to something else.

5. Average distances between gas molecules are great in terms of molecular size   Under ordinary conditions, the distance between gas molecules averages about ten molecular diameters. This estimate makes air and other gases mostly empty space. This assumption was necessary to explain the great compressibility of gases and other phenomena. This assumption also made possible the next one.

6. Forces between gas molecules are negligible except at collisions
Gases are uniform in behavior compared to liquids and solids. Under similar conditions, gases tend to expand, increase in temperature, and increase in pressure equally. This is possible if forces between gas molecules are negligible.

If Newton's laws apply to molecules, gravitational forces exist between molecules. And these forces are in direct proportion to molecular masses $(F = GMm/d^2)$. But with distances between gas molecules relatively great, intermolecular forces are negligible, regardless of mass values.

7. The absolute temperature of a gas is directly proportional to the average kinetic energy of translation of its molecules   At any given temperature, the average molecular speed of a gas is assumed to remain constant. When heat is added to a gas, the molecules move faster. The increase in average speed is shown by an increase in temperature. More specifically, the temperature of a gas is a measure of the average kinetic energy of the gas molecules in their *translatory motion*. No such motion means no temperature in an absolute sense. A substance chilled until its molecules lose their translatory motions has reached an absolute zero in temperature, a point beneath which temperature cannot go. Having kinetic energy means having a temperature above absolute zero, doubling average kinetic energy means doubling temperature above absolute zero, tripling kinetic energy means tripling absolute temperature, and so on. The concept of absolute zero and an absolute temperature scale will be further discussed in a later section.

KINETIC
MOLECULAR EXPLANATIONS

The kinetic molecular model has been highly successful in explaining, predicting, and controlling heat phenomena. By extending Newtonian ideas to molecules, the model opened wide the door of thermodynamics, the science of heat. The following sections consider kinetic molecular explanations in more detail.

Heat Transfer

In kinetic molecular theory, heat transfer basically is the transfer of molecular energies from areas with higher average kinetic energy to those with lower kinetic energy.

When you carelessly touch a poker protruding from a fire, your fingers gain heat by conduction. Metals are good conductors. That means the poker molecules in the fire easily transmit their greater vibration energies to neighboring molecules, which transmit to their neighbors, and so on in succession until the end of the poker touched by your hand is reached. Your fingers in turn are bombarded by the high-energy molecules. And kinetic energy lost by the poker molecules is gained by molecules in your fingers. You feel the effects.

Heat transfer by convection currents (Chapter 11) is transfer by a carrier. Molecules in warm air or water currents lose kinetic energy to molecules of surroundings by collisions on contact and by radiation. Currents may also gain heat (molecular kinetic energy) from warmer surroundings.

Infrared or heat radiation (Chapter 11) as such is not heat. Radiation involves transfer through a vacuum of another form of energy (electromagnetic waves, discussed later) from the sun or other heat sources. Such radiation becomes heat when absorbed by an object. This radiation is able to increase molecular motion within an object being radiated.

Thermal Equilibrium and Energy Conservation

Substances at various temperatures settle at a common temperature when mixed. By kinetic theory, the molecules of the warmer substances lose energies of motion until the molecules of the cooler substances have average kinetic energies equal to their own. And the total kinetic molecular energies lost by the warmer substances are equal to the kinetic molecular energies gained by the cooler: In calorimetry (Chapter 11), heat energy may be conserved. But heat energy may also be transformed *to* other energy forms, as in the steam engine (Chapter 12), or *from* other energies, as in Joule's paddle wheel experiment.

Temperature versus Heat

What is temperature according to kinetic molecular theory? And what is the difference between temperature and heat? A glass of boiling water (Fig. 11–7) has less heat but a higher temperature than a kettleful of warm water. By the kinetic theory each of trillions of water molecules bombarding the walls of the glass or kettle has its own speed (v) and its own kinetic energy ($\frac{1}{2}mv^2$). The individual kinetic energies in each vessel can be added and averaged. If they are just added, we have heat; if they are averaged, we have temperature. The sum is symbolized as $\Sigma\frac{1}{2}mv^2$ (Σ means sum); the average, as $\frac{1}{2}m\bar{v}^2$ ($\bar{v}^2$ represents the average value of the speed squared).

ROTATION

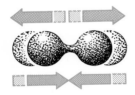

TRANSLATION

VIBRATION

13–5   Three types of molecular motion are translation, rotation, and vibration. Increased temperature is identified with increased kinetic energy of translation. The "dumbbell" is merely a symbol of two atoms joined into a molecule.

The kettle contains more heat than the glass because it contains more water; the kettle has far more water molecules with kinetic energies $\frac{1}{2}mv^2$ to be added. But regardless, the *average* kinetic energy of the molecules in the glass of boiling water is higher than that of the molecules in the kettle of warm water (just as the first two quiz scores a student receives in a course may total 170 points for an average of 85, but his first ten quizzes may total 750 points for an average of only 75). If temperature is a measure of average kinetic energies, the higher the temperature of a substance, the higher the average molecular kinetic energies of translation involved.

Change of State

Gases can become liquids, and liquids can become solids. These changes can then be reversed. How can differences among gases, liquids, and solids be explained by moving molecules? Answers lie in not only the speeds of molecules but also the distances between molecules.

Liquids versus gases   Distances between gas molecules are great enough to keep attractive forces negligible (assumptions 5 and 6). Gas molecules are free to move away from one another, and gases change volume with containers. But intermolecular distances in liquids are smaller, and attractive forces between liquid molecules are significant. Liquids, therefore, do not easily change volume; the attractive forces between liquid molecules are large enough to keep them from increasing their average distance from one another. But the speed of the molecules is enough for the liquid to flow. Liquids, therefore, assume the shapes of their vessels, even if they cannot increase their volumes in them.

That liquid molecules are closer together than gas molecules can be inferred from the following arguments:

Gases can be liquefied by compression under proper circumstances. Explanation: In compressing a gas, molecules are forced more closely together to form a liquid. Release the external pressure, and the molecules tend to move outward; the liquid becomes a gas again.

A sponge, like a gas, can be easily compressed. The sponge has a large amount of space within it. Liquids are difficult to squeeze into smaller volumes. Hypothesis: Liquids have much smaller intermolecular spaces than gases.

If liquid molecules are closer together than gas molecules, molecules in solids are closer than in liquids. Gases contract when condensing into liquids; liquids (except water and type metal) contract when freezing.

Solids versus fluids   Gases change shape and volume; liquids change shape but retain volume; solids, especially crystals, retain both shape and volume. Ice cubes have molecules close enough to hold one another in place. If so, are molecules of solids moving? Kinetic theory answers "yes": Each molecule in a solid vibrates pendulumlike across a fixed central position. The central positions remain fixed, but the molecules oscillate rapidly and regularly. Increase the temperature of an ice cube, and its vibrational energy increases. Heat the cube long enough, and its vibrational energy becomes strong enough for the molecules to break away from fixed central positions. The molecules "break ranks," moving randomly among their fellows as they vibrate. The molecular motion becomes translational rather than just vibrational; the ice becomes liquid and flows.

Heat in a solid thus becomes identified with a vibrational energy of its molecules, and the heat of a liquid becomes identified with vibrational and translational energies of its molecules. The heat of gases has been identified with rotational as well as translational and vibrational energies of their molecules. Figure 13–5 illustrates the three types of motion for such *diatomic* molecules as oxygen or nitrogen in the air. In translation, a molecule moves as a unit in a linear direction. In vibration, "ends" of a molecule move toward and away from each other regularly, as if by springs. In rotation, the molecule moves clockwise or counterclockwise around its center.

The heat content of an object, therefore, is associated with all mechanical energies of its molecules, including translational, vibrational, and rotational. Temperature, however, in gases and liquids is assumed to be identified with average *energies of translation only*. A rise in the temperature of a gas or liquid means an increase in average speed of translation. Molecules of solids do not have translational motion. Therefore, a rise in the temperature of a solid is assumed to be an increase in the *vibrational motion* of molecules about their fixed positions.

In a later section on latent heat, we shall see that in addition to the above three forms of molecular kinetic energy, heat may also take the form of molecular potential energy.

Evaporation and boiling   Evaporation and boiling are processes in which liquids become gases. Evaporation takes place at the surface of liquids at any temperature; boiling takes place throughout liquids at characteristic boiling points (Fig. 13–6).

Evaporation is common experience. Liquid water in a pan gradually "disappears." The water molecules in the pan move in all directions at an average velocity depending on temperature. But some molecules are slower and some are faster than average. At the surface of the water, *faster* molecules are able to escape into the air even against the attraction of slower neighbors. As faster molecules escape, the average velocity becomes less. The temperature of the remaining liquid falls: We say that evaporation is a cooling process.

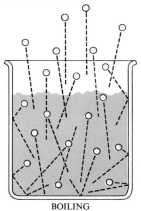

ESCAPING MOLECULES

BOILING

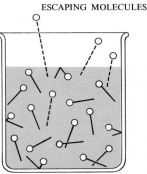

ESCAPING MOLECULES

EVAPORATION

13–6   Evaporation versus boiling. In the evaporation of a liquid, faster molecules escape from the liquid surface at all temperatures. In the boiling of a liquid, molecules escape from all parts of the liquid at a characteristic boiling point.

Heating a liquid speeds evaporation because heating increases the speed of the molecules and more surface molecules can escape. Finally, the boiling point is reached; the molecules have enough speed to escape in telltale bubbles rising through the liquid.

The ocean of air above us exerts 14.7 lb/sq in. at sea level. Should not the bombarding particles of air that produce air pressure above an evaporating or boiling liquid prevent liquid molecules from escaping? *Vapor pressure* is a concept that has arisen in answer to this question. The tendency of molecules to escape from a liquid surface results in the building up of the liquid's own vapor pressure against atmospheric pressure. As the temperature of water, for example, rises, its molecules move faster, and more of them escape from the water's surface. The vapor pressure increases until at the boiling point the vapor pressure equals the atmospheric pressure, and molecules escape from all through the liquid. The boiling point has been reached.

Technically, *the vapor pressure of a liquid at a given temperature is the pressure that its vapor exerts when confined above the liquid.* If a tight cover is placed on a pan of water, the escaping molecules accumulate above the liquid surface as water vapor. As vapor accumulates more and more, vapor molecules collide with each other and the pan, and more of them are forced back into the liquid. Finally, depending upon the given temperature, as many molecules move back into the liquid as leave it. At this equilibrium point between evaporation and condensation, the characteristic vapor pressure of water at the given temperature is obtained. This pressure indicates how readily the molecules of a liquid escape from its surface.

At 100°C the vapor pressure of water equals the atmospheric pressure at sea level. The energies of the water molecules have become great enough to escape, and the water boils away without further rise in temperature. Other liquids have other boiling points (Table 11–3).

A large flame under boiling water does not cook an egg faster than a small one does. It wastes fuel. Once the water boils, it does not reach a higher temperature; it merely becomes a gas faster. Liquid water at 100°C becomes vapor at 100°C; 100°C is 100°C, and you will not get a 4-minute egg in 3 minutes by applying more heat. A pressure cooker, however, increases the pressure above the water and thereby raises the boiling point. The food then cooks at a higher temperature and so cooks faster.

Latent heat Ice melts and water boils without increasing temperature. Yet heat is required (Chapter 11). Where does this heat go? How does the kinetic molecular theory explain latent heat?

It takes energy to lift a weight. When the weight is lifted, it has gravitational potential energy. But gravitation applies to all matter, including molecules (assumption 3). In a solid, molecules are close together and have strong intermolecular gravitational forces. For a solid to become a liquid or for a liquid to become a gas, molecules must be moved apart against the attraction of their neighbors.

It takes heat energy to move molecules apart against intermolecular forces. When the molecules are moved further apart, they have *molecular potential energy*, just as the lifted weight has gravitational potential energy. The heat energy used for boiling water or melting ice becomes molecular potential energy. Latent heat is molecular potential energy.

When water vapor (or any gas) condenses back to a liquid, the molecules "fall" back to closer positions and lose molecular potential energy. The latent heat originally acquired is given back to the surroundings. When water vapor in the air condenses into clouds (myriads of water droplets), the surrounding atmosphere becomes warmer. That is, the molecules of surrounding air particles have an increased energy of motion. Similarly, liquids freezing return the original heat of fusion to their surroundings.

Thus, molecules have potential energy as well as kinetic energy. The heat energy absorbed by a substance does not always increase the kinetic energy of its molecules; in changes of state, the latent heat absorbed gives potential energy to molecules. Here again, the mechanical model of moving molecules effectively explains heat phenomena.

Pressure of Gases

Moving molecules push pistons in Bernoulli's kinetic model of gases (Fig. 13–3) and relate pressure to volume at constant temperature (Boyle's law). But how can moving molecules relate the pressure of a gas to its temperature? When a gas is heated, its molecules move faster and tend to move apart more quickly. But if the gas is confined to a rigid container —for example, steam in a boiler—and if the steam temperature unceasingly increases, watch out! Pressure increases, too. In fact, at constant volume, pressure changes in direct proportion to temperature. That is, $\triangle P \propto \triangle T$. Doubling the *change* in temperature $\triangle T$ doubles the *change* in pressure $\triangle P$; tripling one triples the other; or halving one halves the other.

If heat means *total* molecular mechanical energy and if temperature means *average* molecular kinetic energy of translation, pressure is the molecular *bombardment effect* per unit area on container walls. The bombardment effect, or pressure P, like the temperature T above, changes in direct proportion with the average speed squared $\bar{v}^2$ of the molecules.

Charles's Law and Absolute Temperature

But what if a gas is heated, and the container is not rigid but flexible like a balloon? Suppose an inflated balloon is taken from a 70°F air-

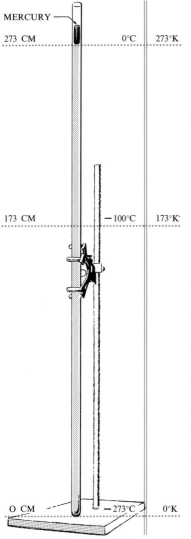

MERCURY —

273 CM   0°C   273°K

173 CM   −100°C   173°K

0 CM   −273°C   0°K

13–7 By the kinetic molecular theory, a "rock-bottom," or absolute zero, temperature (0°K) is reached when a gas approaches a volume of zero and its molecular motion stops. By Table 13–1, this "basement" is reached at about −273° C (or −459° F) and is the bottom of the absolute, or Kelvin (K), scale.

conditioned room to an outside desert temperature of 120°F. The temperature increase is 50°F; the balloon pressure remains constant with atmospheric pressure. What happens to the volume of the balloon?

Jacques Charles (1746–1823) and Joseph Gay-Lussac (1778–1850), two French experimentalists, independently discovered the following famous law now bearing their names: The volume V of a gas kept at constant pressure changes in direct proportion to the temperature T. That is, $\triangle V \propto \triangle T$, or at constant pressure,

$$\frac{\triangle V}{\triangle T} = k,$$

where $\triangle V$ = volume change

$\triangle T$ = temperature change

k = a constant value.

At constant pressure, doubling the *change* in temperature $\triangle T$ doubles the *change* in volume $\triangle V$; tripling one triples the other; and so on.

Accordingly, a decrease in temperature would mean a proportionate decrease in volume at constant pressure.

Further, other things remaining the same, whether hydrogen, oxygen, or nitrogen are in the above balloon, the balloon will change size equally. At the same pressure, all gases have equal changes in volume with the same rise or fall in temperature.

In Fig. 13–7, a gas fills the tube to 273 cm in length at 0°C. A drop of mercury confines the gas and slides back or forth in the stem as the gas temperature decreases or increases. If the temperature is reduced to −1°C, the level of the gas falls to 272 cm. Further drops in temperature of the gas show volume reduction as in Table 13–1. Since the diameter of the tube is uniform, changes in the length of the gas column represent proportional changes in volume. That is, each degree *drop* in temperature from 0°C means a $\frac{1}{273}$ loss in the gas column length, or volume level. For example, a 5°C drop from 0°C means the volume level has reduced to 268 units. The loss in gas volume is $\frac{5}{273}$. Each degree *rise* in temperature means a $\frac{1}{273}$ increase in the gas volume (using its volume at 0°C as a base).

Further inspection of Table 13–1 shows that at −273°C, a gas approaches a volume of 0. Since all matter must occupy some space, it should be impossible for any substance to reach a temperature below −273°C (more precisely, −273.2°C). And at that point, all motion of molecules should stop; the molecular kinetic energy becomes zero. Thus, −273°C (or −459°F) becomes a bottom (basement) temperature. Nothing can become colder. Cold is not an entity; it is an absence of heat, of kinetic molecular motion. In this way, the phenomena repre-

Table 13–1 | GAS TEMPERATURE–VOLUME RELATIONSHIP

TEMPERATURE (°C)	VOLUME LEVEL (CM)
0	273
−1	272
−2	271
−3	270
−4	269
−5	268
. . .	. . .
−100	173
−200	73
. . .	. . .
−273	0

sented in Table 13–1 have become the basis of an absolute, or Kelvin, temperature scale, shown and compared to the Celsius in Fig. 13–7.

The law of Charles and Gay-Lussac expressing the above relationship between the volume V and *absolute temperature* T of a gas may be fully symbolized as follows. At constant pressure, $V \propto T$ or $V/T =$ a constant k.

That is,

$$\frac{V_1}{T_1} = \frac{V_2}{T_2},$$ Equation 13–2

where $V_1 =$ the volume at temperature T_1

$V_2 =$ the volume at temperature T_2.

Thus, kinetic molecular theory easily explains the Charles and Gay-Lussac law. (To explain laws is a function of theories.*) As heat is added to a gas, temperature increases, and so do the velocities of the molecules. With increased velocities at constant external pressure, the molecules occupy more space in motion against a flexible or elastic container (for example, the wall of a balloon).

On the other hand, when temperature decreases, molecular velocities decrease, and consequently so does the space occupied by the molecules. As temperature decreases, eventually molecular motions approach zero, and so does the absolute temperature. By this time, distances between molecules are so small that gravitation forces are effective; with little or no motion, myriads of minute molecules are concentrated in negligible space. In recent years substances have been successfully reduced in temperature to within a fraction of a degree of absolute zero. The volume decreased as expected.

*Theories thus tend to have less certainty and more scope than laws.

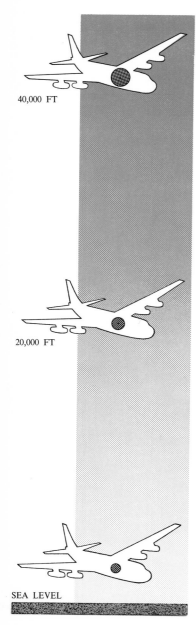

40,000 FT

20,000 FT

SEA LEVEL

13–8 An inflated balloon in an unpressurized plane expands as the plane rises. If the temperature in the plane is constant, the expansion results from reduced atmospheric pressure in accordance with Boyle's law,
$$P_1V_1 = P_2V_2 = a \text{ constant.}$$

Expansion of Gases: The General Gas Law

Let us generalize at this point with respect to the expansion of gases. The three cases below review relevant gas principles discussed so far. The general gas law, following these principles, significantly synthesizes them into one law.

Case 1   Constant T: $P_1V_1 = P_2V_2$ Boyle's law

When a gas is compressed at constant temperature, its molecules are forced closer together; its volume decreases and its pressure increases. When outside pressure upon a gas is reduced, the gas molecules move further apart; the gas volume increases, and its pressure decreases. For example, an inflated balloon in a heated but unpressurized plane expands as the plane rises (Fig. 13–8). The expansion is due to atmospheric pressure changes and not to heat.

Suppose a balloon occupies 1,000 cm³ of space at 1 *atm** of pressure (14.7 lb/in.²). If the temperature remains constant, how much space does the balloon occupy at a pressure of 0.5 atm?

Given: $P_1 = 1$ atm, $V_1 = 1,000$ cm³, and $P_2 = 5$ atm

To find V_2

Solution: $P_1V_1 = P_2V_2$

or

$$V_2 = \frac{P_1V_1}{P_2} = \frac{1 \text{ atm} \cdot 1,000 \text{ cm}^3}{.5 \text{ atm}}$$
$$V_2 = 2,000 \text{ cm}^3.$$

That is, reducing the pressure P_2 on the balloon to one-half (½ atm) doubles its volume V_2 to 2,000 cm³.

Case 2   Constant V: $\dfrac{P_1}{T_1} = \dfrac{P_2}{T_2}$

Charles's and Gay-Lussac's principle

When a gas is heated, its molecules move faster and tend to move further apart. But if the gas is confined in a rigid container, the volume remains constant, and the pressure rises (or falls) in direct proportion

---

*An *atmosphere* is a standard unit of pressure. It is *that* (air) *pressure which will support a column of mercury 76 cm (29.92 in.) high at 0°C, sea level, and 45° latitude.*

to the absolute temperature. Doubling the *absolute* temperature of steam in a boiler from 373°K (100°C) to 746°K (473°C) doubles the steam pressure.

Case 3   Constant P: $\dfrac{V_1}{T_1} = \dfrac{V_2}{T_2}$ Charles's and Gay-Lussac's law

When a gas is heated or cooled at constant atmospheric or other pressure, the gas expands (or contracts) in accordance with the absolute temperature. A balloon expands if the surroundings become warmer at the same atmospheric pressure. For example, at constant pressure, doubling the *absolute* temperature T of a balloon from 173°K (−100°C) to 346°K (73°C) doubles the balloon's volume.

All Cases $\dfrac{P_1V_1}{T_1} = \dfrac{P_2V_2}{T_2}$ general gas law   Equation 13–3

In Equation 13–3 the individual gas laws are combined into one general gas law. Note that in the general law neither temperature T, pressure P, nor volume V needs to be constant. A gas may change in temperature, pressure, and volume all together, as when an inflated balloon is taken to the top of Mt. Whitney. Atmospheric pressure and temperature decreases; volume changes accordingly. The decreased atmospheric pressure tends to inflate the balloon; decreased temperature tends to deflate the balloon. Which way the balloon goes depends on the relative amounts of decrease in temperature and pressure.

It can be seen that the general gas law, Equation 13–3, reduces to Boyle's law, Case 1, when $T_1 = T_2$ (and therefore cancel out); to Case 2 when $V_1 = V_2$ and cancel out; and to Charles's and Gay-Lussac's law, Case 3, when $P_1 = P_2$ and cancel out.

The general gas law is referred to as the "ideal" gas law. Recall that Galileo's law of falling bodies assumes an "ideal" situation of free fall in a vacuum. In actual free fall, allowances must be made for air resistance. Similarly, the general gas law assumes an "ideal" gas whose molecules have no volume and exert no mutual gravitational forces. Real gas molecules do occupy small amounts of space and do have slight gravitational attractions for one another. Allowances for actual volumes and intermolecular attraction are negligible and therefore ignorable under ordinary conditions or at high temperature and low outside pressure, when molecules quickly move away from one another. The allowances become large and important at very low temperatures and high outside pressure, when molecules are forced more closely together.

In any case, it is clear that gases (or liquids and solids) expand not because individual molecules stretch but because the average distances among molecules increase with speed. And if gases expand indefinitely, it is because attractive forces of their molecules are insignificant compared to their molecular velocities.

Diffusion

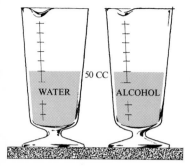

Diffusion is a process of thorough self-mixing of liquids or gases. Agitated molecules of one liquid (or gas) make their way through spaces between agitated molecules of another.

A mixture of alcohol and water may be used as evidence for the existence of spaces between liquid molecules (Fig. 13–9). Fifty cc of alcohol added to 50 cc of water give a mixture totaling only 97 cc. Self-mixing results even when alcohol and water are merely placed in contact. If drops of ink are placed in water, the spontaneous self-mixing can be seen.

Gases diffuse much faster than liquids; there is much more space between molecules. An open gas jet soon makes itself known, as does burned toast. The random motions of the particular gas and air molecules make for a thorough self-mixing.

Figure 13–10 represents a diffusion experiment through air. The open ends of the horizontal glass tube are plugged with cotton. Concentrated hydrochloric acid is poured into the cotton at one end at the same time that a concentrated ammonia solution is poured in at the other end. Hydrogen chloride and ammonia gases immediately evaporating from the solutions begin diffusing toward each other. Where the gases meet, a white cloud (ammonium chloride) forms.

Hydrogen chloride molecules have about twice the mass of ammonia molecules. The myriads of lighter ammonia molecules therefore will diffuse through the air in the tube faster than the hydrogen chloride molecules. And the white cloud will form much closer to the source of the heavier hydrogen chloride.

Both gases are at the same temperature and therefore have the same average kinetic energy $\frac{1}{2}m\bar{v}^2$. That is,

$$\tfrac{1}{2}m\overline{V^2} = \tfrac{1}{2}M\bar{v}^2$$

or

$$\frac{\overline{V^2}}{\bar{v}^2} = \frac{M}{m}$$

or

$$\frac{\overline{V}}{\bar{v}} = \sqrt{\frac{M}{m}},$$

Equation 13–4

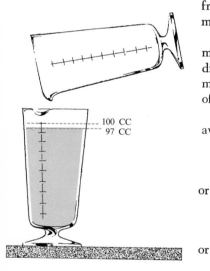

13–9   Fifty cc of alcohol mixed with 50 cc of water total only 97 cc; liquids contain empty spaces.

where m = the molecular mass of the lighter gas (ammonia gas)

M = the molecular mass of the heavier gas (hydrogen chloride)

$\overline{V^2}$ = the larger average velocity squared (ammonia)

$\bar{v}^2$ = the smaller average velocity squared (hydrogen chloride).

The above use of both lower case and capital letters helps to emphasize that molecules with smaller masses m are identified with larger velocities V and larger masses M with smaller velocities v in molecules of different gases at the same temperature.

Equation 13–4 leads to Graham's law of diffusion (1830), which states that at the same pressures and temperatures, the relative rates (or numbers per unit of time) at which gases escape from a small opening are inversely proportional to the square roots of the molecular weights of the gases.

Statistical Law: Order from Disorder

In this way order emerges from disorder; Graham's law orders molecular chaos. And physical laws become statistical; they predict group rather than individual behavior. *Average* velocity, or average kinetic energy, describes group, not individual, behavior, for an average refers to a group.

No one can predict the path of a given molecule. Where any molecule will be at any time is a matter of chance. Yet we can make predictions about groups of molecules. More will tend to randomly move out of than into an area where they are concentrated. The result is diffusion, or self-mixing, at rates predictable from the *average* velocity or average kinetic energy of a *group* of molecules.

The problem of scientifically calling the world to order through mechanisms of random motion or chance is still with us in the 20th century. The problem started in the 18th century, when Bernoulli explained Boyle's law by assuming chance motions of vast numbers of gas particles. We say that Boyle's law is causal in the sense that a change in gas pressure *causes* an *effect*: a change in gas volume. An additional weight on Bernoulli's piston (Fig. 13–3) causes a decrease in space occupied by the gas. And yet *chance* motion of molecules is the mechanism of explanation. Air particles move in all directions; only those particles that happen to move toward the piston are effective in supporting a weight. Randomness provides high probability that there will be sufficient numbers moving in the necessary direction. Bernoulli unknowingly was casting an early focus on a basic problem: To what extent

13–10   A diffusion experiment. Hydrogen chloride gas evaporates into the tube from the hydrochloric acid in the cotton at one end, and ammonia gas evaporates from the ammonia solution at the other end. Before long, a white cloud appearing in the tube shows that the gases are diffusing through the air in the tube and are forming ammonium chloride where they meet. Since hydrogen chloride molecules are heavier and move more slowly than ammonia gas, the gases meet closer to the hydrogen chloride end.

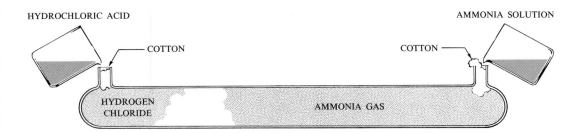

HYDROCHLORIC ACID

COTTON

AMMONIA SOLUTION

COTTON

HYDROGEN CHLORIDE

AMMONIA GAS

are events—and laws predicting events—a matter of cause and effect, and to what extent are they a matter of chance or probability?

SIGNIFICANCE OF THE THEORY—A MECHANICAL MODEL OF HEAT

This chapter reveals the kinetic molecular theory to be a mechanical model of heat. Mechanical concepts of random motion, gravitation, kinetic energy, and potential energy are applied to molecules to explain heat phenomena. There is no need to belabor the point here.

In time, the energy theory won. The caloric theory ran into serious difficulties in explaining heat of friction, easily handled by the kinetic molecular theory. By extending Newtonian ideas to molecules, the model opened wide the doors of thermodynamics (heat dynamics). The kinetic theory was also more promising with respect to conservation principles. The caloric theory had prospered with Black's conservation of heat principle but could go no further in a conservation direction. Unless heat is energy, the mechanical energy of a swinging pendulum gradually disappears without any energy taking its place. A conservation of energy principle requires that heat be energy. How far would physics have developed without equals signs, without the broad conservation idea that the total energies before a process occurs equals the total energies afterward?

LAW OF DISSIPATION OF ENERGY

If all objects are systems of moving molecules, do all matter and all energy eventually degenerate back into molecules in random motion? Gases diffuse into a uniform mixture. Will the universe be leveled off into nothing but molecules moving randomly in a void? If systems of matter and energy emerged from disorder, will system lapse back into disorder?

The law of dissipation of energy, the famous second law of thermodynamics, pessimistically answers "yes," that all other energies gradually become heat and that the universe is running down to a "heat death." Energies transform, with the total amount remaining constant (conservation law, Chapter 12), but *in every energy transformation, some of the original energy changes into heat energy unavailable for further transformations.* So states the law of dissipation of energy as enunciated by the great German scientist Rudolph Clausius (1822-1888). By analogy, suppose the winner of each "hand" in cards places a small portion of his winnings into a "house kitty." With no additional funds feeding in, a gradual, nonrecoverable accumulation of chips results in the "kitty," and the "house" becomes the eventual winner.

With every swing of a pendulum, heat of friction replaces energy of motion—energy is conserved (Chapter 12)—but the heat is lost into the surroundings. How is the increased agitation of air molecules outward to be recovered?

We have seen (Chapter 9) that almost all energies, including muscular, have their origins in the sun. The sun and billions of other stars in billions of galaxies flood the universe with radiation. The earth receives only an infinitesimal fraction of this radiation and itself reflects and radiates back to the universe almost all it receives.

Scientific man finds complex technological energies absorbing and necessary. Various forms of life and his own human energies involve systems of a very high order. Does the degradation of energy from complex to simpler forms apply here, too? Can man not intervene and reverse the process, at least on earth? Do not steam or gasoline engines transform heat to higher-order mechanical energy? Petroleum is certainly "concentrated sunshine" dating back hundreds of millions of years that now provides heat for locomotion.

The French genius Sadi Carnot (1796–1832) was the first to answer such basic questions, at least regarding the steam engine. His theoretical work on ideal engine cycles became the basis of modern theory of heat engines, including rocket motors and steam turbines, as well as of refrigeration and heat pumps. His basic conclusion, an early version of the law of dissipation of energy, states that *heat does not of its own accord flow from cold regions to hot regions.* That is, engines converting heat into locomotion are the same as all other transformation devices. They also have a heat loss into surroundings that cannot be recaptured because heat will not spontaneously flow back from cold to hot regions. Besides, as Clausius later pointed out, in the operation of a piston in an engine cylinder, the molecules of the heated fuel mixture move in all directions; only those moving toward the piston can do useful work. The remaining heat energy is wasted.

Since heat transfers from hot to cold regions, couldn't heat be recovered by creating cold areas through refrigeration in order to bring in heat from surrounding areas? Unfortunately, to refrigerate an area below its surroundings loses more heat energy than what would be obtained. And so the chain goes on and on. There can be no net gain in "reclaiming" heat energy. As long as heat spontaneously travels from hot to cold areas, hot areas tend to become cooler, and cooler areas tend to become warmer until a universal thermal equilibrium is reached. The process certainly seems a leveling one.

We can only get out of this bind scientifically by remembering that we think only in terms of today's knowledge and concepts—not yet in terms of knowledge and concepts to come. There could be a building-up process at work in the universe as yet unknown to us. By rough analogy, mountains are built by earthquakes and volcanic action, and land is leveled by water, ice, and wind. For land to be leveled, areas must also be raised.

According to Einstein's special theory of relativity, matter and energy are equivalent, and matter is a concentrated form of energy. Einstein's $E = mc^2$ involves not only conservation but also more complex organization of matter and energy from simpler organization. Matter, complex energy, has been created from kinetic energy of particles in the Radiation Laboratories at Berkeley. Simpler atoms are being converted into more complex atoms in the stars. And Fred Hoyle's present hypothesis of a steady state universe includes the assumption of constant galaxy formation to fill in space as the universe expands. Such birth of stars and galaxies would involve creation of energy and matter as well—perhaps from such simpler forms as lost or dissipated radiation. Both degradation and uplifting processes may be at work in the universe.

Man as a system of the highest order (that we know of), a conscious being, may reduce himself by war into molecules in a void. But the uplifting process resulting in so complex a system and creature as man could be operating elsewhere in the universe. In any case, we are here merely speculating; future knowledge is necessary. Meanwhile, the universe has billions of years in which to "run down."

CHAPTER REVIEW

1. Why do we believe that molecules exist and move?

2. State the kinetic theory of heat, and discuss its main assumptions.

3. Compare solids, liquids, and gases with respect to the following: (a) freedom of molecular motion, (b) relative closeness of molecules, (c) forces of attraction among molecules, and (d) resistance to change of volume and shape.

4. Why is friction a meaningless concept when applied to molecules?

5. Review the following as early evidences for kinetic theory: (a) Rumford's cannon-boring experiments, (b) Davy's ice experiments, (c) Joule's paddle wheel experiments, and (d) Brownian motion.

6. What bearing did each of the following have in the development of the kinetic molecular theory? (a) Torricelli's barometer. (b) Boyle's J-tube experiment and law. (c) Boyle's "spring of the air" hypothesis. (d) Atomic hypothesis of ancient Greeks. (e) Charles's and Gay-Lussac's law. (f) General gas law. (g) Absolute temperature scale.

7. Discuss assumptions, definitions, hypotheses, laws, theories, and evidences not considered in questions 1–6 that make up the kinetic model of heat.

8. How does the kinetic model explain the following phenomena? (a) Heat transfers by conduction. (b) Heat transfers by convection currents. (c) The sun's radiation warms the earth and its atmosphere. (d) The temperatures of objects change. (e) Substances vary in specific heat capacity. (f) Liquids freeze. (g) Liquids boil. (h) Liquids evaporate and cool their surroundings. (i) Heat generally expands substances. (j) Gases exert pressure on containers. (k) Substances, particularly gases, diffuse.

9. How does the kinetic model explain the following concepts and principles? (a) Heat of fusion. (b) Heat of vaporization. (c) Thermal equilibrium. (d) Heat conservation. (e) Decreasing the volume of a gas at constant temperature increases its pressure ($PV = k$), or increasing volume decreases pressure. (f) Increasing the temperature of a gas at constant volume increases its pressure ($P/T = k_1$), or decreasing temperature decreases pressure. (g) Decreasing the temperature of a gas at constant pressure decreases its volume ($V/T = k_2$), or decreasing temperature decreases pressure. (h) General gas law: pressure P, temperature T, and volume V of a gas sample are inter-related as follows: $PV/T =$ a constant K. (i) Absolute zero temperature. (j) Vapor pressure.

10. Which laws discussed in this chapter apply to gases and not to liquids and solids? Why?

11. Apply the criteria for evaluating a theoretical system (Chapter 3) to the kinetic molecular model.

12. Why was the caloric theory abandoned in favor of the kinetic molecular theory of heat?

13. Use the development of the kinetic molecular theory to illustrate the combined inductive-deductive nature of scientific reasoning.

14. How is the kinetic theory of heat an extension of the mechanical view of the world?

15. Why has the kinetic model been called a statistical model of heat that explains how "order arises from disorder"?

16. (a) What is the law of dissipation of energy? Illustrate. (b) Does this law imply that "disorder emerges from order" and that "the universe is running down"? Explain.

17. Compare the law of dissipation of energy to the law of conservation of energy.

18. How do Chapters 12–13 illustrate that "Science is an interconnected series of concepts and conceptual schemes that have developed as a result of experimentation and observation and that are fruitful of further experimentation and observation" (James Conant)?

19. Is there such a thing as a "crucial" experiment or observation that unquestionably "proves" a given theory or law to be true? Or are there merely significant observations that eliminate alternative principles recognized at a given time? Illustrate.

PROBLEMS

1. Discuss the statement that "cold is nothing but the absence of heat."

2. Smaller dust particles are seen to move faster than larger ones in Brownian motion. Why?

3. When a solid expands, do individual molecules in the solid expand? Explain.

4. (a) How are heat and temperature related by the kinetic theory of heat? (b) What are differences between heat and temperature according to this theory?

5. Explain the following by the kinetic theory of heat: (a) The burning of toast soon becomes apparent. (b) Beads of moisture collect on the outside of ice water pitchers. (c) Sudden compression heats a gas. (d) Live steam produces a more severe burn than boiling water. (e) Water gradually mixes with syrup when placed on it. (f) Doubling the amount of air pumped into a container doubles the pressure on the container.

6. Why does a can collapse if a small amount of water is boiled in it and tightly covered while hot?

7. Does an operating fan actually heat or cool a room? Explain.

8. (a) Is an object at 200°F twice as hot as one at 100°F? Why? (b) Is an object at 200°K twice as hot as one at 100°K? Why?

9. (a) If a mercury barometer has a height of 30.0 in., what is the height in feet of a water barometer? (b) If a mercury barometer has a height of 25.0 in., what is the height in feet of a water barometer?

10. Half of the atmosphere lies below an altitude of 3.5 mi. (a) What is the air pressure at 3.5 mi above sea level? (b) If a toy balloon 1 ft³ in volume rises to a height of 3.5 mi in a nonpressurized plane at constant temperature, how much larger or smaller in volume is the balloon?

11. (a) A pressure of 2 atm is equivalent to how many centimeters of mercury? To how many pounds per square inch? (b) How high a column of water would 2 atm of pressure support?

12. How deep is a lake if an air bubble of 1 in.³ at the bottom becomes 4 in.³ at the surface?

13. Suppose a gauge registers 15 cm of mercury for your blood pressure. What is it in pounds per inch?

14. Thirty ft³ of oxygen are under 2 atm of pressure. What is the volume of the gas if the pressure is increased to 4 atm at the same temperature?

15. Forty liters (1 liter = 1,000 cm³) of air at 0°C are compressed at a constant pressure of 3 atm until the volume is 20 liters. What is the final temperature of the air?

16. A gas has a volume of 100 liters at a pressure of 1 atm and a temperature of 40°C. What is the volume of the gas at a pressure of 0.5 atm and a temperature of 60°C?

17. Show that the general gas law (Eq. 13–3) becomes Boyle's law (Eq. 13–1) when $T_1 = T_2$ and Charles's law (Eq. 13–2) when $P_1 = P_2$.

18. Use the kinetic theory to explain why the value of temperature T used in the gas laws should be the absolute, or Kelvin, value.

19.* Car tires are inflated to a gauge pressure of 30 lb/in.² at the base of Mt. Whittier (elevation over 14,000 ft). (a) Will the gauge pressure reading of the tire be less or more at the top of the mountain? Assume no leakage or temperature change. (b) What is the total pressure of the tires at the base of the mountain if atmospheric pressure is 15 lb/in.²?

20.* Suppose that your car tires are inflated to a gauge pressure of 30 lb/in.² when the thermometer registers 100°F. What is the gauge pressure in the tires if the temperature drops to 50°F that evening?

21. How can a 30-lb gauge pressure in tires support a 3,000-lb car?

22. A 1-ft³ volume of oxygen at 15 lb/in.² of pressure is compressed to half its volume at constant temperature. (a) What is the new pressure of the gas? (b) Does the average speed of its molecules remain the same? Explain.

23. Hydrogen has an average speed of about 1 mi/sec at ordinary room temperature and atmospheric pressure. What is the average speed of an oxygen molecule at the same temperature and pressure if an oxygen molecule is 16 times as heavy?

SUGGESTIONS FOR
FURTHER READING

Einstein, Albert, and Leopold Infeld, *The Evolution of Physics*, Simon and Schuster paperback, New York, 1961, Part 1, "Rise of the Mechanical View."

Holton, Gerald J., and D. H. D. Roller, *Foundations of Modern Physical Science*, Addison-Wesley, Reading, Mass., 1958, Ch. 25.

Conant, James, *Science and Common Sense*, Yale Univ. Press paperback, New Haven, Conn., 1962, Chs. 4–6.

Conant, James, ed., *Harvard Case Histories in Experimental Science*, Vol. 1, Harvard Univ. Press, Cambridge, Mass., 1957, Chs. 1 and 3.

Mott-Smith, Morton, *Concept of Energy Simply Explained*, Dover paperback, New York, 1964, Chs. 8–9.

Gamow, George, *One, Two, Three . . . Infinity*, Mentor paperback, New York, 1953, Ch. 8.

*For tire gauge problems 19 and 20: *Total pressure P = gauge pressure + atmospheric pressure.*

Cheronis, Nicholas D., et al., *Study of the Physical World,* Houghton Mifflin, Boston, 1958, Ch. 19.

Bronowski, Joseph, *Common Sense of Science,* Vintage paperback, New York, 1960.

Kline, Morris, *Mathematics in Western Culture,* Oxford Univ. Press, New York, 1953, Ch. 24.

Butterfield, Herbert, *Origins of Modern Science,* Collier paperback, New York, 1962, Chs. 6–7.

Krauskopf, Konrad B., and Arthur Beiser, *Fundamentals of Physical Science,* McGraw-Hill, New York, 1966, Ch. 9.

Tyndall, John, *Heat as a Mode of Motion,* Appleton-Century-Crofts, New York, 1863.

Cowling, T. G., *Molecules in Motion: An Introduction to the Kinetic Theory of Gases,* Harper paperback, New York, 1960.

14 *Magnetism: Data, Concepts, and Theories*

> To you alone, true men of science, who seek knowledge not only from books but from things themselves do I dedicate these foundations of magnetic science. If any disagree with my opinion, let him at least take note of the experiments and employ them to better use if he is able.
>
> WILLIAM GILBERT, 1600

ANCIENT MYSTERY OF MAGNETISM

Our complex electrical civilization had simple beginnings in pieces of iron ore. Ancient shepherds detected small pieces of black stone clinging to the iron crooks at the ends of their staffs. The force required to remove these bits of black stone in time gave rise to tales of magnetic islands that pulled in ships and held them fast. And there were other myths of submerged mountains that even drew the nails out of ships, collapsing them. In actuality, however, large deposits of lodestone ("leading" stone) were found near Magnesia, in Asia Minor, that mysteriously attracted bits of iron. The Greeks, therefore, named this iron ore magnetite.

Lodestone had a "mystical" property understandable only to the gods. To question further could even invoke the wrath of the gods. Then speculative Greeks or Romans like Thales, Claudian, and Pliny projected humanlike spirits or "souls"—and sex, too—upon magnetic stone. At least the stones could now be examined. Said Thales: "The magnet has a soul because it gives movement to iron." Man explains the unknown through the known, the impersonal through the personal. A man has known personal needs that he consciously satisfies—hunger, for example. A magnet, in attracting filings, shows needs and a "soul" in the same way. Said Claudian (4th century A.D.): "Iron gave life to magnets and nourished them; therefore, magnets sought iron as animals sought food." And Pliny (1st century A.D.) stated: "The moment the metal comes near it, it springs toward the magnet and, as it clasps it, it is held fast in the magnet's embrace." Certainly a projection of living characteristics upon inanimate objects. Further, said Pliny, "The leading distinction in magnets is sex, male and female . . . . The kind that is found in Troas is of the female sex, and consequently destitute of attractive power." (How complimentary!) Another Greek explanation assumed a special "sympathy" to exist between attracting and attracted objects.

On the other hand, Greco-Roman atomists postulated that an invisible material emitted by lodestone is responsible for magnetic attraction. Said atomist Lucretius in his materialistic explanation of attraction:

> First, from this stone there must stream a shoal of seeds in a current
> Driving away with its blows all the air 'twixt itself and the iron.
> Soon as this space is made void and a vacuum fashioned between them,
> Instantly into that void the atoms of iron tumble headlong
> All in a lump; thus the [iron] ring itself moves bodily forward.

That is, magnets emit invisible emanations (after all, flowers emit unseen fragrances); emanations force out air particles between itself and iron filings to create a vacuum; the filings or iron rings move into the void in apparent attraction to the magnet. Certainly a mechanical rather than an animistic explanation!

EXPERIMENTS WITH MAGNETS

Some men simply speculated about the mysteries of magnetism; later, others carefully observed and speculated. The following experiments highlight observations of curious men across the centuries who observed specific magnets and developed concepts for explanation.

Experiment 1—Magnetic Attraction

Bring a magnet close to iron filings, tacks, or paper clips. These materials can be seen to "jump" across space in attraction to the magnet. Approach your magnet close to bits of glass, wood, thread, copper, lead, or paper. These and most other materials do not react to magnets. Those that do react are called magnetic substances.

Experiment 2—Induced Magnetism

Among early keen observations of lodestone magnets are the following words of Plato quoting Socrates: "This stone not only attracts iron rings, but also imparts to them a similar power of attracting other rings ... and all of them derive their power of suspension from the original stone." That is, soft iron is not ordinarily magnetic. But lodestone imparts its power of attraction to previously unmagnetized iron. Place the end of an unmagnetized iron nail near iron filings. The filings are not attracted (Fig. 14–1A). But if you bring a lodestone or other magnet up to or even close to the iron nail, the nail attracts the filings (Fig. 14–1B); the iron nail has become a temporary magnet. Remove the permanent magnet from the nail, and the nail drops the filings (Fig. 14–1C); it has lost most of its magnetism. Soft iron was early found to magnetize and demagnetize quickly. A piece of iron is said to be *magnetized by induction* when it becomes magnetic by being near or in contact with a magnet.

Experiment 3—Permanent Magnets

Elongated pieces of lodestone were early used to magnetize iron rods, bars, nails, or needles more permanently by the ancient Chinese. A Chinese dictionary compiled in 121 A.D. gives instructions on how lodestone, a natural magnet, can make permanent magnets of iron objects. When repeatedly rubbed in the same direction with lodestone (or other magnets) iron and steel become more permanently magnetic.

Magnetize a sewing needle or nail with a bar magnet as just described, and test the magnetism of the needle by dipping it into iron filings before and after the process.

Magnetite (an oxide of iron, Fe_3O_4) is a *natural* magnet, as compared to *artificial*, or man-made, magnets. Artificial magnets today are generally composed of an alloy steel (mostly iron) and are shaped variously into bars, needles, horseshoes, and the like. Nickel, cobalt, alnico (composed of aluminum, nickel, and cobalt), and a few other materials are also magnetic. Magnetized steel, nickel, and alnico remain magnetic permanently.

Experiment 4—Magnetic Poles

Immerse a bar magnet into iron filings. Upon removal of the magnet, filings are found clustered at the ends of the magnet. Such areas are known as *magnetic poles*. Magnetic needles and bar magnets have two poles. Place odd-shaped lodestones or other magnets within filings, and two or more poles will be found, always even in number.

The concept of "poles" offers invaluable insights into magnetic phe-

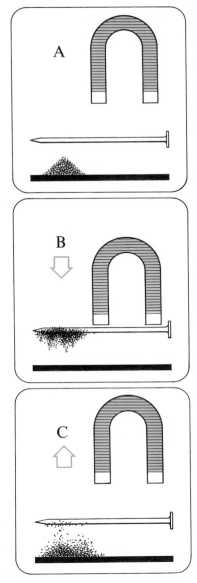

14–1 Induced magnetism. Soft iron magnetizes and demagnetizes easily. When the horseshoe magnet is brought close to the iron nail, filings are attracted to the nail. The nail is magnetized by induction. When the horseshoe magnet is withdrawn, the nail loses its magnetism, and the filings fall off.

nomena, including repulsion. But "poles" are primarily labels, or definitions, describing parts of a magnet to which iron filings are attracted. We actually do not see magnetic "poles"; we see clusters of filings.

Experiment 5—Magnetic Compasses

Ancient Chinese invented the compass sometime before the 2nd century A.D. The ancient Chinese dictionary of 121 A.D. refers to not only stones which magnetize needles but also magnetized needles which point "southward." These needles were displayed as objects of curiosity by Chinese magicians or used as compasses on carriages.

Europeans were probably the first to use the compass at sea. A thousand years after its invention by the Chinese, Alexander Neckham of Paris (1157–1217) described a pivoted compass as part of ship equipment. At about this time magnetic needles set floating on pieces of straw in water were experimentally found to rotate and point northward as compasses. A number of magnetic needles in a row tend to come to rest parallel to one another pointing northward. The north-seeking poles of such magnets became known as *north poles;* the south-seeking as *south poles.* The consistent direction pointing of compasses remained unexplained, however, until William Gilbert (1544–1603), physician in Queen Elizabeth's court.

Experiment 6—Magnetic Repulsion

Magnets repel as well as attract. Lucretius observed magnetic repulsion in the following words:

> There are times also when the nature of iron
> Moves away from this stone, being wont to flee
> And follow it by turn. I have even seen
> Rings of Samothracian iron dance,
> And iron filings leap madly about
> Inside brass bowls, soon as this magnet stone
> Is put beneath; so eager the iron seems
> To escape from the stone.

Pliny (1st century A.D.) attempted to explain magnetic repulsion as a matter of two kinds of lodestone, one that attracts iron and another that repels. Said Pliny in his *Natural History*: "There are two mountains near the river Indus; the nature of one is to attract iron, of the other to repel it; hence if there be nails in the shoes, the feet cannot be drawn off the one or set down on the other." Imagination indeed! Myth becomes science only when imagination is checked by direct observation.

Eleven hundred years later, Roger Bacon (1214–1292) did experimentally observe that the same piece of lodestone may both repel and attract: "If the iron is touched by the north part of the magnet, it follows that part wherever it goes.... And if the opposite part of the magnet is brought against the touched part of the iron, it flees from it as though inimical; as the lamb from the wolf."

Pivot a magnet. Bring an end of a second bar magnet toward an end of the first (Fig. 14–2). Before contact, the first magnet will be either attracted *or* repelled. If it is attracted, bring the other end of the second magnet toward the same end of the first. The suspended magnet will then be repelled. Why? This mystery remained unanswered for hundreds of years after Roger Bacon.

LAW OF ATTRACTION AND REPULSION

The concept of polarity gave insights into magnetic repulsion and attraction and led to an important law of magnetism.

Experiment 7—Poles and Repulsion

Magnets point north and south (experiment 5). And they repel as well as attract (experiment 6). Once magnets are recognized as having pairs of poles and are appropriately labeled, repulsion is predictable. In Fig. 14–2, the north-seeking poles are labeled N and the south-seeking, S. If the N pole of one magnet is brought toward the N pole of another, the poles repel each other (Fig. 14–2B). The S pole of one also repels the S pole of the other. The N pole of either magnet, however, attracts the S pole of the other (Fig. 14–2A). That is, *like magnetic poles repel;*

14–2 Magnets both repel and attract. If one end of a bar magnet attracts an end of a suspended magnet, the other end of the first magnet repels the original end of the suspended magnet.

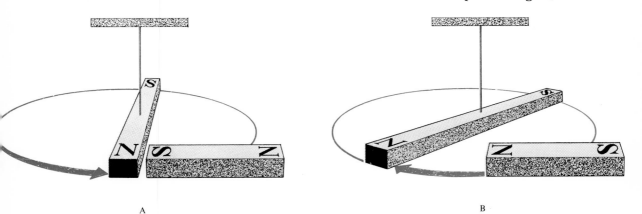

A   B

unlike poles attract. This observation, confirmed countless times, is known as the *magnetic law of attraction and repulsion*. Peter Peregrine (13th century), a friend of Bacon, observed that magnets have pairs of poles. He even noted that whenever a piece of lodestone breaks, a new pair of opposite poles appears at the broken ends. One magnet becomes two. Peregrine could have used his observation to explain magnetic repulsion, a phenomenon unknown to him but noted by Bacon. Although these two gifted men were friends, Peregrine did not know about the repulsion of magnets and Bacon did not know about pairs of poles. Scientific progress requires communication. The connection between repulsion and pairs of poles escaped in the silence.

MAGNETIC DECLINATION AND DIP

Compass needles generally do not point true north or south. A Chinese royal astronomer in the 8th century reported the *magnetic declination* of a compass needle as 3° to the west of south. In other localities, the compass needle was indicated as "off" by different amounts.

Columbus, during his famous voyage in 1492, discovered a place of no declination. He reported in a letter to King Ferdinand and Queen Isabella of Spain: "When I sailed from Spain to the West Indies, I found that as soon as I had passed 100 leagues west of the Azores . . . the needle of the compass, which hitherto had turned toward the northeast, turned a full quarter of the wind to the northwest, and this took place from the time when we reached that line." When the strange behavior of the compass alarmed his men, Columbus pacified them by attributing the behavior of the compass to the North Star.

In any case, Columbus's voyage led to systematic study of compass declinations across wide areas. Governments began publishing maps showing declination by isogonic lines, or lines drawn through locales of equal declination. Figure 14–3 is such a map of the United States giving declination by isogonic lines. Notice a line of no declination (0°) running south from Hudson Bay, across Lake Superior and Lake Michigan, through Ohio, and eventually leaving the country parallel to the Florida coast. In any location east of the 0° line, the compass needle points west of true north, as indicated by the lines marked from 5°W to 20°W. In the western United States, the compass needle points east; isogonal lines marked 5°E to 20°E, therefore, are seen across western states. For example, San Francisco has a declination of about 17°E. That means that around San Francisco, a compass needle points 17° to the east of due north. True, or geographic, north in San Francisco is therefore 17° west of the direction indicated by the magnetic compass. Since declination in any locality changes over the years, declination maps are revised from

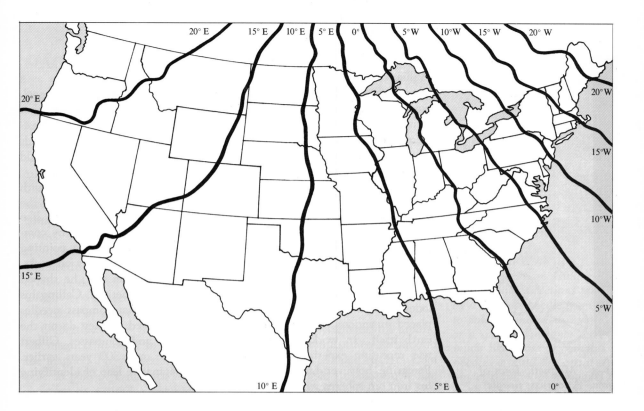

time to time. For example, in London, compasses pointed 11°15′ east of true north in 1580, due north in 1659, and 24½° west in 1823—a change of almost 36° in about 250 years!

About 50 years after Columbus's first transatlantic voyage, Georg Hartmann, a German vicar, discovered that needles had not only an angle of declination but also an angle of dip. A compass needle free to swing vertically dipped toward the earth. This *magnetic dip* occurred only after the needle was magnetized. Hartmann reported his discovery to Count Albert of Prussia, but nothing came of it. In 1576 magnetic dip was rediscovered by the Englishman Robert Norman, who in 1580 also published the first magnetic declination charts. The north-seeking pole of the needle came to rest in London at the large angle of 71°50′ from the horizontal. Later this angle was found to increase as the compass was moved northward and to decrease as it was moved southward. Near the equator, the dip disappears. Beyond the equator, the south-seeking pole of the compass points diagonally to the earth. In the Southern Hemisphere, the angle of dip becomes greater as one travels southward. Magnetic dip at any place changes in time. The 71°50′ reading in London taken in 1576 gradually increased to 74°52′ in 1725—only to drop ever since.

14–3 Isogonic lines in the United States. The wavy lines, called isogonic lines, connect locales of equal compass declination. The 0° line running through Lakes Superior and Michigan is the only line that runs through vicinities in which compasses point due north. All other locales have angles of compass declination from due north, for which the allowances indicated on the map must be made.

If the strength of one pole is doubled? If the strength of both poles is doubled? (c) If the strength of both poles is doubled and the distance between them is reduced to one-half? (d) If the strength of both poles is doubled and the distance between them is doubled?

18. Will the attractive force of a strong magnetic pole upon an opposite weak one be the same as the force of the weak upon the strong pole? Explain.

19. How does the molecular theory of magnetism explain the following? (a) Two magnets with two poles each can be formed by breaking a single magnet with two poles. (b) A needle can be demagnetized by heating it.

20. Would you surmise that the earth obtains its magnetism primarily from its iron ore and other magnetic deposits? Why?

SUGGESTIONS FOR FURTHER READING

Taylor, Lloyd W., *Physics, the Pioneer Science,* Vol. 2, Dover paperback, New York, 1959, Ch. 39.

Priestley, Herbert, *Introductory Physics,* Allyn and Bacon, Boston, 1958, Ch. 18.

Butterfield, Herbert, *Origins of Modern Science,* Collier paperback, New York, 1962, Chs. 5–7.

Farrington, Benjamin, *Francis Bacon, Philosopher of Industrial Science,* Collier paperback, New York, 1961.

Gilbert, William, *De Magnete,* Dover paperback, New York, 1958.

15   Electricity at Rest

A great French philosopher . . . said to me once, "I understand everything in the book except what is meant by an electrically charged body."

HENRI POINCARÉ, 1885

ANCIENT
ELECTRICAL PHENOMENA

Electrical science had origins in lightning, long feared as a punishment
of the gods. Even today children cringe in terror at "the bolt out of the
blue." Knowledge helps: What is lightning? A clue lies in amber. This
resinous material, when polished, has a yellow brilliance that reminded
ancient Greeks of the sun (elector). The Greek word for amber was
therefore elektron. But polished amber does more than gleam. Thales
noted that rubbed amber attracts bits of thread, straw, chaff, and twigs,
much as lodestone attracts iron filings. That amber must first be rubbed
added to the mystery of attraction.

Another mystery was "St. Elmo's fire," an eerie glow often seen at
the tips of masts or spears. A strange ability of the torpedo fish (electric
eel) to shock victims was also known. But while amber and lodestone
effects were considered alike—until William Gilbert emphasized the
differences—lightning, rubbed amber, St. Elmo's fire, and electric eels
went unrelated until the days of Benjamin Franklin.

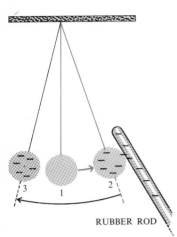

*15–1 Electrical repulsion.
(1) A neutral pith ball first
is attracted to a charged
rubber rod brought close.
(2) With contact, the ball
gains some of the rod's charge
and is repelled (3).*

RUBBER ROD

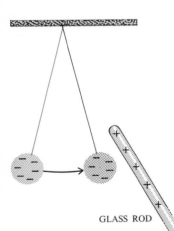

GLASS ROD

*15–2 Two kinds of charge.
A glass rod rubbed with silk
attracts the charged pith ball
repelled by the "minus"
charged rubber rod. The glass
has an opposite, or "plus,"
charge.*

EXPERIMENTS
WITH ELECTRICITY

Electrical Attraction Experiments

Vigorously rub a hard rubber rod with cat's fur or a wool cloth. If you bring the rod close to bits of paper—much as Thales did with amber and chaff over 2,500 years ago—you will find the small particles "jumping" across space to the rod. Notice, however, that a similar unrubbed rod will not attract the paper bits.

Next, vigorously rub a glass rod with silk or rayon, and again you will find paper bits attracted. You are now duplicating experimental efforts of William Gilbert. Twenty-one hundred years after Thales, Gilbert found that not only amber and glass but also diamonds, opals, sapphires, wax, sulfur, and many other substances show definite attractive properties when rubbed.

Gilbert considered these attractions to be uniquely different from magnetic attraction. Why? Bring a bar magnet close to bits of paper. The steel magnet will not attract paper; a rubbed amber rod will. On the other hand, magnets attract iron filings; amber rods do not. Gilbert called materials that attract like amber "electrics."

To test for electrics, Gilbert invented a "versorium." This simple device, a light, delicately pivoted metal pointer, was free to turn when attracted. If placed near an electrified object, the versorium turned toward it. The versorium was thus the first detector of electricity. Substances like rubbed metals that did not attract his detector Gilbert called "non-electrics."

In a sense, Gilbert was the father of electrical science. Through systematic experimentation, he differentiated electrical from magnetic phenomena. But more than that, he gave the new science of electricity a necessary early stage of classification. He operationally defined "electrics" and "nonelectrics" as classes of substances that do or do not "attract as amber does." He then devised the first electrical instrument to test and classify carefully various substances as electrics or nonelectrics in accordance with his definitions. Gilbert's experiments started a chain of non-mathematical investigations into electricity that culminated 2 centuries later in electrical measurements and laws. For that reason alone, Gilbert deserved the tribute of "father."

Electrical Repulsion Experiments

Gilbert, however, did not detect electrical repulsion. Like all great innovators, he lit a torch that he carried just so far. About 30 years after

Gilbert's death, an Italian Jesuit, Nicolo Cabeo (1585–1650), discovered electrical repulsion. In simple experiments, he observed that rubbed electrics sometimes repel objects after attracting them.

Bring a hard rubber rod rubbed with fur toward a suspended pith ball (Fig. 15–1). The ball will move up toward the rod, remain in contact with it for a moment, and then fall back. If you now bring the rod closer to the pith ball, the ball moves further away. Your results, first attraction and then repulsion, are the same as those of Cabeo.

Cabeo, strongly Ptolemaic, hoped to confound Copernicans by the repelling effects. Kepler claimed that a magnetic attraction of the sun keeps the earth and other planets in orbit. "If the sun repels as well as attracts, how can the earth remain in orbit?" rhetorically asked Cabeo. Not until Newton was it clear that the sun's attraction is gravitational, not magnetic or electrical. Cabeo, therefore, could not realize that his discovery of electrical repulsion was not a blow to Copernicanism. Unlike magnetic and electrical forces, gravity does not repel. The sun never repels the earth.

DUFAY'S HYPOTHESIS:
TWO KINDS OF ELECTRICITY

Return to the repelled pith ball (Fig. 15–1). A second electrified rubber rod also repels the ball. Now bring a glass rod well rubbed with silk or rayon toward the ball. Strangely enough, the ball is *attracted* toward the glass rod at the very time that it is repelled by the rubber rods (Fig. 15–2). Can it be that there are two kinds of electricity, one contained by the rubber rod rubbed by fur and the other by the glass rod rubbed by silk? How else are the opposite effects of the two rods on the ball to be explained? In any case, the French scientist Charles Dufay (1698–1739) concluded that there are two kinds of electricity, "vitreous" in rubbed glass and "resinous" in rubbed amber (or rubber). Benjamin Franklin (1706–1790) later substituted the terms "positive" (+) and "negative" (−) electricity for "vitreous" and "resinous," respectively.

LAW OF
ATTRACTION AND REPULSION

An object that acquires the property of attraction when rubbed is today said to have an *electric charge*. The definition is operational; the charge is defined through a process, the process of electrical attraction. The pith ball moves to a rod. The rod is said to attract the ball and therefore to have a charge. The charge is actually not seen. It is assumed in the process of attraction and associated with it. Using the concept of charge, let us see how Dufay's hypothesis of two kinds of electricity actually

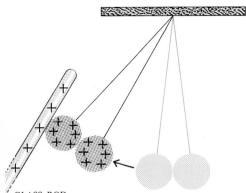

15–3A Like charges repel. Two neutral pith balls are attracted to a positively charged glass rod brought close. On contact, the balls gain some of the rod's positive charge and are repelled (Fig. 15–3B).

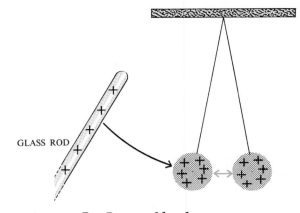

15–3B Because like charges repel, the two positively charged pith balls remain apart.

explains attraction and repulsion. The rubber rod (Fig. 15–1), when rubbed, gains a — charge that gives it the property of attracting the pith ball. With contact, the ball acquires some of the rod's — charge. Both objects now have the same charge. And said Dufay: *"Like charges repel each other."* With like charges, the rod and ball repel each other. The ball remains at a distance as long as both have like charges.

But why does the rubbed glass rod (Fig. 15–2) attract the same ball? The glass rod has a + charge (that is, the "second kind of electricity"), a charge opposite to that of the rubber rod and ball. And said Dufay, *"Unlike charges attract."* Because the glass rod and ball have opposite charges, they attract each other at a time when the rubber rod and ball repel each other. The glass rod and rubber rod also will attract each other because of their opposite charges. On the other hand, two electrified glass rods will repel each other because of like charges, as will two electrified rubber rods. Thus, unseen, opposite charges (+ and —) were assumed to explain electrical attraction and repulsion, just as opposite poles (N and S) were assumed to explain magnetic attraction and repulsion.

Hypotheses are retained only if they successfully predict. Let us see if Dufay's hypothesis (likes repel and unlikes attract) successfully predicts in a new situation. This time, suspend *two* pith balls and approach them first with a glass rod (Fig. 15–3A). Dufay's hypothesis predicts the following results:

1. Both pith balls should be electrically attracted to the glass rod by definition of a charged body (Fig. 15–3A).

2. After contact, both balls should be repelled by the rod; the balls receive some of the rod's + charge, and like charges repel (Fig. 15–3B).

3. The pith balls should settle at a greater distance from each other than before. Since the balls have the same charge $(+)$, they also should repel each other.

4. Bringing the $(+)$ glass rod toward the $(+)$ pith balls should now further repel them from the rod. Again, likes $(+'s)$ repel.

5. If a $-$ charged rubber rod is brought toward the $+$ charged pith balls in place of the glass rod, the balls should tend to move toward the rod. Opposite charges attract.

Actual tests verify the above predictions. In fact, predictions from Dufay's hypothesis have been so well verified under changed circumstances and materials that his hypothesis became a theory and then *a law of electrical attraction and repulsion.* Such changes in status from hypothesis to theory to law indicate increased degrees of confidence in the idea with increased evidence.

EXPERIMENTS IN ELECTRICAL CONDUCTION

In a famous experiment, the English scientist Stephen Gray (1696–1736) supported a student from rafters by silk threads (Fig. 15–4). The boy's *feet* were touched by a large glass sphere well charged by vigorous rubbing. At once the boy's *hand* attracted feathers exactly as expected of an electrified object. Gray concluded that electricity had passed readily through the boy's body from his feet to his hand. The human body is a conductor of electricity! Metals are also good conductors. In earlier experiments, Gray had discovered that electricity applied to one end of a metal rod attracts feathers to cork at the other end. Electrical conduction as an idea emerged from experimental curiosity.

In still other experiments, Gray supported conductors first with dry silk threads and then with brass wires. The brass supports conducted the charge away from the main "line," whereas the silk supports did not. In this way, Gray discovered electrical insulators, or nonconductors. Gray found that amber, sulfur, hair, glass, dry air, and wood are also insulators; they do not tend to transmit electricity.

Gilbert had been unable to "electrify" metals. Gray succeeded by mounting metal objects on insulators. Unaware of electrical conduction, Gilbert had not realized that as fast as he formed charge by rubbing metal objects, the charge was conducted into his body or another absorbing medium. Consequently, his metals did not retain enough charge for his versorium to detect. When insulated, metals retain charge.

On the other hand, Gilbert's electrics or charged objects were all insulators. Amber or glass as insulators do not lead away the charges they acquire when rubbed. Thus, all objects acquire charge when rubbed; conductors may quickly lose theirs but insulators do not.

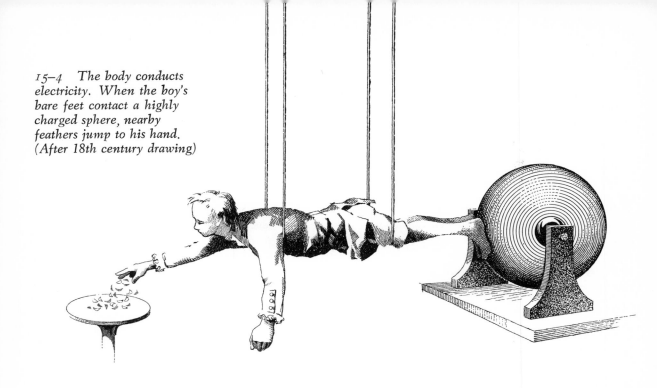

15–4   The body conducts electricity. When the boy's bare feet contact a highly charged sphere, nearby feathers jump to his hand. (After 18th century drawing)

DETECTING ELECTRICITY

An *electroscope* is a detector of charge. Gilbert's versorium was an electroscope; by rotating toward a charge, it detected charge. The suspended pith balls already discussed (Fig. 15–3) were an improved electroscope by John Canton in 1754. The lightweight pith balls could indicate the nature of the charge. For example, if the pith balls were previously charged negatively, an unknown charge is *minus* if it repels the pith balls or *plus* if it first attracts them. Gray's discovery of conductors and insulators led to an even more sensitive detector, the "gold leaf" electroscope, consisting of two leaves of thin metal foil hanging from a metal rod. A glass-walled box protects the foil from air currents; the vertical metal rod passes through a block of insulating sulfur to a metal knob outside the box. Charge on the knob is distributed through the conducting rod to the leaves. The leaves take on like charges and repel each other. The greater the charge, the greater the angle between the leaves. That is, intensity of charge at the knob is estimated by degree of divergence of the leaves.

The "gold leaf" electroscope easily distinguishes conductors from insulators as follows:

1. Place an electroscope about a foot away from a metal sphere or any other well-charged insulated object.

2. Then connect the charged sphere and the electroscope with a copper wire. The leaves of the electroscope fly apart at once (Fig. 15–5); copper is an excellent conductor.

3. Remove the wire and collapse the leaves by touching the knob.

4. Now connect the charged sphere and the electroscope knob with dry silk thread instead of wire. The leaves do not move; dry silk thread is a nonconductor, or insulator.

5. Test a ruler, pencil, glass rod, candle, spike, or what have you as a conductor.

At this point, we generalize. Insights into nature lead to improved instruments of investigation, which, in turn, lead to increased insights leading to improved instruments... and so on in an ascending spiral of scientific progress. Gilbert's insights into differences between electricity and magnetism led to his versorium as a device for detecting the former. Use of such detectors led to ideas of + and − charges (Cabeo, Dufay, and Franklin) and to laws of attraction and repulsion (Dufay)—as when rubbed glass rods attracted rubbed amber but repelled similar glass rods. Discovery of repulsion, in turn, led to the simple pith ball electroscope (Canton) as a more effective indicator of charge. Improved detection techniques resulted in concepts of electrical conduction and insulation (Gray) that led to the gold or aluminum leaf electroscope (Volta and Bennet). This more sensitive detector, in turn, led to many more observations, concepts, and devices, as we shall see, in a spiral of progress furthered by many men of various nations.

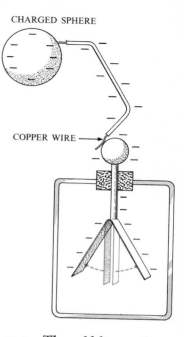

15–5   The gold leaves of an electroscope fly apart when a copper wire or other conductor connects the electroscope knob to a charged object.

CHARGING BY CONTACT AND INDUCTION

When a charged rubber rod touches the neutral knob of an electroscope, negative charges move directly into the knob and spread uniformly through the metal rod and gold leaves. The leaves diverge, and the electroscope is said to be *charged by contact.*

Can an object become charged without being touched by a charged object? We saw (Chapter 14) that magnets attract filings across space by first magnetizing them. Can it be that rubbed amber attracts thread by a *charge induced across space?* Or that charged rods attract pith balls in the same way? To answer these questions, bring a charged glass rod toward an electroscope knob without touching it. Notice that as the rod moves toward the knob, the leaves diverge (Fig. 15–6). Pull the charged glass rod away from the knob, and the leaves come together again. If electroscope leaves repel each other when charged and fall back together when neutral, then the electroscope must be charged by induction as the rod approaches. And if a nearby charged rod induces charges in an electroscope, then it most likely does the same to a pith ball. And by the law of attraction, the positively (+) charged rod must induce an opposite (−) charge on the pith ball, at least on the side facing the rod. By the same reasoning, the electroscope knob should also have a − charge. Accord-

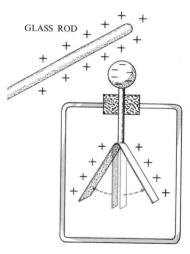

15–6   Charging across space. Without touching the knob, a charged rod causes the electroscope leaves to diverge by an induced charge.

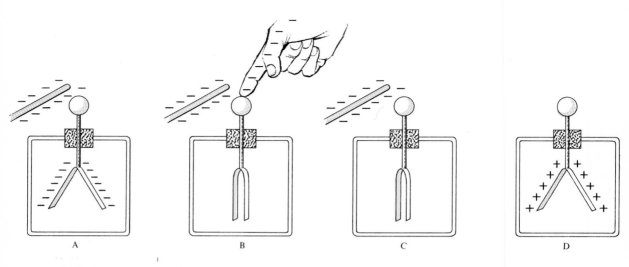

15–7   *Inducing a permanent charge.*

ingly, a nearby — charged rubber rod should induce a + charge upon the side of a pith ball facing it or upon a nearby electroscope knob. The light pith ball moves toward the glass rod because opposite charges attract, but once the two are in contact, enough of the rod's negative charge enters the ball to give the latter the same charge, and the ball is repelled. In the case of the electroscope, there is no contact with the outside rod and no transfer of charge. Therefore, when the rod is pulled away, the electroscope becomes neutral again. The induced charge was temporary. By use of pith ball electroscopes and such reasoning, John Canton made clear the nature of induced charge.

An electroscope can be given a more permanent induced charge, however, by properly applying a finger to the knob. This permanent charge can be demonstrated as follows (Fig. 15–7A–D):

    1. Bring a negatively charged rod near the knob. The leaves diverge, indicating that they are charged (Fig. 15–7A).

    2. Place a finger on the knob. The leaves collapse (Fig. 15–7B); their charge escaped into your body.

    3. Remove your finger. The leaves remain collapsed (Fig. 15–7C).

    4. Lastly, remove the rod, and the leaves diverge again (Fig. 15–7D). Why? The answer requires further concepts developed in succeeding sections.

STORING ELECTRICITY

In 1672 the German scientist Otto von Guericke built the first electrical machine, a sulfur sphere mounted on an axle with an attached handle. By rotating the sphere against his hand, Von Guericke built up stronger electrical charges than his predecessors.

In 1709 George Hauksbee hung a large brass cylinder from the ceiling— and a chain from the cylinder (Fig. 15–8). The bottom of the chain was in contact with a glass globe. As Hauksbee turned the axle, the chain led the charge to the cylinder from the globe. By using the chain as von Guericke used his hand, Hauksbee was able to store a large charge in the cylinder. Good sized sparks jumped between the cylinder and metal objects or hands brought close. Sparks could also be seen between the rotating globe and the dangling chain when contact was broken.

Soon the glass sphere was changed to a wheel with amber insets. When the wheel was rotated, the amber was charged as it brushed across cat's fur. The amber charge was led off to metallic spheres by wires. A large charge could be accumulated, and experimenters approaching such spheres were often met by large sparks. Electrical sparks increasingly fascinated scientists and amused polite society.

In 1746 Peter van Musschenbroek, a Dutch professor, carried the idea of storing electricity a step further. From a horizontal steel rod (an old gun barrel) suspended by silk threads, he hung a piece of wire (Fig. 15–9A). The lower end of the wire passed through a cork into a suspended flask of water. Van Musschenbroek's idea was that as the rod was charged with electricity, the charge could be conducted to and stored in the water. His results were too good. After feeding a considerable charge to the steel rod, the professor touched the rod with one hand and the glass bottle with the other. The results he never forgot. The electrical shock incapacitated him for two days. But he had invented the now famous Leyden jar condenser for storing electricity.

Abbé Nollet (1700–1770) of France heard of Van Musschenbroek's experiment. In Louis XV's palace, he arranged a 900-foot ring of Carthusian monks to receive a large electrical discharge. What a sight when at the instant of discharge, the monks, hands connected, leaped into the air to a man! What a way to serve science, king, and God! Fortunately, the shock did no harm.

A form of Leyden jar is still used in experimental work. A large glass jar is lined inside and out with tin foil (Fig. 15–9B). A brass rod with a knob at the upper end terminates below in a chain touching the inner foil instead of water. To charge the Leyden jar, its knob is connected to a terminal of an electric machine, and the outer foil is connected with the ground. As shown in the illustration, a — charge applied to the knob distributes itself through the rod and chain to the inner foil. By induction, the *inner* surface of the outer foil develops a + charge. The — charge tending to form on the *outer* surface of the outer foil is repelled into the ground. Glass is an insulator that keeps the — charge of the inner foil and the + charge of the outer foil apart. Human hands or any other conductor placed between the — charged knob and the + outer foil results in a surge of electricity; unlike charges attract.

15–8 Storing electricity. George Hauksbee accumulated electrical charge by connecting a brass cylinder to a glass globe and rotating the globe.

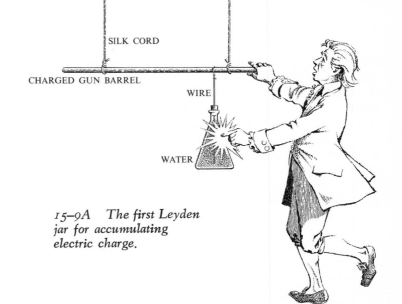

CHARGED GUN BARREL

WIRE

WATER

15–9A   The first Leyden jar for accumulating electric charge.

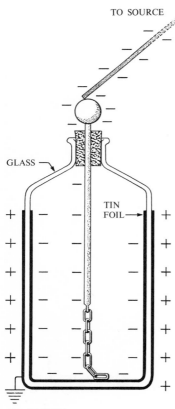

TO SOURCE

GLASS

TIN FOIL

TO GROUND

15–9B   Charging a Leyden jar. Electric charge applied at the knob is distributed along the inner foil. An opposite charge is induced on the outer foil with the aid of a grounded wire.

The Leyden jar is now but one form of electrical condenser for concentrating charges in a small space. Its essential element, first noted by Franklin, is the glass insulation separating the two foils. A simpler condenser consists of two metal plates insulated by air instead of glass. Most of us are familiar with the variable condenser and its set of rotating metal plates in radio sets. We turn such plates relative to a second stationary set each time we change radio stations.

ELECTRICAL SPARKS AND LIGHTNING: FRANKLIN'S KITE EXPERIMENT

By the time of Benjamin Franklin, electrical sparks were in the air, figuratively and literally. In 1708 Dr. William Wall of England suggested that the crackling and light around amber after vigorous rubbing are thunder and lightning on a minute scale. A spark between a piece of rubbed amber and a needle brought to the amber reminded Newton of lightning in 1716. Stephan Gray in 1731 went a step further and reported to the British Royal Society that sparks seen in the dark between rubbed glass tubes and a nearby finger represented electricity passing between the two objects. Then in 1735, Gray speculated that the flash and noise of electric discharge from a friction machine is small-scale lightning and thunder.

In 1748 Benjamin Franklin became so intrigued with electrical phenomena that he sold his printing business, newspaper, and Almanac to devote himself completely, he hoped, to research. He was particularly interested in lightning. From where did it arise? If the origins of lightning were supernatural, why were churches targets? If lightning was a huge electric spark due to natural causes, couldn't lightning be controlled?

A further clue to lightning was St. Elmo's fire at the tips of masts or steeples. Franklin, and Gray before him, noticed that charged spheres produce sparks more readily toward objects with sharp points than toward others. In a famous letter to the Royal Society in 1750, Franklin said:

> Points have a property by which they can *draw on* as well as *throw off* the electrical fluid, at greater distances than blunt bodies can . . . . If these things are so, may not the knowledge of this power be of use to mankind in preserving houses, churches, ships, etc., from the stroke of

15–10 Franklin investigating lightning. Franklin was lucky to survive this famous kite experiment. Within a year, a French and a Russian scientist were killed in similar attempts to determine whether lightning is a huge electrical spark. (Brown Bros. photograph)

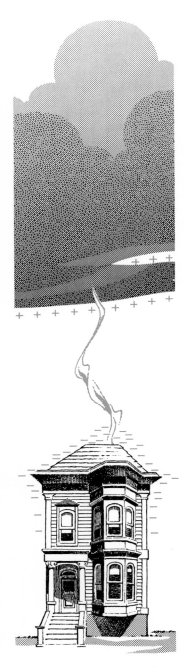

lightning.... Would not pointed rods probably draw the electrical fire silently out of a cloud before it came nigh enough to strike, and thereby secure us from that most sudden and terrible mischief?

At the time, the British Royal Society did not take Franklin's idea of treating lightning as a huge electrical spark seriously. The proposal did not receive a place in their proceedings. Franklin's ideas had a more positive reception in France. Inspired by Franklin, two French scientists, Delibard and Delor, individually carried out experiments in 1752 "to determine the question whether the clouds that contain lightning are electrical or not." Delibard used a pointed iron rod 40 feet high, and Delor, one about 100 feet high, to draw electricity from storm clouds. Both reported sparks up to an inch and a half long at the lower ends of their rods. Fortunately, the two French experimenters were not killed. A third Frenchman was killed the following year in a similar experiment.

Aware of the French experiments, Franklin in 1752 took one more experimental step to convince himself that sparks from clouds are the same as those from charged objects on earth and that lightning itself is a huge electrical spark. The poles of his French colleagues had not reached into the clouds; perhaps the sparks obtained had not originated from the clouds. Besides, the sparks had not been gathered into a Leyden jar for further electrical checking. Perhaps these sparks were not the same as those from friction machines. Franklin therefore reached into a storm cloud with a kite (Fig. 15–10). The results are well known. He too was fortunate in remaining alive; a year later, a Russian scientist was killed in a similar attempt. Franklin used metal points on his kite to draw charge. From the points, a wet string stretched to where Franklin stood under cover in the rain. Franklin held the string with a dry silk cord. At the end of the string was a key. Loose fibers of string began to bristle as they became electrified. When Franklin moved his knuckle toward the key, a spark jumped from the key. Franklin quickly lowered the key and charged his Leyden jar. He later found that the charge in his jar tested the same as if from a friction machine. He had established the hypothesis that lightning is a huge electrical spark. Lightning was a natural phenomenon rather than divine punishment. It was Franklin's contribution to an Age of Reason well buttressed by Newtonian mechanics.

In the turbulence and friction of cloud formation, parts of clouds become positively charged, and other parts become negatively charged. By induction, nearby clouds and the earth below become oppositely charged (Fig. 15–11), much like the outer foil of a Leyden jar (Fig. 15–9). The air between charged clouds or between clouds and buildings is ordinarily a good insulator, like glass between metal foils in a Leyden jar. But if the charge becomes large enough or the clouds come close enough, a lightning discharge occurs. Since light travels faster than sound, we see the flash before hearing it as thunder. More discharges occur between

15–11   Lightning is a huge electrical spark that occurs between an oppositely charged cloud and a building or other object.

clouds than between clouds and earth because of shorter distances between charged clouds.

Franklin followed through and invented lightning rods. These metal rods extend from a point slightly above a building into moist earth below. For example, positively (+) charged clouds drifting over a building tend to induce a negative (−) charge upon it. Pointed lightning rods on the building tend to dissipate the induced charges as they form (Fig. 15–12). And metals, remember, are excellent conductors. If a sudden discharge should occur, the rods lead the discharge into the ground to protect the building. Blind resignation to fate is a poor substitute for the understanding and control of nature. Franklin and his lightning rods illustrate the point.

In automobiles, metal frames provide lightning protection. Lightning that strikes a car tends to find its way into the ground through the chassis. The inside upholstered materials are protective insulation. On the other hand, lone trees on open fields are dangerous places in storms. The trees are high and tend to draw a discharge. Since wood is a poor conductor, the discharge tends to destroy the tree and objects beneath it.

"ARTIFICIAL LIGHTNING" MACHINES

If lightning is a huge spark, then in an opposite sense electrical sparks are miniature lightning flashes. In that sense, the Wimshurst machine (Fig. 15–13) is an "artificial lightning" machine. This experimental machine often has its own built-in Leyden jars for charging. Two parallel glass plates rotate in opposite directions when a handle is turned. The plates and their metal insets rotate against brushes where, through induction, two types of charge are formed. A pair of conducting rods leads − charges to the knob of one Leyden jar; another pair of conductors results in + charges at the knob of the other jar. The knobs are like two clouds with opposite charges. When enough opposite charge accumulates at the two knobs, a discharge leaps across the "spark gap," much like lightning between clouds. Men attempt to control nature by imitation as well as by understanding. Today's Van de Graaf electrostatic generators induce tremendous charges for accelerating atomic particles in modern nuclear research.

THEORIES OF ELECTRICITY

So much for electrical phenomena. What about their explanation? It is one thing to identify lightning as electricity and another to explain what electricity is. What is it that passes from cloud to cloud or from amber rod to electroscope knob?

15–12 Lightning rods on a building dissipate induced electric charges.

15-13 The Wimshurst "artificial lightning" machine. The knobs are like two clouds with opposite charges. With enough unlike charge at the knobs, a discharge leaps across the "spark gap," much like lightning between clouds. (Pip Photos, Inc. by Ullstein Verlag. Mme. Curie is the experimenter in the photograph.)

Fluid Theories

Abbé Nollet concluded that electricity is a fluid, an invisible substance like caloric, that becomes apparent as a spark through its effects on another unseen substance, air. But there are two electrical fluids, the resinous (−) and the vitreous (+). An uncharged object has both fluids in equal amounts; a charged object has an excess of one of the fluids. Amber and fur ordinarily are unelectrified; each has equal amounts of the two fluids. Rubbing causes some exchange of fluids. The amber acquires extra resinous fluid from the fur, and the fur acquires extra vitreous fluid from the amber. Each becomes electrified in an opposite way. In the same way glass and silk become oppositely charged by rubbing. The two-fluid theory could thus explain electrification of objects by rubbing. The theory could also explain such phenomena as conduction, insulation, repulsion, attraction, or induced charges. For example, good conductors have ample passageways for transmitting electrical fluids; insulators do not. Electrical fluid particles tend to repel each other but to be attracted toward particles of ordinary matter and particles of the other electrical fluid. Thus, when a piece of amber with resinous electrical fluid is brought near a neutral pith ball, the resinous fluid in the pith ball is repelled to a further region. The section closer to the amber now has an excess of the opposite vitreous fluid, which is attracted to the resinous amber and brings the lightweight pith with it. And so on.

Franklin opposed the two-fluid theory with a one-fluid theory. He had a water analogy in mind. If adjacent twin containers, each half full of water, are joined by a pipe, water will not flow (Fig. 15–14A). Transfer some water from one container into the other, and water will flow from the higher to the lower until the levels are equal again (Fig. 15–14B). If the original water level is considered neutral, the higher water level may be indicated as + and the lower level −. The water flows from + to − until equality of the two levels is again reached (Fig. 15–14C). The excess water of one container neutralizes the water deficiency in the other. The total amount of water remains the same regardless of flow.

To Franklin, by analogy with water, there was just a single electrical fluid. A neutral or unelectrified object has a given normal amount of this fluid. In gaining more fluid, the object becomes positively (+) electrified. In losing some fluid, the neutral object becomes negatively (−) electrified. When unelectrified glass is rubbed with silk, some electrical fluid transfers from the silk to the glass. The glass, in gaining fluid has + electricity, and the silk, in losing fluid, has − electricity. It is the *excess* (+) and the *deficiency* (−) of the fluid rather than the fluid itself that results in electrification. Electrical fluid flows from + (higher levels) to − (lower levels) just as heat travels from higher temperature to lower, or water from higher places to lower places. Lower (−) will not go uphill to higher (+). A beautiful example of reasoning by analogy! And yet analogies often break down. Such phenomena as electrical attraction or conduction could be explained by the water analogy: Negatively charged objects take on fluid from neutral or positively charged

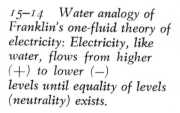

15–14 Water analogy of Franklin's one-fluid theory of electricity: Electricity, like water, flows from higher (+) to lower (−) levels until equality of levels (neutrality) exists.

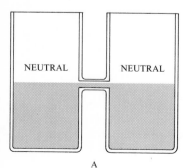

A

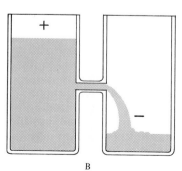

B

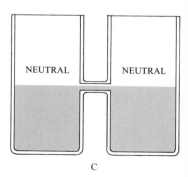

C

objects. But the water analogy could not explain repulsion. Water flows downhill to water in seeming attraction or remains stationary (neutral) at the same levels, but no shifting of water levels in two containers gives repelling effects. Water does not repel water. Why do negatively charged objects repel negatively charged objects? Franklin himself could not answer this question. Franklin's one-fluid theory could not supply an answer. The two-fluid theory could. With two kinds of fluids (+ and −), unlikes could attract, and likes repel.

The one-fluid theory was simpler than the two-fluid, but simplicity may not be enough in a complex universe. In time, both fluid theories of electricity had to be discarded, but Franklin's terms of + and − (charges) were retained in electrical theory and applied to the makeup of everyday matter. Perhaps the most important contribution of the one-fluid theory is the principle of conservation of charge that it indicated— the principle that *electrical charge can be neither created nor destroyed.* Specifically, a given amount of fluid transferring from silk to rubbed glass rod gives the glass just as much excess (+) fluid as the silk has a deficiency (−) of fluid. The fluid that the glass gains is lost by the silk; the two objects develop equal and opposite electrifications, or charges. That is, individual objects gain and lose fluid in transferring it, but the total amount of fluid (and therefore charge) in the universe remains the same, just as does the total amount of water when water flows from one container to another. Discarded theories often leave behind inferences that take hold on their own. And discarded theories may leave behind vestigial terms as well: The expression electrical "juice," a carry-over from fluid theory, is still heard today.

Theory of Electron Transfer

At the heart of electrical explanation today is the theory of electron transfer. Seven assumptions of this theory are given below. The first three assumptions are retained from electrical fluid theories.

1. A neutral body contains equal amounts of positive (+) and negative (−) charge (for example, an insulated metal sphere).
2. Insulated conductors can be electrified by induction and show a + and a − charge in different sections (for example, an insulated metal sphere approached by a charged glass rod should have a − charge facing the rod and a + charge away from the rod).
3. All matter is composed of atoms.
4. Atoms are composed of three basic particles: *protons, neutrons,* and *electrons.* The protons and neutrons form a nucleus around which electrons orbit. The protons carry + charges, and the neutrons are electrically neutral. The electrons are the lightest known carriers of − electrical charges.

5. Atoms themselves are ordinarily neutral. Each atom has as many electrons as protons; the — charges neutralize the + charges in the atom as a whole.

6. Electrons transfer out of and into atoms more readily than do other particles. They are outermost and lightest.

7. It is the transfer of electrons between and within solid objects that charge or electrify them.

A negatively charged solid has an excess of electrons. Ordinarily, neutral amber gains electrons when rubbed with fur. The extra electrons make the amber negatively charged as a whole.

A positively charged solid has a deficiency of electrons. The fur, having lost some of its electrons, has more + charges than — charges and is positively charged as a whole. A glass rod when rubbed loses some electrons to the silk cloth and becomes positively charged. The cloth becomes negatively charged.

In short, modern atomic and electron theories of matter assume that matter itself is basically electrical in nature and can be used to explain electrical phenomena, whether rubbed amber or lightning. That is, matter itself is made up of particles carrying two distinctly opposite charges (shades of two-fluid theory here!). But in solids only one of these charges, the electron, is the active one (shades of one-fluid theory here!). Assumptions 4–7 above of the electron theory thus can be seen as a synthesis of the best features of the opposing one-fluid and two-fluid theories. Ingenious reconciliations of formerly contradictory ideas are frequent in modern science. Further discussion of atomic and electron theories is postponed to later chapters of the book because of their complexity and importance. Meanwhile, see if you can explain the phenomena illustrated in Figs. 15–1 to 15–14 by electron transfer as suggested in the seven points listed above.

COULOMB'S LAW OF ELECTROSTATIC FORCE

By Newton's laws of motion, electrical forces are associated with electrical charges. The gold leaves of a charged electroscope repel each other against gravity (Fig. 15–5); electrical forces must be acting upon them. The gold leaves separate, and gravity does not bring them back together. Pith balls when charged also move apart and stay apart. These charged objects repel each other equally; opposite and equal forces are involved. Newton's mechanical view thus extends to electrical situations. But what determines how large electrical forces become? Gravitation involves an inverse square law, and by analogy, electrical forces do, too, reasoned Bernoulli in Switzerland, Priestley and Cavendish in England, and Coulomb in France.

Each independently and contemporaneously attempted to show that electrical forces become larger as the square of the distance between two charged objects becomes smaller. That is, $F \propto 1/d^2$, where F is the electrical force and d^2 is the distance squared between the charged objects.

But Coulomb went further than the others in precisely measuring electrical forces and distances directly with charged spheres. Coulomb used a sensitive torsion balance technique much like that later developed by Cavendish (Fig. 9–10) to test gravitational inverse squares. The force of repulsion on the charged ball at the end of the horizontal rod was proportional to the angle of twist of the suspension fiber. Through the corresponding angle of rotation of the rod, Coulomb could therefore make comparisons between repulsion forces as the distance between the charged balls was changed. Coulomb repeated this repulsion experiment many times. He also tested electrical forces of attraction. The result was an inverse squares law for electrostatic forces: $F \propto 1/d^2$.

But distance between charges is not the only factor in the size of electrical forces. Coulomb assumed also that an electrical force varies directly "as the product of the *electrical masses* of the two balls." This was by analogy with Newton's law of gravitation,

$$F = G \; \frac{m_1 m_2}{d^2}.$$

Coulomb substituted "electrical masses" for gravitational masses and electrical forces for gravitational forces. The idea of "electrical masses" is expressed today as quantities of charge q. The electrical force F between two charged objects depends upon three factors: (1) the quantity of charge q_1 in the first object; (2) the quantity of charge q_2 in the second object; and (3) the distance squared between the two objects d^2. These factors are related in the following manner:

1. $F \propto \dfrac{1}{d^2}$ (by direct measurement [Coulomb])

2. $F \propto q_1 q_2$ (by analogy with gravitational forces and masses and confirmed by Coulomb's torsion balance tests)

3. $F \propto \dfrac{q_1 q_2}{d^2}$ (by combining 1 and 2)

4. $F = C \left(\dfrac{q_1 q_2}{d^2}\right)$ (by introducing proportionality constant C).

Equation 15–1

Equation 15–1 is now known as *Coulomb's law of electrostatic force*. The law says that *the electrostatic force between two bodies is directly proportional to the quantities of charge of the two bodies and inversely proportional to the square of the distance between the two bodies.*

In honor of the man, the *coulomb* has become the name of a unit for quantity of charge q. The coulomb is that charge which repels a like charge 1 meter away in a vacuum (or air) with a force of 9×10^9 newtons. That is, in the mks system: Force F is expressed in newtons, quantities of charge q_1 and q_2 in coulombs, and distance d in meters:

$$F = C \frac{q_1 q_2}{d^2}.$$

In air or in a vacuum, the value of the constant C is 9×10^9 (that is,

$$9 \times 10^9 = C \frac{1 \times 1}{1^2}).$$

FARADAY'S FIELDS

Observations of lodestone led to the theory of magnetism and its concepts of poles, forces, and fields. Similarly, observations of rubbed amber led to the theory of electricity and its parallel concepts of charges, forces, and fields. It was Michael Faraday who first projected fields of force into spaces around electrical charges. Faraday was concerned with how electrical forces could act on objects from a distance. Was there anything in space through which electrical forces act? Faraday proposed "tubes" (or lines) of force around charges analogous to those around magnets. And in the process he advanced one of the great conceptual models of our time, the model of fields—electrical fields, magnetic fields, gravitational fields, and as we shall see, composite electromagnetic fields.

A + charged balloon and a − charged balloon are attracted to each other. Can it be that lines of electrical force like unseen elastic bands pull the balloons together? If lines of force form fields around magnets, why not around charges? Faraday's conceptual model of electrical fields of force is illustrated in Fig. 15–15.

15–15   Electric fields: (A) around a single positive charge, (B) between opposite charges, and (C) between like (positive) charges. The direction of lines of force is from + to − charges.

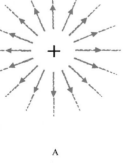

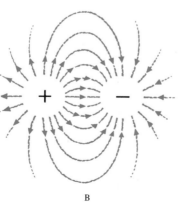

A   B   C

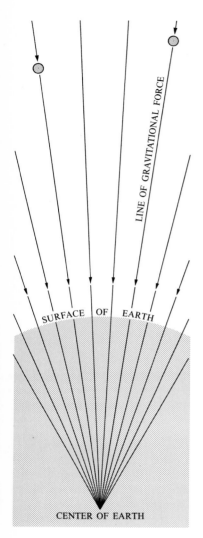

LINE OF GRAVITATIONAL FORCE

SURFACE OF EARTH

CENTER OF EARTH

15–16A   Lines of force in the earth's gravitational field.

Figure 15–15A represents the field pattern of a + charged balloon alone. Lines of force spread radially outward from the balloon surface; the divergence of the lines represents a weakening of the electric field with distance.

In Fig. 15–15B, another balloon of the same size has been placed nearby with an equal but opposite charge. The two charged balloons have a common electrical field with lines of force tending to pull the two charged objects together. Faraday gave lines of electrical force a direction from + charge to −, analogous to the extension of lines of magnetic force outward from N pole to S pole.

Figure 15–15C represents balloons of the same size and equal + charge repelling each other. The fields here separate rather than join, and they appear to "buck" or repel each other, carrying the balloons back. The field contains the energy and exerts the forces on the balloons.

Fine bits of hair in thick oil surrounding two highly charged metal objects can be used to demonstrate electric field patterns. The hair clippings tend to take the patterns described in Fig. 15–15 in accordance with whether the charged objects are alone, equal and opposite, or alike. The hairs line up in patterns much like iron filings around magnets.

Faraday's fields of force were real to him and could explain known electrical phenomena. For example, a + charged cloud is surrounded by an electric field. The field, stretching to roofs and ground, induces opposite charges on them (Fig. 15–11). Franklin's lightning rod promoted safety by tending to draw the opposite charges, the lines of force and field toward itself.

FIELD AND GRAVITY

Fields of force, once established for magnets and electric charges, were worked out for the earth's gravity. If a field of force is a "region of space where forces are present," then a gravitational field surrounds the earth or any object. A rock falling from high above the earth's surface tends to fall in a straight line toward the earth's surface (Fig. 15–16A). That path represents a line of gravitational force. A second rock dropped from another point gives a second gravitational line of force. No matter from where above the earth a rock is dropped, a line of force can be drawn toward the earth. The system of radial lines drawn in to the center of the earth, therefore, symbolizes the earth's lines of gravitational force and field. The direction of the lines is toward the earth's center, where supposedly the lines meet.

Notice in Fig. 15–16A that the lines of gravitational force become more dense as they converge toward the earth. The closer in to the earth, the greater is the number of lines piercing a cross-sectional area; the further away, the less dense the lines. The number of lines penetrating

1 sq cm (or other unit area) is therefore a measure of the density of lines of force and the strength of the gravitational field.

Suppose there are 4 lines of force to 1 sq cm on the earth's surface (Fig. 15–16B). These 4 lines/sq cm represent the strength of the gravitational field at the earth's surface. Now imagine these lines extended to a sphere 8,000 miles above the earth's surface. Since these lines diverge, they corner *nine* squares rather than *one* square on the outer sphere. In short, *tripling* the distance from the center of the earth decreases the average number of lines to a square to *one-ninth* of its former value (that is, from four to four-ninth lines)—the inverse square relationship again! Obviously, Newton's inverse square law is well represented by the field model. Figure 15–16B further illustrates this inverse square relationship between line densities or gravitational forces upon an object at various positions above the earth.

Similar representations around an electrical charge (Fig. 15–15A) show a decrease in the density of lines of force as the square of the distance from the charge increases. Thus, the density of lines graphically indicates the strength of the electrical force or field at any point around a charged object in accordance with Coulomb's electrostatic inverse square law.

In the same way, illustrations of field around an isolated magnetic pole (Fig. 14–6) show decreased density of lines of force with distance squared from the magnetic pole. And the density of lines indicates the strength of the magnetic force or field at any point around the pole in accordance with Coulomb's inverse square law for magnetism.

In summary, Gilbert's work and the definite patterns of iron filings around magnets suggested to Faraday "tubes" or lines of electric force around charges as well as lines of force around magnets. Lines of force act as mechanical structures in space that exert force on certain objects. Lines of force around magnets and charges, therefore, are not "emanations" from them but unseen mechanisms that transmit Coulomb forces to particular reacting objects (for example, filings, hair clippings). Electrical lines of force form total patterns called electrical fields, just as magnetic lines of force form magnetic fields and just as gravitational lines of force form gravitational fields.

COULOMB'S LAWS AND THE MECHANICAL VIEW

In the budding sciences of magnetism and electricity, Newton's mechanics thus further triumphed as an approach to the universe. There were now three main forces and associated fields in the universe: gravitational, magnetic, and electrical. All three forces acted directly across space between objects, had similar formulations as summarized in the equations below, and involved inverse squares laws. Determine the position and

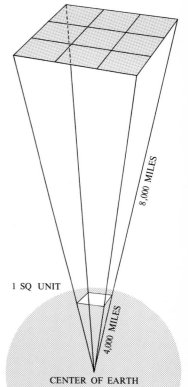

9 SQ UNITS

8,000 MILES

1 SQ UNIT

4,000 MILES

CENTER OF EARTH

15–16B   Newton's inverse square law and gravitational fields. Lines of force diverge away from the earth. Tripling the distance from the earth's center reduces the number of lines of force per unit area (gravitational field strength) to one-ninth.

velocities of all objects in the universe as well as their gravitational masses, charges, and polar strengths, and you will then know all forces at work. You will have all that you need to predict future events.

FORCES AT A DISTANCE

GRAVITY	MAGNETISM	ELECTRICAL FORCES
$F = \dfrac{Gm_1m_2}{d^2}$	$F = \dfrac{Kp_1p_2}{d^2}$	$F = \dfrac{Cq_1q_2}{d^2}$

CHAPTER REVIEW

1. Describe some electrical phenomena observed in nature.
2. What is an electric charge?
3. How were electric charges first produced by men?
4. How does electrical attraction differ from magnetic attraction?
5. What observations suggest the following concepts? (a) Positive and negative electric charges. (b) Induced charge. (c) Electrical conductors. (d) Electrical insulators. (e) Electrical force. (f) Electrical field.
6. Define the concepts in question 5.
7. Describe evidences for the following laws: (a) law of electrical attraction and repulsion and (b) inverse square law of electrical force.
8. (a) Why is William Gilbert sometimes called the "father of electrical science"? (b) Did the science of electricity really begin with Gilbert? Explain.
9. How can electric charges be detected? Explain.
10. Why may an electrically charged body have only one kind of charge, while a magnet must have both kinds of poles?
11. How did Benjamin Franklin show that lightning is a huge electrical spark?
12. Electricians often refer to electricity as "juice." Why "juice"?
13. How could Franklin have believed that electricity is a single "fluid" and still have originated the idea that electricity can be positive or negative?
14. (a) Describe and compare the following theories of electricity: Franklin's one-fluid theory, the two-fluid theory, and the theory of electron transfer. (b) Is the electron transfer theory closer to the one-fluid or the two-fluid theory?
15. (a) What are assumptions of the electron transfer theory? (b) Which of these assumptions were retained from electrical fluid theories?
16. Who was the greater innovator in electrical science, William Gilbert or Benjamin Franklin? Is it correct to compare their contributions? Why?

17. Use the electron transfer theory to explain the following phenomena: (a) A rubbed glass rod attracts bits of paper. (b) A pith ball is attracted to a rubbed rubber rod, remains in contact for a moment, and then falls back. (c) When the rod in (b) is brought toward the pith ball, the ball moves further away. (d) A well-charged glass rod applied to one end of a metal rod attracts feathers to cork at the other end. (e) A spark may result if you reach for a doorknob after walking across a thick rug. (f) A charged rod placed on the knob of an electroscope causes the suspended gold leaves to fly apart and stay apart. (g) A charged rod merely approaching but not touching an electroscope knob causes the gold leaves to move apart. When the rod is removed, the leaves collapse. (h) In (g), if a finger is placed on the electroscope knob before the rod is removed, the leaves do *not* collapse. (i) Rotating a sphere against a hand gives electric charge to both the sphere and the hand. (j) Electricity may be stored in Leyden jars. (k) The Wimshurst electrical machine can be used to produce charge, store charge, and produce "artificial lightning."

18. By Coulomb's law, what three factors determine the strength of an electric force? What assumptions exist in this law?

19. Will the repelling force of a strong electric charge upon a weak one be more than the force of the weak charge upon the strong one? Explain.

20. Compare similarities and differences among Newton's law of gravitation, Coulomb's law of magnetic force, and Coulomb's law of electrical force.

21. Show similarities and differences between (a) electrical and magnetic phenomena and (b) electrical and magnetic theory.

22. How does Coulomb's law of electrical force illustrate the extension of the mechanical view to electrical phenomena?

23. Give illustrations of how imagination contributed to electrical science development.

24. Show how the development of electrical science crossed national boundaries.

PROBLEMS

1. If you run a comb through your hair, the comb will attract small pieces of paper. How do you know this is electrical attraction rather than magnetic attraction?

2. Why do gasoline trucks often drag chains behind them?

3. Explain why when two objects are rubbed together to produce an electric charge, one object becomes positively charged and the other negatively charged.

4. A charged rod is brought near a positively charged electroscope. The leaves fly further apart. Is the rod charged positively or negatively? Explain.

5. Prove that unlike electric charges repel each other.

6. What is lightning? How does it originate? Where does it go? Why?

7. (a) How do lightning rods protect a building? (b) Why does a tall brick chimney need lightning rods more than a steel smokestack?

8. The earth and the clouds with the air in between have been called a condenser such as the one used in your radio set. How does lightning prove this?

9. Suppose that two similar positive charges placed 1 cm apart repel each other with a force of 2 gm. What would the force become (a) if the distance is increased to 2 cm? (b) If one charge is tripled? (c) If both charges are doubled? (d) If one charge is doubled and the distance is doubled?

10. What happens to the force between two electric charges (a) if the distance between them is halved? Tripled? Quadrupled? Explain. (b) If one charge is doubled? (c) If one charge is doubled and the other tripled? (d) If one charge is doubled, the other tripled, and the distance is tripled?

SUGGESTIONS FOR FURTHER READING

Taylor, Lloyd W., *Physics, the Pioneer Science,* Vol. 2, Dover paperback, New York, 1959, Ch. 40.

Conant, James, ed., *Harvard Case Histories in Experimental Science,* Vol. 2, Harvard Univ. Press, Cambridge, Mass., 1957, Ch. 8.

Editors of *Scientific American, Lives in Science,* Simon and Schuster paperback, New York, Ch. 4, "Benjamin Franklin."

Ripley, Julien A., *Elements and Structure of the Physical Sciences,* Wiley, New York, 1964, Ch. 13.

Wightman, William, *Growth of Scientific Ideas,* Yale Univ. Press, New Haven, Conn., 1953, Ch. 18.

Schneer, Cecil, *Search for Order,* Harper, New York, 1960, Ch. 13.

16   Electric Currents
and Electromagnetism

Chance favors the prepared mind.

LOUIS PASTEUR, 1870

Sparks jumping from Franklin's key to his knuckle were not *electric currents*, but they were a step toward them. An electric spark is a *discharge*, a brief, fast flow of charge to an opposite charge. How did man improve upon nature by creating a steady flow of charge?

"ANIMAL ELECTRICITY"

Another step toward electric currents was the accidental discovery of "animal electricity" by Luigi Galvani (1737–1798), professor of anatomy at the University of Bologna. The story is that Galvani's assistant touched an exposed nerve in the leg of a dead frog while a nearby electric machine was sparking. Galvani noticed that with each spark, the leg jerked. Perplexed, Galvani took over the scalpel; his results were the same. A frog's leg was responding to electrical sparks at a distance. Galvani then wondered whether a dead frog would also respond to lightning. Attaching an iron wire to the foot of a frog, he dropped the other end of the wire into a well (Fig. 16–1). He ran a second wire from the nerves of the frog's leg to the top of his house. And there it was: The frog's leg jerked with the flashes of lightning. Would the same thing occur in good weather? Galvani then hung a number of prepared frogs with projecting brass

16–1 Apparatus for Galvani's experiment with "animal electricity." (Pip Photos, Inc. by Ullstein Verlag)

hooks from an iron railing. Nothing happened until, in Galvani's words, "I began to press the brass hooks against the iron railing . . . . I did observe frequent contractions." Clearly, the contractions were to be attributed to something in the experimental setup rather than to the weather. But to what in the setup? Galvani continues:

> When I transferred the animal to a closed room, had laid it on an iron plate and begun to press the hook which was in the spinal cord against the plate, behold, the same contractions, the same motions! I repeated the experiment by using other metals at other places and on other hours and days; with the same result, only that the contractions were different when different metals were used, being more lively for some and more sluggish for others. At last it occurred to us to use other bodies which conduct electricity only a little or not at all, made of glass, rubber, resin, stone or wood and always dried, and with these nothing similar occurred, no muscular contractions or motions could be seen. Naturally such a result excited in us no slight astonishment and caused us to think that possibly *the electricity was in the animal itself.*

The frog's legs had contracted without lightning or an electric machine present. What could be more plausible than that the contractions were due to electricity originating within the animal itself, and that the electricity showed itself when the animal's body made a complete circuit with the conducting metals (the brass hook and iron plate)? An alternative to Galvani's "animal electricity" hypothesis did exist: Two *different* metals were in contact with the frog. When both the hook and the plate were of the *same* metal, iron, and were pressed together, the legs did not jerk. But Galvani remembered that in the earlier experiment at the well, the frog's leg had jerked with distant lightning flashes, although only conducting wires were used. Galvani insisted on his hypothesis of animal electricity.

VOLTA'S BATTERIES: CURRENTS FROM CHEMICALS

Galvani's countryman Alessandro Volta (1745–1827), physics professor at Pavia, however, believed that Galvani's electricity originated somehow in the two different metals rather than in the frog. For further evidence, Volta stacked discs of zinc and silver alternately. Between each pair of the two metals, he inserted a piece of brine-soaked cardboard (Fig. 16–2A). When he connected the two end discs of his pile he obtained a small spark at the point of contact. But more than that, he got a continuous current as long as contact was maintained. Two different metals replacing a frog gave an electric current. Here was the world's first source of steady current, the battery. Volta experimented further, to find that other metals in pairs gave currents. And the higher his pile of alternate discs, the greater was Volta's shock in touching both ends. Although Volta acknowledged that the effects of his battery were not as striking as discharges of electric machines or Leyden jars, he noted that his battery "infinitely surpasses the power of these [jars] in that it does not need, as they do, to be charged in advance by means of an outside source; and in that it can give the disturbance every time that it is properly touched, no matter how often." That is, his batteries afforded not temporary discharges but continuous currents originating from pairs of different metals.

Volta also substituted bowls of water with brine or lye in place of moist cardboard to originate a "wet" cell, the ancestor to today's storage battery. As described by Volta:

> We set up a row of several cups or bowls half-full of pure water, or better of brine or of lye; and we join them all together in a sort of chain by means of metallic arcs of which one arm *A* which is placed in one of the goblets is of . . . copper and the other Z which is placed in the next goblet is of tin or better of zinc . . . . The two metals of which

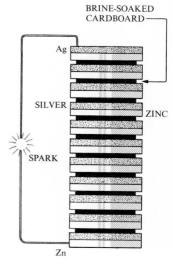

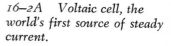

16–2A Voltaic cell, the world's first source of steady current.

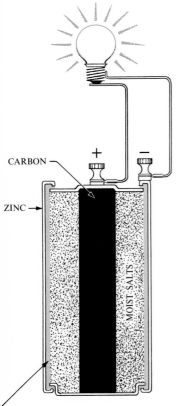

CARBON

ZINC →

MOIST SALTS

INSULATION

16–2B   Cross section of today's "dry" cell.

each arc is composed are soldered together somewhere above the part which is immersed in the liquid.

In today's "dry" cell (Fig. 16–2B) carbon and zinc are used effectively as the two metals. A carbon cylinder acts as a metal in the center of a container made of zinc. Moist salts fill the container. The carbon terminal is labeled as +, and the zinc as −. If the terminals, or *electrodes,* are connected by wire, an electrical current is produced.

In summary, Volta orginated batteries and electric currents to support the idea that two unlike metals (and not the frog) gave Galvani his electricity. The frog had merely conducted the current and responded to it by muscular contraction. Volta recognized a basic principle for steady electric currents that Galvani had stumbled upon but did not accept. Yet regardless of error about its origins, Galvani had accidentally discovered that electricity could exist independently of rubbed objects or lightning. And although Volta was basically correct in his interpretation of Galvani's frog experiments, Galvani did have a point regarding animal electricity. We know today that all animals and humans do produce electricity. In particular, the electric eel shocks victims through internal muscular plates that produce electricity. In a number of experiments with an electric eel, Faraday showed that there is no basic difference between the electricity of·an eel and that of a battery. Figure 16–3 illustrates a setup in the New York Aquarium in which an electric eel, whenever disturbed, lights a lamp by completing a circuit through an electrical discharge into the water. A terminal in the water at each end of the tank is connected to an auxiliary current source and to the lamp. Ordinarily, however, currents produced by animals or men are too minute to be detected except by very sensitive apparatus.

PREREQUISITES OF A CURRENT

The work of Volta made it clear that there are two prerequisites for a current: (1) a source (for example, a dry cell) and (2) a complete, or closed, circuit. An *electric circuit* is an unbroken conducting path along which a flow of electricity may take place. Copper wires connecting terminals in a dry cell, hard water in the eel's tank, or frog tissue all serve as circuit-completing conductors. Circuits include appliances or indicators, whether light bulbs or the convulsive leg of a frog (Fig. 16–1). A flashlight illustrates the prerequisites of a current: The dry cells provide the source; the light bulb, the appliance; and the metal case, a completed circuit when the switch is flicked.

But why do two different metals properly arranged act as a source of current? Since Volta's time, the answer has been found in chemical action. There is chemical action of frog body fluids upon the brass screws and iron plates, of electric eel body fluids upon muscular plates, and of

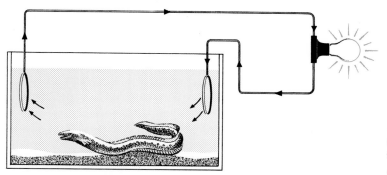

16–3 An electric eel originates a lamp-lighting current in the New York Aquarium.

moist salts upon zinc and carbon electrodes of dry cells. Experiments show that if a copper strip and a zinc strip are immersed without touching in a dilute sulfuric acid (Fig. 16–4), the zinc strip becomes negatively charged and the copper strip positively charged. Some of the zinc, "attacked" by the acid, has gone into the solution, leaving the remaining zinc with an excess of electrons to become negative. The copper strip, meanwhile, has dissolved in the solution much less than the zinc, has fewer extra electrons, and is therefore positive relative to the zinc. The resulting electrical difference between the two strips is called a *potential difference,* or *voltage.* When the metal strips are externally connected by wire, electrons flow through the wire from the zinc (−) to the copper (+). And moving charges constitute a current. Thus, an internal circuit exists within the cell or source itself between the plates and liquid, and an external circuit through conductors between plate terminals. In a so-called dry cell, moist salts replace the acid in chemical action upon the zinc container to give a − zinc electrode and a + carbon electrode in the center of the container. The − electrode is called a *cathode;* and the + electrode, an *anode.* Although electron direction in the wire is from the − to the + electrode, we often read that currents flow from

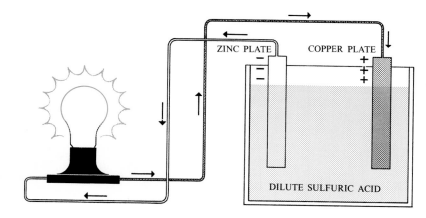

ZINC PLATE COPPER PLATE

DILUTE SULFURIC ACID

16–4 A simple wet cell produces an electric current. By chemical action at the plates, an exterior current flows from the negative to the positive plate.

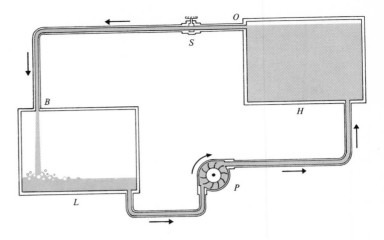

16–5 *Water analogy of an electric current in which a pump acts as an electric cell.*

+ to − electrodes. This convention dates back to Benjamin Franklin's one-fluid theory (Chapter 15) which assumed that electricity flows from higher (+) to lower (−) electrical levels. Theories often leave traces long after they have been abandoned.

WATER ANALOGY OF ELECTRIC CURRENTS

In 1820, a great French physicist, André Ampère (1775–1836), distinguished between what he called "electric tension" and "electric current," between the electrical condition within the eel that tends to cause electricity to flow and the flow itself. Today the terms are "voltage" and *"amperage"* in honor of Volta and Ampère and what they investigated.

A dry cell, by analogy, may be considered to pump electricity much as a water pump circulates water through pipes. In Fig. 16–5, the bottoms of two water tanks L and H at different levels are connected by pipes and a pump P. This setup corresponds to two electrodes and a connecting solution in a voltaic cell. The upper parts of the tanks are connected by an overflow pipe and a valve S in analogy to the exterior circuit or wiring between electrodes. When the tanks are partly filled with water and the pump started, water is forced from the lower tank to the higher tank. When the water in tank H rises to the overflow level at point O, water flows through the outer pipe back to B for a completed circle. Close the valve and tank L is emptied in a short internal flow of water, but external flow has stopped. Falling water can turn wheels; so can moving electrons.

Close the valve with the pump operating and tank L is emptied in a short internal flow of water, but the external flow has stopped. Closing the valve is similar to breaking a connection (switching off) between terminals in an external circuit. Electron flow stops, even though chemical activity continues briefly within the cell.

How can an electrical current be measured if electrons cannot be seen? Perhaps the water analogy can offer further clues. Quantities of water and rates of water current flow are measured even if water molecules are not seen. Water may be measured in cubic feet or gallons, and the rate of flow of water in gallons or cubic feet per second. Similarly, a quantity of electricity may be expressed in units called coulombs (Chapter 15), and the rate of flow of an electric current (past an imagined position on the wire) may be expressed in units called coulombs per second or amperes. The coulomb as a workable unit of electrical charge equals the combined charges of 6.25×10^{19} (62,500,000,000,000,000,000) electrons. Obviously, the charge of an electron is not workable as a unit for everyday currents. *One* coulomb, or 6.25×10^{19} electrons, considered flowing by in 1 second gives a current rate, or intensity, of 1 ampere. *Two* coulombs flowing by per second means 2 amperes, or twice the intensity of current. *Two* coulombs in 2 seconds means a current intensity of only 1 ampere, since the amperage is the number of coulombs in *1* second. That is,

$$I = \frac{Q}{t}$$

or

$$Q = It,$$

where I = intensity, or strength, of current in amperes

Q = the charge in coulombs

t = time in seconds.

Georg Ohm (1787-1854), a German contemporary of Oersted and Ampère, felt the allure of the new field of current electricity. He was particularly interested in the resistance of electrical conductors. Ampère had differentiated between the voltage of a source V and the strength of current I in conducting wires. And it was clear that the more the voltage of the source, the more the resulting current. But unconsidered was the slowing effect of the conducting wires in currents. Water flowing through a pipe is slowed by friction. The longer, narrower, and rougher the pipe, the greater the resistance to the water flow. Shouldn't there be friction slowing the flow of current within wires? And shouldn't this resistance vary with the length, width, material, or temperature of the wire? Fifty years earlier, Cavendish had anticipated Ohm's concept of electrical resistance, but due to Cavendish's secretiveness, his ideas were unknown to Ohm. After diligent, careful experimentation, Ohm found that the resistance R of a wire (1) depends on the material, (2) is directly proportional to the wire's length l, and (3) is inversely proportional to its cross-sectional area a. Stated in algebraic shorthand:

$$R = k\frac{l}{a},$$

Equation 16–1

where k is a constant called resistivity, the value of which depends on the material. Copper, with a low value of k, has a low resistance to current flow. With low resistance, it is of course an excellent conductor of electricity; in fact, it is the best except for silver. Even the best conductors offer some resistance to electrical flow.

Sooner or later, a physical science passes from a descriptive to an analytical mathematical stage based on establishing units and measuring objects. In comparing different materials of the same dimensions and temperatures to copper with respect to ease of electrical conduction, Ohm certainly did his part in mathematizing electric currents. Eventually, an international unit of resistance called the *ohm* was established. The standard ohm is the resistance to a current flow of a column of mercury 106.3 centimeters long and 1 square millimeter cross section at $0°C$.

OHM'S LAW AND ELECTRICAL MEASUREMENT

Ohm's mathematical methods were not confined to comparing resistance of wires. He achieved fame in seeking relationships of the wire resistance R to the voltage V and the intensity of current I. The relationships he found are known as Ohm's law. The law states that "The magnitude of the current in a galvanic current is directly as the sum of all the tensions, and inversely as the entire reduced length of the circuit." Today we say: *The intensity of an electric current (amperes) along a conductor equals the potential difference (volts) divided by the resistance (ohms)*, or

$$\text{current} = \frac{\text{potential difference}}{\text{resistance}}.$$

In symbols,

$$I = \frac{V}{R},$$

Equation 16–2

where I = intensity of current in amperes

V = potential difference in volts

R = resistance in ohms.

From Eq. 16–2, it is clear that a current flowing through a conductor is directly proportional to the potential difference applied across the conductor and inversely proportional to the resistance of the conductor. Also,

$$V = IR. \hspace{4cm} \text{Equation 16–3}$$

That is, the voltage applied across a conductor equals the product of the current in the conductor and the resistance of that conductor. An applied voltage results in a current against resistance. The more the resistance, the less the current expected from a given voltage source (since the product of the current and resistance remains the same.)

The unit for potential difference is the volt. Ohm's law actually became the basis for defining the volt, as seen in the following definition: *the work done in sending a current of 1 ampere through a resistance of 1 ohm.* That is, $V = IR = 1 \cdot 1 = 1$. We have a volt when $I = 1$ ampere and $R = 1$ ohm.

Ohm referred to an analogy between heat and electricity: A greater temperature difference between neighboring objects results in a faster flow of heat, just as a greater potential difference (voltage) between the electrodes of a battery results in a faster flow of electrons (greater amperage). In fact, this heat-electricity analogy may have led Ohm to his law. Once again, we can see the invaluable role of analogies in the development and understanding of science.

But we must also emphasize again that the best of analogies have limitations and can lead to errors. For example, voltage has been called electro-motive *force*. Pumps exert mechanical pressure on water to circulate it through pipes. By analogy, therefore, batteries and other electrical sources have voltage as electrical pressure or force for driving currents through wires. But the word "force" is a misnomer for voltage. Voltage is closer to a concept of work than of force, as shown in the mks system of units, which defines a volt as a joule per coulomb. The joule, of course, is the metric unit of work (Chapter 10). Voltage as basically a concept of work can be more clearly understood through another kind of emphasis in the water system analogy. The *work* of the pump in lifting water to tank H (Fig. 16–5) is transformed into gravitational potential energy of water, and the potential energy of the water in the tank is to be differentiated from its energy of motion when falling. Similarly, the chemical energy within a battery is transformed into a potential difference of the two electrodes, with electrical potential energy being involved in the potential difference. And the potential energy of an electrical source is to be differentiated from the energy of electron flow in wires when connected. Potential energy of a dry cell is lost when electrodes are connected, and a current results that heats, lights, lifts, or otherwise works on objects. And of course, in line with the conservation of energy principle, the original chemical energy lost in the battery equals the total energies gained in the current flow. When "spent" batteries are recharged, the energy process is reversed; the external electrical energy applied to a battery is converted into chemical energy within the battery.

ELECTRICAL POWER AND ENERGY

Ohm's law led indirectly to concepts of electrical power and energy. If the voltage V of a circuit is multiplied by the intensity of current I, the answer will be in units of electrical power. That is,

$$P = VI, \hspace{4cm} \text{Equation 16–4}$$

where P = watts (w) *

V = voltage

I = amperage.

Thus, a watt is the power developed when a current of 1 ampere flows under an electrical pressure of 1 volt. For modern commercial purposes, the watt is often too small a unit. The kilowatt (kw)—"kilo" means 1,000—has therefore been introduced as a unit of 1,000 watts. That is, the kilowatt = 1,000 watts.

The relationship of mechanical and electrical power is given as follows:

1 hp = 746 w (or about ¾ kw)

1 kw = 1⅓ hp.

Energy = power · time. Electrical energy is no exception. To determine the amount of electrical energy used in a circuit, we must know the rate of use (power) and for how long (time). Electrical power may be expressed in watts or kilowatts, and time in seconds or hours. A 12-volt battery giving a 0.5-ampere current may be operated for 5 seconds, 30 minutes, or 2 hours. The power or wattage P involved, $V \cdot I = 12 \cdot 0.5 = 6$ watts, is the same regardless of how long the battery is operated. But the total energy consumed must, of course, increase with time. Units of electrical energy are the *watt-second* (wsec), or joule; the *watt-hour* (whr); and the *kilowatt-hour* (kwhr).

6 w power used for 5 sec give 30 wsec electrical energy;
6 w power used for 2 hr give 12 whr electrical energy;
500 w power used for 30 hr give 15,000 whr electrical energy.
(.5 kw)   (15 kwhr)

*The unit of electrical power was named the watt after James Watt of steam engine fame.

The watt-second is too small a unit for ordinary commercial uses. Electric bills are paid in terms of kilowatt-hours. If the rate of payment for electrical energy is 7c per kilowatt-hour, the cost for operating 500 watts for 30 hours is $1.05.

In summary, if watts = volts · amperes, and kilowatts = watts/1,000 then

$$\text{kilowatt-hours} = \frac{\text{volts} \cdot \text{amperes} \cdot \text{hours}}{1,000}$$

$$\text{cost} = \text{kilowatt-hours} \cdot \text{rate}.$$

MAGNETISM FROM ELECTRICITY: OERSTED'S EXPERIMENTS

Accidental discoveries are significant in the development of science. Galvani's accidental discovery was followed by a momentous one made by Hans Christian Oersted (1777–1851). Oersted, professor of physics at the University of Copenhagen, was about to heat a platinum wire by sending a galvanic current through it. According to one of his students, a compass needle happened to lie under the conducting wire and parallel to it in its northern direction. As soon as the current was on, the magnetic needle quickly swung to a direction perpendicular to the wire (Fig. 16–6). An *electric* current was exerting a perpendicular force on a *magnet!* Oersted reversed the direction of the current by switching the ends of

16–6 Oersted's accidental discovery of electromagnetism. Oersted was amazed to find that an electric current changes the direction of a compass needle. (Culver Pictures, Inc.)

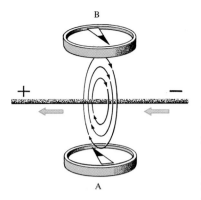

16–7 *Electric currents form magnetic fields.*

STATIONARY CHARGE

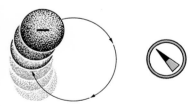

MOVING CHARGE

16–8 *A moving charge is a current; the compass needle deflects when the electric charge moves.*

the two wires to opposite battery terminals. The needle immediately swung halfway around again to a right angle position. A *perpendicular* force rather than a direct attracting or repelling force was acting on the needle. A perpendicular force is contrary to Newtonian expectation. Besides, why magnetism from electricity? In later experiments (Fig. 16–7), Oersted moved the needle from below to above the wire to find that the needle reversed its direction again. There seemed to be a circular magnetic field around current-carrying conductors. When the current was cut off, the needle settled back to its usual northern direction; the wire lost its effect on the needle. Oersted's discoveries were momentous; they established a relationship between electric currents and magnets. Electricity and magnetism were no longer completely separate sciences; electric currents created magnetic fields. The fact was there without an explanation.

A later famous experiment of the American physicist H. A. Rowland (1848–1901) makes Oersted's experiment more clear. A charged sphere, mechanically rotated, replaced Oersted's wire-borne current around a magnetic needle (Fig. 16–8). After all, a moving charge is a current. When the charge was stationary, the compass needle did not change direction; there was an electric field—no magnetic field. But with rotation of the charge, the magnet was deflected by a perpendicular force. There was now also a magnetic field. A stationary charge has an electric field only; a moving charge has a magnetic as well as an electric field. And the faster Rowland's charge moved, the more marked was the deflection of the needle from its original position toward a right angle with the plane of the rotating charge. That is, a faster electric charge was giving a stronger magnetic field. A faster charge means a higher amperage. Strength of magnetic fields depends upon strength of current.

ELECTROMAGNETS AND FIELDS

That an electric current is surrounded by a magnetic field is easily demonstrated (Fig. 16–9). Send a current up a vertical wire passing through a horizontal square of cardboard. Then sprinkle iron filings on the cardboard while gently tapping the cardboard; the filings arrange themselves in concentric rings around the wire. The rings represent lines of force in a plane at right angles to the wire. A small compass placed at various positions on the cardboard shows the lines of force to have a clockwise direction. If the current is off, the filings do not form rings or show a magnetic field. Thus, other metals besides iron can show magnetism, but only while currents flow through them. In this way, a connection between magnetism and electricity becomes clear. In fact, a basic rule suggested by Ampère further established this connection. As seen in Fig. 16–9: *If the wire is grasped with the left hand so that the thumb points in the direction of the current, the fingers will point* *in the direction of the magnetic field.* Ampère's rule* enables us to determine the direction of a magnetic field near a conductor if we know the direction of a current, or conversely, to determine the direction of a current from the direction of the magnetic field.

Several scientists (Ampère, Arago, and Sturgeon) found that by winding wire in a coil around an iron core, the magnetic effects of a current are greatly increased. Such devices are called *electromagnets.* The more the turns of wire and the stronger the electric current, the greater the magnetic effect of an electromagnet. Such a magnet, of course, is a temporary magnet. It drops its load when the current is switched off.

Magnetic lines of force about a wire coil carrying an electric current form a field much like that of a bar magnet (Fig. 16–10). If the fingers of the left hand represent the direction of the current in the coil, the thumb points to the N pole of the electromagnet.

ELECTRIC CURRENTS FROM MAGNETIC FIELDS: THE ELECTRIC GENERATOR

If electric currents produce magnetism, then why not the reverse? Why shouldn't magnets produce electricity? With this question, Faraday and Joseph Henry (1799–1878), the noted American physicist, independently completed the fusion of electricity and magnetism into one science of electromagnetism. And with this question, electrical generators and modern civilization emerged. Electric machines give only temporary currents; batteries offer permanent currents of limited strength. But the dynamo effect, the principle of electrical generators independently discovered by Faraday and Henry, is another matter. And the principle is simple. Faraday and Henry in 1831 found that there are only three requirements for obtaining electric currents from magnets: (1) a magnet, (2) a coil of wire, and (3) proper relative motion between the magnet and the field.

If a bar magnet is moved in or out of a coil of wire with its ends connected for a complete circuit, a current will be generated in the wire; moving magnets produce electric currents. Or the coil may be moved and the magnet held still (Fig. 16–11). A current appears in the wire as long as lines of force of the magnetic field are "cut" by the wire.

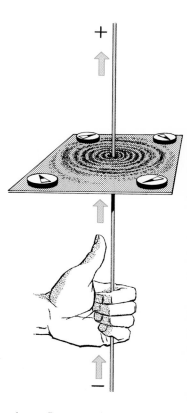

16–9 Left-hand rule: If the thumb points in the direction of the current, the fingers indicate the direction of the magnetic field.

*The rule was originally a "right-hand rule," based on the theory that external currents flow from + to − electrodes. In modern theory the current (electron) flow in wires is from − to + terminals, and Ampère's right-hand rule has become a left-hand rule.

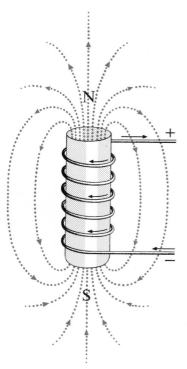

A properly placed compass needle will indicate the current. If neither the wire nor the lines of force move, no current appears. (A knife cuts an apple whether the knife moves through the apple or the apple is pressed against the knife, but not when both are stationary.) Such production of currents from relative motion between magnetic lines of force and turns of wire is called electromagnetic induction. The currents are called *induced currents* because they are formed in the presence of a magnetic field without direct contact with electrons. Magnets and turns of wire properly combined to generate such currents are called *electric generators.* Electrical generators beautifully illustrate the transformation of mechanical energy (specifically, the kinetic energy of magnets or coils) into electrical energy.

Suppose now that part of a single turn of wire (Fig. 16–11) were moved *upward* through the lines of force of a horseshoe magnet. In which direction in the wire is the induced current, or electron flow, moving? Such a question is answered by Fleming's rule as follows: Extend the thumb, forefinger, and center finger of the *left* hand—left for *electron* flow direction—at right angles to one another. If the thumb points in the direction in which the conductor moves through the field (*up* in this case), and the forefinger points in the direction of the magnetic lines of force (toward the south pole), the center finger points in the direction of the electron flow in the wire (toward you, in this case).

If the wire is then moved *downward*—that is, reversed—Fleming's rule (or compass needle) shows the current to reverse in the wire and to move *away* from you. The direction of the current has reversed in just one cycle of up-down of the wire. The current generated is therefore called an *alternating current.* The strength of the induced current (amperes) can be increased by increasing the number of turns of wire, the strength of the magnetic field, and the speed of the coil (or magnet). Huge, modern 60-cycle (per second) alternating current generators of hundreds of thousands of volts have resulted from the fast relative motion of many giant coils with innumerable turns of wire moving in powerful fields created by huge electromagnets.

16–10   An electric current in a wire coil forms a magnetic field like that of a bar magnet.

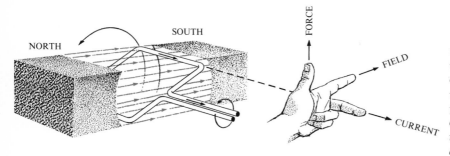

16–11   Fleming's rule: If the thumb of the left hand points in the direction in which a conductor moves through a magnetic field and the forefinger points in the direction of the magnetic lines of force, the center finger points in the direction of the current.

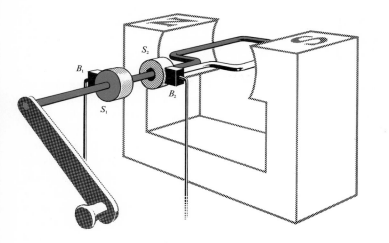

16–12 *Alternating current generator (classroom model).*

16–13 *Commutator, or split ring. Substituted for slip rings, the commutator changes an alternating current generator into a direct current generator.*

There are many types of generators. The classroom hand demonstration model (Fig. 16–12) is a mere toy, but it illustrates the use of several horseshoe magnets for a magnetic field. In addition to an *armature* (moving coil of wire) in a magnetic field, every alternating current generator has two slip rings, S_1 and S_2, fastened to the armature. Two brushes, B_1 and B_2, always in contact with the rings as the armature turns, feed the current as generated to the outside circuit for use.

For a direct current in the outside circuit, a *commutator*, or divided ring, is substituted for the two slip rings (Fig. 16–13). Each end of the armature wire is fastened to a segment of the commutator. The brushes are in contact with the rotating commutator. But the brushes are placed so as to come in contact with the next section of the commutator just as the current reverses in the armature. In this way, the current always enters the external circuit through the same brush and returns to the generator through the other. The result is a current in the external circuit that always travels in the same direction.

A generator is a device for transforming mechanical energy into electrical. For a generator to produce electricity, mechanical energy must be applied in some way to the generator. The armature wires must be kept moving in order to cut the magnetic lines of force, or there is no current. That is why huge, modern generators are often constructed near dam sites. Falling water can turn wheels on shafts that turn armatures that electrify our civilization. And like the house that Jack built, the process goes back to the sun, which evaporates the water that falls as rain that flows into the dam . . . . Again that conceptual house called conservation of energy!

MECHANICAL ENERGY
FROM ELECTRICAL:
GALVANOMETERS AND MOTORS

Other direct results of Oerstad's discovery of magnetic effects of a current were the galvanometer and the electric motor. The galvanometer, named after Galvani, permitted precision in electrical measurement; the motor technically revolutionized society. A compass needle forced from its usual position by a current is, of course, indicating the presence of the current. Any magnet properly suspended by a thread will turn in response to an electric current. The stronger the current, the further the magnet will turn against the thread resistance from its original position. In one type of galvanometer (D'Arsonval), a lightweight coil of wire is mounted between the poles of a horseshoe magnet. The coil acts as an electromagnet. When a current flows through it, the coil turns against thread resistance so that its N pole is closer to the S pole of the horseshoe magnet (and its S pole is closer to the N pole of the magnet). A pointer attached to the coil moves over a scale. The larger the current, the further the pointer moves. If the current is reversed, the direction of the coil reverses, too. Thus, a properly mounted coil can indicate the amount and the direction of current, or with modification, the potential difference in a circuit.

But when a current turns a compass needle or a coil of wire, mechanical energy is obtained from electrical energy. A sewing machine can be electrically operated. Mechanical work can be done.

The above galvanometer effect led to a *motor effect*, independently observed by Faraday and Henry. The electric current has a magnetic field, and so, of course, does the compass needle or electromagnetic coil. When the current is switched on, the two fields interact. The compass needle or coil is pivoted, and the current is fixed; therefore, in the interaction of fields, the compass needle moves. If part of the circuit wire were pivoted and a bar magnet (or electromagnet) fixed, why shouldn't the circuit wire move in the interaction of fields when the current is on? Faraday and Henry raised and answered this question in separate experiments similar to the one represented in Fig. 16–14. When the fixed bar magnet was placed under the movable current wire, the wire did move. And what is most important, the wire moved sideways. The push of the magnetic field on the wire was perpendicular to the magnetic field and current. That push, the motor effect, is another contradiction of Newtonian laws requiring that forces be attractive or repelling, but not sideways or perpendicular!

The *electric* motor is one of the most effective devices for transforming electrical energy into mechanical energy. Developed from Faraday's and Henry's motor effect, today's motor, like the generator, consists of an electromagnet, an armature, and a commutator with brushes. In fact,

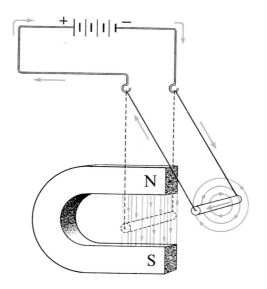

16–14   Motor effect. The movable wire swings sideways when the current is on; electrical energy transforms into mechanical energy.

the motor is a generator in reverse. In a generator (Fig. 16–12), mechanical energy (of falling water or of steam) acting on a shaft turns an armature coil in a magnetic field to give electricity. In a motor (Fig. 16–14), a current through an armature coil in a magnetic field turns a shaft to run machinery (a sewing machine, for example). Turned by a shaft in a magnetic field, the armature gives electricity; turned by a current in a magnetic field, the armature moves a shaft. Thus, the illustration of an alternating current generator in Fig. 16–12 is the reverse of the illustration for the alternating current motor in Fig. 16–14.

TRANSFORMERS

Coil 1 (Fig. 16–15) is connected to an electrical source; coil 2 is not. Can an alternating current in (primary) coil 1 light the lamp in the separate (secondary) coil 2? If what counts is that magnetic lines of force be cut by a conductor (principle of electromagnetic induction), the answer is yes.

A 60-cycle alternating current changes direction 120 times per second. Each reversal means an instant of no current followed by a current buildup to maximum value and a decline back to zero. At zero, a vertical loop of armature wire in the generator (Fig. 16–16) moves parallel to the magnetic field. Then, as the loop turns through 90°, it cuts ever more lines of force to give ever more current moving in the direction *ABCD*. At a horizontal position of the loop, the current is strongest, and then declines

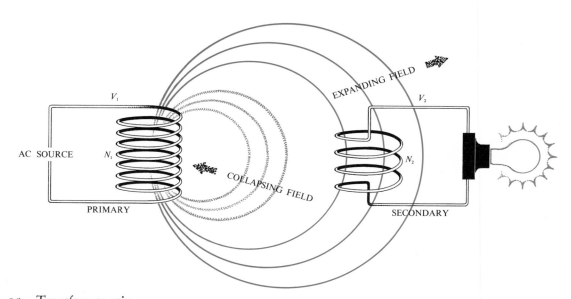

V₁   EXPANDING FIELD   V₂

AC SOURCE   N₁   COLLAPSING FIELD   N₂

PRIMARY   SECONDARY

16–15   Transformer principle. With alternations of current in the primary coil, an electromagnetic field from that coil alternately expands and contracts across the secondary coil. The lines of force moving across the turns of wire in the secondary coil create a current that lights the lamp.

as the wire cuts fewer lines of force. At 180° of turn, the loop again moves parallel to the magnetic field, and the current is zero. From that point on, the current moves in the opposite direction *DCBA*. Those parts of the loop that were moving upward are now downward and vice versa by the left-hand rule. As currents reverse in direction and rise and fall in strength, so do the magnetic fields built up around them. This means, in effect, that as the alternating current in coil 1 increases at a given instant from zero, magnetic lines of force expand outward across wires in coil 2. Such cutting of lines of force by the wires induces an alternating current in the wires as the field alternately expands and contracts 60 times a second.

Two such separate coils placed close together around a core of soft iron are called a *transformer*. The transformer coil fed an alternating current from an outside source is called the primary coil; the coil with the induced current is the secondary coil. Transformers are ineffective in direct currents. A direct current does not give the necessary expansions and contractions of a magnetic field from a primary to a secondary coil that generate a current in the secondary coil.

Transformers are indispensable in our alternating-current civilization. Through them, currents can be stepped up to hundreds of thousands of volts for long cross-country transmission and then stepped down to the 110 or 220 volts ordinarily used. Also, the correspondingly low amperages at very high voltages across country mean very little energy loss during transmission.

The greater the number of turns of wire in the secondary coil, the greater is the voltage induced in it by the alternating current in the primary coil. Stepping up or stepping down voltages in transformers, therefore, is a simple matter of increasing or decreasing the number of turns of wire in the secondary coil relative to the number of turns in the primary coil. If both coils have 100 turns of wire, the coils have about equal voltages, let us say, 120 volts. If the number of turns in the secondary is doubled to 200, its voltage is also doubled to give 240 volts. The voltage is "stepped up." If the number of turns in the secondary is reduced to one-tenth, or 10 turns, its voltage is reduced to one-tenth, or 12 volts. The voltage is "stepped down." In general, the voltage produced in the secondary coil V_2 is to the voltage of the primary V_1 as the number of turns N_2 in the secondary is to the number of turns N_1 in the primary. Symbolically,

$$\frac{V_2}{V_1} = \frac{N_2}{N_1}.$$ Equation 16–5

Watts are the electrical unit of power. By the law of conservation of energy, the wattage P_2 in the second coil should equal the wattage P_1 induced in the first coil (heat losses are small in transformers). That is,

$$P_2 = P_1 \qquad \text{(conservation law)}$$

$$V_2I_2 = V_1I_1 \qquad \text{(watts } [P] = \text{volts } [V] \cdot \text{amperes } [I])$$

$$\text{or } \frac{V_2}{V_1} = \frac{I_1}{I_2} \qquad \text{Equation 16–6}$$

$$\text{and } \frac{I_1}{I_2} = \frac{N_2}{N_1}. \qquad \text{Equation 16–7}$$

16–16 Alternating current. The strength and direction of an alternating current varies with the position of the armature turning in a magnetic field.

MAGNETIC FIELD

Faraday in his laboratory at the British Royal Institute. (The Bettmann Archive, Inc.)

Equation 16–6 indicates that if a transformer *increases* the number of volts, it proportionately *decreases* the number of amperes. Or, a decreased voltage means a proportionately increased amperage. For example, if the voltage is "stepped *down*" to one-tenth from 120 volts to 12 volts, a primary current of 1 ampere is "stepped *up*" to 10 amperes (assuming no heat losses). Equation 16–7 implies that the induced current in the secondary coil depends on the ratio of turns of wire in the two coils. A greater number of turns of wire in the secondary means less current; fewer turns mean more current.

ENERGY TRANSFORMATIONS AND OUR ELECTRICAL AGE

We have traced the development of electricity from separate "frictional," chemical, and mechanical origins. Involved were transformations from chemical and mechanical forms of energy to electrical. "Frictional" electrical machines gave spectacular sparks that aroused interest and effort. Batteries initiated steady electrical currents of limited application from chemical sources. The generator ushered in electrical power of startling cultural impact by relative motion between magnets and wires. Once an extensive, potentially unlimited electric energy was achieved, the Morses and Bells and Marconis and Edisons got to work. A deluge of electrical appliances began to convert electrical energy into heat, light, sound, motion, radio, television, and other energy forms for the reduced labor and increased convenience of men. With all its dangers, the new technology can increase labor productivity, relieve drudgery, prevent and heal sickness, limit birth, and extend life. The extent to which technology can free men for living with dignity, curiosity, culture, and wisdom depends on our social intelligence. Men need not be slaves to machines nor slaves for lack of them.

DECLINE OF THE MECHANICAL VIEW

Electromagnetism not only introduced an electrical era, it eclipsed the mechanical view. All nature can no longer be reduced to laws of mechanics. Newtonian forces are forces of attraction or repulsion acting in a straight line between objects, whether in gravity, magnetism, or electrostatics. They are not perpendicular forces. Why, then, does a current-bearing wire pull a compass needle to a position at right angles to itself? The perpendicular force here neither attracts nor repels; it does not act on a line between the wire and needle, but on another plane. Or, why must a wire be mechanically moved *perpendicular to* magnetic lines of force to induce a current that flows within the wire in still another perpendicular direction? In general, why do left-hand (or right-hand) rules in electromagnetism involve magnetic lines of force, current direction, and wire motion *at right angles* to each other? Such right-angle phenomena do not conform to a mechanistic pattern and cannot be explained by it. The mechanical view—overwhelmingly successful until then—failed with electromagnetic phenomena. The mechanical view since then has been supplemented, in fact superseded, by a view that explains nature primarily in electrical terms.

So far, in the history of scientific ideas, large, unifying ideas have had a way of taking over for a time, successfully unifying, explaining, and predicting experience until contradictions appear that limit these ideas within a more fundamental framework or that reject them entirely. So it was with the mechanical view of nature. The succeeding chapters of this text describe essentially successful extensions of an electrical view, whether it be to light phenomena, other forms of radiation, atomics, or chemical transformations of matter.

CHAPTER REVIEW

1. What is the relationship between Franklin's experiment with lightning and your car lights?

2. How did the jerking of a dead frog's leg lead to the production of electric currents?

3. How did Volta overthrow Galvani's theory of "animal electricity" in inventing his "dry" cell or battery?

4. How could Galvani be an important contributor to the development of electrical science if he operated from a rejected theory of "animal electricity"?

5. How does a dry cell, or battery, convert chemical energy into electrical?

6. What is an electric current? What are the prerequisites for one?

7. Use a water analogy to explain the differences between voltage and amperage in a current.

8. How does the water analogy illustrate the strengths and limitations of analogies in the development of science?

9. Why is measurement important in electrical science?

10. What other factor besides voltage and amperage is important in understanding and measuring currents? How does Ohm's law relate these three basic factors of an electric current? Illustrate.

11. Explain and illustrate the differences among volts, watts, and kilowatt-hours. Why are these units and their differences important?

12. How did the following experiments and devices show specifically that magnetism and electricity are not distinctly separate sciences but closely inter-related? (a) Oersted's experiments. (b) Rowland's experiment. (c) Electromagnets. (d) Generators. (e) Motors. (f) Transformers.

13. Relate Oersted's accidental discovery of the magnetic effects of a current to the invention of the electrical generator.

14. (a) Illustrate a left-hand rule in electromagnetic science. (b) Why is the existence of such a rule highly significant in the decline of the mechanical view of nature?

15. What is an electromagnetic field?

16. What transformations of energy are involved in each of the following processes? (a) Use of a battery. (b) Charging a battery. (c) A lightning discharge. (d) Water falling on a turbine. (e) Bread toasting. (f) Operation of a generator. (g) Operation of a motor. (h) Oersted's experiments. (i) A galvanometer in use. (j) A transformer in use. (k) An electromagnetic hoist lifting junk metal.

17. How did each of the following inventions extend the law of conservation of energy? (a) Edison's light bulb. (b) Bell's telephone. (c) Morse's telegraph.

18. Give several illustrations from this chapter or elsewhere of how "Chance favors the prepared mind."

PROBLEMS

1. (a) Explain how a flashlight converts chemical energy into electrical energy and light. (b) Trace the complete circuit in a flashlight.

2. How can copper wire be made magnetic?

3. How can the N pole of an electromagnet be determined? Be reversed?

4. If an electromagnet is too weak to lift a tremendous block of steel, how could its strength be increased?

5. How can you produce an electric current with a wire and a magnet?

6. How can the energy of falling water or of steam be converted into electricity?

7. What is the difference between a DC current and an AC current?

8. What is the difference between a generator and a motor?

9. Why are the following practices dangerous? (a) Touching bare or dangling wires. (b) Placing fingers or metal objects in a socket or outlet. (c) Inserting a knife or fork into an electric toaster. (d) Using pennies as fuses. (e) Testing electrical objects with wet hands or when in a bathtub of water.

10. Do you pay your electric bill for amperage, voltage, power, or electric energy? Explain.

11. (a) What voltage sends a current of 125 amperes through a 96-ohm lamp? (b) The lamp uses how many watts?

12. (a) A 300-watt lamp has what amperage when operating on 120 volts? (b) What resistance does the lamp have?

13. (a) What is the cost of using a 300-watt lamp for 4 hours at 3c a kilowatt-hour? (b) What is the cost of using a 1,000-watt iron for 2 hours at 3c a kilowatt-hour?

14. If a current of 20 amperes "blows" a house fuse on a usual 120-volt line, will a 1,000-watt iron, a 900-watt iron, and a 1,100-watt coffeemaker used togther blow the fuse?

15. An electric heater draws 4 amperes on a 110-volt circuit. (a) What resistance does the lamp have? (b) How many watts does the heater use? (c) What is the cost of using the heater for 10 hours at 4c a kilowatt-hour?

16. Explain how the power companies step down the 22,000 volts in the outside lines to the 110 volts in your home.

17. Why will a transformer not work on a direct current?

18. A transformer has an input voltage of 120 volts and an output voltage of 6 volts. The primary coil has 2,000 turns. Assuming no heat loss, (a) how many turns of wire has the secondary coil? (b) If the transformer uses 500 watts, what is the amperage in the primary coil? (c) What is the current strength in the secondary coil?

19. A step-down transformer changes 2,200 volts to 110 volts. (a) If there are five turns of wire in a secondary coil, how many turns are there in the primary coil? (b) If the amperage in the secondary coil is 60 amperes, what is the current strength in the primary coil?

SUGGESTIONS FOR
FURTHER READING

Cheronis, Nicholas D., et al., *Study of the Physical World,* Houghton-Mifflin, Boston, 1958, Chs. 31–32.

Einstein, Albert, and Leopold Infeld, *The Evolution of Physics,* Simon and Schuster paperback, New York, 1961, Part 2, "Decline of the Mechanical View."

Taylor, Lloyd, W., *Physics, the Pioneer Science,* Vol. 2, Dover paperback, New York, 1959, Ch. 42.

Lemon, Harvey B., *From Galileo to the Nuclear Age,* Univ. Chicago Press, Chicago, 1949, Chs. 26–27.

Meyer, Jerome S., *The ABC of Physics,* Pyramid paperback, New York, 1962, Ch. 11.

17   Light and Color

If a poet could at the same time be a physicist he might convey to others the pleasure, the satisfaction, almost the reverence which the subject inspires . . . . Especially is its satisfaction felt in the branch which deals with light . . . . These beauties of form and color so constantly recurring in the varied phenomena of refraction, diffraction, and interference are, however, only incidentals; and though a never-failing source of aesthetic delight, must be resolutely ignored if we would perceive the still higher beauties which appeal to the mind . . . . These laws . . . [are for] the scientific investigator to discover and apply. In such successful investigation consists at once his keenest delight as well as his highest reward.

A. A. MICHELSON, 1903

MYSTERY OF THE RAINBOW

The rainbow in all its poetic splendor has intrigued man ever since he could observe and speculate. It has explanations in mythology; it enters into the Bible; it fascinated Greek natural philosophers. It allured the mathematically minded Newton.

What is a rainbow? From where arise its colors? Adequate answers depend upon satisfactory solutions to other questions, such as those given below:

1. Why does sunlight leave shadows behind trees (unlike flood-waters, which completely surround obstacles)?

2. Why does an oar partially submerged in water appear bent?

3. Why does the rising or setting sun appear more red than the midday sun?

4. If you extend a right hand to your mirror image, why does the image extend a left hand back?

5. Does a color exist if no eye is there to see it?

The above five questions involve relationships among light, sight, and color that took man almost his whole history to understand. A synthesis was finally made by Newton in a superb model of experimentation that answered the question of rainbow colors. But 2,000 years earlier, Greco-Roman natural philosophers were laying foundations for Newton.

EARLY MIRROR EXPERIMENTS

In 300 B.C., Euclid observed that "light travels in straight lines called rays." In so doing, this great thinker was applying mathematical techniques to nature. He was arbitrarily reducing light into rays. In so doing, he was calling the world of light to order and, incidentally, explaining shadows. Water waves bend around obstacles; light rays traveling in straight lines do not and thereby leave shadows.

Hero of Alexandria (1st century A.D.) experimentally established Euclid's hypothesis by "bouncing" narrow beams of light off plane mirrors. The path of the beams, although broken by the mirror, was straight in approaching and leaving the mirror. But even more significantly, Hero found that the angle at which a beam approaches the mirror always equals the angle at which it leaves the mirror (Fig. 17–1). The perpendicular dashed line PO to the mirror surface forms an *angle of incidence* $\angle i$ with the approaching ray IO; the same dashed line forms an *angle of reflection* $\angle r$ with the reflected ray OR. Hero's discovery that the angle of incidence equals the angle of reflection is a basic law of reflection and may be symbolized as $\angle i = \angle r$. Note in the illustration that the incident ray, the reflected ray, and the perpendicular all lie in the same plane (the plane of the page of the book).

Light reflected from mirrors or smooth, polished surfaces gives images. Parallel rays of light from a mirror remain parallel when reflected, but they are changed in direction. Your image in a mirror appears as if behind the mirror (Fig. 17–2), and the left hand of your image appears to meet your outstretched right hand; we "intuitively" react to light rays as if they travel in unbroken straight lines. The direction that "counts" is the direction from which the ray enters the eye from the mirror. The eye does not catch the change in direction at the mirror when the incident ray becomes a reflected ray.

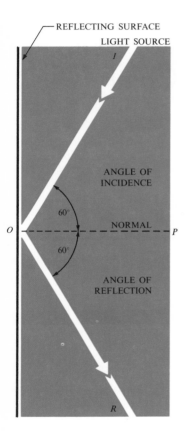

17–1 Reflection of light. The angle of incidence equals the angle of reflection ($\angle i = \angle r$).

Light reflects from points of rough, unpolished surfaces also in accordance with the law of reflection, but the irregularities of the surface result in a haphazard reflection of the originally parallel rays and lose the image formation.

THE BENDING OF LIGHT

But light rays are not always just reflected back upon striking the surface of objects; they may also be absorbed or transmitted. Some rays are reflected from water surfaces to give a mirror effect; other rays may be absorbed by muddy water or transmitted by clear water. Oars are seen in water when light rays penetrating the water are reflected back by the oars. Aristotle was among the first to describe correctly the broken appearance of oars in water. But Ptolemy, the astronomer, was the first to explain the broken appearance through the concept of *refraction,* or bending, of light rays. In the fifth volume of his treatise on optics, Ptolemy writes:

> Visual rays may be altered in two ways: (1) by reflection, i.e., rebound from objects called mirrors, which do not permit penetration by the visual ray, and (2) by refraction, in the case of media which permit of penetration and [are transparent]. It has been shown ... (1) that a visual ray proceeds along a straight line and may be naturally bent only at a surface between two media of different densities, (2) that the bending takes place not only in the passage from rarer and finer media to denser ... but also in the passage from a denser medium to a rarer, and (3) that this type of bending does not take place at equal angles but that the angles, as measured from the perpendicular, have a definite quantitative relationship.

Refraction is illustrated in Fig. 17–3. The ray *AO* entering from the less dense medium (air) to the more dense medium (glass) takes the new direction *OB*. A dashed perpendicular *PQ* forms the angle of incidence *POA* and the angle of refraction *QOB*. This new direction *OB* of the ray

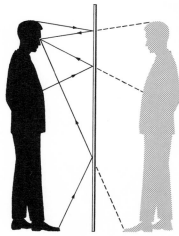

17–2   Your image results from the reflection of light rays at a mirror surface. Since your eye does not catch the rays' change in direction, you see yourself behind the mirror.

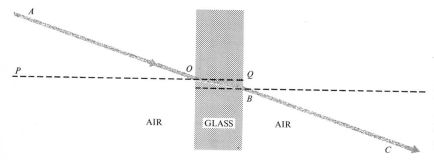

17–3   Bending of light. A light ray (AO) passing from a less dense to a more dense area bends toward the perpendicular (PQ). In passing from a more dense to a less dense area, a light ray bends away from the perpendicular.

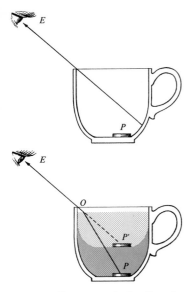

17–4 *Because of the bending of light rays, the unseen coin appears when water is poured into the cup.*

in the denser medium is closer to the perpendicular PQ, and the angle of refraction is less than the angle of incidence. When the same ray leaves the glass to enter air again at point B, the new direction BC is further from the perpendicular drawn through point B. The ray, in passing from the more dense medium (glass) to the less dense (air), bends away from the perpendicular. The coin can not be seen at point P (Fig. 17–4) until water is poured into the cup. With water a light ray bends away from a perpendicular to the surface at point O, and therefore, in entering the eye at E, appears to be coming from the point P^1. The coin therefore appears at P′ within the line of sight somewhat above its actual position at P.

Ptolemy's table of refractions (Table 17–1) lists the angles of refraction that he measured for light rays moving from (1) air into water, (2) air into glass, and (3) water into glass. The angles of refraction in columns 2, 3, and 4 correspond to the particular angles of incidence of the light rays. Note that in each case (air to water, air to glass, and water to glass), (1) the light ray moves from a less dense to a more dense medium, and (2) the value of the angle of refraction without exception is less than the corresponding angle of incidence. Ptolemy, in optics as in astronomy, was a scientist as well as a natural philosopher. He sought generalizations or laws of nature by reasoning from nature in precise terms with measurements systematically recorded.

Table *17–1* | *PTOLEMY'S TABLE OF REFRACTIONS*

	ANGLES OF REFRACTION		
ANGLE OF INCIDENCE	AIR TO WATER	AIR TO GLASS	WATER TO GLASS
10	8	7	9½
20	15½	13½	18½
30	22½	20½	27
40	28	25	35
50	35	30	42½
60	40½	34½	49½
70	45	38½	56
80	50	42	62

SNELL'S LAW OF REFRACTION

But there was a hidden generalization in his data that Ptolemy did not see. Fifteen hundred years later, the Dutch mathematician Willebrord Snell (1591–1626) recognized a constant mathematical relationship between the angle of incidence and the angle of refraction of a ray passing between two given media. To understand this relationship, called Snell's law of refraction, consider a light ray traveling from air (less dense) to water (more dense). The angle of incidence will be larger than the angle of refraction (Fig. 17–5). We measure equal distances from point O on the incident and refracted rays (that is, $AO = BO$). A dashed (normal) line XY is drawn perpendicular to the surface through point O. Then perpendiculars AC and BD are drawn to the normal XY from points A and B. AC will measure a definite number of times larger than BD regardless of the angle of incidence. If AC should be 4 inches, BD would be 3 inches. If AC is 8 inches, BD would be 6. If AC is 12, then BD is 9. That is, there is a constant ratio AC/BD equal to 4/3, or 1.33, for the same two substances. Changing the angle of incidence does not change the ratio. This important ratio (in this case, 1.33 for water and air) is called the *index of refraction*.* Crown glass, for example, has an index of refraction ranging from 1.48 to 1.61; flint glass from 1.53 to 1.96; and diamond 2.417. Each index given refers to the bending of light between air and the given substance.

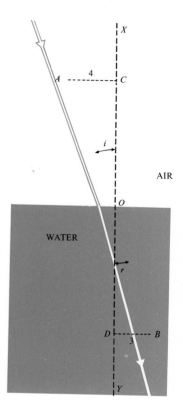

17–5   *The path of a light ray traveling from air to water. The angle of incidence i is greater than the angle of refraction r ($\angle i > \angle r$).*

SENECA'S RAINBOW

A century before Ptolemy, Seneca (3 B.C.–65 A.D.), the Roman natural philosopher (and adviser to Nero) seriously reflected upon the rainbow. He was concerned with questions of appeal today: What causes the rainbow? Why after rain? From where arises the variety of colors? Why the semicircular shape and the large size? Why is the bow seldom found during midday in the summer?

Seneca's thesis or hypothesis in his book *Naturales Questiones* essentially was that the rainbow is an image of the sun distorted by hollow clouds as imperfect mirrors. Seneca, like Aristotle before him, had no ideas of light bending. These men, familiar with the "bent oar" and other refraction phenomena, attributed such things to "weaknesses of the eyes." The most advanced concepts of light at the time relevant to the rainbow were the ideas of mirror reflection. These ideas, along with speculative writings of contemporaries, and his own observations and brilliant reasoning, were all Seneca had to work with. Ptolemy lived a century later. Experimenta-

*For students familiar with trigonometry, this ratio may be expressed as follows in Snell's law of refraction:

$$\frac{\text{sine of } \angle i}{\text{sine of } \angle r} = \frac{AC/AO}{BD/BO} = \frac{AC}{BD} = \text{index of refraction.}$$

Remember that the *sine* of an angle by definition is the ratio of the side opposite the angle to the hypotenuse of the right triangle and that in this case, the hypotenuse AO = the hypotenuse BO.

tion was not a socially developed or recognized tool of knowledge. But Seneca's ideas and methods are worth analyzing as gems with many facets.

Seneca opens his discussion of the rainbow with the question of its origin. His approach is one of calling attention *to the conditions under which the phenomenon occurs*:

1. Water forced from a burst pipe shows "the appearance of a rainbow."
2. Water "spurted by a fuller" on clothes shows the colors of the bow.
3. "A rainbow never occurs except when there are clouds about."

Through observational evidence, he establishes the presence of moisture or clouds as a first factor in the rainbow's origin. He then begins his mirror analogy: Each raindrop of the cloud is a mirror of the sun, and the "rainbow is a blending of innumerable images." In typical proof by analogy, he points out that single drops of water on separate leaves of a plant will each have an image of the sun. He really slips here, however, when he states as further proof that in sectioning off a pond, there will be an image for each section of the pond. A little actual checking would certainly have made a difference.

Then, with acknowledgments to Aristotle, he attributes to "weakness of human eyes" the fact that the rainbow is seen as a single blurred mass instead of as many distinct images of the sun. Without realizing the refraction involved, he then brilliantly uses excellent examples of refraction as evidence of the "weakness of eyes": the broken appearance of an oar in water or the magnified appearance of apples through glass. The broken oar contains a key to the rainbow, refraction, but the knowledge of the time was not ripe enough for the significance of the broken oar to be recognized. Reasoning and analogy are always at a disadvantage without sufficient knowledge.

The sun is a second factor of rainbow origin. Here Seneca's observations are sharp: "the [rainbow] image is never seen except opposite the sun, high up or low down, *in inverse relation** just as he sinks or elevates his course." Or, again: "The bow never appears when the sky is clear, and never when it is so cloudy as to hide the sun."

The third factor of rainbow origin is the observer, or rather the position of the observer relative to the clouds and the sun: Rainbows are never seen unless the observer is facing water drops with the sun over his shoulder.

In further elaboration of his mirror thesis, Seneca points out that just as objects do not actually exist within a mirror, so the rainbow does not actually exist within the clouds. He again uses observational evidence

*The italics are the present writer's.

of sudden appearance and disappearance of the rainbow, as when an intervening cloud shuts out the sun.

So much for the origin of the rainbow. How did Seneca handle the question of its colors? In seeking to explain the variety of rainbow colors, Seneca looks to basic factors in a rainbow's origin: the sun and the clouds. Impressed by the fiery color in the rising and setting of the sun and by the "dull" shades of clouds, he attributes the red in the rainbow to the sun, and the dark blue to the clouds. He considers the other colors to be an interplay or blending of these basic two. Notice, first of all, the scientifically analytical and empirical character of his explanation in going back to origins, to the sun and clouds for color. It is true that his analysis is merely on a descriptive or qualitative basis, but what other basis could there have been 19 centuries ago for such analysis? Although he did not have any color theory with which to work, he is very close to Young's idea, 18 centuries later, of three primary colors of red, blue, and green, with all the other colors a blending of these three.

But Seneca is not satisfied merely to explain the variety of rainbow colors as a blending of primary colors; he is interested in the mechanism involved. He points out that clouds have an infinite variety of shapes and thicknesses in the transmission of sunlight and that "this difference in consistency causes alternations of light and shade, and produces that marvelous variety" of color in the rainbow. He also points out that the angle at which light strikes or leaves an object is a factor in color. We shall see that he is getting close here when we later consider Newton's concept of color dispersion. Then, in further support of his "blending" theory, he uses gems of analogy with all the attendant advantages and dangers:

1. Some dyed clothes vary in color according to the angle and the distance at which they are viewed.
2. "A purple garment does not always come out to exactly the same tint from the same dye. Differences depend upon the length of time it has been steeped, the consistency and the amount of moisture in the dye: it may be dipped and boiled more than once."
3. "The neck of the peacock shines with varied colors as often as it is turned hither and thither."
4. A glass stick placed obliquely in the rays of the sun will show colors of the rainbow, in this case, of course, glass taking the place of the cloud.

The first three analogies eloquently speak for themselves: Reflective phenomena are being used in brilliant analogy to support a theory based entirely on reflection. The fourth analogy is of particular interest: It is the correct analogy, one based on refraction, but the underlying principle, as with the broken oar, lies hidden below. Seneca here in a prism analogy comes as close to the answer of the rainbow's color as he can without knowing refraction. Here again, we must emphasize that the knowledge of the time was not yet ripe enough; Seneca did not make Newton's leap—16 centuries intervened.

Thus coming as close to the answer as he could for the times, but still missing, Seneca then moves further away and even stumbles in attempting to use an eventually correct analogy (a prism) as evidence for an incorrect or incomplete theory (cloud mirror). To reconcile the fact that in the color effects of the glass, one does not obtain an image of the sun, he states that if the glass were symmetrical in shape and "suitably constructed," it would "reflect as many images of the sun as it had faces. But since the sides are not distinctly separated from each other, and not bright enough to serve as mirrors, the images get confused through being crowded together, and are reduced to the appearance of a single band of color." The point is that here he "leaves himself open" by not actually checking the underlying assumption of "as many images as faces." We emphasize again, however, that his is not yet a time when rigorous empirical checking becomes a criterion of scientific methods. It is Roger Bacon, 12 centuries later, who begins to insist on such a criterion. The above example is another illustration of the dangers and yet the advantages that lie in analogies as indispensable tools of science: dangers of relationships that may be superficial, and yet advantages in revealing truths that may lie beneath.

The bow appears a great deal larger than the sun. Seneca handles the question of the large size of the bow not on the basis of the much greater distance of the sun—not much was known in those days about quantitative distances of heavenly phenomena—but by consistently following through with his mirror analogy. He discusses actual mirrors that magnify, stars that appear larger when seen through moisture, and the magnification of objects placed in water. Here again, we note that he strives to substantiate his ideas by observational evidence and analogy. He even suggests that the reader place a ring in water to observe the ring's magnification.

In summary, we have enough here to reveal the nature of Seneca's problem solving with the rainbow. Weaknesses are apparent. In his book, Seneca presents his material in a somewhat rambling and unsystematic fashion; he often generalizes from too few cases, and he is not always careful about his evidence. Yet for the following reasons, his handling of the rainbow is essentially good science for his day:

1. He goes directly to the phenomenon itself.
2. In so doing, he calls attention to the natural conditions under which the rainbow phenomenon occurs, as for example, the presence of the sun, of moisture, and of an observer, as well as to certain relationships among them.
3. He poses and discusses various questions concerning the phe-

nomenon, such as origins, color effects, shape, size, and seasonal variation.

4. He makes the best use of the knowledge of his time through brilliant imagination, observation, analogy, inference, and ideas of others.

5. He constantly strives for evidence or "proof" for his arguments by reference to observations, to known analogous situations, to "mathematical proof," or to "authorities" like Aristotle. If his evidence is not always empirical, he still emphasizes evidence. And if the considerable observational evidence that he does have is based on memory rather than on written records, remember that we are applying today's criterion of rigorously controlled experimentation to a period 19 centuries ago. Like anything else, science—its definitions, concepts, methods, content—changes with time and with the accumulation of knowledge and experience.

With respect to content, Seneca, without knowing refraction, weaves close to and around it while establishing the origin of the rainbow in a positional relationship between the sun, clouds, and an observer. His hypothesis, based on a mirror analogy, is incomplete, even erroneous. Yet with his hypothesis, he makes headway in establishing facts about rainbows, as for example, the three basic factors of origin and their relationships. Modern physics cannot always do better. We shall see, for example, that recent advances in optics have been made through contradictory, incomplete hypotheses that light, on the one hand, consists of continuous waves and, on the other hand, of streams of separate particles.

NEWTON'S PRISM EXPERIMENTS: COLOR DISPERSION

Newton solved the mystery of the rainbow's colors. It took 16 centuries and Newton to come up with today's basic answers, but how far would Newton have gone with analysis of sunlight without previous refraction ideas, including Snell's law? Archbishop Antonio de Dominis (1566–1624) and Descartes had correctly applied principles of refraction and reflection in explaining the rainbow. But neither could adequately explain how refraction results in color. Newton became interested in the fringes of color that blur telescope images. In systematically investigating such color phenomena with prisms, he determined that white light is a blend of colors and that prisms, lenses, and raindrops act as refraction agents for separating the component colors of white light. As Newton reported in a letter to the Royal Society:

Having darkened my chamber and made a small hole in my window-shuts to let in a convenient quantity of the Sun's light, I placed my Prisme at his entrance, that it might be thereby refracted to the opposite wall. It was at first a very pleasing divertisement to view the vivid and intense colours produced thereby; but after a while applying myself to consider them more circumspectly, I became surprised to see them in an *oblong* form, which, according to the received laws of Refraction, I expected should have been *circular*.

They were terminated at the sides with straight lines, but at the ends, the decay of light was so gradual, that it was difficult to determine justly what was their figure; yet they seemed *semi-circular*.*

Newton named the band of colors a *spectrum* and established seven colors in analogy with seven notes of a musical scale: red, orange, yellow, green, blue, indigo, and violet (Fig. 17–6). It was not the colors appearing in a prism in gradual transition from one to another that surprised Newton; men had noticed rainbow effects in glass long before Seneca. What intrigued Newton was that these colors formed an oval with semicircular ends. Why this shape when the light streamed upon the prism through a round hole? (Figs. 17–6 and 17–10 to 17–12 may be found in the color insert.)

Newton's Cambridge professor, Isaac Barrow, and others thought that prisms themselves create colors by "*condensation* of the original white light" at the red end and by *rarefaction* at the violet end. To disprove this idea, Newton placed a second prism behind the first (Fig. 17–7): The colored beams were reunited into a narrow white beam again. If Barrow's idea were correct, the second prism would further condense and rarefy the colored beams rather than reunite them. White light thus was not an elemental color; it was a blend of various rainbow colors! The glass in the first prism merely separated component colors already present in white light by refracting them at different angles. The prism was an agent for *dispersion;* it did not create the colors. Newton's second prism reversed the color dispersion of the first prism. To further prove his point, Newton placed a small screen between the two prisms. A small opening in the screen allowed a single color at a time from the first prism to strike the second prism (Fig. 17–8). Each of the colored rays was refracted in the second prism, but no new color appeared. The prism did not form anything not already there. The basic nature of light is not changed in passing through glass.

As further evidence that white light is a blend of colors, Newton refers to a color disc. The "Newton color disc," based on a principle of the Arab Alhazen, is divided into seven sections for the seven basic spectral colors. When rotating quickly, the colors of the disc appear to the eye as a grayish white blend.

Each color of light has its own angle of refraction, whether in glass, water, or other media. Sunlight through a triangular bottle of water in place of a prism also would have given Newton a spectrum in the same order of colors, but less dispersed. (The index of refraction of water is less than that of glass.) In a rainbow, raindrops replace a prism as a color-dispersing medium for sunlight.

*Italicized by the present writer.

Rainbow at Nevada Falls,
Yosemite National Park.
(Photograph by Ansel Adams)

Rainbow effects of a prism. Newton using a glass prism to produce rainbow colors from sunlight. (Bausch & Lomb photograph)

17–6 Color spectrum. The colors dispersed from white light in a prism are red, orange, yellow, green, blue, indigo, and violet.

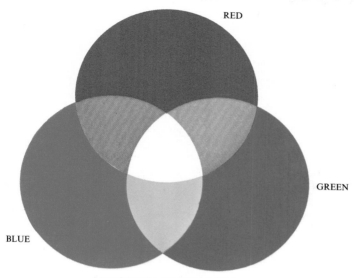

RED

GREEN

BLUE

ADDITIVE PRIMARIES

17–10   Color addition. Light of the three primary colors (red, green, and blue) may be added in various proportions to give any other color of light. Focusing red and green lights together gives a yellow blend. Blue light added to the yellow blend gives white light.

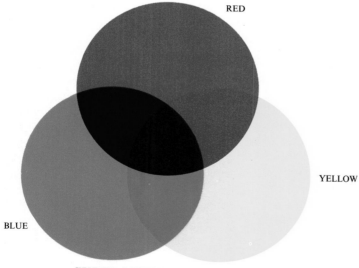

RED

YELLOW

BLUE

SUBTRACTIVE PRIMARIES

17–11   Color by subtraction. Mixing paints is a color subtraction process because paints are substances that absorb light and are not light itself. Blue paint absorbs components of white light, to subtract from white light. Yellow paint subtracts other components from white light. Together, blue and yellow paints absorb all colors from white light except green, which is reflected to the eye. Mixing blue and yellow paints thus results in green paint by subtraction.

17-12 Three kinds of spectra: continuous, absorption and bright line.

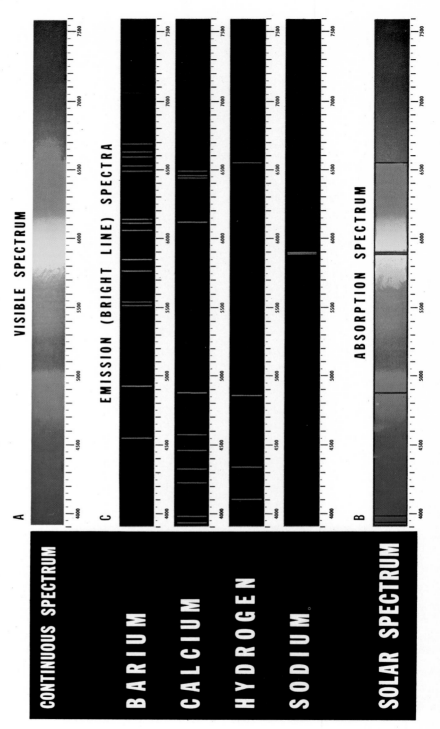

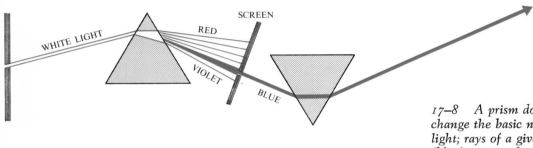

17–7   White light is a blend of colors. The first prism merely separates the colors already there by bending each at a different angle. The second prism reunites the colors into white by bending them variously toward the thicker part of the glass.

17–8   A prism does not change the basic nature of light; rays of a given color (blue) passing through the screen and second prism remain the same (blue).

THE RAINBOW EXPLAINED

In summary, the explanation of the rainbow below drew on the work of many men. Culminating details of reflection and refraction within the bow are the work of Descartes; color dispersion, the work of Newton.

For a rainbow, three conditions are necessary: (1) the presence of water drops in a cloud or mist; (2) the sun shining on the drops; and (3) an observer with his back toward the sun and his eyes toward the mist or clouds.

As illustrated, however (Fig. 17–9), rays from the sun may form two bows, the brighter primary, and the fainter secondary, not always seen. If both are visible, the secondary is above the primary, and its colors are in reverse order. In tracing through light rays from the sun, it can be seen that given rays forming a secondary bow experience *two* refractions, or bendings—one on entering and one on leaving the drops—as well as *two* reflections within the drops. On the other hand, in the case of the primary bow, there is only *one* internal reflection with the two refractions. Since some light is lost with each reflection, the primary bow is brighter than the secondary—the secondary cannot always be seen.

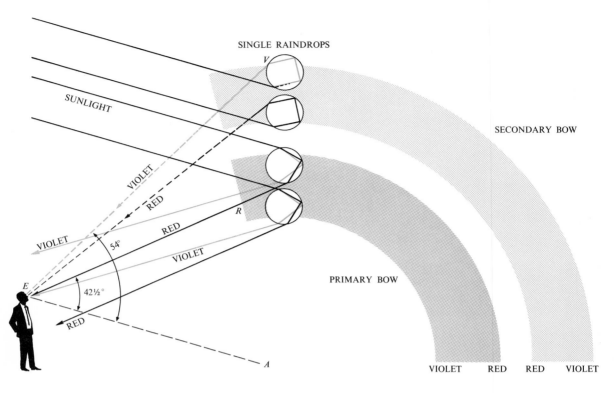

SINGLE RAINDROPS

SECONDARY BOW

PRIMARY BOW

VIOLET   RED   RED   VIOLET

*17–9   Rainbow formation.
Drops of water refract, reflect,
and disperse sunlight. To see
a bow, an observer must face
a mist and have his back to
the sun.*

In being refracted, ordinary white light from the sun is separated into its constituent parts of red, orange, yellow, green, blue, indigo, and violet because of the differences in refractive angles of these different colors. To see the bows, the eye E must have a position relative to the sun and to the drops such that when the rays are refracted and dispersed by the drops, a definite angle is formed with the line AE parallel to the sun's rays. This angle varies from color to color, since the index of refraction varies according to the refractive angles of each color. In the primary bow, the angles vary from 42½° in angle REA for the red to 40° in angle VEA for the violet. In the secondary bow, the angles vary from 54° for the violet to 51° for the red. The explanation for the semicircular shape of the rainbow involves the locus (path) of a point representing a given color, say, red, in the primary bow that forms the 42½° angle REA. The locus of such a point is half or part of a circle forming part of the base of a cone, with the eye at the vertex of the cone, as was emphasized by Roger Bacon but not fully explained until Descartes. Rays of various colors are leaving each drop, but for each drop in a given section of the bow, only the ray of the particular color seen strikes the eye. Because of the differences in refractive and reflective angles, other rays from the same drop fall long or short. This, along with the fact that the secondary bow, in addition to two refractions, has two reflections, while the primary bow has only one reflection, is the explanation for the secondary bow's having a reversed order of colors. This is made clear in Fig. 17–9.

Newton's prism experiments show that light bends or refracts increasingly as we move from the red end of the spectrum to the violet. The blue component of sunlight refracts in the prism far more than red. If by the same token we assume that blue light is scattered far more than red by dust or other fine particles in the atmosphere, we can explain why the sun appears redder when it is setting than it does at noon. At sunrise or sunset, with the sun at the horizon, sunlight passes through a larger mass of atmosphere to reach the eye of the observer than it does at other times of the day. The red component scatters less than the blue, and more red comes through directly to the eye. Objects at the horizon opposite to the sun take on a bluish cast because of the much greater scattering of the light. Also, it is the scattering by the atmosphere of the blue in sunlight at any time of the day that gives the heavens their general blue color. Balloon and rocket observations above ordinary atmosphere and scattering show the sun as a glaring white disc in a black sky.

COLOR BY SELECTIVE REFLECTION

Greenness is not in grass itself but is a sensation in your eye. By the principle of selective reflection first recognized by Newton, the color of an *opaque* object depends upon the color of the light that it *reflects* to the eye. White light is a blend of all the colors of the rainbow. Grass absorbs most light radiations of the sun and reflects primarily the green radiation. What determines the green sensation is not the radiation that the grass absorbs, but the remaining radiation that the grass reflects to your eyes. The color in grass is everything but the green you see. Similarly, the red is not in a rose that reflects primarily red radiation. Minor amounts of a few other color radiations along with red give a sensation of a shade of red rather than a pure red.

In the study of heat, it was necessary to differentiate between heat radiation and heat itself. Heat radiation from the sun becomes heat when absorbed by molecules. It is the same with light; color radiations from an object become color sensations after entering an eye mechanism. Color is an interaction, not a property. Just as your weight involves an interaction between you and the earth, the red that you see is an interaction between light radiations, the rose, and you. A pure red object appears black under a blue, green, or pure yellow light that furnishes no red radiation for reflection. And pure green grass appears black when under a blue, red, or yellow light not containing green radiation to reflect to the eye. An object reflecting all radiations of white light quite equally appears white—for example, a page of this book. An object that absorbs all color radiation, and therefore reflects none, appears black—the print on this page, for example.

Newton also recognized a principle of selective color by transmission. In this case, the color of an object depends upon the color of light it *transmits* rather than reflects. Red glass transmits primarily red radiation and absorbs other color radiations. Ordinary window glass is colorless because it transmits all components of white light.

COLOR BY ADDITION

Color is a sensation in response to light radiation. Without an eye, there is no color, only light radiation, just as without molecules, there is no heat, just heat radiation. Without a world of objects, there is nothing to view, nothing to reflect or absorb radiation. The sun, the eye, and a world of form and color go together. In his *Opticks* (1704), Newton included a "Query" about color vision: "May not the harmony and discord of Colours arise from the proportions of the Vibrations propagated through the fibres of the optick Nerve into the Brain as the harmony and discord of Sounds arise from the proportions of the Vibrations of the Air?" Newton was concerned with the specific roles of the eyes, nerves, and brain in color vision.

By 1801 Thomas Young (1773–1829), an English physician-turned-physicist, had applied himself to the subjective, or human, aspect of color. An ordinary person can distinguish about 130 separate hues of the color spectrum. Young did not believe the retina has a separate photoreceptor for each hue that could be recognized and that there would be enough duplications of 130 receptors across the retina to respond to rays wherever they fell. Young believed that if colored lights could be blended on a screen, they could be blended on the retina. He settled upon three basic color receptors, each sensitive to a specific color: red, green, and blue. These three colors were *primary* colors. All other colors and shades were blends of these three in various proportions and combinations. This idea can be experimentally verified by rapidly rotating a disc with separate colors or by focusing beams of different colors on the same spot (Fig. 17–10). Therefore, only three different color receptors, one for each of the three primary colors, should handle light of any hue entering the eye.

Young's theory was not taken seriously at the time. About 50 years later, Hermann von Helmholtz (1821–1894), German physicist-physiologist, and James Maxwell revived the three-color theory. Helmholtz made an important modification that added his name to the Young theory. He suggested that any of the receptors are activated mostly by one characteristic color radiation and to a much lesser extent by the other two. Pure red light activates the red-sensitive receptors strongly and the other two types of receptors weakly to give a sensation of red. Pure yellow light stimulates the red and green receptors considerably and the blue slightly to give a sensation of yellow.

In summary, the Young-Helmholtz theory offers a process of color by addition. Light of the three primary colors can be added to give any other colored light. Three types of nerve receptors in the retina respond to the primary components in the entering radiation. The brain gives us a sensation of the blend.

COLOR BY SUBTRACTION

Considerable confusion about color exists because color is a sensation. The confusion is overcome by differentiating between light radiation that enters the eye and the color sensations that result when color receptors are activated in the retina. A great deal of confusion about color also exists if color of light is not distinguished from color of paints or pigments. The mixing of different colors of light is an addition process; the mixing of paints is a subtraction process. Focusing blue and yellow lights together gives *white* light; mixing blue and yellow paints gives *green* paint (Fig. 17–11). Blue light stimulates primarily the blue receptors; yellow light activates the red and green receptors, since each color receptor is somewhat sensitive to spectral colors on each side of its main color. (Yellow is closely between red and green in the color spectrum.) Consequently, blue and yellow light together stimulate all three types of receptors to give a white light sensation. Two colors of light that combine to give white are called *complementary colors*. Other pairs of complementary colors are red and blue-green, orange and green-blue, and green and purple. Complementary colors can be demonstrated by rotating color discs or by focusing spotlights.

Paints or pigments, when mixed, are subtractive because they are substances rather than light. A blue paint absorbs certain components of white light, therefore subtracting from it; a yellow paint absorbs other components from white light. When blue and yellow paint are mixed, together they subtract more of the white light than either singly. In fact, together they absorb all components from white light except that component reflected and seen as green.

TYPES OF SPECTRA

At first glance the color spectrum of the sun is continuous. When dispersed by a prism, the seven colors gradually fade one into the other. In 1802, the English scientist William Wollaston reported seven dark lines irregularly spaced across such a solar spectrum. Several years later Fraunhofer, a German, independently found and classified hundreds of such dark lines not only in sunlight but in the spectra of bright stars. The dark lines were in different relative positions for each star. These lines, now called Fraunhofer lines, are believed to result when light from the very hot inner portion of the sun or stars passes through cooler outer gaseous layers. The cooler outer layers absorb some of the light. The dark lines indicate the colors of light absorbed. Since different chemical substances absorb different colors, much information about the composition of the sun and stars has been obtained by analysis of their spectra. A spectrum like that of the sun with dark lines is called an *absorption spectrum* (Fig. 17–12B), as compared to an unbroken *continuous spectrum* (Fig. 17–12A). Very hot gases under high pressure (without any enveloping cooler gases), white hot solids (such as wires in electric lamps), and luminous liquids ordinarily give continuous spectra.

A third type of spectrum is the *bright line spectrum* given off by luminous gases under ordinary pressures. In this spectrum, instead of the full band of colors, a number of bright lines appear through a prism. Each gas has its own characteristically colored bright lines (Fig. 17–12C). Table salt dipped in a Bunsen flame turns the flame yellow and shows yellow only in its bright line spectrum. Neon, argon, and mercury vapors in electric tubes show light of characteristic colors that are blends of characteristic bright lines (Fig. 17–12C). The bright lines of various elements fall into the exact positions of dark lines of these elements to give confidence in identifying elements in the sun and stars or on earth. The element helium was found in the sun before it was known on earth. Helium first appeared as unidentified dark lines in the solar spectrum. When the unknown element was sought and found on earth, the bright emission lines of this gas on earth matched the dark emission lines of helium in outer layers of the sun. The new element was named helium after the Greek word for sun, *helios*.

The spectrometer, originated by Fraunhofer, is an effective instrument for examining spectra. The instrument consists primarily of a *collimator* tube, a triangular prism, and a telescope properly arranged. A slit in the collimator tube permits only a narrow beam to enter the tube. A lens within the tube refracts the beam into parallel rays. The prism disperses the rays. The telescope affords effective examination of the spectrum. Mounting the collimator tube and the telescope on a large protractor permits refraction measurement for the various colors or lines.

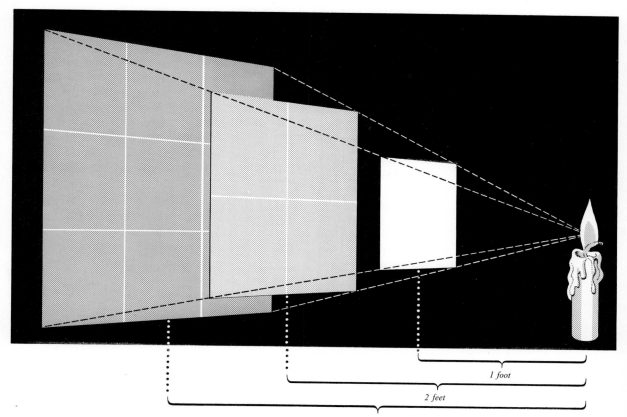

1 foot

2 feet

3 feet

17–13 "Inverse square" illumination. Illumination on a printed page decreases in intensity with the square of its distance from a source, much like equal pats of butter spread on increasingly larger slices of bread.

"INVERSE SQUARE" ILLUMINATION

Intuitively we recognize that the amount of light received by an object decreases with its distance from a light source. But to what extent? Gravitational, magnetic, and electrical forces involve inverse square laws; so does *intensity of illumination*. It is easily shown that intensity of illumination decreases as the *square* of the distance increases (Fig. 17–13). At a distance of 2 feet from a point source, a beam of light spreads over four times as much area as at 1 foot; and at 3 feet, across nine times as much area as 1 foot. That is, at 3 feet from a lamp, the page of your book receives only about one-ninth as much illumination as at 1 foot. Your page at 5 feet from a lamp receives only about one-twenty-fifth as much illumination as at 1 foot. Distance really counts!

SPEED-OF-LIGHT EXPERIMENTS

When we flick a switch, does light flood the room all at once (that is, at infinite speed), or does it move across the room at some other speed too fast for the eye to see? The speed of light was an ancient topic of speculation. Empedocles (490–435 B.C.) was one of the first natural philosophers to believe that light moves at a limited but very great speed. The Roman Pliny (23–79 A.D) noted that "light is swifter than sound because it is certain that a lightning flash is seen before the thunder is heard, though they both take place at the same time." A noted Arabian scientist, al-Biruni (973–1048), and Roger Bacon also speculated about a finite but great speed of light. But later, Kepler and Descartes believed that light has infinite speed. Here again, brilliant men speculated on both sides of a question for ages. How was the question of an infinite versus finite speed of light to be settled? Galileo made the first known attempt to measure the speed of light. He and an assistant, stationed on hilltops nearly a mile apart, flashed lanterns back and forth. When Galileo quickly uncovered his lantern and the light reached his assistant, the latter uncovered his own lantern for a return of light to Galileo. Meanwhile, Galileo hoped to measure the time taken for light to make the round trip. Although the two had practiced considerably to "acquire such skill in uncovering and occulting their lights that the instant one sees the light of his companion he will uncover his own," Galileo was not "able to ascertain with certainty whether the appearance of the opposite light was instantaneous or not." Galileo's basic method and reasoning were sound, but the swift speed of light was lost in the time it took the experimenters to react. Another 2 centuries were needed for precise enough apparatus in the hands of French physicists Armand Fizeau (1819–1896) and Leon Foucault and of American Albert Michelson (1852–1931) to measure the speed of light directly.

17–14   Roemer's determination of the speed of light. Roemer found that as the earth moved from A to B, the period of revolution of Jupiter's moon appeared to increase. He reasoned that the increase was due to the time taken for light to travel the extra distance from Jupiter's moon as the earth receded. From the extra distance and extra time, he calculated a finite speed for light.

But meanwhile in 1666, the young Danish astronomer Ole Roemer (1644–1710) indirectly but successfully determined a finite speed for light. His discovery was accidental in the sense that he did not have the speed of light in mind when he came upon it. He was systematically observing one of Jupiter's moons at the Paris Observatory as it passed into and out of Jupiter's shadow (Fig. 17–14) around the planet and into the shadow again. He expected the time between successive passages of the moon into Jupiter's shadow to remain the same. He was amazed to find that the period of the moon's revolution first increased for six months when the earth receded from Jupiter (positions A to B). The period then decreased for six months when the earth approached Jupiter (positions B to A). Specifically, with the earth at position A, Roemer found that it took the moon 42.5 hours to go from its position shown at P around Jupiter and back to its original eclipse position P'. The small distance that Jupiter meanwhile moved can be ignored. As the earth moved from A to B, the 42.5-hour period for Jupiter's moon increased until, when the earth was at B, that period had increased by 16 minutes and 36 seconds, or about 1,000 seconds. Roemer concluded that the speed of light was involved. If light had an infinite speed, then the moon's period viewed from the earth would remain constant whether the earth was at A or B. Roemer reasoned, therefore, that the extra 1,000 seconds was the time taken for the light from Jupiter's moon to travel across the earth's orbit from A to B. Using today's value of 186 million miles as the average diameter of the earth's orbit relative to Jupiter, the speed of light c is calculated as follows:

$$c = \frac{\text{distance light traveled}}{\text{time of travel}} = \frac{186{,}000{,}000 \text{ mi}}{1{,}000 \text{ sec}}$$

$$c = 186{,}000 \text{ mi/sec.}$$

The speed of light is amazingly high—fast enough to carry light over seven times around the earth in a second! Roemer's value of about 140,000 miles per second for the speed of light was low but was still the first value determined, and it was accurate enough to show that the speed of light is not infinite.

In 1849 Fizeau adapted Galileo's laboratory method to determine the speed of light. In place of a human assistant, he used a mirror 5 miles away (Fig. 17–15). Instead of a lantern, Fizeau used a candle and a cogwheel turned by a weight and pulley device. The candle was arranged so that before the wheel turned, light from the candle traveling a round trip of 10 miles could be seen reflected from the mirror between cogs (teeth) of the wheel. When the wheel turned, the beam was broken up by the teeth in rotation; and the slower the speed of the wheel, the longer the length of each beam seen. With care, the wheel could be made

MIRROR

LIGHTLY SILVERED
MIRROR

5 MILES

OBSERVER

17–15 Fizeau's technique for determining the speed of light. An observer sees a continuous beam of light in his mirror if the beam makes the 10-mile round trip in the time taken for cog 2 to get to the position of cog 1. The distance and time involved can be used to determine the speed of light.

to rotate slowly enough so that the beam was continuous. That is, a beam leaving the source between cogs 1 and 2 could be returning between cogs 2 and 3, and so on, to give continuity. This also meant that the time it took cog 2 to get to the position of cog 1 was the time it took for light to travel 10 miles—in this case, almost 1/20,000 of a second. Fizeau obtained this time value by dividing the time for a rotation of the wheel by the number of cogs. Fizeau's answer of about 194,00 miles a second for the speed of light was closer than Roemer's a half century before; but a year later, Fizeau's colleague, Foucault, substituted a rotating mirror for the cogwheel, and with the same technique he obtained a closer answer by today's standards. Finally, by great refinement of the rotating-mirror technique, in repeated experiments on Mount Wilson, California, Albert Michelson in 1926 established our present approximation of 186,000 miles per second for the speed of light.

CHAPTER REVIEW

1. What is a rainbow? What are the three prerequisites for its formation? How do its colors originate?

2. Compare Seneca's explanation of the origin of a rainbow to present ideas.

3. (a) Describe Seneca's hypothesis that "the rainbow is an image of the sun distorted by hollow clouds acting as imperfect mirrors." (b) What assumptions did he use? (c) What appeals to observation did he make? (d) What appeals to authority? (e) What appeals to reasoning? (f) What appeals to imagination?

4. Distinguish among reflection, refraction, dispersion, absorption, and diffusion of light. Illustrate.

5. How does a rainbow illustrate (a) reflection of light? (b) Bending of light? (c) Dispersion of light?

6. Explain and illustrate the law of reflection.

7. Explain and illustrate the law of refraction.

8. What direct or indirect contributions did the following men make to present understanding of the rainbow? (a) Euclid. (b) Seneca. (c) Hero of Alexandria. (d) Ptolemy. (e) Snell. (f) Archbishop A. de Dominis. (g) Descartes. (h) Newton.

9. What was Newton's hypothesis about the origin of rainbow colors? How did he test his hypothesis?

10. Compare Newton's problem solving with the rainbow to Seneca's with respect to (a) knowledge available at the time of each man. (b) The approach of each to the problem. (c) The assumptions of each man. (d) The nature of the evidence each used to support his ideas.

11. Is ordinary sunlight a "pure" yellow or a blend of many colors? How can this be shown?

12. Without an eye to observe, does color exist? Explain.

13. What is the principle of selective reflection of light? Illustrate.

14. What is the principle of selective color by transmission? Illustrate.

15. Describe and illustrate color by addition.

16. Describe and illustrate color by subtraction.

17. What are the three types of spectra? Illustrate.

18. Under what conditions do these three types of spectra arise? Why are they significant?

19. How are spectroscopes used to determine the composition of stars?

20. How could the element helium have been discovered in the sun before it was found on earth?

21. What relationship exists between intensity of illumination and distance from a light source?

22. Without apparatus for measurement, what early evidence existed that light travels faster than sound?

23. How did the astronomer Roemer determine the speed of light without originally intending to do so?

24. To what extent does the speed of light change as light travels from air to glass?

25. What reasons exist for believing that light travels in straight lines?

PROBLEMS

1. When you look in a mirror, do you see yourself as others see you? Why?

2. Show by a diagram how you can see your entire image in a plane mirror half your height.

3. Use a diagram to show why your mirror image appears to extend a left hand to your outstretched right hand.

4. If the hands of a clock reflected in a mirror indicate 3:00 P.M., what time is it?

5. Through a diagram, show how an oblique beam of light is bent as it enters and leaves a pane of glass.

6. Use a diagram to show why an oar partially submerged in water appears bent.

7. Use a diagram to show why another person looks shorter to you when he is standing in a swimming pool than when he is on dry land.

8. If you are obliquely spearing a fish, would you aim at, above, or below it? Why?

9. Using the refraction principle, show how it is possible to see the sun after it sets. What effect does such refraction of the sun's rays have upon the length of daylight?

10. Use a diagram to show how a glass prism separates white light into component colors.

11. Why does the sun when it is setting appear more red than it does at midday?

12. What is a luminous body? How are nonluminous bodies seen?

13. Distinguish among opaque, transparent, and translucent objects. Illustrate.

14. What determines the color of an opaque object? Of a translucent object?

15. Why is ordinary glass colorless?

16. Why does blending all colors of light give white, whereas a mixture of all pigments produces black?

17. Explain why a piece of red cloth appears black when seen under blue light.

18. Explain why the American flag appears black and red under a red light.

19. Before purchasing a suit or dress, why should you take the garment into daylight or under "daylight" lamps?

20. What color would red cloth appear to be if it is illuminated by (a) a mercury vapor lamp? (b) A sodium vapor lamp? (c) The sun?

21. What kind of spectra do the following show? (a) A piece of white-hot platinum. (b) Molten iron. (c) An electric discharge in a partially evacuated tube.

22. Why do white walls aid in the illumination of a room?

23. A lamp is moved from a distance of 5 feet to 1 foot from a printed page. How much greater is the illumination on the page?

24. A lamp is lowered from 4 feet to 3 feet above a table. By what percentage is the illumination on the table increased?

25. How many miles does light travel in a year? What is a light-year?

SUGGESTIONS FOR
FURTHER READING

Taylor, Lloyd W., *Physics, the Pioneer Science,* Vol. 2, Dover paperback, New York, Chs. 29–30 and 34–35.

Priestley, Herbert, *Introductory Physics,* Allyn and Bacon, Boston, 1958, Ch. 24.

Newton, Isaac, *Opticks,* Dover paperback, New York, 1952.

Lodge, Oliver, *Pioneers of Science,* Dover paperback, New York, 1960, Lecture 10.

Coleman, James A., *Relativity for the Layman,* Signet paperback, New York, 1962, Ch. 1.

Helmholtz, Herman N. L., *Popular Scientific Lectures,* ed. Morris Kline, Dover, paperback, New York, 1961, Series 1, Lecture 4, "Recent Progress in Theory of Vision," and Series 2, Lecture 2, "On the Relation of Optiks to Painting."

18   Theories of Light: Wave versus Particle

We can scarcely avoid the inference that light consists in the transverse undulations of the same medium which is the cause of electric and magnetic phenomena.

JAMES CLERK MAXWELL, 1856

Thinking men do not stop with phenomena. They wish to know what is behind the outer forms of things. What *is* light? What is the rainbow a manifestation of? What is it that reflects, refracts, disperses, or travels at 186,000 miles per second? Running through the ages have been two opposing theories of the nature of light: wave theories and particle theories. Still contending today are Maxwell's electromagnetic wave theory (quote above) and Einstein's photon theory.

EARLY THEORIES OF LIGHT

So what is light? And how does it travel? To ancient atomists, all phenomena were to be understood in terms of atoms in motion. Light, therefore, consists of a stream of minute particles emitted by a source that upon entering an eye gives vision. Pythagoreans amplified the corpuscular idea; they held that the emitted light particles are seedlike miniatures of the emitting objects. We see objects as they are through their miniatures' entering our eyes. Plato kept the emanations but reversed the direction. The eye is an active agent. It searches for objects by emitting streams of light (feelerlike). Said Plato, "Of the sense organs of the human body, the gods first made light-bearing eyes. They caused the pure fire within us . . . to flow through the eyes as a smooth stream . . . . Whenever the vision collides with an obstructing object, it thus brings about the sensation of seeing." Empedocles (490–435 B.C.), a century before Plato, stated that vision results when emanations from a luminous object are met by rays from the eyes.

To Aristotle, no particle theory was satisfactory. A particle theory meant that a ray of light was discontinuous, that a void existed between particles. All nature was continuous and would not tolerate a void. Light traveling like water waves as vibrations through transparent media provides a continuity lacking in all particle theories. The term *ether* as a universal medium for light and other radiation has its origin in Aristotle's idea of an ethereal substance comprising and extending through the entire heavens. The wave concept of light, perpetuated by Arabian astronomers, was emphasized by Roger Bacon, who stated in his *Opus Major* that "light is not an emanation of particles but the transmission of a movement." Leonardo da Vinci, Galileo, and Descartes considered light to be a wave by analogy with sound and water. Descartes also assumed a universal "subtle and very fluid material" different from celestial body material that he called aether, in which light waves traveled. Newton's contemporaries Hooke and Huygens continued the chain of light wave theorists.

NEWTON'S
CORPUSCULAR THEORY

Newton, however, resurrected the particle theory. At first Newton had been attracted to the wave theory. Even his later writings show that he was not entirely satisfied with light as just a stream of particles. But he did not see how else light could travel in straight lines. Light waves, like water waves, would spread around obstructions, and customary shadows would hardly exist behind objects. In Newton's words, light as a wave would show "a continual and very extravagant spreading and bending in every way into the genescent medium." But Newton adds: "Assuming the rays of light to be small bodies emitted every way from shining substances, those when they impinge on any refraction or reflecting superficies must as necessarily excite vibrations in the aether as stones do in water when thrown into it." Newton's particle theory included elements of wave theory. Particles were primary, but waves were there too, at least as ether vibrations when the material light particles struck objects.

To be acceptable, a hypothesis or theory must be expanded to explain and predict diverse events. This Newton did with his particle theory. Light sources eject light particles much as machine guns eject bullets. The particles move at great speeds in all directions. When striking objects, the bulletlike particles either are reflected off an opaque surface, enter and are absorbed in the material, or penetrate through so-called translucent substances.

Newton's corpuscular theory easily explained the reflection of light. A billiard ball is reflected by the side of the table it strikes. In an elastic collision, the angle at which the ball strikes equals the angle at which it leaves (Fig. 18–1). Each light particle in a stream does the same against opaque surfaces. The angle of incidence of each particle equals the angle of reflection to satisfy the law of reflection.

Newton explained refraction, that is, the bending of light moving between materials of different densities as follows: Light particles entering glass from air should tend to be attracted to the thicker part of the glass by Newton's law of gravitation. Experience shows that light rays entering prisms and lenses do bend toward the thicker part of these glass objects to give an angle of refraction smaller than the angle of incidence (Fig. 17–7). But gravitation does not repel; on what basis some of the light particles would be reflected—that is, repelled at the surface of glass while others were attracted—is not clear. Also, light particles should have a greater speed in glass than in air because of the gravitational attraction of the glass. Sound travels about 15 times as fast in glass as in air and over four times as fast in water as in air. What is true for sound could be true for light. A crucial test showing light to move more slowly in glass or water than in air would of course contradict Newton's particle or substance theory of light. But measuring techniques had not yet arrived at the point where the speed of light could be measured in glass or water.

Newton could also explain color dispersion by his theory. Each color has corpuscles of different mass. Gravitational forces on corpuscles increase with greater mass from red to violet. When sunlight enters glass prisms or raindrops, gravitational forces should be strongest on corpuscles at the violet end and weakest at the red end. Corpuscles of violet light, therefore, bend the most, and those of red, the least—to give the beautiful separation of colors from red to violet observed in rainbows and prisms.

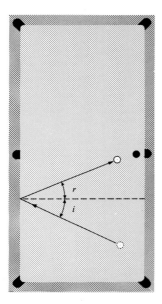

18–1   Corpuscular explanation of the reflection of light. The angle at which a billiard ball strikes the side of a table equals the angle at which the ball is reflected. By analogy, the angle of incidence (∠ i) at which a light particle in a beam strikes a smooth surface equals the angle of reflection (∠ r) at which the particle is reflected.

WAVE CHARACTERISTICS

The great Dutch physician-physicist Christian Huygens (1629–1695) opposed Newton's corpuscular model with a wave model. In 1678 Huygens became aware of Roemer's value for the speed of light and was convinced that nothing material could travel "more than six hundred thousand times

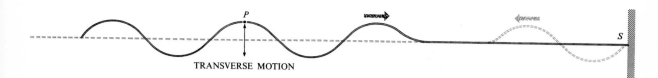

TRANSVERSE MOTION

the velocity of sound." To him, light could travel that fast only as a wave disturbance in a universal elastic medium, an ether. Using as an example a row of marbles struck at an end, Huygens emphasized that "the motion passes as in an instant to the last of them, which separates itself from the row . . . . Whence one sees that the movement [not the marbles themselves] passes with an extreme velocity . . . . But it is certain that this progression of motion is not instantaneous, but successive, and therefore it must take time."

Huygens used not only marbles but water waves and sound waves as analogies for light. To understand light waves, we must first understand waves in general. As conceptual models, waves are in two main forms involving vibrating sources, transmission media, velocities, frequencies, wavelengths, and amplitudes.

Two main wave forms are *transverse* and *longitudinal*. Attach one end of a rope to a support S and sharply jerk your hand up and down at the other end of the rope several times (Fig. 18–2). Several waves chase each other down and back. The hand is a vibrating source, and the rope a flexible medium for the waves. The waves are called transverse because a point on the rope medium moves vertically as the waves themselves move horizontally toward the support. The motion of a particle of the medium is differentiated from the wave motion and is perpendicular to it. Water waves are also primarily transverse waves; a cork at the water surface bobs up and down as waves move horizontally.

For a second main type of wave, a compressional or longitudinal wave, consider a spiral spring (Fig. 18–3). With one hand at B, pull back a turn of the spring toward the other hand at A, and release the hand at B. A compressional pulse will move along the spring to the support S, and back. This pulse involves a region of condensation in which wire turns are closer together, followed by a section of rarefaction in which turns are correspondingly further apart. Such pulses of condensations and rarefactions are called longitudinal or compressional waves because a point P of the spring vibrates longitudinally, that is, parallel to the direction of the

18–2   Transverse waves. A given point P on a wave oscillates perpendicularly to the direction of the wave itself.

18–3   Longitudinal waves. A given point P on a wave oscillates in a direction parallel to that of the wave itself.

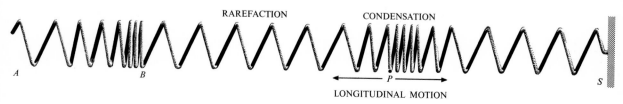

RAREFACTION   CONDENSATION

LONGITUDINAL MOTION

compressional pulse itself. Sound waves are compressional waves. The hammer of a bell visibly vibrates the gong against air to send air pulsations in all directions. The air disturbances in turn vibrate eardrums with a resulting sound. Sound, therefore, is a sensation with three prerequisites: a vibrating source (the bell), a transmitting medium (air), and a receiving mechanism (an ear). Without an ear, there is no sound, just silent, vibrating objects and generally unsensed disturbances of the air or other media. Remove air from a large jar encasing a ringing bell and an eerie silence remains with a visibly moving bell hammer—a silence much like that experienced on the moon. (The moon has no atmosphere.) For sound, a transmitting medium is necessary. Of course, stop the hammer, return the air, and no sound is heard, either. Clearly, sound is an interaction between organisms and their surroundings.

By analogy, a wave model for light must also have a vibrating source, a transmitting medium, and a receiving mechanism. Just as Huygens's marbles had to be struck, water disturbed by wind, or a bell gong vibrated, an originating source of disturbance must exist for light, whether it be sun, candle, or lamp. Vibrating charges as originating sources of light were first visualized by Maxwell in 1854 and were pinpointed as vibrating electrons within atoms by Bohr in the twentieth century. An ether was assumed by Huygens as an elastic transmitting medium for light everywhere. That without an eye there is no color, just original light sources and light radiation—in waves for Huygens—has already been discussed. Huygens assumed light to travel in longitudinal waves like sound until the English physician-physicist Thomas Young (1773–1829) and the French engineer Augustin Fresnel (1788–1827) about a century and a half later produced evidence for a transverse wave model of light.

Once Roemer gave a first estimate of the speed of light, further characteristics of hypothetical light waves were possible. By analogy with water waves (Fig. 18–4), light waves have a *wavelength* λ from crest to crest or from any given point on a wave to the same point on the next wave. They also have a *frequency* f representing the number of waves passing a given point per second.

18–4 By water wave analogy, v = nλ. The velocity (v) of a wave equals the number (n) of waves traveling past a given point (P) in a second, times a wavelength (λ).

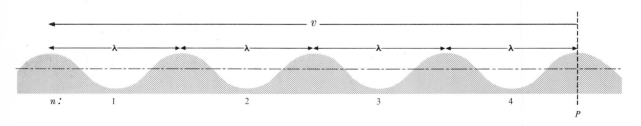

If v is the velocity of the waves,

$$v = \lambda f.$$

Equation 18–1

That is, the velocity of a wave equals the product of its frequency and its wavelength.

If the velocity of light waves, unlike water or sound waves, always has the constant* value c:

$$c = \lambda f.$$

Equation 18–2

Clearly, with a constant velocity c for light, the greater the wave frequency n, the smaller the wavelength λ (n and λ are inversely proportional). In this way, a relationship is established between the velocity, wavelength, and frequency of waves in general and of unseen hypothetical light waves in particular. Science and mathematics again calling the world to order!

Waves also have an *amplitude,* or altitude, measured from a point midway between the top of the crest and the base of the trough. A large amplitude means large intensity, and vice versa. For example, a larger amplitude in sound means greater loudness; a large amplitude in light waves, more brightness.

HUYGENS'S WAVE THEORY OF LIGHT

The great contribution of Christian Huygens to the wave model of light was the principle that every point on an advancing wave front acts as a source from which secondary waves continually spread. Let AB be a wave front from a source S (Fig. 18–5), and p, q, r, s, and t be points on that wave front. From each of these points, secondary waves will spread out as if from new original light sources. The secondary waves are represented by arcs at p', q', r', s', and t'. Secondary waves from all points on AB form the new position A^1B^1 of the moving wave front. Each point on $A'B'$ then becomes a new source of secondary waves in a continuous process. With this principle for the spreading out of waves, Huygens was able to explain straight-line propagation of light, reflection, refraction, and other phenomena. For example, any dashed line from the source S through p and p', q and q', and so on represents a ray moving in a straight line and indicates the direction in which the front is traveling. The direction is always perpendicular to the wave front. With his wave

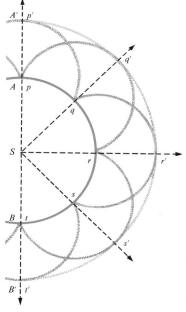

18–5 Huygens's wave model of light. From light source S emanates a wave front AB. Any point p, q, r, s, or t on AB may be treated as a new point source of light from which emanate new waves with further point sources p', q', r', s', or t' for a new wave front A'B'. Dashed arrows Sp', Sq', Sr', and so on show how straight-line propagation of light may be explained through a wave model.

---

*Reasons for assuming a constant speed for light are discussed in Chapter 22.

model, Huygens met Newton's argument that a wave theory could not account for light rays moving in straight lines. On the other hand, Huygens argued that the wave theory more reasonably accounted for the fact that beams of light cross one another without apparent interference; if light were particles, wouldn't some strike each other and be deflected? Also, if different colors involve particles of different masses, as Newton assumed, then how could the heavier particles move as fast as lighter ones? How could all light particles travel together through space?

Once straight lines perpendicular to a moving wave front could be used to represent rays that give the direction of the wave front, Huygens's wave model could explain reflection of light (Fig. 18–6). The incident ray represents the direction of the wave front before striking a mirror surface. When the wave hits the surface, it is reflected back, with the wave taking the direction of the reflected ray and with the angle of incidence equal to the angle of reflection.

Let us also illustrate how wave theory explains refraction of light (Fig. 18–7). The parallel lines represent a light beam in air diagonally approaching a water surface WX. The water slows the motion of the front. The end A of the front enters the water before end B and temporarily moves more slowly than B. When end B is at the water surface, its speed is reduced to that of end A. The wave front therefore takes the new direction A'B' as compared to AB. Since BB' is a greater distance traveled than AA', the beam is bent to a direction closer to the dashed normal PQ. An analogy is often made of a column of soldiers marching from smooth to very rough terrain (Fig. 18–7). The man at A reaches the rough ground before the one at B. A is slowed down; B continues at the original pace. A travels through only AA' while B covers BB'. Automatically the line swings to a direction closer to PQ. Light beam paths are reversible. If a beam passes from water to air rather than from air to water, all that is necessary is to reverse directions of motion in the diagram. In the reversed case of a beam moving from a more dense to a less dense medium, it is clear from the diagram why the beam is bent to a direction further from the normal.

Recall that light should travel *faster* in a dense medium by Newton's gravitational particle theory and *slower* by Huygens's wave theory. An experiment set up to determine whether the speed of light in glass or water is more (or less) than in air would have been significant in the controversy between Newton and Huygens. But experimental techniques had not yet advanced to that point. Roemer had just made his accidental discovery of the speed of light in planetary space. It wasn't until 1850 that Foucault successfully measured the speed of light in various media, to find that Huygens was right. The speed of light in air is 30 percent greater than in water and 50 percent greater than in glass. Obviously, the knowledge process is limited by the techniques as well as the ideas of any given period. In the intervening 2 centuries, most scientists

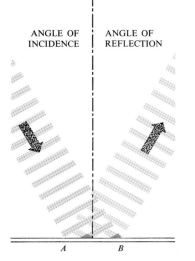

ANGLE OF INCIDENCE   ANGLE OF REFLECTION

A   *B*

18–6 Light reflection by the wave theory. The (lower) part of a wave front arriving first at a mirror surface (A) leaves the mirror first as the upper part of a reflected wave. In the direction change of the entire front, the angle of incidence equals the angle of reflection. A wave front arriving at a perpendicular (dashed line) to the mirror surface at AB reverses its direction on that perpendicular.

followed Newton's corpuscular theory with more assurance than that great scientist originally had himself. Newton's all-embracing mechanical system gave him more prestige than Huygens. And Newton's disciples followed Newton often as rigidly as Aristotelians did Aristotle.

YOUNG'S DIFFRACTION EXPERIMENTS AND THE INTERFERENCE PRINCIPLE

Not all scientists of that intervening period were corpuscular theory advocates. A most effective wave adherent was Thomas Young (1773–1829), the English physician whose contributions in optics stemmed from human eye research. He strongly reinforced Huygens's wave model with an ignored principle of *interference,* suggested by Robert Hooke at the time of Newton. This principle also was based upon a water wave analogy:

> When two undulations from original sources coincide either perfectly or very nearly in direction, their joint effect is a combination of motions belonging to each . . . . It has been shown that two equal series of [water] waves proceeding from centres near each other, may be seen to destroy each other's effects at certain points, and at others to redouble them; and the beating of two sounds has been explained from a similar interference.

That is, two or more waves can reinforce each other to give a higher, more powerful wave; waves can also cancel each other out. If light is a wave, then light should show evidence of reinforcement and cancellation. Young looked for such evidence of mutual interference by light rays. And he found it in phenomena called *diffraction.* Light passing through a single pinhole forms a spot on a screen. With care, color fringes can be found about the spot. An Italian mathematics professor, Francesco Grimaldi, had reported such color fringes back in 1665. Newton's explanation had been that corpuscles of light vary in mass according to color, and that corpuscles moving through a pinhole are separated by a different pull of matter on them, much as with color dispersion in prisms. In his famous diffraction experiment, Young, however, used two adjacent pinholes. Alternately covering up each pinhole, he let light of a single color through the other. He found two distinct spots on his screen as expected. But when light passed through both holes at the same time, he found a central light spot *between* the two pinholes rather than directly opposite them, as would be expected by a corpuscular theory. And even more significantly, he found alternate light and dark stripes around the central spot (Fig. 18–8). Just as with

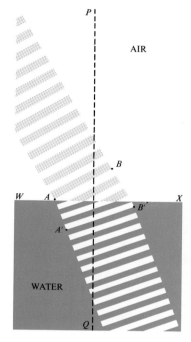

18–7 Bending of light waves passing from air to water. Point A on wave front AB reaches the water surface before point B does and is slowed down by the water before point B is. This earlier slowing of A causes the front to swing to the new direction A'B'.

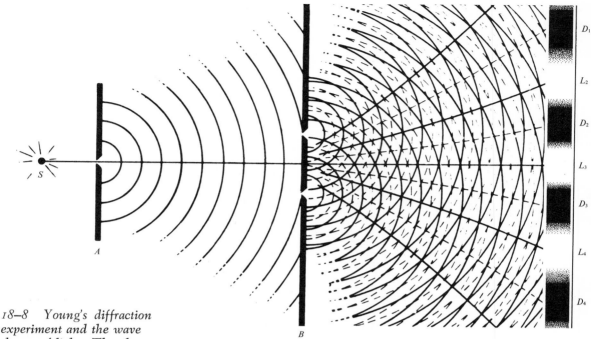

18–8 *Young's diffraction experiment and the wave theory of light. The alternate bright and dark lines on the screen are easily explained by wave theory as due to light waves from the two slits in B that alternately reinforce and cancel each other.*

water waves, here was a case of rays of light interfering with each other. The light stripes were light waves reinforcing each other (constructive interference); the dark stripes were waves canceling each other (destructive interference). Applying Huygens's wave model to Young's diffraction experiment gives the following explanation (Fig. 18–8):

From a point source S, light proceeds through a single slit in A and then symmetrically through the double slit in B. The two parallel slits can be treated like two point sources sending out waves simultaneously. The solid arcs are wave fronts, or crests; the dashed lines are troughs one-half wavelength behind the crests. A crest of a wave (solid arc) from one slit meeting the crest of a wave from the other slit are in *phase* and fully support each other. The solid radial lines L_1 to L_5 indicate where waves meet in phase and reinforce each other; the broken dark streamers D_1 to D_4 indicate where the waves cancel each other. Where lines L_1–L_5 strike the screen are areas of light stripes. Where lines D_1–D_4 touch the screen are dark bands. The alternations of light and dark bands around a central light area were thus easily explained by Young.

Young also easily explained ordinary color dispersion by associating color with wavelength and frequency. Wavelength decreased from red to blue in the spectrum. With the longest wavelength, red refracted the least; with the shortest wavelength, blue refracted the most.

In fact, with his interference principle, Young easily explained specific

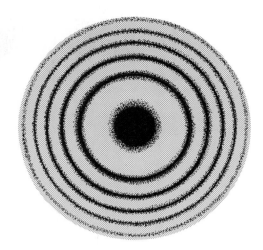

18–9   Newton's rings. Newton found alternate blue and black rings when he placed a thick convex lens on a flat piece of glass under blue light (see Fig. 18–10). Under sunlight, the rings were in various colors.

color phenomena that Newton handled with considerable uncertainty— for example, the shifting, glistening colors of soap bubbles or the spectacular circles of color called "Newton's rings." A bubble is a film with an inner and outer surface. Newton, in investigating soap bubble colors, had placed a very thin *convex lens* on a flat piece of glass by analogy with the two soap bubble surfaces (Fig. 18–9). Newton was amazed at what he saw: Around the center contact point were a succession of colored rings not at all in rainbow color order! Then when he used blue light, Newton found alternate rings of blue and black (Fig. 18–9); with pure red light, he found alternate rings of red and black. Why the succession of alternate rings? And why did the spacing between rings vary with the color? In his explanations, Newton came very close to wave theory without actually arriving, just as Brahe moved up to Copernican theory and stopped short in a Ptolemaic compromise. (Recall that Newton did not see how a wave theory could explain light traveling in straight lines and that Brahe was unable to find stellar parallax as evidence for Copernicanism.)

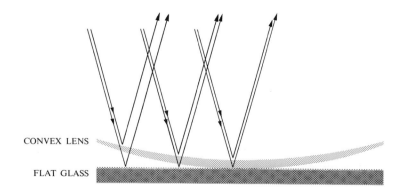

CONVEX LENS

FLAT GLASS

18–10   Young's explanation of Newton's rings. Thomas Young theorized that Newton's rings resulted from the very gradual change in the small distance between the reflecting surfaces of the flat glass and the lens. Wavelengths of different colors could alternately reinforce and cancel each other out at different points.

Newton blowing bubbles.
(Brown Bros. photograph)

Young explained soap bubble colors and "Newton's rings" as wave interference effects. In both cases, two reflecting surfaces are very close together. Different colors are associated with different wavelengths. With minute gradual changes in the distance between the lens and the flat piece of glass (or an uneven thickness of the soap bubble film), wavelengths of different colors could reinforce and cancel each other out at different points (Fig. 18–10). The uniformity and shape of the rings was due to the symmetry of the lens touching the flat glass at the center.

But accepted conceptual models are not easily shaken. Newton's corpuscular theory otherwise was well established in the early 19th century, and Young's reinforcement of wave theory was not taken seriously. One of Young's critics referred to

the absurdity of this writer's "law of interference," as it pleases him to call one of the most incomprehensible suppositions that we remember to have met with . . . . This paper contains nothing which deserves the name of experiment or discovery; and it is, in fact, destitute of every species of merit . . . . We . . . dismiss, for the present, the feeble lubrations of this author in which we have searched without success for some traces of learning, acuteness, and ingenuity, that might compensate his evident deficiency in the powers of solid thinking.

To be an innovator is difficult. Copernicus did not publish *Revolutionibus* until just before his death. Galileo could not coax some of his colleagues to look through his telescope. Newton published *Principia* and *Opticks* years after completion, and only upon the insistence of friends. Then, when Newton was accepted, his monumental work stopped some followers from thinking further. In answer to critics, Young said, "Much as I venerate the name of Newton, I am not therefore obliged to believe he was infallible. I see . . . with regret that he was liable to err, and that his authority has perhaps retarded the progress of science." Newton himself had said, "Tis true that from theory I argue the corporeity of light but I do so without any absolute positiveness . . . . I knew that the properties which I declared of light were in some measure capable of being explicated not only by that, but by other mechanical hypotheses." It is often better to deal with the principal than with an agent!

In time, Young's ideas began to take hold through the brilliant experimentation and support of the French engineer Augustin Fresnel (1788–1827). With Foucault's demonstration of 1850 in contradiction to Newton that light slows down in media denser than air, the corpuscular theory was totally eclipsed. The wave model reigned supreme for over 50 years, until it was seriously challenged by Einstein's photon theory of light.

LIGHT AS AN ELECTROMAGNETIC WAVE

Huygens, Young, and Fresnel through 2 centuries established light as a wave. But what kind of wave? The term "wave" tells more about how light travels than what it is.

Oersted, Faraday, and Henry linked electricity to magnetism, but it was the English mathematical physicist James Clerk Maxwell (1831–1879) who extended electromagnetism to light and predicted that Newton's color spectrum was a narrow, visible strip in a vast *electromagnetic spectrum*. A band of electromagnetic radiation so vast has resulted from Maxwell's prediction that it ranges from radio waves miles long at a low-frequency end to gamma rays with wavelengths in minute fractions of an inch at a high-frequency end. In between are merging wavelength ranges now designated as infrared (below red) radiation, light, ultraviolet (beyond violet) radiation, and X rays. All such related radiations move with the speed of light c and show reflection, refraction, reinforcement, and other characteristics of light. Every so often, a genius appears who sweepingly and successfully organizes and predicts. But like other

19 miles were emitted for use in radio telegraphy. It was also Hertz who experimentally showed that all electromagnetic radiations show the characteristics of light predicted by Maxwell. They reflect, refract, reinforce, and interfere like light.

Maxwell's electromagnetic spectrum was another one of the great unifiers of knowledge and nature with vast technological, social, and cultural implications. Table 18–1 and Fig. 18–12 offer current details of the electromagnetic spectrum. Because of the minute wavelengths of light and higher frequency radiation, the *angstrom* has been introduced as a unit of length, with 1 centimeter $= 10^8$ angstroms (or 1 angstrom $= 10^{-8}$ centimeters). Notice in Table 18–1 that the wavelengths of light as determined by the human eye vary from about 7,500 angstroms (red) to about 3,800 angstroms (violet) for a range of just 1 octave* in 60. We can hear through about 10 octaves of sound vibrations.

Table 18–1 | *ELECTROMAGNETIC SPECTRUM*

KIND OF WAVE	WAVELENGTH λ (APPROX.), METRIC UNITS	FREQUENCY *f (APPROX.), CYCLES/SEC
Long electromagnetic	over 16 km (10 mi)	under 20,000
Radio waves	16 km to 30 m	20,000 to 10,000,000 (or 10^7)
Microwaves	30 m to .01 cm	10^7 to 3×10^{12}
Infrared rays	.01 cm to .000075 cm	3×10^{12} to 4×10^{14}
Visible light	7.5×10^{-5} cm to 3.8×10^{-5} cm (7,500 A† to 3,800 A)	4×10^{14} to 8×10^{14}
Ultraviolet rays	3,800 A to 100 A	8×10^{14} to 3×10^{16}
X rays	100 A to .1 A	3×10^{16} to 3×10^{19}
Gamma rays	below .1 A	above 3×10^{19}

*All electromagnetic waves travel at the speed of visible light; $c = 3 \cdot 10^8$ m/sec. And $c = l \cdot n$ (that is, wavelength · frequency).
†"A" symbolizes angstrom (1 A $= 10^{-8}$ cm, or 1 cm $= 10^8$ A).

"ELECTRIC EYES"
AND PHOTON PARTICLES

At the end of the 19th century, light seemed entrenched as electromagnetic radiation emitted in continuous waves by vibrating electric charges in luminous bodies. Newton's color spectrum was part of a far more

*An *octave* is the interval from a given frequency either to half or twice that frequency.

extensive electromagnetic spectrum. But sooner or later, situations arise that the best of conceptual models cannot explain. Just when the electromagnetic wave theory seemed most firm, a *photoelectric effect* was observed that contradicted it. Light falling on a metal plate ejected electrons (negative charges) from the plate (Fig. 18-13) to positively charge the plate. How is it possible for light waves to have impact on electrons? Water waves have impact on objects, but water is a material thing. Perhaps light is not "pure" energy after all!

The difficulty really began, however, when the intensity of the light on the photoelectric plate was increased. Instead of electrons leaving the plate with more speed, there were just more electrons leaving with the original speed. If light consists of waves, more intense light should mean higher waves with nastier "wallops" on plate electrons. The electrons should move more quickly. If light consists of bulletlike particles, more intense light would mean more "bullets" at the same speed. A given electron hit by a light particle would not be affected by the additional "bullets." More "bullets" would just mean that more electrons would be hit and emitted. From the results, light seemed more like bullets. Maybe light is not a wave phenomenon after all!

In any case, Albert Einstein (1879-1955) assumed in 1905 that light is a stream of energy particles that he called *photons.* Einstein's photons are not minute bits of matter like Newton's corpuscles; they are particles of *energy* that act like matter. The energies of Einstein's photons are directly proportional to the color frequencies given in the electromagnetic spectrum. Violet light has a higher frequency than red light. Therefore, photons of violet light are larger than red light photons. The larger photons of violet striking metal should cause electrons to move faster than the smaller red photons do. Experiments showed this to be so. In his photon idea, Einstein was applying to light an energy packet, or *quantum,* idea that Max Planck (1858-1947) had successfully applied to heat phenomena. Einstein assumed that the energy E of each particle of energy was represented by:

$$E = hf,$$

Equation 18-3

where *h* is a now-famous universal constant of nature called Planck's constant (with a value determined at 6.62×10^{-34}), and where *f* is the frequency of the particular radiation in the electromagnetic spectrum.

In the transfer of a photon's energy to an electron in the photoelectric effect, Einstein emphasized that

$$hf = \tfrac{1}{2}mv^2 + w,$$

Equation 18-4

where *hf* equals the energy of the light photon, $\frac{1}{2}mv^2$ is the kinetic energy of the expelled electron, and *w* is the energy necessary to remove the

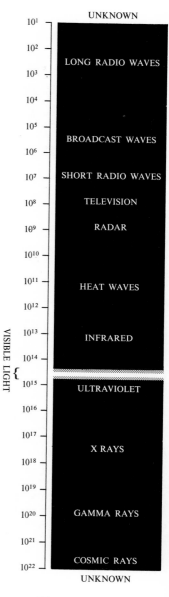

18-12 Electromagnetic spectrum. Visible light (3,800 A to 7,500 A) is a narrow, 1-octave range of color in a 60-octave band of electromagnetic waves stretching from long radio waves to cosmic rays.

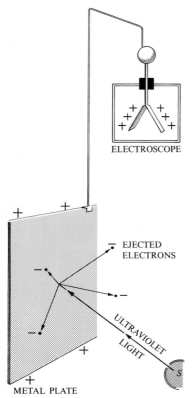

ELECTROSCOPE

EJECTED
ELECTRONS

ULTRAVIOLET
LIGHT

METAL PLATE

*18–13   Photoelectric effect.
Light falling on a metal plate
ejects electrons from the
plate, to charge the plate
positively. The electroscope
leaves repel each other, indicating that the plate is
charged.*

electron from the metal. This famous photoelectric equation earned for
Einstein a Nobel prize.

Today photoelectric cells (popularly called "electric eyes") open super-
market doors for customers, but the photon theory that explains this
operation cannot explain diffraction phenomena. Bulletlike photons, in
passing through a single pinhole, should create a spot on a screen directly
in line with the hole. But alternate light and dark rings are also found.
And photons through two pinholes should show two spots on a screen.
Instead, a series of alternate light and dark stripes are found around a
single spot midway between the two pinholes. The photon theory is also
unable to explain how light bends around obstacles. But the opposing
wave theory cannot explain the photoelectric effect. The nature of light
thus seems relative to the experimental setup. Light is wavelike in a
pinhole situation and particlelike in a photoelectric cell. But how can
light be both a continuous wave and a discontinuous particle? Perhaps
waves and particles are aspects of a bigger picture. Different situations
may display light in its different aspects, just as at different angles "the
neck of the peacock shows different colors."

CHAPTER REVIEW

1. What is light? Is it matter or energy, particles or waves, or what?
2. Describe the following particle theories of light, and indicate the
assumptions of each: (a) particle streams of Greek atomists, (b) seedlike
emanations of the Pythagoreans and of Plato, (c) Newton's corpuscular
theory, and (d) Einstein's photon theory.
3. Show how the successive theories in question 2 are alike.
4. What was new or different as particle ideas changed from 2a to 2d?
5. Give whatever experimental or other evidence you can for the
successive particle ideas in question 2.
6. Why did Newton believe in the corpuscular theory of light?
7. How did Newton's corpuscular theory explain the following light
phenomena? (a) Reflection. (b) Absorption. (c) Passage through translucent objects. (d) Bending, or refraction. (e) Color dispersion. (f)
"Newton's rings" or soap bubble colors.
8. Describe the following wave theories of light, and indicate the
assumptions of each: (a) Aristotle's light vibrations in a universal medium,
(b) water and sound wave analogies of light, (c) Huygens's model of
light waves, and (d) Maxwell's electromagnetic wave theory.
9. Use diagrams of a spring coil to illustrate (a) a longitudinal wave
and (b) a transverse wave.

10. Use water waves to show the relationship among wave velocity, wavelength, and wave frequency.

11. Compare water, sound, and light waves with respect to the following characteristics: (a) transverse or longitudinal wave form, (b) vibrating sources, (c) media of transmission, (d) velocities (e) frequencies, (f) wavelengths, (g) amplitudes, and (h) effects upon receiving mechanisms.

12. How does Huygens's wave model explain the following light phenomena? (a) Reflection of light. (b) Refraction of light.

13. On what basis did the corpuscular theory gain dominance over the wave theory?

14. What is Young's interference principle of light?

15. How did Young's diffraction experiments reinforce the Huygens wave theory?

16. How does the Huygens-Young wave theory account for "Newton's rings" or soap bubble colors, explained with difficulty by the corpuscular theory?

17. What significant experiment decidedly favored the wave theory over the particle theory of light during the last half of the 19th century? Explain.

18. What are electromagnetic waves? Describe the electromagnetic spectrum.

19. How did light waves come to be regarded as electromagnetic waves?

20. What does it mean to say that light rays are electromagnetic waves to which the eye and brain respond?

21. Explain the following as interactions between an organism and its surroundings: (a) sound and (b) color.

22. (a) What is the photoelectric effect? (b) How did it contradict the electromagnetic wave theory?

23. How did the photoelectric effect help to reinstate the particle theory of light?

24. What advantages does the photon theory have over Newton's corpuscular theory?

25. (a) How does the electromagnetic wave theory explain color differences in light? (b) How does the photon theory explain these color differences?

26. How does Einstein's photon theory explain diffraction phenomena?

27. How does Maxwell's electromagnetic wave theory explain the photoelectric effect?

28. Summarize the advantages and disadvantages that wave and particle theories have with respect to each other.

29. How can light be an electromagnetic wave and also a stream of photons? How can the two apparently opposed theories of light be acceptable at the same time?

PROBLEMS

1. If light consists of waves, why do shadows exist?

2. Illustrate the difference between light rays and light waves.

3. Use a diagram to show what is meant by constructive and destructive interference of light waves.

4. Why do films of oil often show bands of different colors?

5. (a) In what ways are light waves, infrared radiation, radio waves, ultraviolet rays, and X rays alike? (b) How do these radiations differ?

6. (a) Arrange the following radiations in the order of increasing wavelength: X rays, red light, violet light, radio waves, gamma rays, and ultraviolet light. (b) Which of these radiations has the greatest frequency? Which has the least?

7. Arrange the following types of stars in a sequence of increasing surface temperature: yellow stars, blue stars, red stars, and white stars. (Surface temperatures increase with wave frequency corresponding to color.)

8. Specifically what does it mean to say that we can hear through 10 octaves of sound waves but see through only 1 octave of electromagnetic waves?

9. (a) How does the electromagnetic wave theory explain differences in the colors of light? (b) How does the photon theory explain these differences?

10. Why do stars twinkle when seen from the ground but not when seen from space above the atmosphere?

11. (a) Is red or violet light bent most by a prism? (b) Use the wave theory of light to explain how a glass prism disperses white light into component colors.

12. Use the corpuscular theory to explain how a glass prism separates white light into component colors.

13. Why doesn't a thick, flat pane of glass separate sunlight into component colors?

14. By the corpuscular theory, should light travel faster upon entering a glass prism from air? Why?

15. By the wave theory, should light travel faster upon entering a glass prism from air? Why?

16. Foucault in 1850 was the first scientist to determine that light slows down in media denser than air. Why did this lead to the rejection of the particle theory of light for 50 years?

17. What is the frequency of ocean waves 500 feet long traveling 60 feet per second?

18. What is the wavelength of radio waves whose frequency is 900,000

vibrations per second? (All electromagnetic waves travel at 186,000 miles per second.)

19. How can we show that light primarily is a form of energy rather than matter?

20. How is it possible for radio signals to be arriving from outer space?

SUGGESTIONS FOR FURTHER READING

Taylor, Lloyd W., *Physics, the Pioneer Science*, Vol. 2, Dover paperback, New York, 1959, Chs. 36–38.

Priestley, Herbert, *Introductory Physics*, Allyn and Bacon, Boston, 1958, Ch. 22.

Lemon, Harvey B., *From Galileo to the Nuclear Age*, Phoenix paperback, Chicago, 1961, Chs. 35–36 and 38.

Bragg, William, *Universe of Light*, .Macmillan, New York, 1934, Chs. 7 and 9.

Ripley, Julien A., *Elements and Structure of the Physical Science*, Wiley, New York, 1964, Ch. 16.

Holton, Gerald J., and D. H. D. Roller, *Foundations of Modern Physical Science*, Addison-Wesley, Reading, Mass., 1958, Chs. 30 and 32.

Schneer, Cecil, *Search for Order*, Harper, New York, 1960, Ch. 14.

MacDonald, David K. C., *Faraday, Maxwell, and Kelvin*, Anchor paperback, Garden City, N. Y., 1964.

PART FOUR

Matter
and Its Transformations

19   Atoms and Elements

Atomism has proved the power of the intellectual imagination to identify aspects of an objective truth deeply rooted in the nature of things. Hidden in the history of atomism . . . there must be still concealed a trustworthy foundation for the human intellect . . . . No one is so brilliant that he can afford to neglect what history can teach him.

L. L. WHITE, 1961

Atomism originated among ancient Greeks in search of a basic alphabet of nature. Atoms were an idea long before they became a fact of technical power that will either solve basic human problems or destroy civilization.

ANCIENT GREEK
IDEAS OF MATTER

Have you ever considered that the countless ideas in thousands of volumes in a library are arrangements of but 26 letters of the alphabet, ten numerals, and a few punctuation marks? And have you ever wondered whether all the rich profusion of objects around us are formed of a basic alphabet of nature itself in various combinations? Or wondered what the character of nature's "building blocks" would be? Ancient Greeks did wonder about such things. They were intrigued by the diverse, changing, temporary character of objects around them. But they were confident that the universe is one, and they looked for something unifying and eternal in the variety and flux of things. In the search for order, Alcymneon likened the universe to the human body, with all parts correlated to the whole. This analogy gave astrologers something to grasp. The relationships of the stars to man and his activities became all the more apparent as the working and relationships of parts in a whole. Plato reinforced this in animistic analogy. The universe is a living organism of body, mind, and soul. Any particular material object has an importance that is secondary, changing, and temporary to the underlying, permanent reality of the whole—just as the cells and tissues of each one of us undergo wear, tear, and replacement in the more fundamental reality of our entire selves. Common origins of poetry, religion, philosophy, art, and science in man's search for order (and survival) are revealed by such analogies. Ionian Greeks were the first materialists. They reduced all objects to elemental components for explanation of variety and transformations in matter. Their idea was to look into matter itself to understand matter. Successors attempted to reduce objects to minute particles. When Leucippus pictured these unseen particles as hard, indivisible, unchanging, and eternal, atomism was born. "Atom" means "indivisible" in Greek. Things change, but irreducible units composing them can be permanent.

Plato, Aristotle, Seneca, and Lucretius describe Greek ideas of matter in detail; yet these men based their own ideas upon predecessors whom they acknowledged. Lucretius, in his *The Nature of the Universe*, provides a vivid exposition in poetic form of Epicurus's atomism, which, in turn, was originated by Leucippus and further developed by Democritus. Plato, in his *Timaeus*, falls back upon the Pythagorean idealization of number and geometric forms as the essence of things. Aristotle, in several works, elaborates the idea of the four elements air, earth, water, and fire, which he attributes to Empedocles. Chart 19–1 summarizes Greek ideas of matter and provides insights into the theoretical foundations of chemistry. Conceptual emphasis is on the nature of elements and on transformations of matter.

One Basic Element

The one-element Ionians (Chart 19–1) were the first systematic natural philosophers in Greece. They had a naturalistic, materialistic bent. It is not easy to clarify the meaning of "naturalistic." It is definite, however, that the Ionians sought causes and explanations in terms of the eternal working of things themselves rather than in any divine, mythological, or supernatural intervention. Looking for a single basic reality, each Ionian believed that all things have their origin in a single knowable element: water, air, fire, or some indeterminate, nebulous substance.

To Thales, the originator of the Ionian school, the primary element was water. As Seneca states it, "Water is, according to Thales, the most

Chart 19–1 | ANCIENT GREEK IDEAS OF MATTER

	NATURE OF THE ELEMENTS	TRANSFORMATIONS OF MATTER
THE ONE-ELEMENT IONIANS		
Thales ca. 624 B.C.–?	Water.	Cycle: Water → Bodies of plants and animals → Air → Earth → Water
Anaximander ca. 611–547 B.C.	An unlimited, eternal, indeterminate substance.	Eternal primary substance → Various substances, e.g., water / Eternal primary substance, and Opposite substances, e.g., fire. Transformation through separation and "strife" of opposites, moist, dry, etc.
Anaximenes 6th century B.C.	Air.	Stones ⇄ Earth ⇄ Water ⇄ Air ⇄ Fire. When rarefied. When condensed. Differences among all substances merely quantitative.
Heraclitus of Ephesus ca. 540–475 B.C.	Ethereal fire of everlasting, driving character.	Cycle: Primordial fire → Various substances, e.g., wood → Primordial fire; Other substances, e.g., smoke
THE FOUR-ELEMENT PHILOSOPHERS		
Empedocles ca. 490–435 B.C.	Fire, air, water and earth. Empedocles proved that air is a substance by showing that water can enter a vessel only as air escapes.	1. Four elements *not* intercovertible. 2. All substances are combinations of four elements caused by attraction (love) or repulsion (strife).
Pythagoreans From 5th century B.C. on Philolaus 480 B.C.–?	1. Numbers are elemental realities of everything. 2. Fire, air, earth, and water are built up out of regular geometric solids: a tetrahedron, octohedron, icosohedron, and cube, respectively. 3. The geometric solid dodecahedron is a fifth	The multiplicity of things is understandable in the relationships and transformability of numbers and of geometric forms.

Plato 427–347 B.C.:	1. Ideal types or qualities of things are the permanent realities giving temporary form to substances as we know them. 2. In his *Timaeus*, Plato also subscribed to the Pythagorean version of the four elements.	
Aristotle 384–322 B.C.	1. Primary essence of matter: four qualities of *hot, cold, dry,* and *moist*. 2. Fire, earth, water, and air, derived by combinations in pairs of the above four qualities as: E.g., fire, hot and dry; earth, dry and cold, etc. 3. A fifth ethereal element of eternal, almost divine quality beyond the human sphere.	1. Fire, earth, water, and air *are* interconvertible. 2. All substances consist of the four elements variously combined in different amounts of the four qualities in pairs. 3. The fifth ethereal element is not transformable.

THE IONIAN OF COUNTLESS ELEMENTS

Anaxagoras 510–428 B.C.	*"Seeds"* Each substance is infinitely divisible into "seeds" of itself.	No transformation: There is a "portion of everything in everything."

THE ATOMISTS

Leucippus ca. 500 B.C.–? Democritus ca. 460–370 B.C. Epicurus ca. 342–270 B.C. Lucretius ca. 98–55 B.C.	*Atoms* 1. Eternal. 2. Indestructible. 3. Minute. 4. Solid. 5. Indivisible. 6. All identical in substance. 7. But variable in size, shape, and weight. 8. Constantly moving.	 Individual atoms and void — separations — Groups of atoms — collisions Substances, once formed, vary according to size, shape, weight, and grouping of atoms.

powerful of the elements. He thinks it was the first of them, and that all the others sprang from it. Also, the whole earth is upborne by water, and floats just like a boat." Why did Thales select water as primary? Any answer to that question is speculative. We can merely guess that he was impressed by the widespread prevalence of water, whether on the earth's surface—three-fourths is water—in the air, in plants, in animals, in almost everything, everywhere. Perhaps he was impressed by the falling of rain, by the melting of ice or snow, by the weathering of soil and rock. In the freezing of water, he saw the formation of solid matter. In the boiling of water, he saw the formation of vapor, of what he considered air. In this process, he also may have noticed the slight residue of solid matter that the water left behind. Nowhere does Thales account for fire, however, or give specifics about how matter transformations take place. Thales and his successors, however, showed awareness of physiological changes in which air, food, and water taken in by plants and animals are altered when eliminated.

Anaximander's primary element is an eternal, endless substance that Aristotle referred to as a kind of primal "chaos" or nebula. Evidently, Anaximander was not satisfied that water or, for that matter, fire, air, or earth is primary. There has to be something common to all of them, since in freezing, boiling, or other processes, one seems to transform into the other. In a world of changing substances and one in which Anaximander recognized a strife of opposites (water versus fire or coldness versus hotness), the primary element has to be permanent, eternal, and boundless. Otherwise, the universe would run down in the continual waste and destruction of ordinary things we know. He visualized all substances as originating from an eternal primary mass through separation of opposite qualities, such as hot and cold, wet and dry, to form water, fire, air, earth, and a world of things. Then from the "strife" of opposite substances previously formed comes the continual formation of fresh or new substances. Yet Anaximander believed that everything would eventually settle back and disappear into the general "indeterminate" mass— just as is heard today that the universe is running down or leveling off because of an irreversible dissipation of heat in *natural processes* (second law of thermodynamics, Chapter 13).

To Anaximenes, all things originated from air. Here again, we can only speculate about why he believed this. He may have been influenced by the fact that air is everywhere around us, even within us, and that in air all kinds of things are observed: solid objects such as dust, snow, or the moon; liquids, such as clouds or rain; or vapors, as indicated by odors. We do know, however, that he ingeniously explained the transformation of air into other substances by condensation and rarefaction. For example, air rarefied becomes fire; air somewhat condensed becomes wind; more condensed, becomes water; still more condensed, earth; still further condensed, stones; and so forth. Thus, all substances vary quantitatively only; the only differences are ones of density.

Heraclitus, like Anaximander, was primarily impressed by two things in the world around him: first, the continual state of change and flux he saw everywhere; second, the ever present struggle of opposites. With everything temporary, limited, changing, and in strife, to him there had to be a single, underlying reality, permanent and driving in character. Fire was such a dynamic force-substance. He visualized a primordial ethereal fire, ever burning, consuming fuel, and releasing smoke, taking some substances into itself, and, on the other hand, giving off other substances—as against the indeterminate nebulous substance of Anaximander. Like the latter, Heraclitus also believed that just as everything originally arose from his primordial substance, fire, everything would eventually settle back into it. And Seneca chimes in: "We Stoics also say that it is fire that lays hold upon the world and changes all things into its own nature." So fire is the beginning and the end.

The Four Elements

Both Aristotle and Lucretius attributed the concept of four elements (Chart 19–1), earth, water, air, and fire, to Empedocles. Pythagorean contemporaries also used the idea. The Pythagoreans, however, emphasized the primacy of geometric forms as the essence of the four elements rather than the primacy of the four elements themselves. Most likely they fitted Empedocles's idea into their own.

The Egyptians had long recognized four elements, with qualities of male or female. For example, earth is male when it has the form of boulders and crags; female when it is cultivable land. When air is windy, it is male; when cloudy or sluggish, female. John Read, in his *Prelude to Chemistry,* claims that in both India and Egypt, the four elements were a fundamental idea since about 1500 B.C., and that the Chinese, as early as the 12th century B.C., had five elements, the above four and wood, together with five virtues, tastes, colors, tones, and seasons. It is merely speculative as to whether the number "5" had significance here to the Chinese, just as the number "4" did to the Pythagoreans in their original designation of four basic geometric forms and four elements of matter.

In any case, Empedocles was the first Greek natural philosopher to claim there is not one but four basic elements. He was aware that Ionian philosophers had chosen water, air, and fire singly as primary elements. Empedocles could not see that any one of these alone would adequately explain the tremendous varieties and complexities of substances. He believed that Heraclitus's fire had to have elements of water within itself to give rise to its opposite, water. Empedocles believed that he solved the problem by considering all four instead of one of the elements as primary. That would enable him to consider all four of them "indestruct-

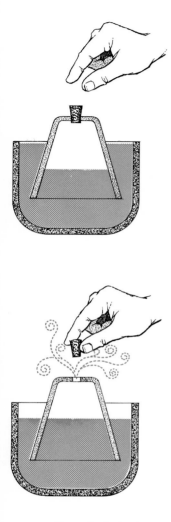

19–1 Empedocles's air experiment. When the stopper is removed, the water in the inverted glass rises. Conclusion: Escaping air is invisible matter that occupied space taken by the water.

ible, unchangeable, and permanent." That would also enable him to use all or various proportions together to explain the large diversity of objects, just as present-day chemistry uses its more than 100 elements. To Empedocles, elements do not transform one *into* the other; they *combine* with one another to form the world of things. That is what makes them basic. He explained, for example, that bones consist of a proportion of 2:1:1 of fire, earth, and water, as against a 1:1:1: ratio of these elements for flesh and blood. A crude chemistry indeed, but one that seeks answers within things themselves. In fact, in his emphasis on different fixed ratios of elements in different substances, Empedocles was over 2,200 years ahead of his time!

Operating universal "forces" of Love and Strife, attraction and repulsion, were behind combinations and recombinations of Empedocles's elements. Strife was the struggle of opposites emphasized by Anaximander and Heraclitus, to which Empedocles added the attraction principle of Love. The elements and all substances were attracted into and out of combination with one another under the influence of these universal "forces."

Empedocles also proved the material nature of the element air by demonstrating that more water enters an inverted container as air escapes (Fig. 19–1). No longer could vacuum, air, and space be synonymous.

To the Pythagoreans, numbers were "the reality of everything." Numbers were identified with space and matter in the following way: The number 1 is a point, or a unit, for indicating position and size. Arrangements of such points give geometrical figures: Two points determine a line; three points, a surface; and four, a solid (Fig. 19–2). The number 4, representing solids, applied to Empedocles's four elements. Empedocles's fire, air, water, and earth were explainable as different regular geometric solids: the tetrahedron, octahedron, icosahedron, and cube, respectively (Fig. 4–2).

Aristotle's physical ideas of matter may be summarized as follows:

1. His ideas were an elaboration of Empedocles's four elements, already described.

2. He rejected Empedocles's idea that the elements earth, water, air, and fire cannot be transformed one into another. He did so by making Anaximander's two pairs of opposite qualities (hot and cold, dry and moist) primary to the four elements, and in combinations the essence of them. For example, fire is formed from the qualities of *hot* and *dry*, earth from *dry* and *cold*, water from *cold* and *wet*, and air from *wet* and *hot* (Chart 19–1, Aristotle). To transform fire into earth, all that is necessary is to replace *hot* with its opposite, *cold*; or to obtain earth from water, supplant *wet* with its opposite, *dry*. However, not only do the elements transform one into another through these qualities, but in various combinations of the four elements with pairs of the four qualities, all worldly, sublunar substances are formed. Only two

of the four qualities can be used at any time with the four elements, "for it is impossible for the same thing to be both hot and cold, or moist and dry."

3. Aristotle introduced a fifth element. This fifth element, however, unlike the first four, cannot be "generated, corrupted, or transformed." This pure, eternal, ethereal substance makes up the heavens and all their unchangeable objects. Beneath the lunar sphere, the many products of the terrestrial four elements ceaselessly transform. While the four elements ever seek their various places (Chapter 6), the fifth element reveals its divine, ethereal quality in perfect, circular motion. Aristotle points out, however, that although all substances of the four elements are individually "generated, corrupted, and transformed, the universe as a whole is ungenerated and indestructible." Thus, in him also we find a conservation of matter concept.

Seeds of Matter

Anaxagoras in his "seeds" idea (Chart 19–1) was unwilling to submerge the tremendous varieties in things into any common denominator, whether it be the concrete water of Thales, the air of Anaximenes, or the intangible ethereal fire of Heraclitus. He preferred to accept the immediate diversity of things as is. In his reasoning, every object is infinitely divisible. Every tree can be a sliver; every sliver, a speck; and every speck halved without end. No matter how far this process goes, what is left would have characteristics of the original substance. That is, the broken-down speck has the characteristics of wood in the same sense that today a molecule has basic properties of the substance it composes. We, however, stop at the atom or molecule for similar properties, while as Lucretius pointed out 2,000 years ago, Anaxagoras did not stop at all. Anaxagoras was intent, however, in making his basic point that every item is made up of unique miniatures of itself.

That brings us to the very interesting question of the transformation of matter. If all substances are derived from unique seeds of themselves, how can one substance develop into another? How does the potato you eat become body fat? Anaxagoras's answer was that every substance down to the most minute fragment contains a portion of everything else within itself. That it is one substance rather than another is only because of the relatively greater amount of itself that it contains. If you eat potatoes and get fat, it is because potatoes provide fat as well as starch and water. Your body stores the fat. Such a conception of a minute substance containing something of everything within itself seems fantastic until we realize that today, in referring, for example, to the "half-life" of a meson, we are talking in terms of billionths of a second. Can we really conceive of how small a billionth of a second is? Because something is inconceiv-

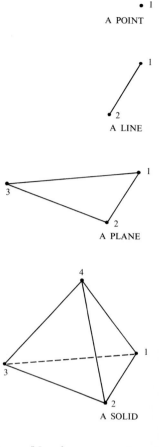

19–2 Numbers are to be identified with points that determine lines, planes, and solids (Pythagoreans).

able to us does not necessarily make it incorrect. Our own present limitations are involved.

The contribution of Anaxagoras's concept of "seeds" was its refinement, its idea of taking substances as they are and breaking them down minutely in order to know more about them. No scientist today will argue against analyzing things. Anaxagoras's seeds, however, were too complex. Anaxagoras was passing down the complexities of a large-scale object to unseen miniatures of itself. And since these miniatures were infinitely divisible, a fundamental unit was lacking.

Indivisible Atoms

The Leucippus-Democritus atom (Chart 19–1) combined features of the Ionian single element, Anaxagoras's "seeds," and Empedocles's four elements and yet was an improvement over all of them. Let us see why. There was the great benefit of simplicity in the single-element idea of the Ionians, but the idea was too simple. A single element, water or air, could not account for the endless number of different things in the world without changing its quality or losing identity as an element. Empedocles attempted to give flexibility by using all four elements as basic. What is more, he established elements as permanent, indestructible, and unchangeable; they did not lose identity. Yet they could not get far enough in a complex world. As Lucretius argues in his *The Nature of the Universe*, if these four elements are combined:

In the wild congress of this varied heap
Each thing its proper nature will display,
And air will palpably be seen mixed up
With earth together, unquenched heat with water,
But primal germs in bringing things to birth
Must have a latent unseen quality.

In other words, the above four elements would form mixtures of themselves only, not new substances, unless they contained something more primary than themselves. Besides, said Lucretius, earth, air, water, and fire are too "soft" to be elements. In the actual world they are destructible, changeable, variable.

Let us see how Leucippus's atoms combined to good advantage the simplicity of the Ionians, the indestructible, unchanging, and indivisible unit idea of Empedocles, and Anaxagoras's analysis of individual objects. "Atom" means "not divisible" in Greek. That term was intentionally chosen by Democritus to emphasize a particle so small that it could no longer be divided. To Leucippus and Democritus, originally and basically the universe consisted entirely of "atoms" and a "void" in which atoms moved. Thus, the atom in its "solid singleness," as Lucretius expressed it, became a particle common to all substances. The atom is eternal; there was no need to look for anything primary or Primary to it (definite materialism here). Eternal, the atom is indestructible and unchanging.

Atoms are all of the same substance, but by varying in size and shape, can be used to explain the large variety of objects they compose. Water, for example, "as a liquid has its atoms smooth and round, gliding over each other, while atoms of iron are hard and rough." Lucretius believed that substances like air, earth, and water are soft because there is "void" (vacuum) between the atoms composing them. On the other hand, hard substances like iron are so only because the iron atoms, themselves hard and solid, are more concentrated.

However, differences in size, shape, and weight were only part of the explanation of diversity. All atoms, like today's molecules, are continually in motion and remain that way naturally unless stopped—advance shades of Galileo's inertia! Democritus visualized these atoms moving in all directions in a whirl. Atoms group, and a world of substances results. In the general whirl, atoms of like size, shape, and weight are sorted out and thrown together to form large concentrations of a given substance, just as by centrifugal force we separate skimmed milk from cream.

Lucretius visualized atoms as moving in orderly, parallel fashion rather than in whirls, but with "a little swerve at times." These "swerves," of course, result in collisions, substances, and worlds, although not all collisions are fruitful. "All visible objects are compounds of different kinds of atoms," explained Lucretius. Atoms of different sizes and shapes may be thrown together, separate, and regroup variously. Individual atoms, solid, eternal, and indestructible, always maintain their identity in uniting or separating. It is the union and separation of atoms that is temporary and that results in the transformation of objects. The total number of atoms remains the same as atoms group and separate in transformations of matter. The result is the principle of conservation of matter: Matter is neither created nor destroyed but is transformed.

Individual atoms have no color, sound, odor, or heat. These are all secondary characteristics of a group of atoms that change as the group changes. These characteristics are applicable to perishable objects and not to the eternal individual atoms composing objects.

After the atomists, the ideas of Plato and Aristotle on the nature of matter may seem almost an anticlimax. Without, however, the possibility of experimentation or the refinements of measurement, the Greek atomic theory, as it turned out, did not have a chance against the authority of Plato and particularly that of Aristotle. Besides, the four-element theory had evidence of its own, as illustrated by a lit candle (Fig. 19–3). The dancing flame apparently is the element *fire* escaping from the candle as the wax burns down. Warm *air* also can be felt rising above the visible flame. Place a cold piece of glass above the flame, and small drops of *water* can be found forming on the glass. After the candle has burned out,

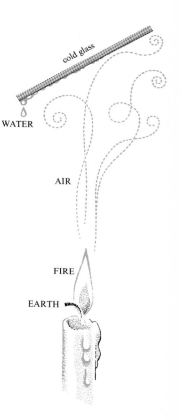

19–3 Four-element theory "evidence": Earth, fire, air, and water replace a burning candle.

remaining ash and soot are the *earth* element left behind. In the burning process, the elements fire, air, water, and earth have been freed from their union in the candle and return to their natural places in the universe. In reverse, living creatures breathe air, drink water, eat food, and have warm bodies. Heated food contains "fire." The four elements are compounded within.

We, of course, no longer accept air, water, earth, and fire as basic elements. We now have over 100 of our own, and the number continues to mount. But the concept "element" was a milestone in the advance of ideas. And the attempt to understand objects in terms of the workings of parts was inspiration. In general, ideas of any given period can best be understood against the framework of their own times. Each individual—even if he be an Aristotle, a Newton, or an Einstein—rests upon the accumulated knowledge of his day, and if he is outstanding, he takes a step forward from there. We have seen that whether it was the Ionians who emphasized a single element, Anaxagoras and his "seeds," the atomists, Empedocles and the four elements, the Pythagoreans, Plato, or Aristotle, one borrowed from the other in stepping forward. Even when the thinking took different lines or directions, as with the atomists and Aristotle, they could still be traced back to common roots. The atomists developed from and in reaction to ideas of single elements, and so did Empedocles and Aristotle. The thinking of all was conditioned and limited by the particular accumulation of knowledge of the time. The atomists were the closest to present-day ideas of matter. But experimental techniques and knowledge had not yet reached the point where they could prevent the atomists from being eclipsed by Aristotle—and experimental techniques and knowledge are social accumulations. Who knows what ideas, eclipsed today, will emerge illuminated tomorrow?

ALCHEMY AND THE FOUR ELEMENTS

The Aristotelian four elements dominated ideas of matter until the 17th century. Centuries of medical practitioners followed the famous Greek physician Galen in Aristotelian prescriptions of *dry* medicines for *moist* diseases, *cold* applications for *hot*, feverish patients, and the like. And for centuries, alchemists sought a mystical "philosopher's stone" that would change "base" metals into gold and endow perfect health and perpetual youth. This was in accord with Aristotle's fifth element, the ether, which could transform one substance into another. Plato, Aristotle's teacher, taught that the universe is a permanent living organism of body, mind, and soul, with all particular objects in it temporary, changing, and secondary—in analogy to the human being. And that only "form ideas or types of things have a full being and reality." Beauty as a reality is something with a capital "B" in the realm of ideals and perfections, rather than with a small "b," which in everyday things withers away. Table as a reality is the Idea of a perfect Table rather than a particular table that is temporary and will decompose. If so, then ordinary matter is but "a passive recipient upon which qualities can be imposed."

These Platonic Ideas, reinforced by Aristotle's idea of Being and Becoming, left the way open for alchemists to work temporary, base metals toward higher, more real essences. Gold was a step on the way, a step where most alchemists would have been willing to stop. Arabian alchemists early in the Middle Ages added three elements, or principles—sulfur, mercury, and salt—to Aristotle's four material elements. Mercury gave objects metallic *luster;* sulfur made them *combustible,* and salt made them *soluble.* The Swiss physician Paracelsus (1493–1541) wrote favorably about alchemists as follows:

> They diligently follow their labors, sweating whole days and nights by their furnaces. They do not spend their time abroad for recreation, but take delight in their laboratory. They wear leather garments with a pouch, and an apron wherewith they wipe their hands. They put their fingers among coals, into clay and filth, not into gold rings. They are sooty and black like smiths and colliers and do not pride themselves upon clean and beautiful faces.

Again, with respect to the alchemist's laboratory:

> A gloomy, dimly lighted place, full of strange vessels and furnaces, melting pots, spheres, and portions of skeletons hanging from the ceiling, the floor littered with stone bottles, alembics, great parchment books covered with hieroglyphics, the bellows, the hourglass, and over all cobwebs, dust, and ashes.

Paracelsus himself, a conscientious experimenter, was rooted in alchemical theories of matter. But he was a bombastic, traveling medical crusader who refused to confine himself to books and herbs of ancients and who prescribed metallic and chemical medicines. A maverick in transition from alchemy, he eventually was called the "father of medical chemistry." He knew and used the only known laboratory techniques, those of the alchemist, not for gold or eternal youth, but for remedies for specific diseases of men. Ether, the anesthetic, was his product that he called "stupefying vitriol salts."

Previous alchemists, in a mad search for gold, had discovered the three most important acids used by chemists: nitric, hydrochloric, and sulfuric acids. In the "clay and filth" of centuries, alchemists came up with antimony, arsenic, bismuth, and phosphorus, four present chemical elements. Other discoveries of alchemists were alum, borax, cream of tartar, plaster of Paris, red lead, iron and silver salts, and barium sulfide, the first substance known to glow after exposure to light. The alchemists originated many of today's chemical tools as flasks, retorts, water baths, and crude balances as well as such basic processes as *distillation*. Francis Bacon (1561-1626) very aptly compared the alchemist "to the man who told his sons he had left them gold buried somewhere in his vineyard; where they, by digging, found no gold, but by turning up the mould about the roots of the vines, procured a plentiful vintage." For specific knowledge and techniques inherited by chemists, alchemists have been called illegitimate "grandfathers of chemistry." Rogues among the illegitimate grandfathers successfully fleeced money even from kings wanting gold. And the sincere craftsmen among them were born too soon to separate science from mystical trappings. The great Isaac Newton (17th century) practiced alchemy in a small laboratory of his own while Warden of the Mint. Even genius is relative to given areas and does not make creative leaps at all frontiers.

ATOMS, ELEMENTS, AND THE SCIENTIFIC REVOLUTION

The four elements were too simple an idea. Men search for order through a few unifying principles. But nature has a way of seeping through categories set for it. Meanwhile, men gain detailed knowledge of their surroundings and develop more sophisticated concepts, techniques, and unifying principles. Experimentation, becoming respectable in the Scientific Revolution, eventually showed that earth, water, air, and fire can be resolved into simpler substances and that the Aristotelian elements are not elements after all. Or that they are more appropriate as states of matter that apply to every substance. That is, substances called "earths" are solids; "water," liquids; "air" and "fire," gases.

Francis Bacon was the trumpeter of the Scientific Revolution, which Copernicus sparked unknowingly. Bacon was aware of the work of Galileo, Kepler, Gilbert, and other experimenting contemporaries. In place of science by authority, he appealed for experimentation. He expressed respect for men of antiquity who "used to deliver the knowledge which the mind of men had gathered in observation . . . [and who invited] men both to ponder that which was invented and to add and supply further." But he sharply criticized his own contemporaries for whom "sciences are delivered to be believed and accepted, and not be examined and further discovered." "Go to the horse's mouth and count teeth rather than quote authorities," Bacon challenged. Roentgen, the discoverer of X rays 3 centuries later, had the idea when he said: "What did I think? I didn't think. I began to experiment." Rather than force facts into set ideas, go to nature, get the data, and then form conclusions. Bacon was a crusader for a fact-finding, inductive approach to nature.

Bacon took issue with alchemists for not being inductive and for explaining endless failures by "either supposing a misunderstanding of the words of authors, which maketh him listen after auricular traditions; or else a failing in the true proportions and scruples of [the alchemist's own] practice, which maketh him renew infinitely his trials." In his best-known work, *Novum Organum* (1620), Bacon wrote, "But to resolve nature into abstractions is less to our purpose than to dissect her into parts, as did the school of Democritus, which went further into nature than the rest." Bacon sought a revival of the Democritus atom in preference to Aristotle's elements unquestionably accepted. "The theory of Democritus relating to atoms is, if not true, at least applicable with excellent effect to the exposition of nature." And "If we could discover the original or primary component Particle of Matter so as clearly to discern their Arrangements and Compositions, whereon the Form or properties of different Bodies depend..."

Lord Bacon was a highly placed political and literary figure in Elizabethan England who himself did not have time for scientific experiments. His trumpet was heard, however, by Robert Boyle, who devoted a lifetime to experiments described in Boyle's book *The Skeptical Chymist* and elsewhere. (Fortunately, he had a private income that permitted this.) He was among the first of modern chemists. He urged the alchemist craftsmen to study matter for its own sake. He believed that all matter is basically the same unknown "stuff," which changes into different forms through "corpuscular" (atomic) components. But he insisted that matter can be better known only when systematic observation rather than gold is a basic objective. (As a matter of fact, mercury was finally converted into gold by 20th century scientists testing atomic theory rather than searching for gold.) In place of the four elements, he proposed that all substances be divided into elements and compounds. An element is a substance that can not be broken down in a laboratory into simpler substances. A compound is a substance that can be broken down into simpler substances. That is, elements are to be determined by thorough laboratory testing.

After a life of experimentation, Boyle was too cautious to name any elements. But he started an investigation of the dynamics of air that stimulated considerable chemical interest in air. Boyle's law of gases and "spring of the air" hypothesis were described in Chapter 13. We saw that Boyle's hypothesis drew attention to corpuscles or atoms of matter. Previously, Bacon and Galileo had accepted the Greek atom. D. Sennert, a German physician, had applied atomic theory to such specific natural processes as recovering gold from an acid solution. Pierre Gassendi (1592–1655), influential French mathematician and philosopher, developed an extensive nonmathematical atomic theory. Boyle, in keeping with developments, also considered a kinetic theory of gases in which corpuscles are in agitated motion within gases. Boyle, a founder of the

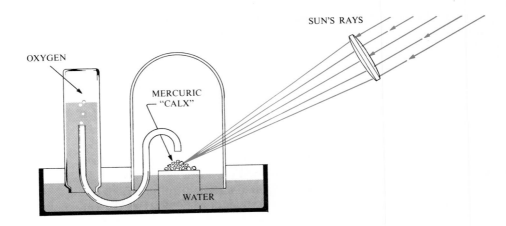

OXYGEN

SUN'S RAYS

MERCURIC
"CALX"

WATER

*19–6 Priestley's "dephlo-
gisticated air" (oxygen).
Priestley concentrated the
sun's rays upon mercuric
"calx" (ore) in a bell jar.
When he inserted a burning
candle into the gas collected
in the inverted bottle, the
flame was especially bright.*

passed through a tube and into a bottle of liquid mercury (or water). The
gas collected over the liquid (Fig. 19–6). This method of collecting gases
—minus the lens—is still used. In one of the most significant experiments
in chemical history, Priestley one day placed a solid called mercuric "calx"
in the bell jar. When he heated the "calx," gas collected in the bottle.
Priestley noticed a candle burning nearby. Curiously, he placed the candle
into the gas and was amazed to find the candle burning with special
brilliance. A glowing piece of charcoal which he excitedly inserted into
the gas burst into a rapid flame; a red-hot iron wire sizzled like a sparkler.
This "air" was unique. And then, wrote Priestley, "I procured a mouse
and put it into a glass vessel containing the air from the red powder of
mercury. Had it been common air, a full-grown mouse, as this was,
would have lived for about a quarter of an hour. In this air, however my mouse lived a full half hour." Priestley called his product
"dephlogisticated air."

He had discovered oxygen and did not know it. The big ideas under
which we operate determine the interpretation of what we see. Thinking
in terms of phlogiston theory, Priestley reasoned that this new "air" had
less phlogiston in it than ordinary air and therefore absorbed phlogiston
more readily from burning objects. The resulting faster flow of phlogiston
showed itself in a larger, more active flame. In contrast to this "dephlogisticated air" was "fixed air" (from limestone or beer) which, supposedly
saturated with phlogiston, could absorb no more. The flow of phlogiston
stops in "fixed air," and the candle flame in this air goes out.

Once again we see the role of chance in scientific discovery. In his
recollections of the above experiment, Priestley said:

I cannot at this distance of time recollect what it was that I had
in view in making this experiment; but I had no expectation of the
real issue of it. If I had not happened to have a lighted candle before
me, I should probably never have made the trial, and the whole train

of my future experiments relating to this kind of air might have been prevented .... More is owing to what we call chance than to any proper design or preconceived theory.

Once again "chance favors the prepared mind,"—and the curious mind. If Priestley had not been experimentally curious, he would not have made "chance" discoveries.

That brings us to the highly gifted, prepared mind of Antoine Lavoisier (1743–1794). Lavoisier saw more in Priestley's chance discovery than another "air." He saw revolutionary implications for the nature of burning. And he paid particular attention to the question of weight, the changed weight of a burned or transformed substance.

Lavoisier describes his own classic repetition of Priestley's experiment (1774) as follows:

> I introduced four ounces of pure mercury into the matrass [sealed glass vessel]. I lighted a fire in the furnace which I kept up almost continually during twelve days. Nothing remarkable took place during the first day. On the second day, small red particles began to appear on the surface of the mercury: These during the four or five following days gradually increased in size and number, after which they ceased to increase in either respect. At the end of twelve days, I extinguished the fire.

The above experiment had three results that revolutionized ideas of matter and gave Lavoisier the title of "father of modern chemistry":

1. The "small red particles" helped Lavoisier to replace the phlogiston theory with a new theory of burning. Through these particles Lavoisier showed that Priestley's "dephlogisticated" air was a new element, oxygen, that was a component of air and a key to the understanding of fire. Fire was primarily a process, not an element.

2. The air remaining in his vessel turned out to be another new element, nitrogen. Here was still another component of air. Air was certainly not an element.

3. An increase in the weight of the red mercury product *equaled* a loss in the weight of the air in the vessel. The consequence was a law of conservation of matter in the quantitative form of chemical equations (Chapter 20). Chemical equations represented transformations of matter and greatly deepened man's insights into nature.

Lavoisier's Theory of Burning

The silvery-colored liquid mercury in Lavoisier's vessel gained weight in changing to solid red particles. Priestley's interpretation was that due to the heat of the furnace, phlogiston flowed from the mercury to the air, leaving a red mercury "calx." The red "calx" was a "pure" earth element. The silvery mercury was a compound of this earth element and phlogiston. Due to the sustained heat of the furnace, the phlogiston left the silvery mercury. The phlogiston left behind the "pure" mercury calx and saturated the air in the vessel to give "fixed" air. But why, asked Lavoisier, did the silvery mercury *gain* weight when the phlogiston left it, and why did the air lose weight when the phlogiston joined it? Priestley's answer was that phlogiston had negative weight; phlogiston subtracted weight from anything containing it. Dissatisfied with "negative weight," Lavoisier insisted that instead of giving off a nonexistent phlogiston, the silvery mercury took on a substance (now called the element oxygen) from the air and therefore increased in weight. The air, having lost oxygen, lost weight. The silvery mercury, therefore, was an element that combined with oxygen from the air to become a red compound, mercuric oxide. From this idea of *oxidation* (of an element like oxygen uniting with other substances) resulted Lavoisier's theory of burning or combustion. Mercury combines with oxygen slowly, but other substances, like wood, combine very quickly with oxygen when sufficiently heated. Combustion, or burning, is fast oxidation. Burning is the chemical union between a burnable substance and oxygen. Fire ceased to be a substance. It involved a process that gives off heat and light and is characterized by a flame.

Law of Conservation of Matter

To ancient atomists, the total count of atoms in the universe was constant. The total amount of matter, therefore, remained the same regardless of changes. The atomists had a conservation principle, but no one counted atoms in those days.

When Lavoisier checked the weight gained by the mercury against the weight lost by the air, he had a conservation principle in mind: Weight lost = weight gained. He was providing a backbone for experimental study of matter in specific experimental situations. Weight was something that could be measured. To an "=" sign, Lavoisier added a chemical balance. Lavoisier wrote, "As the usefulness and accuracy of chemistry depend entirely upon the determination of the weights of the ingredients and products, too much precision cannot be employed in this part of the subject, and for this purpose we must be provided with good instruments."

Lavoisier tested his conservation of matter ideas with many substances, even a burning candle. His conservation hypothesis in this case was that the hot wax combined with oxygen from the air to form water vapor and carbon dioxide ("fixed air"). In equation form:

candle wt + oxygen wt = "fixed air" wt + water vapor wt.

Lavoisier measured the weight of the candle before burning it and the weight of the oxygen that combined with it. He also measured the weights of the "fixed air" and the water vapor that had formed and been trapped. He found that the weights of the first two equaled the weights of the second two. His hypothesis was again confirmed. The original candle, of course, weighed less than the gases formed from it. The difference was the weight of the oxygen required for combustion.

In 1789, Lavoisier wrote: "We must lay it down as an incontestable axiom, that in all the operations of art and nature, nothing is created! An equal quantity of matter exists both before and after the experiment . . . and nothing takes place beyond changes and modifications in the combination of these elements. Upon this principle, the whole art of performing chemical experiments depends." In brief, Lavoisier's conservation law is that all matter existing within *any* closed system constitutes the universe for a specific experiment. (A "closed" system here is one in which outside matter does not enter and inside matter does not leave.)

Air as a Mixture

When Lavoisier, in his famous "burning" experiment, tested the remaining gas in the vessel, he found that it extinguished a lighted chip of wood. Since oxygen supports a flame, the remaining gas was something else. This gas was another element, nitrogen, and further established the fact that air is a mixture of substances. In a mixture, substances retain their individual properties and do not form new substances. Oxygen unites with burning substances whether nitrogen is in the air or not.

Techniques were soon developed for finding the amount of oxygen in the air. Here is a simple technique for you to try. Soak a wad of steel wool in vinegar and wedge it in the bottom of a large glass. Then invert the glass in a dish of water (Fig. 19–7). The iron in the steel wool rusts, taking oxygen from the air in the glass. Water rises in the glass as oxygen leaves the air. The water rises for a number of hours to a level about one-fifth of the way up. Since water is replacing oxygen, the process stops when oxygen in the air is depleted. The amount of oxygen in the air is therefore about 20 percent. The 80 percent of the air left in the glass is mostly nitrogen.

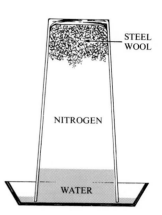

STEEL WOOL

NITROGEN

WATER

19–7 Determining the amount of oxygen in air. As the iron in the steel wool rusts, the water in the glass rises to a level one-fifth of the way up. Since water is replacing oxygen, one-fifth of the air is oxygen.

Water Decomposes

In 1781, Henry Cavendish sent an electrical spark through approximately 400 parts, by volume, of hydrogen gas ("burning air") and 1,000 parts of ordinary air suitably arranged within an unsealed glass cylinder. In Cavendish's words "all the [hydrogen] and about one-fifth of the com-

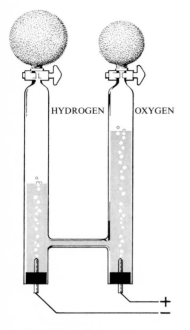

19–8 Electrolysis of water. Water breaks down electrically into hydrogen and oxygen gases, two volumes to one volume, respectively.

mon air [oxygen] condensed into a dew which lined the glass." Cavendish had found that oxygen comprises one-fifth of the air by volume. But far more significantly, he found that water is not an element. It contains simpler substances. It forms from hydrogen and [oxygen in] common air. The ratio is 2:1—specific indeed!

The Frenchman Fournoy shortly afterward burned over 37,000 cubic inches of hydrogen in oxygen for a week and obtained pure water only. Several years later, Deiman and Van Troostwik reversed the process. They sent sparks from an electrostatic machine through water to decompose it into hydrogen and oxygen. Again, the ratio was two volumes of hydrogen to one of oxygen. Electrical decomposition of water, called electrolysis of water (Fig. 19–8), was established.

MIXTURES VERSUS COMPOUNDS

Air, the Aristotelian element, turned out to be a mixture; and water, a compound. Both mixtures and compounds are composed of elements. What is the difference between them? To review Boyle's definitions: An element is a substance that cannot be chemically broken down into simpler substances; a compound is a substance composed of two or more elements with individual properties different from those of the combination. Water is a compound; it has components, hydrogen and oxygen, that have lost their identity. *A mixture is a substance composed of two or more elements or compounds that keep their individual properties when together.* Nitrogen and oxygen are a mixture comprising 99 percent of the atmosphere; they do not lose their individual properties when together there. Oxygen keeps a candle burning whether pure or in the atmosphere; nitrogen never supports a flame. The same two elements as a compound are "laughing gas" (nitrous oxide).

Stir a pinch of salt and a bit of sand together and taste the product. The salt retains its characteristic taste; the sand still has a gritty feel on the tongue. The product is a mixture.

Next stir well together a handful of iron powder and a handful of powdered sulfur (Fig. 19–9A). The black of the iron and yellow of the sulfur can still be recognized. Move a magnet through the product; iron will be found clinging to the magnet. The product is a mixture.

Now heat the iron-sulfur mixture (Fig. 19–9B). The product changes color. And nothing clings to a magnet sent through it. The product is a compound and is called iron sulfide. This compound, found in nature in crystal form, has been called fool's gold because of its color and appearance.

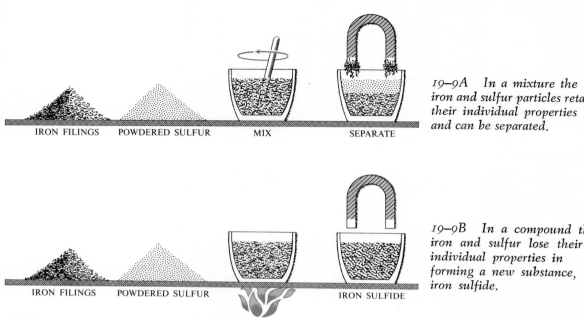

19–9A In a mixture the iron and sulfur particles retain their individual properties and can be separated.

19–9B In a compound the iron and sulfur lose their individual properties in forming a new substance, iron sulfide.

IRON FILINGS   POWDERED SULFUR   MIX   SEPARATE

IRON FILINGS   POWDERED SULFUR   IRON SULFIDE

STATES OF MATTER

When "earth," "water," and "air" disappeared as elements, solids, liquids, and gases replaced them as a parallel set of concepts that covered all matter. "Earth" actually represented solids; "water," liquids; "air" and "fire," gases. But the later concepts were general states rather than components of matter. Any substance can change from one state to another and retain the same elements or components. Liquid water may change to ice by cooling or to water vapor by heating. But in all of these three states, water contains the same elements, hydrogen and oxygen. Its composition need not change with its state.

PHYSICAL CHANGES
VERSUS CHEMICAL CHANGES

In the 19th century, awareness of two kinds of change in matter developed: physical and chemical. (Nuclear change was added in the 20th century.)

A change in which a substance entirely retains its original composition is a physical change. Changes of state are physical changes. So is sugar dissolving in water. Drink the water and the unseen sugar can be tasted. Evaporate the water and the sugar appears in its original form and color. When rocks are crushed, pencils sharpened, or irons heated, physical changes are involved. Composition is not changed.

A change in which a substance loses its original composition and one

Lavoisier at work. (Brown Bros. photograph)

or more new substances are formed is a chemical change. A burning candle involves chemical changes of wax into carbon dioxide, water vapor, and soot. A chemical change occurs when water decomposes to hydrogen and oxygen. Iron and sulfur ground to a powder and mixed illustrate physical change. But when the iron-sulfur mixture is heated and forms the new substance iron sulfide, the change is chemical. Mixing flour, eggs, milk, fruit, and other ingredients for a cake results in physical changes. Actually baking the mixture results in chemical changes.

In summary, each of the four elements broke down on experimental investigation into simpler substances. They were not elements. Air became plural "airs" or gases: "fixed" air (carbon dioxide), a compound;

"burning" air (hydrogen), an element; "dephlogisticated" air (oxygen), an element. The air we breathe became a *mixture* of gases, mainly oxygen and nitrogen. Water decomposed to new elements, to hydrogen and oxygen gases. Fire disappeared as a substance and became a light and heat manifestation of a burning process. Earth became diverse solid elements, compounds, and mixtures. In short, the former elements were too simple. Earth, air, and water became identified as solids, liquids, and gases, states of matter applying to all substances. And fire became identified with energy of burning in Lavoisier's new principle of combustion. Equal amounts of matter by weight exist before and after the burning of an object. All changes of matter are changes in form, not the creation or destruction of matter itself.

But a new organizing idea for elements was needed. And a new system of names and symbols. In May 1787, Lavoisier and three collaborators, Berthollet, Napoleon's chemistry instructor; De Morveau, a lawyer; and Fourcroy, orator of the French Revolution, completed a treatise on a new nomenclature for chemistry. Their list of 33 elements was accepted by the French Academy of Science and became the basis of our present series of elements.

It was left to atomist successors of Lavoisier to develop conservation equations in terms of atoms and molecules and to give such equations their modern symbolic form. In 1794 Lavoisier lost his head to the guillotine. He was not involved in politics, but he was a descendant of lesser nobility and had served as a tax farmer under the king. Taxes in those days were collected by tax farmers, who paid set amounts in advance to the government and kept whatever taxes they collected. There is evidence that Lavoisier was more humanistic than most tax farmers. But unfortunately, Lavoisier had gained the personal and professional animosity of a mediocre chemist, Marat, who was a prominent activist in the French Revolution. He denounced Lavoisier as a

> master of charlatans, son of a rent collector, apprentice chemist, tax collector, steward of ammunition and saltpetre, administrator of discount funds, secretary to the King, member of the Academy of Sciences. Just think of it, this little gentleman enjoyed an income of forty thousand livres and has no other claim to public gratitude than to have put Paris in prison by intercepting the circulation of air through it by means of a wall which cost us poor people thirty-three million francs, and to have transferred the gunpowder from the Arsenal to the Bastille the night of the 12th or 13th of July, a devil's intrigue to get himself elected administrator of the Department of Paris. Would to heaven he had been hanged from the lamppost!

Through such demagoguery, the French Revolution and the world, in building from feudal society, lost one of the great scientific minds of all time.

CHAPTER REVIEW

1. What is matter?

2. Is matter continuous or discontinuous? What evidence is there for continuity in matter? For discontinuity?

3. Does matter contain basic elements or particles that in constant combination and separation form the endless variety and changes of substances? How can we know?

4. Are these assumed "building blocks" of matter separate, minute particles, or are they extended primary substances? What is the evidence?

5. What answers did Greek philosophers of nature give to questions 3 and 4?

6. What sense did it make in ancient Greece to consider the following to be the basic elements of which all substances are composed? What evidences were there? (a) Water. (b) An indeterminate primordial substance. (c) Air. (d) Fire. (e) Earth, water, air, and fire.

7. How can a world of objects be formed and continuously transformed from a single element according to ancient Greeks proposing the idea?

8. What did Anaxagoras mean by "each substance is infinitely divisible into seeds of itself," or that there is "a portion of everything in everything?" Illustrate.

9. What did the Pythagoreans mean by "numbers are elemental realities of everything"?

10. What did Plato mean by "ideal types or qualities of things are the permanent realities giving temporary form to substances as we know them"?

11. How can a world of objects be formed and continuously transformed from four elements according to Empedocles and Aristotle?

12. (a) Describe atoms and their motions as originally proposed by Leucippus and Democritus. (b) What were the basic assumptions of the Greek atomists?

13. Were the ancient concepts of the atom a matter of science or natural philosophy?

14. What are the similarities and differences among Democritus's atoms, Anaxagoras's seeds, and Aristotle's elements?

15. Why do you think the Ionians and the Greek atomists have been called the "first materialists"?

16. Were ancient atoms hypotheses, theories, facts, or what?

17. Were ancient ideas of the atom science or natural philosophy? Explain.

18. What is alchemy? Why should alchemy be considered in this science text?

19. What did Francis Bacon mean by "Go to the horse's mouth and count its teeth"? Why did he say it?

20. What is meant by an inductive approach to nature?

21. In what sense did Robert Boyle make the idea of elements scientific?

22. Why was Boyle's emphasis upon a concept of compounds an important scientific contribution?

23. Describe the following experiments, and show how they contributed to a scientific revolution in chemistry: (a) Joseph Black's discovery of "fixed air" (carbon dioxide) in fire and air experiments, (b) Henry Cavendish's discovery of hydrogen in experiments with fire and air, (c) Joseph Priestley's discovery of "phlogisticated air" (oxygen) in fire and air experiments, (d) Antoine Lavoisier's investigation of burning, (e) Lavoisier's experimental finding that air is a mixture, and (f) Cavendish's decomposition of water.

24. What was the phlogiston theory? How was it related to the concept of fire as a basic element? Illustrate how this theory explained burning.

25. Show how Priestley actually discovered oxygen and did not know it because of the phlogiston theory. To what extent should Priestley receive credit for the discovery of oxygen?

26. Why was Lavoisier's theory of burning successful against the phlogiston theory?

27. Show how the experiments in question 23 disproved the Aristotelian four-element theory.

28. Why should the phlogiston theory be studied if it has been rejected?

29. Describe and illustrate the law of conservation of matter.

30. Why is Lavoisier called the "father of modern chemistry"?

31. Differentiate between the Greek conservation of matter principle and Lavoisier's conservation law. Are we justified in reserving the term "law" for Lavoisier's work? Why?

32. Explain and illustrate the difference between a mixture and a compound.

33. What is meant by "states of matter"? Illustrate.

34. Show how the Greek elements earth, water, air, and fire correspond to the present categories of solid, liquid, and gaseous states of matter.

35. Differentiate between and illustrate physical changes and chemical changes.

PROBLEMS

1. What made Black think that his "fixed air" (carbon dioxide) was not ordinary air?

2. How could Lavoisier be sure that Priestley's "dephlogistated air" was a new element, oxygen?

3. Why was Cavendish sure that the gases formed in his electrolysis of water were not ordinary air?

4. What is fire?

5. Explain why a lighted candle goes out shortly after a jar is placed over it.

6. How can you show that the air is about 20 percent oxygen?

7. Why is air called a mixture rather than a compound?

8. Why is rust called a compound rather than a mixture?

9. Are the following changes physical or chemical? Explain in each case. (a) The rusting of iron. (b) The burning of a candle. (c) The change of water into steam. (d) The change of water into hydrogen and oxygen. (e) The dissolving of sugar in water. (f) The change of red mercuric oxide to mercury and oxygen.

10. Use a burning candle to illustrate the law of conservation of matter.

SUGGESTIONS FOR FURTHER READING

Lucretius, *The Nature of the Universe,* Penguin paperback, Baltimore, 1964.

Jaffe, Bernard, *Crucibles: The Story of Chemistry,* Premier paperback, New York, 1960, Chs. 1–5.

Conant, James, *Science and Common Sense,* Yale Univ. Press paperback, New Haven, Conn., 1962, Chs. 3 and 7.

Conant, James, ed., *Harvard Case Histories in Experimental Science,* Harvard Univ. Press, Cambridge, Mass., 1957, Case 2.

Asimov, Isaac, *Short History of Chemistry,* Anchor paperback, Garden City, N.Y., 1965, Chs. 1–4.

Farrington, Benjamin, *Francis Bacon: Philosopher of Industrial Science,* Collier paperback, New York, 1961.

Taylor, F. Sherwood, *The Alchemists: Founders of Modern Chemistry,* Collier paperback, New York, 1962.

Feinberg, Joseph G., *Story of Atomic Theory and Atomic Energy,* Dover paperback, New York, 1960, Chs. 1–2.

Butterfield, Herbert, *Origins of Modern Science,* Collier paperback, New York, 1962, Chs. 5–6, 11–12.

Aristotle, *Of Generation and Corruption,* Oxford Univ. Press, London, 1922.

Plato, *Timaeus,* Scribner's, New York, 1921.

Seneca, *Physical Science,* Macmillan, New York, 1910.

20   Atoms, Molecules, and Chemical Changes

The scientific method is merely a formalization of *learning by experience.*

MARSHALL WALKER, 1963

Is matter continuous or discontinuous? Does matter consist of particles separated by spaces, or is it internally continuous like a wave? This question was not settled by Greek natural philosophers, nor is it completely settled today. We now speak of "matter-waves," matter with properties of both waves and particles.

PARTICLES VERSUS CONTINUITY IN MATTER

At first glance, objects may appear continuous or unbroken. A glass of water appears to be without holes. But how could sugar or salt dissolve in water if there were no empty spaces in the water for them to disappear into?

A pint of water added to a pint of alcohol gives a mixture that is *less* than two pints (Fig. 13–9). There must be many holes within each for one liquid to work its way into the other. Otherwise, how could the volume of the mixture be less than two pints?

How could we smell a skunk if the atmosphere did not have spaces within it through which fluid particles can travel?

Gold bars and silver bars kept well pressed together for a number of months show an exchange of particles across contact surfaces when separated. Would this diffusion be possible if the substances were without inner empty spaces?

Considerable evidence exists for the atomist belief that substances, whether solids, liquids, or gases, contain vacuums or "voids." But that does not necessarily mean that matter is in the form of atomic particles. Matter could still be intertwined like threads with spaces in between.

Similar concerns and more captured the attention of John Dalton (1766–1844), English Quaker schoolmaster. The four-element theory was gone. Principles were needed to explain changes and differences in matter, and Lavoisier's theory of burning was only a start. Bacon had been correct up to a point; exploratory fact-finding is necessary. Otherwise, inadequate or outmoded ideas can hardly be eliminated. But after some fact-finding, organizing ideas are needed again. Dalton had no formal theoretical instruction in physics or chemistry, and he could therefore start fresh. If all changes in matter are changes in form (conservation of matter principle), then what is the underlying matter that goes through the changes? Could it be atoms? Does matter consist of particles separated by spaces, or is it continuous like a wave? A scientific answer must be specific. It must involve specific materials in specific changes, and it must solve specific problems. Dalton was after specificity.

Dalton assumed atoms and continued from there. Atoms had been used successfully to explain such physical phenomena as heat or the expansion of gases by Boyle, Bernoulli, Gassendi, Newton, and others. The brilliant Serbian scientist Roger Boscovich (1711–1787) had even developed an ingenious mathematical theory of atomism to explain general physical behavior of matter. But chemically speaking, the atom came of age with Dalton. He was interested in the atom as a unit for explaining specific chemical changes. Dalton used atoms to explain why 9 pounds of water decomposed to 8 pounds of oxygen and 1 pound of hydrogen.

LAW OF DEFINITE PROPORTIONS BY WEIGHT

But *is* water the same everywhere? In general, are the elements of a compound always there in exactly the same proportions by weight? These questions existed in a running controversy between Dalton's French contemporaries Bertholet, friend of Lavoisier, and Joseph Proust, an apothecary. Lavoisier had made chemists weight-conscious. Bertholet's position was this: Ratios of ingredients for bread vary; why shouldn't ratios of hydrogen and oxygen in water? Or ratios of sodium and chlorine in salt? For 8 years, an experimental duel raged in which each contestant decomposed compounds and weighed elements. Proust won. His answer

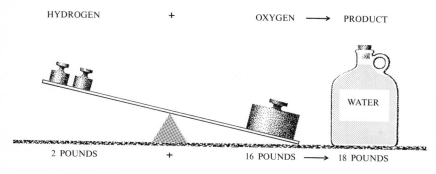

HYGROGEN + OXYGEN ⟶ PRODUCT

WATER

2 POUNDS + 16 POUNDS ⟶ 18 POUNDS

20–1   *Law of definite proportions. Elements in a chemical compound always combine in the same definite proportions by weight.*

is now a pillar of chemistry called the *law of definite proportions: Elements in a chemical compound are always combined in the same definite proportions by weight* (Fig. 20–1). If 9 pounds of rainwater yield 1 pound of hydrogen and 8 pounds of oxygen, so do 9 pounds of lake water. Eighteen pounds of water contain 16 pounds of oxygen; 27 pounds of water contain 24 pounds of oxygen. The ratio of hydrogen to oxygen is 1:8 for any amount of water anywhere. In charcoal, there are always three parts of carbon to eight parts of oxygen by weight. "We are forced to recognize," Proust said, "that the composition of true compounds is as invariable as their properties; between pole and pole they are identical in these two respects. The cinnabar of Japan has the same properties and composition as that of Spain; silver chloride is identically the same, whether obtained from Peru or Siberia." Bread and other mixtures may vary in ratio of components, but not "true compounds," claimed Proust.

LAW OF
MULTIPLE PROPORTIONS

Dalton repeated Proust's experiments and developed another pillar of chemistry from them. He noticed that carbon unites with oxygen in a ratio of 3:4 by weight to form a poisonous gas (compound), carbon monoxide. Carbon also unites with oxygen in a ratio of 3:8 by weight to form the harmless gas carbon dioxide, present in the atmosphere. The ratios were 3:4 and 3:8. The amount of oxygen combining exactly *doubled*. Why should oxygen increase in a ratio of *small whole* numbers, 2:1? Why not in a ratio of 9½:4 or 11:4? For Dalton, the question pointed to an answer in terms of atoms. But whatever the answer, Dalton's experimental results are summarized in the *law of multiple porportions* (1804): *When any two elements form a variety of compounds, the ratios of the weights of one element to that of another are small whole numbers.* That is, the different amounts by weight of one element (for example, oxygen) that unite with a given weight of another element (for example, carbon) are exact *multiples* of each other.

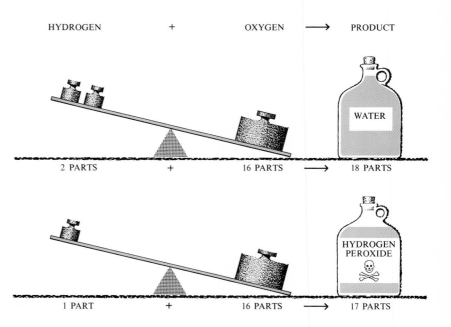

HYDROGEN + OXYGEN ⟶ PRODUCT

2 PARTS + 16 PARTS ⟶ 18 PARTS

WATER

1 PART + 16 PARTS ⟶ 17 PARTS

HYDROGEN
PEROXIDE

20–2   Law of multiple proportions. When two elements form a variety of compounds, the ratio of the weight of one element to that of another is small whole numbers. One part of hydrogen to 16 parts of oxygen gives a poison, hydrogen peroxide. Two parts of hydrogen to 16 parts of oxygen gives water.

Hydrogen unites with oxygen to form water, but half the amount by weight of hydrogen unites with the same amount of oxygen to form hydrogen peroxide, a bleach discovered by a French chemistry instructor, Louis Thenard, in 1818 (Fig. 20–2). Dalton compared the composition of hydrogen peroxide to water. The former had 1 part by weight of hydrogen to 16 parts of oxygen, as compared to water, with 2 parts of hydrogen to 16 parts oxygen. Thus, the ratio of the weights of hydrogen combining with oxygen to give two different compounds is 2:1, again a "small whole number" or "multiple."

DALTON'S ATOMIC MODEL: ASSUMPTIONS AND SYMBOLS

It was the "small whole numbers," the "multiples," that convinced Dalton that atoms exist. The observable large objects could be explained by the unseen small components. If copper is chipped from bars at random, two chips would seldom weigh twice as much as one chip. But if identical pennies are made from a copper bar, then two pennies would weigh twice as much as one. If the element oxygen is made of identical indivisible atoms, then two atoms would weigh twice as much as one, and three atoms would weigh three times as much as one. Only whole numbers would be involved, not fractions. All weights of oxygen would be multiples of the weight of one atom. The laws of definite proportions and of multiple proportions could them be easily understood.

The main assumptions of Dalton's atomic theory that made it quantitative and workable for experimentation are as follows:

1. Each element consists of minute basic particles, atoms.
2. All atoms of any element are identical. Weights, sizes, and shapes are exactly alike.
3. Atoms are indestructible units. They cannot be divided, created, or destroyed.
4. If two or more elements combine to make a compound, their atoms unite to form a unit (now called a molecule) of the compound.
5. Atoms generally join together in small numbers. (Since atoms are indestructible units, the numbers are whole numbers.)

In assumption 1, ancient atomists would have emphasized "all matter" rather than "each element." Dalton essentially unites the formerly opposing concepts of "elements" and "atoms." Assumption 2 standardizes the weights of unseen atoms and facilitates a table of relative weights. In the "new chemistry," weights are significant. Assumption 2 no longer holds today; almost all elements have some atoms different in weight or mass. Assumption 3 made atoms dependable units for chemical changes and for the law of conservation of matter. It took almost a century to discover that atoms *do* break down. Assumption 4 is at the heart of the conservation of matter. If atoms are indivisibly hard spheres, compounds are stable arrangements of these spheres. The weight of the whole (a molecule) equals the sum of the weights of its parts (atoms). The weight of a carbon dioxide molecule, for example, equals the total weight of the indestructible carbon atom and the two indestructible oxygen atoms that comprise it. Dalton needed the first four assumptions to explain the laws of definite and multiple proportions already described. These four assumptions also made chemical equations possible to describe and predict chemical changes.

Symbolic drawings for elements and compounds did not begin with Dalton. Alchemists intent on secrecy used obscure language and symbols. There was some uniformity among alchemists, however, in symbols for known metals. The symbol for gold was ○ (symbol of the sun and perfection); for silver, ☾ (symbol of the moon); mercury, ☿ ; iron, ♂ (Mars, god of war); and copper, ♀ (Venus, goddess of love).

Dalton represented all atoms by circles. But he placed different markings in the circles to show unlike atoms for different elements. Dalton's symbol for gold was ⊙ ; and for mercury, ⊛ . Dalton had new elements to represent in chemical combinations. His symbol for oxygen was ○ ; for hydrogen, ⊙ ; for carbon, ● ; for nitrogen, ⊖ ; and for sulfur, ⊕ .

Dalton represented the union of atoms to form molecules as follows:

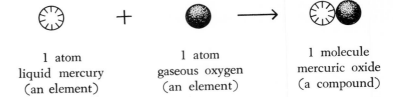

1 atom	1 atom	1 molecule
liquid mercury	gaseous oxygen	mercuric oxide
(an element)	(an element)	(a compound)

The above symbolizes Lavoisier's theory of oxidation. An atom of liquid mercury combines with an atom of oxygen to form a molecule, or smallest particle of the compound mercuric oxide. Dalton was apt to speak about the "atom" instead of the molecule of a compound. We now carefully distinguish between the smallest particle characteristic of an element (mercury) and the smallest particle characteristic of a compound (mercuric oxide).

The development of chemistry symbols was like that of language in general: symbolic drawings preceded letters of the alphabet. But Dalton's geometric shorthand, although unwieldy, was a long step toward the use of formulas and equations.

ATOMIC WEIGHT

Lavoisier emphasized measurement of weight in changes of matter, as did Joseph Black before him in heat transformation. And Dalton prepared the first table of *atomic weights* (1803). Atoms are so tiny that billions upon billions of them are in the dot of an "i." How could atoms possibly be weighed?

Basically, weights are relative. Comparisons are always made to some weight arbitrarily set as a standard, whether it be a pound, kilogram, or gram.

The relative weights of observable quantities of elements were tackled before atomic weights were. For 20 years after Lavoisier's insistence upon the use of balances in chemistry, experimenters attempted to obtain the relative weights of elements forming compounds. Hydrogen was found to be the lightest of elements. For example, when the weights of equal volumes of various gases are compared at the same temperature and pressure, hydrogen has the lowest weight. Ratios can then be made of the weights of other elements and compounds to hydrogen.

Dalton assumed that all the atoms of the same element have the same weight, but that the atoms of different elements have different weights. He also assumed that the lightest element, hydrogen, has the lightest atoms. He used hydrogen as his standard and gave it an atomic weight of 1. A whole equals the sum of its parts. Nine pounds of water decompose into 1 pound of hydrogen and 8 pounds of oxygen. Whatever the number of atoms in a molecule of water, the ratio of the atomic weights of hydrogen and oxygen is 1:8. If a molecule of water consists of one atom of hydrogen and one atom of oxygen (HO), then the oxygen atom would be eight times as heavy as the hydrogen atom. But if a molecule of water consists of two atoms of hydrogen and one atom of oxygen (H_2O), the one oxygen atom weighs eight times as much as the two hydrogen atoms together. Or, the one atom of oxygen would weigh 16 times as much as either atom of hydrogen. Oxygen then would have an atomic weight of 16, not 8. Dalton considered a molecule of water—he said, "atom of water"—to contain one atom each of hydrogen and oxygen (HO). By the scientific principle of parsimony, the simplest answer is the best, other things being the same. (Dalton's relative atomic weight for oxygen actually was only 7.) Once weights of such common elements as hydrogen and oxygen were set, chemists in Dalton's time determined relative atomic weights of other elements in the same way as with oxygen. They weighed substances before and after chemical reactions and used known atomic weights to calculate the unknown atomic weights of the other elements. Because oxygen commonly combines with many more substances than hydrogen, chemists shortly after Dalton began using oxygen as a standard. As chemical techniques became more precise, the atomic weight or mass of hydrogen compared to oxygen became 1.008. Table 20–1 alphabetically lists atomic weights of elements as known today in *amu*, the abbreviation for *atomic mass units*. Sixteen amu, the weight for oxygen, is 6 $\times$ 10^{-25}, or 0.000,000,000,000,000,000,000,000,6 of a pound!

THE LANGUAGE OF CHEMISTRY: SYMBOLS, FORMULAS, AND EQUATIONS

Chemistry has its own language of *symbols, formulas,* and *equations.* Symbols represent elements; formulas, compounds; and equations, transformations of matter. Lavoisier emphasized the importance of a common language for the "new chemistry," and in 1789 he published a book in such a language with precise, operational (rather than mystical) terms. Dalton used drawings to symbolize atoms in chemical processes. In 1814, the great Swedish chemist Jöns Berzelius (1779–1848) introduced the present system of notation in chemistry with these words:

> It is easier to write an abbreviated word than to draw a figure. The chemical signs ought to be letters for the greater ease of writing. I shall therefore take for the chemical sign the initial letter of the Latin name of each chemical element, thus, C, H, N, O, S, and P. If the first letter be common to two metals, I shall use both the initial letter

and another letter they have not in common, as gold (aurum), Au; silver (argentum), Ag; antimony (stibium), Sb; tin (stannum), Sn.

Berzelius listed more than 50 elements with letter symbols. Today's list of elements (Table 20–1)—twice as long—follows Berzelius's pattern.

Molecules and Formulas

Chemical elements are represented by letter symbols—for example, Hg for mercury and O for oxygen. Compounds are shown by chemical formulas, symbols of elements composing compounds placed side by side. HgO is the chemical formula of the compound mercuric oxide, composed of mercury Hg and oxygen O. The symbols Hg and O each represent an atom of an element; the formula HgO represents a molecule of the compound. CO is the formula for the compound carbon *mon*oxide, representing a molecule composed of one carbon atom and *one* oxygen atom. What if there were two oxygen atoms? CO_2 is the formula for the compound carbon *di*oxide, representing a molecule composed of one carbon atom and *two* oxygen atoms. The subscript "$_2$" or any small number at the right of and below a symbol indicates the number of atoms of the particular element present in the molecule. No subscript in a formula means only one atom of a given element is present in a molecule. H_2O represents a molecule of water composed of two atoms of hydrogen and one atom of oxygen. How would two molecules be shown? The large "2" in $2H_2O$ indicates that there are two molecules of water. A "3" or any other number before H_2O indicates the quantity of molecules (as compared to the subscript indicating the number of atoms of an element within *each* molecule). In this way, Berzelius contributed to a symbolic language of chemistry through which the union and separation of atoms could be described with chemical equations.

Chemical Equations and
Transformations of Matter

Chemical equations represent chemical processes and incorporate the principle of conservation of matter. Formulas of substances entering into a reaction are placed on the left side of the equation, and the products or end substances of the reaction are on the right side. Every atom on the left side must be accounted for on the right side. Otherwise the conservation principle would be broken. There would not be "an equal quantity of matter before and after the operation"; atoms would have been either

Table 20–1 | INTERNATIONAL ATOMIC WEIGHTS*

ELEMENT	SYM-BOL	ATOMIC NUMBER	ATOMIC WEIGHT	ELEMENT	SYM-BOL	ATOMIC NUMBER	ATOMIC WEIGHT
Actinium	Ac	89	227	Mercury	Hg	80	200.59
Aluminum	Al	13	26.9815	Molybdenum	Mo	42	95.94
Americium	Am	95	(243)	Neodymium	Nd	60	144.24
Antimony	Sb	51	121.75	Neon	Ne	10	20.183
Argon	Ar	18	39.948	Neptunium	Np	93	(237)
Arsenic	As	33	74.9216	Nickel	Ni	28	58.71
Astatine	At	85	(210)	Niobium	Nb	41	92.906
Barium	Ba	56	137.34	Nitrogen	N	7	14.0067
Berkelium	Bk	97	(249)	Nobelium	No	102	254
Beryllium	Be	4	9.0122	Osmium	Os	76	190.2
Bismuth	Bi	83	208.980	Oxygen	O	8	15.9994
Boron	B	5	10.811	Palladium	Pd	46	106.4
Bromine	Br	35	79.909	Phosphorus	P	15	30.9738
Cadmium	Cd	48	112.40	Platinum	Pt	78	195.09
Calcium	Ca	20	40.08	Plutonium	Pu	94	(242)
Californium	Cf	98	(249)	Polonium	Po	84	210
Carbon	C	6	12.01115	Potassium	K	19	39.102
Cerium	Ce	58	140.12	Praseodymium	Pr	59	140.907
Cesium	Cs	55	132.905	Promethium	Pm	61	(145)
Chlorine	Cl	17	35.453	Protactinium	Pa	91	231
Chromium	Cr	24	51.996	Radium	Ra	88	(227)
Cobalt	Co	27	58.9332	Radon	Rn	86	(222)
Copper	Cu	29	63.54	Rhenium	Re	75	186.2
Curium	Cm	96	(245)	Rhodium	Rh	45	102.905
Dysprosium	Dy	66	162.50	Rubidium	Rb	37	85.47
Einsteinium	E	99	(254)	Ruthenium	Ru	44	101.07
Erbium	Er	68	167.26	Samarium	Sm	62	150.35
Europium	Eu	63	151.96	Scandium	Sc	21	44.956
Fermium	Fm	100	(252)	Selenium	Se	34	78.96
Fluorine	F	9	18.9984	Silicon	Si	14	28.086
Francium	Fr	87	(223)	Silver	Ag	47	107.870
Gadolinium	Gd	64	157.25	Sodium	Na	11	22.9898
Gallium	Ga	31	69.72	Strontium	Sr	38	87.62
Germanium	Ge	32	72.59	Sulfur	S	16	32.064
Gold	Au	79	196.967	Tantalum	Ta	73	180.88
Hafnium	Hf	72	178.49	Technetium	Tc	43	(99)
Helium	He	2	4.0026	Tellurium	Te	52	127.60
Holmium	Ho	67	164.930	Terbium	Tb	65	158.924
Hydrogen	H	1	1.00797	Thallium	Tl	81	204.37
Indium	In	49	114.82	Thorium	Th	90	232.038
Iodine	I	53	126.9044	Thulium	Tm	69	168.934
Iridium	Ir	77	192.2	Tin	Sn	50	118.69
Iron	Fe	26	55.847	Titanium	Ti	22	47.90
Krypton	Kr	36	83.80	Tungsten	W	74	183.85
Lanthanum	La	57	138.91	Uranium	U	92	238.03
Lawrencium	Lw	103	(257)	Vanadium	V	23	50.942
Lead	Pb	82	207.19	Xenon	Xe	54	131.30
Lithium	Li	3	6.939	Ytterbium	Yb	70	173.04
Lutetium	Lu	71	174.97	Yttrium	Y	39	88.905
Magnesium	Mg	12	24.312	Zinc	Zn	30	65.37
Manganese	Mn	25	54.9380	Zirconium	Zr	40	91.22
Mendelevium	Mv	101	(256)				

*Based on the exact number "12," the assigned atomic mass of the main carbon isotope. A value given in parentheses is the mass number of the isotope of longest known half-life.

created or destroyed. To illustrate, when iron and sulfur are heated, they form iron sulfide. The chemical equation expressing this process is

$$Fe + S \longrightarrow FeS.$$

That is, iron plus sulfur (when heated) forms iron sulfide. An atom of iron and an atom of sulfur combine to form a molecule of iron sulfide. The conservation principle is easily seen in this case. A single iron (Fe) atom on the left side is balanced by one on the right; a single sulfur atom S is accounted for on the right.

Carbon from burning coal and oxygen of the air unite to form carbon dioxide (CO_2). How can this be shown? Each molecule of the product contains one atom of carbon C and two atoms of oxygen O. The equation describing the process is

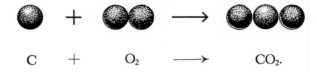

$$C \quad + \quad O_2 \quad \longrightarrow \quad CO_2.$$

The two atoms of oxygen from the air are symbolized on the left-hand side as O_2, a molecule of two atoms rather than 2O, two separate atoms of oxygen. The Italian chemist Amadeo Avogadro (1776–1856) suggested that atoms of oxygen and a number of other gaseous elements, such as hydrogen, nitrogen, and chlorine, ordinarily exist in pairs as O_2, H_2, N_2, or Cl_2, and that such pairs of atoms are molecules of elements. O_2 is a molecule of the element oxygen that unites with carbon C to form carbon dioxide. On each side of the equation, one atom of carbon and two atoms of oxygen are found.

How can the process of decomposing water (H_2O) into hydrogen and oxygen be shown? We may be tempted to say

$$H_2O \longrightarrow H_2 + O,$$

but we cannot. Remember that oxygen and hydrogen atoms, when free, are in pairs O_2 and H_2. This must be shown in the equation. Suppose we then write

$$H_2O \longrightarrow H_2 + O_2.$$

We are again in difficulty, this time with the law of conservation of matter. One atom of oxygen is shown on the left side of the equation and two atoms on the right. Where did the second oxygen atom come from? Equations must be balanced. We can balance the equation by considering two molecules of water $(2H_2O)$. The equation could be

$$2H_2O \longrightarrow 2H_2 + O_2.$$

That is, two molecules of water break down to yield two molecules of free hydrogen and one molecule of free oxygen. This removal of oxygen atoms from a molecule is called *reduction*. Reduction is the opposite process of Lavoisier's principle of oxidation. In oxidation, oxygen atoms join others to form molecules, as when hydrogen is burned in oxygen to form water. That is,

$$2H_2 + O_2 \longrightarrow 2H_2O.$$

AVOGADRO'S MOLECULAR HYPOTHESES

Avogadro was the first to claim that water has two atoms of hydrogen and one of oxygen. Why do we follow Avogadro's formula of H_2O rather than Dalton's HO? Dalton's formula is simpler, and no one has directly counted atoms within a water molecule.

Electrolysis of water (Fig. 19–8) always shows that when water breaks down, twice as much hydrogen forms, by volume, as oxygen. But why would twice as much space occupied by hydrogen mean twice as many hydrogen as oxygen atoms in water? Avogadro's answer (1811) was the famous hypothesis that *equal volumes of all gases under the same conditions of temperature and pressure are composed of the same number of molecules.* Whether the gas is hydrogen, oxygen, nitrogen, or any other, a cubic foot of it would have the same number of molecules as any other gas at the same temperature and pressure—regardless of the differences in size of molecules in different gases and regardless of some gases being elements and some, like carbon dioxide, being compounds. Basing his thinking on a definition of a molecule as "the smallest particle of a substance with characteristics of that substance," he proposed a second hypothesis that some elements as well as compounds have molecules, that gaseous elements, like hydrogen and oxygen, ordinarily have two identical atoms joined as a molecule. The paired atoms, or molecule, of such an element act as a unit rather than as individual atoms in chemical reactions.

The diagram below illustrates Avogadro's concept of diatomic—"*di*" means two—molecules of hydrogen and oxygen combining to form water vapor. In this diagram:

1. 2 vol of hydrogen and 1 vol of oxygen form 2 vol of water.

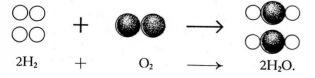

$$2H_2 \qquad + \qquad O_2 \qquad \longrightarrow \qquad 2H_2O.$$

2. Each molecule of water has two atoms of hydrogen and one of oxygen (H_2O).

3. Each atom of hydrogen and oxygen existing before the chemical reaction is accounted for in the water molecules after the reaction.

Avogadro was impressed by the fact that not only in water vapor formation but in all chemical reactions of gases, volumes of reacting and product gases show similar small whole number ratios. In the case of water, the volume ratios were 2 (hydrogen):1 (oxygen):2 (water).

The French chemist Joseph Gay-Lussac (1778–1850), however, had also obtained such consistent experimental results as:

1 vol nitrogen + 1 vol oxygen ⟶ 2 vol nitric oxide gas
N_2 + O_2 2NO

1 vol nitrogen + 3 vol hydrogen ⟶ 2 vol ammonia gas
N_2 + $3H_2$ $2NH_3$

2 vol carbon monoxide gas ⎰
+ 1 vol oxygen   ⎱ ⟶ 2 vol carbon dioxide gas
$2CO$ + O_2 $2CO_2$

1 vol oxygen + carbon (a solid) ⟶ 2 vol carbon monoxide gas
O_2 + $2C$ 2CO.

Somehow, no fractions appeared in the relationships between gas volumes in the above and other experimental results of Gay-Lussac—*just small whole numbers*. That is, *1* volume of nitrogen and 3 volumes of hydrogen form—not 1½ or 2¾ volumes, but precisely—2 volumes of ammonia gas; or 2 volumes of carbon monoxide gas and *1* volume of oxygen form—not 1⅘ or 2½ volumes, but—2 volumes of carbon dioxide gas. Such results by Gay-Lussac convinced Avogadro of the soundness of his own two hypotheses ascribing molecules to gaseous elements and equating the numbers of molecules in all gases through volumes of gases.

Gay-Lussac's conclusion that *the relation between the combining volumes of gases and the volumes of their gas products may be expressed in small whole numbers* soon became a *law of combining volumes*. But Avogadro's hypothesis explaining Gay-Lussac's law and sharply differentiating between atoms and molecules as units in chemical reactions was forgotten for 50 years—along with his H_2O formula for water. Dalton had strongly rejected Avogadro's ideas, and Dalton's prestige was high. Meanwhile, oxygen had an atomic weight of 8 instead of 16. And by 1860, chaos and confusion reigned in atomic weight tables and chemical formulas. Atomic theory was falling into serious disrepute. Difficulties arose particularly in ambiguous use of the concepts of atom and molecule. Chemists spoke about an "atom of water," a compound, in the same way they did about an atom of oxygen, an element. An atom was the smallest

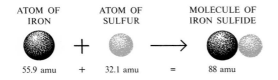

ATOM OF
IRON

ATOM OF
SULFUR

MOLECULE OF
IRON SULFIDE

55.9 amu   +   32.1 amu   =   88 amu

20–3   Molecular weight.
The weight of a molecule is
the sum of the weights of
its component atoms.

particle of any substance. Some used the term "compound atom." We have seen that Dalton himself had used the concepts atom and molecule interchangeably. Clarification and revision of ideas were imperative. In 1858, an Italian professor of chemistry, Stanislao Cannizzaro (1826–1910), forcefully revived and extended Avogadro's ideas in a pamphlet, *Sketch of a Course of Chemical Philosophy.* Cannizzaro showed that when these ideas of Avogadro were applied, confusions in chemical formulas and atomic weights disappeared.

In summary, these ideas were the following: An atom is the smallest unit of a chemical element. Atoms unite to form molecules. A molecule is the smallest unit of a compound that retains the properties of that compound; and a molecule's weight is the sum of the weights of its component atoms (Fig. 20–3). Gaseous elements like oxygen and nitrogen are composed of like atoms joined in pairs or larger groups. Each pair (or more) of such identical atoms is a molecule, just as the smallest unit of a compound is. Each pair acts as a unit of chemical reaction rather than as separate atoms. Oxygen atoms broken down from pairs would have properties different from ordinary oxygen, just as oxygen in molecules of three atoms (O_3) does. O_3 is familiar to us as ozone, found near electric machines. Its sharp, characteristic odor distinguishes it immediately from ordinary oxygen (O_2), as does its weight, one and one-half times that of oxygen. And most important of all, equal volumes of all gases (regardless of their weights or whether they are elements or compounds) have equal numbers of molecules if temperature and pressure are the same. A congress of chemists in 1860 officially and overwhelmingly accepted Avogadro's ideas as elaborated by Cannizzaro. Chemical formulas and atomic weight tables were revised and stabilized. Water was definitely H_2O, and oxygen was set with an atomic weight of 16.000 as the basis of comparison for all other atomic weights. With increased technical precision, the atomic weight of hydrogen compared to oxygen became 1.008. Since the weight of a molecule is the total weight of component atoms, the relative molecular weight of water (H_2O) is 2 × 1.008 plus 16.000, or 18.016.

By the turn of the century, Avogadro's hypothesis of "equal gas volumes" became Avogadro's law. Physicists Millikan, Perrin, and others experimentally determined the number of molecules in a given volume of gas; 22.4 liters of any gas at O°C and standard air pressure were found to contain 6.02 × 10^{23} molecules. That is, under such conditions, 22.4

liters of hydrogen weighs 2 grams and contains 602,000,000,000,000,000,-000,000 molecules. Or, one molecule of hydrogen weighs 0.000,000,000,-000,000,000,000,003,3 of a gram! And 1 gram is only about 1/28 of an ounce. The number 6.02×10^{23} molecules applying to all gases at the volume, temperature, and pressure given is now called *Avogadro's number*. Through this number, molecules of any gas can be "counted" by measuring the space they occupy.

In recent years Irving Langmuir, U.S. Nobel prize winner in chemistry, successfully broke down molecules of hydrogen gas to find that they had two atoms, as Avogadro predicted. Avogadro's second hypothesis about gas molecules is now also a law. Avogadro had based his ideas on current experiments, but he was 50 years ahead of his time in interpretation. Just as important as experimental observation is the reasoning from it.

PERIODIC
TABLE OF ELEMENTS

In 1860, the congress of chemists at Karlsruhe, Austria, saved the atomic-molecular theory. Adoption of the Avogadro-Cannizzaro suggestions resulted in standardized atomic weights and molecular formulas. At that time, over 60 elements were known, each with a different atomic weight and a different array of properties. Great chemists like the Russian Dmitri I. Mendeléyev (1834–1907) and German Julius Lothar Meyer (1830–1895) for a generation were collecting data about elements from everywhere and also experimenting themselves. (It was Meyer who had successfully championed the Avogadro-Cannizzaro atomic molecular ideas at the 1860 congress.) In 1869 Mendeléyev had notations on cards for 63 elements. There were odorless invisible gases like hydrogen (H), oxygen (O), and nitrogen (N). Or chlorine, the greenish-yellow gas with a strong, irritating odor. Hydrogen was inflammable; oxygen, life-giving; chlorine, poisonous; and nitrogen, inactive. There were liquid elements, like silvery, metallic mercury (Hg); and dark red, foul-smelling bromine (Br), with a poisonous vapor. Most elements were solids. There were durable metals of ancient times: gold (Au), silver (Ag), copper (Cu), iron (Fe), lead (Pb), and tin (Sn), each with characteristic hardness, color, or luster. Iron easily rusted; silver tarnished; and gold maintained its polish. Soft, whitish metals like sodium (Na) and potassium (K) were highly active; sodium reacted furiously in water, and potassium was dangerous to bare hands. Mercury was 13.6 times as heavy as water, but the metal lithium (Li) floated on water. There were highly active nonmetals such as fluorine (F), which set fire to water; chlorine (Cl), the poison gas; or iodine (I), known for its beautiful violet vapor and disinfectant qualities. Iodine solids sublimated directly into a vapor, bypassing the liquid state. Carbon (C) was black, and phosphorus (P), white. Metals were good conductors of heat and electricity but varied considerably as conductors. Elements had different boiling and freezing points. Some elements combined with one oxygen atom; others with two, three, or four. How could such diversity be unified as building blocks of all matter? A search for order among elements did not stop with the ancient Greeks or the alchemists.

Back in 1815, William Prout, a London physician, hypothesized that the atoms of all elements are made up of "fused" or "condensed" hydrogen atoms. The atomic weight of the element hydrogen would, of course, be 1. An oxygen atom with an atomic weight of 16 would be a composite of 16 "condensed" hydrogen atoms. But, of course, such elements as chlorine with an atomic weight of about 35.5 created difficulties. There was no such thing as half a hydrogen atom to make a total chlorine atom of 35.5 hydrogen atoms. And when the atomic weight of oxygen became standard at an atomic weight of 16 amu, careful weighing gave hydrogen an atomic weight of 1.008. How could the extra 0.008 be reconciled with Prout's idea? (Strangely enough, with the development of the proton and other 20th century atomic concepts, Prout's hypothesis of hydrogen as a building block of all elements began to make sense.)

Prout or no Prout, atomic weights were still a clue for organization of the elements. Before Mendeléyev and Lothar Meyers, several chemists in different countries explored possible connections between atomic weights and properties of the known elements. Instead of an alphabetical arrangement of atomic weights, they started with tables in order of increasing atomic weights from hydrogen (1 amu) to uranium (238 amu). These men were aware of "families" of elements with like chemical behavior. There were the very active "soft" metals, the less active, more durable "hard" metals, and the highly volatile nonmetals called the halogen (or "salt-forming") family. Elements of the halogen family, for example, include fluorine (F), chlorine (Cl), bromine (Br), and iodine (I). All of these react violently with many metals to form white crystalline salts. The most common example is ordinary table salt (NaCl), a compound of sodium (Na), the dangerous solid, and of chlorine (Cl), a poisonous gas.

Noticeable was that member elements of such families did not have atomic weights close together (Tables 20–2 and 20–3). Along with regular spacing in atomic weights, there was also a regularity of increase or decrease in certain properties. Notice in Table 20–2 or in Table 20–3 that as atomic weights increase regularly, so do the densities or the melting and boiling points.

The English chemist J. A. R. Newlands even went so far with his list of atomic weights as to say, "the eighth element starting from a given one is a kind of repetition of the first, like the eighth note in an octave of music." Beautiful, if true! Certainly partly Pythagorean and partly "true." With later knowledge, the "eighth" or "octave" did not go all the way through the list. Among other things, Newland did not allow for undiscovered elements.

Table 20–2 | PROPERTIES OF THE HALOGENS

NAME	SYMBOL	ATOMIC NUMBER	ATOMIC WEIGHT	DENSITY, GM/CM^3 AT 20°C	MELTING POINT, °C	BOILING POINT, °C
Fluorine	F	9	19.00	1.14 (liquid)	−223	−188
Chlorine	Cl	17	35.45	1.51 (liquid)	−101	− 35
Bromine	Br	35	79.91	3.12 (liquid)	− 7.2	58
Iodine	I	53	126.90	4.93	114	183

Table 20–3 | PROPERTIES OF THE ALKALI (SOFT) METALS

NAME	SYMBOL	ATOMIC NUMBER	ATOMIC WEIGHT	DENSITY GM/CM^3 AT 20°C	MELTING POINT, °C	BOILING POINT, °C
Lithium	Li	3	6.94	.53	186	1,370
Sodium	Na	11	22.99	.97	98	892
Potassium	K	19	39.10	.86	63	770
Rubidium	Rb	37	85.47	1.53	39	700
Cesium	Cs	55	132.91	1.87	28	670

All these findings were pieces for a general pattern that Mendeléyev and Lothar Meyer independently sought. Mendeléyev arranged his 63 cards with data of the elements in order of increasing atomic weight. He placed hydrogen alone and started a row under hydrogen with lithium, the "soft" metal (Table 20–4*). (Helium was still unknown.) The row of seven elements was lithium (Li), atomic weight 7; beryllium (Be), atomic weight 9.4; boron (B), 11; carbon (C), 12; nitrogen (N), 14; oxygen (O), 16; and fluorine (F), 19. The next element, sodium (Na), 23, was like lithium (Li). He therefore started a second row of seven elements under lithium. The seventh element in this row was chlorine (Cl), 35.5. Fluorine and chlorine were both very active nonmetals of the halogen family. The next element was the highly active "soft" metal potassium (K), 39, which he placed under the active metal sodium. The next element, calcium (Ca), 40, had common properties with the group above it, but titanium (Ti), 48, did not seem proper for a group with boron and aluminum (Al), 27.3. Mendeléyev therefore left a space and placed titanium under much more similar carbon and silicon (Si), 28. He decided the empty space represented an undiscovered element and

*In Table 20–4, the blue section represents elements known to Mendeléyev.

eventually found that he had to start a new eighth column with that row to accommodate iron (Fe), 56; cobalt (Co), 59; nickel (Ni), 59; and copper (Cu), 63. In the next row he found that he had to leave two empty spaces for the last three elements to be properly grouped. For example, bromine (Br), 80, belonged with halogens above it.

When finished, Mendeléyev had worked the 63 elements into eight vertical family groups (Table 20–4, Columns I–VIII), each one of which shows a periodic recurrence of properties of elements. Between Groups I and VII, there are gradations from active metals (Col. I) to less active metals to moderately active nonmetals to volatile nonmetals (halogens Col. VII). Within each family group, extending vertically in a column are regular increases or decreases of traits. Mendeléyev was so sure of himself that he placed tellurium (Te), atomic weight 127.61, before iodine (I), atomic weight 126.91. Iodine in chemical behavior belonged with the halogens in Column VII, space 53. Its atomic weight order placed it in column VI, space 52. If he had to choose between atomic weights and consistent grouping, he chose the latter—and claimed that the atomic weights were in error. The same thing occurred with gold (Au), space 79, and platinum (Pt), space 78. He placed gold in space 79 instead of platinum to satisfy family grouping, in spite of platinum's being listed at a higher atomic weight at that time. More precise techniques later showed that gold actually has a higher atomic weight than platinum and belongs after it. Mendeléyev was also correct in his placing of iodine after tellurium, not because of errors in atomic weight data, but for principles of internal atomic structure unknown in his time.

Mendeléyev's completed table (revised in 1872) was like a large jigsaw puzzle with 63 pieces that showed a general pattern, but with a number of pieces missing. But he did not stop with just boldly asserting that the empty spaces represented unknown elements and that all the "pieces" would be found. He predicted some specific properties of undiscovered elements according to the horizontal and vertical positions of the empty spaces representing them—for example, Group III, row 4; Group III, row 5; and Group IV, row 5. The position of an empty space in a row gave general family or group traits, such as reactance and luster. Some families were more chemically active than others. Or some families were metals with distinctive traits. The vertical position of an empty space gave trait variations within its family, as in density and boiling point (Tables 20–2 and 20–3). In this way, Mendeléyev discerned group differences between families and individual differences within each family well enough to pinpoint missing members. Here was a grand scheme inter-relating all the elements through regularly occurring and predictable properties—a great synthesis of accumulated data in chemistry equal to Kepler's organization of planetary data in astronomy or Maxwell's electromagnetic spectrum in physics. But was Mendeléyev's conceptual model valid? Would his predictions hold true? Three new elements, gallium,

Table 20-4
Periodic Table of Elements*

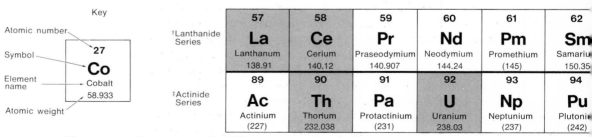

Group Period	Alkali Metals I	Alkaline Earths II						Transition Elements		
	1 H Hydrogen 1.00797							Metals		
1										
2	**3** Li Lithium 6.939	**4** Be Beryllium 9.0122								
3	**11** Na Sodium 22.9898	**12** Mg Magnesium 24.312								
4	**19** K Potassium 39.102	**20** Ca Calcium 40.08	**21** Sc Scandium 44.956	**22** Ti Titanium 47.90	**23** V Vanadium 50.942	**24** Cr Chromium 51.996	**25** Mn Manganese 54.9380	**26** Fe Iron 55.847	**27** Co Cobalt 58.933
5	**37** Rb Rubidium 85.47	**38** Sr Strontium 87.62	**39** Y Yttrium 88.905	**40** Zr Zirconium 91.22	**41** Nb Niobium 92.906	**42** Mo Molybdenum 95.94	**43** Tc Technetium (99)	**44** Ru Ruthenium 101.07	**45** Rh Rhodium 102.90
6	**55** Cs Cesium 132.905	**56** Ba Barium 137.34	**57-71** †Lanthanide Series	**72** Hf Hafnium 178.49	**73** Ta Tantalum 180.88	**74** W Tungsten 183.85	**75** Re Rhenium 186.2	**76** Os Osmium 190.2	**77** Ir Iridium 192.2
7	**87** Fr Francium (223)	**88** Ra Radium (227)	**89 - 103** ‡Actinide Series						

Key

Atomic number → 27
Symbol → Co
Element name → Cobalt
Atomic weight → 58.933

†Lanthanide Series	**57** La Lanthanum 138.91	**58** Ce Cerium 140.12	**59** Pr Praseodymium 140.907	**60** Nd Neodymium 144.24	**61** Pm Promethium (145)	**62** Sm Samarium 150.35
‡Actinide Series	**89** Ac Actinium (227)	**90** Th Thorium 232.038	**91** Pa Protactinium (231)	**92** U Uranium 238.03	**93** Np Neptunium (237)	**94** Pu Plutonium (242)

*The elements in blue are those in Mendeléyev's original periodic table.
All atomic weights are based on the exact number "12," an assigned atomic mass of the main isotope of carbon.
The values in parentheses are mass numbers of the most stable known isotopes of the particular elements.

			III	IV	V	VI	VII	VIII
								2 **He** Helium 4.0026

Nonmetals

			5 **B** Boron 10.811	6 **C** Carbon 12.01115	7 **N** Nitrogen 14.0067	8 **O** Oxygen 15.9994	9 **F** Fluorine 18.9984	10 **Ne** Neon 20.183
			13 **Al** Aluminum 26.9815	14 **Si** Silicon 28.086	15 **P** Phosphorus 30.9738	16 **S** Sulfur 32.064	17 **Cl** Chlorine 35.453	18 **Ar** Argon 39.948
28 **Ni** Nickel 58.71	29 **Cu** Copper 63.54	30 **Zn** Zinc 65.37	31 **Ga** Gallium 69.72	32 **Ge** Germanium 72.59	33 **As** Arsenic 74.9216	34 **Se** Selenium 78.96	35 **Br** Bromine 79.909	36 **Kr** Krypton 83.80
46 **Pd** Palladium 106.4	47 **Ag** Silver 107.870	48 **Cd** Cadmium 112.40	49 **In** Indium 114.82	50 **Sn** Tin 118.69	51 **Sb** Antimony 121.75	52 **Te** Tellurium 127.60	53 **I** Iodine 126.9044	54 **Xe** Xenon 131.30
78 **Pt** Platinum 195.09	79 **Au** Gold 196.967	80 **Hg** Mercury 200.59	81 **Tl** Thallium 204.37	82 **Pb** Lead 207.19	83 **Bi** Bismuth 208.980	84 **Po** Polonium (210)	85 **At** Astatine (210)	86 **Rn** Radon (222)

63 **Eu** Europium 151.96	64 **Gd** Gadolinium 157.25	65 **Tb** Terbium 158.924	66 **Dy** Dysprosium 162.50	67 **Ho** Holmium 164.930	68 **Er** Erbium 167.26	69 **Tm** Thulium 168.934	70 **Yb** Ytterbium 173.04	71 **Lu** Lutetium 174.97
95 **Am** Americium (243)	96 **Cm** Curium (245)	97 **Bk** Berkelium (249)	98 **Cf** Californium (249)	99 **Es** Einsteinium (254)	100 **Fm** Fermium (252)	101 **Md** Mendelevium (256)	102 **No** Nobelium (254)	103 **Lw** Lawrencium (257)

Dalton observing. (Brown Bros. photograph)

scandium, and germanium, were found in 1875, 1879, and 1886, respectively. All three fit into empty spots in Mendeléyev's table (rows 4 and 5), with properties as predicted. The periodic table illustrates well the value of systematic classification of data in man's search for order.

In 1852, the English chemist Edward Frankland introduced and defined the concept of *valence* as *the number of hydrogen atoms with which one atom of an element can combine.* Hydrogen (H) is the standard set, with a valence of $+1$. In forming a molecule of hydrogen chloride (HCl), one atom of chlorine (Cl) combines with one atom of hydrogen (H). Chlorine, therefore, has a valence of 1, actually -1. Since hydrogen is $+1$, chlorine is given a minus sign. By electrical analogy, opposites combine. In forming a molecule of ammonia gas (NH_3), one atom of nitrogen (N) combines with three atoms of hydrogen. Nitrogen thus has a valence of -3. In forming a molecule of methane gas (CH_4), one atom of carbon combines with four atoms of hydrogen. Carbon thus has a valence of -4.

Mendeléyev's periodic classification neatly incorporated the concept of valence. Illustrations follow:

    1. Atoms of elements in Group I tend to combine with oxygen atoms at a ratio of 2:1. Hydrogen is in Group I, and oxygen is in Group VI. Since one oxygen atom combines with two hydrogen atoms for each water molecule (H_2O), oxygen has *twice* the valence of hydro-

gen, or −2. The two hydrogen atoms, with a valence of +1 each, equalize the one oxygen atom with a valence of −2.

2. Atoms of Group II tend to combine with oxygen atoms at a 1:1 ratio and, therefore, to have a +2 valence. Mercury (Hg) is in Group II. A molecule of mercuric oxide (HgO) has one atom of mercury with a +2 valence that equalizes the −2 valence of the one oxygen atom.

3. Atoms of elements in Group III tend to combine with oxygen atoms at a ratio of 2:3 and to have a valence of +3. Aluminum (Al) is in Group III. A molecule of aluminum oxide (Al_2O_3) has two atoms of aluminum (Al_2) and three atoms of oxygen (O_3). Two aluminum atoms, each with a valence of +3, equalize three oxygen atoms, each with a −2 valence.

4. Atoms of Group IV elements tend to combine with oxygen atoms at a 1:2 ratio and to have a +4 valence. Carbon (C) is in Group IV. A molecule of carbon dioxide has one atom of carbon and two of oxygen. The one atom of carbon, with a +4 valence, equalizes two oxygen atoms, with a −2 valence each. Group IV elements, such as carbon, may combine with hydrogen or metals. They then have minus valences.

5. Groups V, VI, and VII tend to have negative valences, or combining powers with hydrogen, of −3, −2, and −1, respectively. Nitrogen (N) is in Group V, with a combining power of −3; oxygen in Group VI, with −2; and fluorine (F) in Group VII, with −1. The lower the valence number, the more active the element; fluorine (valence −1) is more active than oxygen (−2), which is more active than nitrogen (−3).

Also notice the valence symmetry found across Groups I–VII: +1, +2, +4, −3, −2, −1. Elements with + valences unite with elements having − valences. Metals are in the first four groups and are + in valence.

The highly active metal sodium (Na) is in Group I, and the highly active halogen chlorine is in Group VII. The sodium in table salt, sodium chloride (NaCl), has a valence of +1, and the chlorine, a valence of −1.

6. Eventually, inert gases were found that seldom, if ever, combine with other substances. These in later periodic tables (Table 20-4) were listed as zero valence (Group VIII).

7. In time, many elements were found to depart from usual valences. In methane gas (CH_4), carbon has a valence of −4. But in ethane gas (C_2H_6), carbon has a valence of −3.

Mendeléyev read his paper *On the Relation of the Properties to the Atomic Weights of the Elements* before the Russian Chemical Society in 1869. In 1870, Lothar Meyer published his independently written paper on periodic classification of elements. Mendeléyev did more in the way of specific prediction of unknown elements and their properties from gaps in his table. But the work of the two men was comparable and

Dmitri I. Mendeléyev, 1834–1907. (Culver Pictures, Inc.)

simultaneous enough for the British Royal Society to present the Davy Medal to both men jointly. Each had effectively shown that if the elements are listed in the order of atomic weights, elements with like properties appear at regular intervals. Once again, two highly gifted men of different nations working independently at the same problems at the same time from a common international heritage came up with the same big idea.

The entire Table 20–4 is the periodic table of elements brought up to date with elements beyond 100. In comparison to Mendeléyev's table (in blue), notice the filled-in gaps. Notice again the new family Group VIII, known as inert or noble gases. Almost without exception, they do not unite with other substances. Gaseous elements with single atoms, odorless, and invisible, they remained unknown until the last part of the 19th century.

Group VIII had its origins in the solar eclipse of August 1868, a year before Mendeléyev's paper. A spectroscope turned toward the sun's atmosphere showed an orange-yellow spectral line (Chapter 17) different from that of sodium. Unknown on earth, the new element was called *helium* after "helios," the Greek word for sun. Since nothing else was known about helium, the new element passed unnoticed even by Mendeléyev and Meyer. Sir William Ramsay, in 1894, sent a spark through an unknown inactive gas discovered by the U.S. geochemist Dr. W. F. Hillebrand in 1888. Ramsay found that the spectral line of Hillebrand's gas matched that of the sun's element helium. Earlier that year, the same Ramsay and a collaborator, Lord Rayleigh, had discovered traces of another inert gas, argon, in the air. Spectral lines had shown the inactive argon not to be nitrogen. Argon is now known to make up about 1 percent of the atmosphere. Ramsay devoted himself to the pursuit of additional unknown inert gases in liquid air. Through exceedingly precise apparatus and techniques, he isolated from 120 tons of air minute amounts of new inert elements—neon, krypton, xenon, and radon. Of the six inert gases in Group 0, only xenon and argon have ever been successfully united with another element, and that was only recently.

Also notice in the present table of elements that the space in Group III, row 8, is occupied not by a single element, but by 15 elements known as rare earths, all very close in chemical properties. The space in Group III, row 9, is occupied by an open-ended actinide series still being completed by man-made artificial elements. Elements with similar properties are no longer occurring at regular intervals of 8, but at intervals of 2, 8, 18, or 32 elements apart. Again, nature turns out to be more complicated than anticipated by unifying ideas.

Can you find several instances in the modern table in which higher atomic weights are placed before lower ones due to family properties? Do such inconsistencies have implications for Mendeléyev's and Meyer's unifying ideas? In any case, a new concept of *atomic number* eventually replaced atomic weight as an organizing principle of the periodic table.

CHAPTER REVIEW

1. To what extent are the following observations evidence that matter is composed of atomic particles? (a) Sugar dissolves in water. (b) A drop of ink spreads in water. (c) Burning toast soon makes itself known.

2. Is water chemically the same everywhere? Why do we think so? How is the conclusion expressed in the law of definite proportions by weight?

3. Why is it important to know that "a compound always has the same proportions by weight"?

4. What is Dalton's law of multiple proportions? Illustrate.

5. Differentiate between Proust's law of definite proportions and Dalton's law of multiple proportions. Illustrate.

6. Discuss the two laws in question 5 as cornerstones of chemistry.

7. What assumptions did Dalton have in common with the Greek atomists, and what atomic innovations did he make?

8. How could Dalton ascribe weights to atoms that he could not see or weigh?

9. Why was the development of tables of atomic weights highly important for chemistry?

10. What is a molecule? How are atoms related to molecules? Illustrate.

11. How are molecular weights obtained? Illustrate.

12. Why was Dalton's use of symbols significant for chemistry?

13. Why is the atom said to have become a scientific concept with Dalton? If it was not a scientific concept among Greek or Roman atomists, what was it?

14. Compare Berzelius's symbols for a water molecule to Dalton's. What advantages did Berzelius's symbols have?

15. Illustrate the difference between a chemical formula and a chemical equation.

16. Illustrate how the law of conservation of matter is symbolized in chemical equations.

17. What is Gay-Lussac's law of combining volumes? Illustrate. What is the law's significance in the understanding of matter?

18. How does the electrolysis of water point to a formula of H_2O rather than HO?

19. Do equal volumes of all gases under the same conditions of temperature and pressure contain the same number of molecules? Why did Avogadro think so? What bearing does this hypothesis have upon the idea that water is H_2O?

20. Why do we believe that free oxygen atoms travel in pairs? What significance did the hypothesis that gaseous elements may consist of molecules of two identical atoms have in establishing atomic theory?

21. How can the number of molecules in a given volume of gas be known without molecules being seen and counted?

22. What is "valence"? Explain and illustrate the role of this concept in the development of chemistry.

23. Discuss the periodic table of elements as a major conceptual model of chemistry. Around what basic idea was the table developed?

24. Describe eight families in the periodic table of elements, giving characteristics of each family and illustrating with two members of each family.

25. How did Mendeléyev predict the existence of unknown chemical elements through his periodic table? Illustrate with one of Mendeléyev's predicted elements.

26. How does the periodic table illustrate the significance of classification in science?

27. How was it possible for Mendeléyev and Lothar Meyer, working independently in two different countries, to develop almost simultaneously the highly significant periodic table?

28. How do the following laws or organizing principles specifically strengthen the atomic theory? (a) Law of definite proportion by weight. (b) Law of multiple proportions. (c) Law of combining volumes. (d) Avogadro's law. (e) Avogadro's molecular hypothesis of gaseous elements. (f) Avogadro's number. (g) Periodic table.

29. What sense did it make for Proust to suggest that "all elements are built up from hydrogen"? Why was the idea abandoned?

30. Einstein and Infeld stated that "creating a new theory is like climbing a mountain, gaining new and wider views, and discovering unexpected connections between our starting point and its rich environment." Show how this applies to atomic theory.

31. Conant emphasized "certain principles of the tactics and strategy of science." These principles are (a) "New concepts evolve from experiments or observations and are fruitful of new experiments and observations," (b) "Significant observations are the result of controlled experiments or observations," and (c) "New techniques arise as a result of experimentation and influence further experimentation." Illustrate these principles from materials in the development of a new science of chemistry in Chapters 19 and 20.

PROBLEMS

1. Assume eight parts of oxygen to one part of hydrogen exist by weight in water. (a) Thirty-six kilograms of water contain how much hydrogen? How much oxygen? (b) What is the ratio by volume of hydrogen to oxygen in the electrolysis of 36 kilograms of water?

2. (a) What is the ratio by weight of hydrogen to oxygen in 100 pounds of water? How many pounds of hydrogen and oxygen would result from electrolysis of the water? (b) What is the ratio by volume of hydrogen to oxygen in the electrolysis of 100 pounds of water?

3. Assume the formula of water to be HO and the atomic weight of hydrogen to be 1. Also assume eight parts of oxygen to one part of hydrogen by weight in water. (a) What would be the atomic weight of oxygen? (b) What would be the molecular weight of water?

4. Assume the formula of water to be H_2O, the atomic weight of hydrogen to be 1, the weight ratio of hydrogen to oxygen to be 1:8, and Avogadro's molecular hypothesis to be correct. What is the (a) atomic

weight of oxygen? (b) Molecular weight of water? (c) Molecular weight of hydrogen? (d) Molecular weight of oxygen?

5. Assume that carbon has an atomic weight of 12, and oxygen, an atomic weight of 16. (a) What is the molecular weight of CO? Of CO_2? (b) What is the ratio by weight of carbon and oxygen in CO? Of carbon and oxygen in CO_2?

6. Express the union of carbon and oxygen to form carbon dioxide in Dalton's symbols and in Berzelius's symbols. Indicate the atomic and molecular weights involved.

7. Express the union of carbon and oxygen to form carbon monoxide.

8. Write the equation that symbolizes the electrolysis of water.

9. In accordance with Avogadro's molecular hypothesis, if 1 gallon of hydrogen gas contains 1×10^{23} molecules, how many molecules would each of the following volumes of gas contain at the same temperature and pressure? (a) 6 gallons of hydrogen. (b) 6 gallons of oxygen. (c) 2 gallons of nitrogen. (d) 1 gallon of carbon dioxide.

10. How could 100 cubic centimeters of alcohol mixed with 100 cubic centimeters of water give about 195 cubic centimeters of mixture without evaporation?

11. If hydrogen has a valence of $+ 1$, what is the valence of (a) oxygen in H_2O? (b) Chlorine in HCl (hydrogen chloride)? (c) Carbon in CO_2 (carbon dioxide)? (d) Nitrogen in NH_3 (ammonia gas)?

12. Give all the information indicated by the formulas in question 11 that you can.

13. Read the following equations:

$$H_2 + Cl_2 \longrightarrow 2\ HCl$$

$$2C + O_2 \longrightarrow 2\ CO$$

$$2HgO \longrightarrow 2Hg + O_2$$

$$Zn + S \longrightarrow ZnS$$

$$2H_2O \longrightarrow 2H_2 + O_2$$

$$CuO + H_2 \longrightarrow Cu + H_2O.$$

14. (a) Insert atomic and molecular weight values under the members of each equation in problem 13. (b) In each equation show that matter is neither lost nor gained.

15. Which family of elements is missing in Mendeléyev's periodic table? How would you explain Mendeléyev's unawareness of an entire family of elements?

SUGGESTIONS FOR
FURTHER READING

Holton, Gerald J., and D. H. D. Roller, *Foundations of Modern Physical Science,* Addison-Wesley, Reading, Mass., 1958, Chs. 22–24.

Conant, James, ed., *Harvard Case Histories in Experimental Science,* Harvard Univ. Press, Cambridge, Mass., 1957, Case 4, "The Atomic Molecular Theory."

Jaffe, Bernard, *Crucibles: The Story of Chemistry,* Premier paperback, New York, 1960, Chs. 6–7, and 9.

Feinberg, Joseph G., *Story of Atomic Theory and Atomic Energy,* Dover paperback, New York, 1960, Chs. 3–6.

Faraday, Michael, *Chemical History of a Candle,* Viking paperback, New York, 1960.

Omer, Guy C., Jr., et al., *Physical Science: Men and Concepts,* Heath, Boston, 1962, Chs. 23–30.

Rapport, Samuel B., and Helen Wright, *Science: Method and Meaning,* Washington Square paperback, New York, 1964.

Hecht, Selig, *Explaining the Atom,* Viking paperback, New York, 1954, Ch. 1.

21   Atoms Break Down: The Electrical Nature of Matter

Great ideas emerge from the common cauldron of intellectual activity, and are rarely cooked up in private kettles from original recipes.

JAMES R. NEWMAN, 1947

"It seems probable to me that God in the beginning form'd Matter in solid, massy, hard, impenetrable, moveable Particles," said Newton. Yet atoms had been breaking down for billions of years. Not until the 20th century did men begin to stumble upon the clues and catch the signals. Systems of ideas and technology are social heritages. Newton inherited elemental ideas of atoms, but not the experimental techniques or expanded ideas for operating at an atomic level. Men interpreted lightning as the "wrath of God" until they accumulated sufficient ideas and techniques for testing lightning. Men were unaware of radio signals from the stars until they developed ideas of electromagnetic waves and invented radio wave receivers. And men had to operate with ideas of atoms as units before recognizing that atoms break down into electrical components and emit signals. The atom first had to be an entity before the entity could have parts and before matter could be found to be basically electrical in nature.

IONS IN LIQUIDS

Men like Faraday asked why an electric current could split a water molecule into hydrogen and oxygen atoms. Why did hydrogen bubbles always form at negative electrodes and oxygen at positive (Fig. 19–8)? Charges attract opposites. Is the hydrogen electrically positive, and the oxygen, negative? Faraday raised questions and investigated further. Ordinary dry table salt does not conduct a current, nor does distilled water (Fig. 21–1A). But place the salt in the water, and a current is conducted that heats a wire or lights a bulb (Fig. 21–1B). Why? Does the water make the salt a conductor or vice versa? Is the salt or the water basically electrical in nature? What about other materials? Faraday found that any *salt, acid,* or *alkali* in water conducts a current and that chemical changes take place in the solution. Substances that conduct a current when in a water or other solution are called *electrolytes.* Place blue copper sulfate salt in water, and a negative electrode becomes plated with pure copper. The electroplating of gold, silver, or other metals resulted from such discoveries that metals of salts in solutions coat negative electrodes. And in ore refining, pure metals are obtained at the cathode, or negative terminal, of an electrolytic cell by placing ore at the positive terminal, or anode (Fig. 21–2). The impurities either remain at the anode or go into the solution. But in Faraday's time, electrolysis experiments raised more theoretical questions than they answered. Why water solutions of such substances as sugar, alcohol, or glycerin do not conduct a current was unknown.

As a brilliant young Swedist schoolboy, Svanté Arrhenius (1859-1927) came up with some electrical answers. Atoms could be positively charged, negatively charged, or neutral, he said. A charged atom or group of atoms he called an *ion.* A molecule of table salt, sodium chloride, is electrically neutral. In the molecule, a "positively charged sodium atom" is neutralized by "a negatively charged chlorine atom." An electrical force of attraction

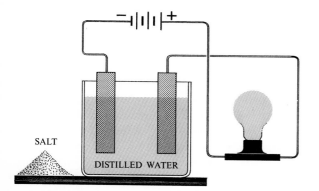

21–1A *Salt or distilled water separately does not conduct a current.*

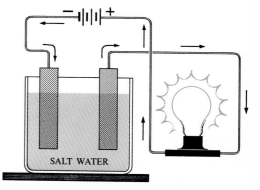

21–1B *Salt in water does.*

keeps the atoms together. When salt is dissolved in water, the sodium and chlorine atoms are forced apart by water molecules to become sodium and chlorine ions. The process is represented as follows:

$$NaCl \longrightarrow Na^+ \text{ (sodium ion)} + Cl^- \text{ (chlorine ion)}.$$

The salt, previously neutral, breaks down into electrical particles. The water solution becomes a conductor of electricity. After all, when electrically neutral amber is rubbed with neutral cat's fur, both become electrical. Why shouldn't an electrifying process be possible in a liquid? Sugar molecules do not break down in water; the molecules remain electrically neutral. The mixture therefore does not conduct a current. It is well to bear in mind two main differences between an atom and an ion: (1) An atom is electrically neutral; an ion is charged positively or negatively. (2) An atom involves only one element; an ion includes one or more elements. An ammonium ion $(NH_4)^+$, for example, includes nitrogen and hydrogen with a combined single $+$ charge.

An ion may have a charge of more than one. If the salt zinc chloride is dissolved in water, the process is shown by:

$$ZnCl_2 \longrightarrow Zn^{++} + 2Cl^-.$$

A molecule of zinc chloride breaks down in water into one zinc ion with two positive $(+)$ charges, and two chlorine ions, each with one negative $(-)$ charge. The reasoning is that metals become positive ions, and nonmetals tend to be negative. Zinc, a metal with a chemical combining power, or valence, of 2 (Chapter 20), should also have two charges as an ion, both positive. A molecule of zinc chloride contains one atom of zinc and two atoms of chlorine. The one zinc atom has twice the combining power of each of the two chlorine atoms. A molecule of zinc chloride is also electrically neutral. Each of the two chloride ions can have only one negative charge to electrically neutralize the single zinc ion with two positive charges. Significantly, the charge of an ion becomes identified with its valence as an atom. The chlorine atom has a valence of -1; the chloride ion, a charge of -1.

Arrhenius's ions were rejected by his schoolmaster and by chemical authorities at the time. But Arrhenius started something that eventually gave him the Nobel prize in chemistry. The combining power, or valences, of atoms after awhile were seen as electrical. Atoms in a molecule were recognized as held together by electrical forces originating from charges in atoms. Matter itself seemed to be electrical in nature. But specific questions remained. An ion is chemically different from an atom. Sodium atoms are silvery metal particles that react violently with water; sodium ions are colorless particles with no known reactions with water. What is added or subtracted from an atom that gives it charge and makes it an ion? If anything is subtracted, how could atoms be indivisible?

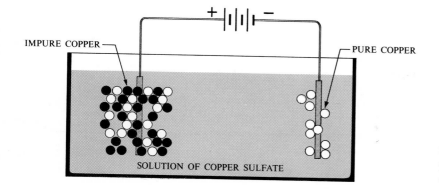

IMPURE COPPER

PURE COPPER

SOLUTION OF COPPER SULFATE

21–2 Ore refining. If copper ore is placed at the anode, pure copper accumulates at the cathode.

ELECTRONS IN TUBES

Men sent currents through not only liquids but also gases in tubes. An electrostatic machine sends sparks through the air. In 1853, Masson, a French scientist, wondered what would happen if sparks were sent through a glass tube from which air was removed. He sealed wires from terminals of an electric machine into the ends of such a tube and found that a spark jumped across a greater gap inside the tube than it did outside the tube.

The German scientist Geissler investigated further. He used a stronger current and tried different gases inside a glass tube at a higher vacuum. Instead of a visible spark, each gas gave a characteristic glow: neon, a red glow; mercury vapor, blue; sodium, yellow; ordinary air, reddish purple. Electrical sparks had become colored light within tubes.

But what are sparks? Benjamin Franklin's "artificial lightning" was now insufficient. In the 19th century, scientists tried to understand observable events in terms of unseen components. Light and heat associated with sparks are outer signs of something unseen passing through; what is the original something? To answer such a question, the Englishman William Crookes, in 1878, exhausted more air than ever from a tube and watched the strange, flickering red-purple glow increase in intensity. As his pump continued to remove air, the soft light became weaker and gradually disappeared. The tube interior was dark, but the glass itself now had an eerie pale green glow. What was happening inside? Curious scientists in many nations experimented with high vacuum "Crookes tubes." Zinc sulfide or certain other powders placed within the tube became fluorescent from something unseen within striking them. Investigations continued. The unseen ray exciting the fluorescent powder—was it a stream of matter or an unbroken wave, like light? A paddle wheel was inserted within a sealed tube (Fig. 21–3). The wheel moved; matter must be striking it. But the wheel always moved away from the cathode (negative terminal) of the tube; particles from the cathode must be striking

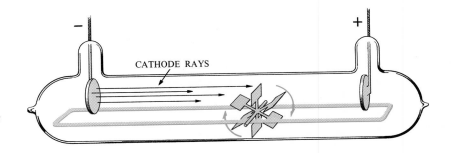

21–3 Cathode ray particles turn a paddle wheel in a vacuum tube.

the wheel. The ray, called a *cathode ray,* seemingly consisted of particles streaming from the cathode to the positively charged end of the tube. A small cross inserted into the tube threw a shadow on the tube wall opposite the cathode. The direction of the ray was confirmed.

Do the minute, unseen particles have charge as well as weight? A second pair of oppositely charged electrodes was sealed within a cathode ray tube. The straight ray curved toward the positive plate as if composed of negatively charged particles (Fig. 21–4). A magnet brought close also deflected the ray in a direction characteristic of negatively charged particles. From where did these negatively charged material particles arise? Were they forced from cathode metal and from gas atoms in the tube? In any case, the English physicist G. J. Stoney in 1891 named these invisible negative particles of electricity *electrons.*

But for the electron to be more than a hypothesis, specific characteristics of individual electrons must be known. The English physicist J. J. Thomson, master of such masters as Ernest Rutherford, set out to obtain some specific data. He used different metals as electrodes in a Crookes tube. He varied the gas in his tube. Repeatedly, he swerved the rays by placing magnets or electric plates near them and measured the deflection of the rays.

Something in the rays showed charge and mass at a constant ratio. Thomson was unable to obtain the specific value of the charge e or the mass m separately, but he did get a specific value for the ratio of e/m of the two (1.76×10^{-8} coulombs per gram). The speed of the particles was around 10,000 miles per *second.* And regardless of what cathode metal or gas was used in the tube, the particles always showed the same charge-to-mass ratio. Thomson concluded that cathode rays are electrons common to all matter and that these particles all have the same mass and negative charge. Thomson had discovered the electron, previously theorized within electric currents and cathode rays. He had not directly seen the electrons—nor has anyone since—but he knew them by the light they created, and he measured them through the magnetic or electrical deflection of that light.

An electrical particle common to all matter fascinated many men as a clue to the atom itself. Electron investigation mushroomed. The

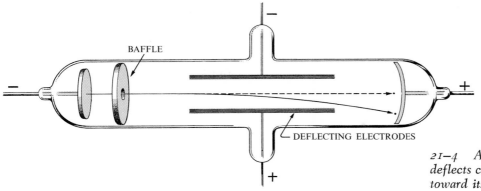

21–4   A positive electrode deflects cathode ray particles toward itself.

American inventor Thomas Edison tested glowing wires in electric light bulbs. He noticed that negative particles "evaporated" from the red hot wire (filament) to a positive plate sealed within the bulb. Other scientists pinpointed these evaporating particles as electrons. Einstein's photoelectric effect has already been described (Chapter 18). Light falling upon certain metals caused electric currents to flow from them just as if from a battery. When tested with magnets in cathode ray tubes, these currents deflected exactly like any other cathode rays or electron streams. Electricity originated in matter.

MILLIKAN'S OIL DROP EXPERIMENT

J. J. Thomson discovered the electron, and Robert Millikan (1868–1953), the University of Chicago physicist, established it as a basic unit of charge.

J. J. Thomson at work. (Cavendish Laboratory, Cambridge)

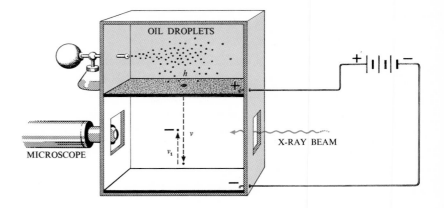

21-5 Millikan's oil drop experiment. Millikan electrically balanced oil droplets against gravity to determine the amount of electrical charge in an electron.

Millikan did so in a very delicate experiment in which he electrically balanced oil droplets against gravity (Fig. 21–5). His technique is simplified below:

1. Tiny oil droplets are sprayed from an atomizer into a space above the top + plate of a battery.

2. The droplets drift down through a small hole h in the top plate into the electric field between the plates.

3. The speed v at which uncharged drops fall is observable through a microscope.

4. Electrons are stripped from falling drops by means of radium or X rays nearby. When negatively charged, oil drops tended to move back up toward the + plate against gravity.

5. Stronger upward electrical forces on a droplet are possible by adjusting the current to the plate. With a strong enough electric field, the electrical force upward balances gravity downward.

6. Given a strong enough electric field against gravity, the oil drop moves up with a speed v_1. By knowing the original speed downward v of an uncharged drop (step 3) and the speed upward v_1 of the drop when charged, Millikan could calculate the amount of charge necessary for the observed change in speed $(v - v_1)$.

For 3 years, until 1911, Millikan and his assistants patiently balanced oil, mercury, or glycerin droplets carrying various amounts of charge. Regardless of material, they found that the charge q was always a multiple of a minimum unit charge close to 4.8×10^{-10} *electrostatic units* (esu), or 1.6×10^{-19} coulombs. That is, in esu, the answers for charge were $4.8, 9.6, 14.4, 19.2 \times 10^{-10}$, and so on upward. The smallest answer as well as the closest difference between answers was always about 4.8×10^{-10} esu. What else could this be but that the electron has a constant unit charge of 4.8×10^{-10} esu, and that every additional negative charge in an oil drop means another 4.8×10^{-10}? That is, the relationships are as follows:

CHARGE VALUES ($\times 10^{-10}$ ESU)	NUMBER OF ELECTRON CHARGES
4.8	1
9.6	2
14.4	3
19.2	4
24.0	5
.	.
.	.
.	.

Obviously, there were no fractions in the number of electron charges at 4.8×10^{-10} esu. The situation is like that of nickels in small piles. If the nickel is the only coin used, then the number of nickels is always a whole number, no fractions. The smallest possible money value in a pile is 5c, the closest possible difference between values in piles is 5c, and the total value of each pile is a multiple of 5c.

We have seen that J. J. Thomson determined a constant value for the charge-to-mass ratio ($e/m = 1.76 \times 10^{-8}$ coulombs per gram) of an electron. It was therefore easy for Millikan to place his value for charge ($e = 1.60 \times 10^{-19}$ coulombs) in the ratio to solve for the mass m of an electron. His value confirmed Thomson's previous relative value of an electron's mass as about 1,850 times less than that of a hydrogen atom. Atoms were definitely not the smallest units of matter. Electrons were smaller. And electrons were absolutely uniform in charge and mass. Were they not a basic component of atoms themselves?

POSITIVE RAYS

If electrons stream in a cathode ray tube, are there positive rays, too? In 1885 the German physicist E. Goldstein decided to find out. Positive particles in a tube should be attracted to the cathode. He used a cathode full of holes in a tube and observed rays extending like "canals" back through the holes (Fig. 21–6). Momentum was carrying particles through.

21–6   Positive rays stream through holes in a perforated cathode opposite in direction to cathode rays.

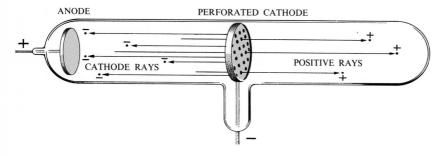

ANODE   PERFORATED CATHODE

CATHODE RAYS   POSITIVE RAYS

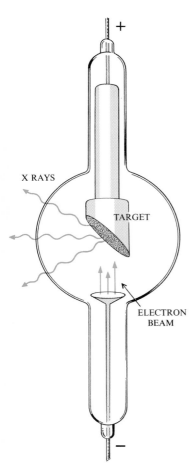

In 1888 another German physicist, Wilhelm Wien, showed that such "canal" rays were attracted by a negative plate and repelled by a positive plate. Wien concluded that the rays consisted of positively charged particles. Wien also found that these positive particles were deflected by magnets or electric plates much less than the cathode ray particles were. The positive particles were therefore much heavier than electrons. Soon other scientists found that the relative weight of the positive particles changed as the gas in the tube was changed. But in all cases, the positive rays were heavier than the negative rays. Seemingly, ions replaced gas atoms or molecules in the tube. Were not the ions originally positive parts of gas atoms? If so, once again matter seemed electrical in nature. Crookes tube techniques and atomic concepts were paying off in significant insights into matter.

X RAYS FROM TARGETS

Arrhenius had made the world conscious of ions; and Thomson, of electrons. The time was ripe for a couple of momentous, chance discoveries. In 1895 the German scientist Wilhelm Roentgen was experimenting in a dark room with a cathode ray tube at a very high voltage. The tube was completely enclosed in a black cardboard box. A fluorescent screen happened to be nearby. When Roentgen operated the tube, he noticed a glow in the dark. The screen was outside the tube. Why the glow? Neither light nor cathode rays from the tube could pass through the opaque box and reach the screen. Invisible, penetrating rays from the tube must be exciting the minerals coating the screen. At a loss for a name, Roentgen called the unknown rays X rays.

Roentgen continued experimenting. "What did I think? I didn't think. I began to experiment," said Roentgen. He placed various objects between the operating tube and the screen. Paper, wood, cloth, or thin sheet metal did not stop the glow; a thin lead plate did. When he placed his hand between the tube and screen, he was amazed to see the skeleton of his hand. The rays passed through flesh but were partly stopped by bones. Also, photographic plates were affected by the rays. Medical practitioners, almost at once, pressed for the use of X rays. Inner structure and functions of the body could be examined without surgery. Photographs could be taken. The medical benefits of X rays are now common knowledge and need no listing here.

The higher the tube voltage, the more penetrating the X rays. Inserting a metal target between the cathode and anode (Fig. 21–7) gives X rays that are far more effective. Somehow, the quick stop of electrons at the target results in the emission of X rays from the target metal. Could the rays arise from within atoms of the metal? Almost two decades were needed for an adequate answer. Meanwhile, X rays found a place in

21–7 X-ray tube. X rays are emitted from the metal target struck by fast-moving electrons.

Maxwell's electromagnetic spectrum. They turned out to be electromagnetic waves at a higher frequency than light and therefore unseen and more penetrating (Fig. 18–12).

The first Nobel prize, awarded in 1901, went to Roentgen for his discovery of X rays. Rarely has a revolutionary discovery been so quickly appreciated. The time was ripe indeed!

URANIUM'S SPONTANEOUS RAYS

Roentgen's chance discovery of X rays led to another one even more momentous. The French physicist Henri Becquerel (1852–1908) wondered whether X rays have sources other than cathode ray tubes. He knew that phosphorus and certain other substances glow in the dark after exposure to sunlight. Cathode ray tubes in operation emit both X rays and light, thought Becquerel. Do "phosphorescent" substances also emit X rays when they glow? If so, uranium and other phosphorescent minerals could be simple sources of penetrating radiation. To test this possibility, Becquerel tightly wrapped photographic plates in heavy black paper opaque to ordinary light but transparent to more penetrating rays. After keeping some uranium salt in the sun for several hours, he rested his sample on the covered film plates. When developed, the plates showed spots directly below where the salt had been set. The salt had given off penetrating rays like X rays and had photographed itself!

Roentgen and his rays.
(Culver Pictures, Inc.)

Becquerel did not check to see if uranium salts would emit penetrating rays even if *not* first exposed to sunlight. Like all his colleagues, he assumed that uranium is a typical phosphorescent mineral. But an accident of weather took care of that. Becquerel had decided to repeat his uranium salt experiment, but cloudy skies delayed him. Becquerel wrote:

> . . . as on [the two previous] days, the sun only showed itself intermittently. I kept my arrangements all prepared and put back the holders in the dark in the drawer of the case, and left in place the crusts of uranium salt. Since the sun did not show itself again for several days, I developed the photographic plates on the first of March, expecting to find the images very feeble. The silhouettes appeared on the contrary with great intensity.

Becquerel had not exposed the uranium to sunlight, but amazingly, the salt in the darkness of the drawer had strongly fogged the covered film plate. Rays were spontaneously arising from the salt itself.

Becquerel tested further. He tried different uranium salts and combined these salts with other substances. And he finally tried pure uranium metal. The results were always the same: The photographic effect on the plates was always proportional to the amount of uranium in the substance tested. The radiation was pinpointed to the uranium rather than to other elements in the salts. And no matter how Becquerel heated, compressed, or physically altered a uranium salt, the rate of radiation did not change. Becquerel's rays arose spontaneously from uranium and were unaffected by physical or chemical conditions. The rays were truly unique.

But what about the conservation of energy? Phosphorus transforms visible or ultraviolet rays from elsewhere into light of its own. Uranium emits rays spontaneously. From what are these rays transformed? How could energy arise from nothing? An enigma remained—either an enigma or an overthrow of the law of conservation of energy.

Becquerel had discovered *radioactivity,* and for his discovery he shared a Nobel prize in 1903 with the Curies. He had accidentally caught inner atomic signals, but he did not yet know that the signals meant atoms were breaking down. How could he know that his spontaneous rays would start an avalanche to an atomic era? The masterly search of Marie and Pierre Curie for a new radioactive element radium was needed to illuminate the significance of "Becquerel rays."

RADIUM—A NEW
RADIOACTIVE ELEMENT

The story of Marie Curie has been often told in books, films, and articles. Few details are needed here. It is the story of the patience, devotion, and skill of a great scientist.

Marie Sklodowska Curie (1867–1934) was born in the then Russian Poland. Her father, a physics teacher in Warsaw, encouraged the talented young Marie in her early study of physics and chemistry. In 1891 Marie finally was able to realize her dream of going to Paris for study, research, and teaching. In spite of severe poverty, she obtained preliminary degrees in physics and mathematics at the Sorbonne. There she met Pierre Curie, a highly gifted young physicist, whom she married in 1895 to form the most famous man-and-wife team in the history of science—almost equaled by the present French team of Joliet-Curie (Irene Curie, daughter of Marie and Pierre).

Marie and Pierre were fascinated by Becquerel's discovery of what Marie later named radioactivity. Could it be that spontaneous rays were not unique for uranium but were characteristic of other elements, too? Implications were tremendous. The very nature of matter was involved, atoms and all.

After the birth of their daughter Irene in 1897, Marie was ready to work for a doctoral thesis. Not much was being done with Becquerel's discovery of a year before. At the moment, Roentgen's X rays were more

M. and Mme. Curie experimenting with radium. (After a drawing by André Castigne, 1903. The Bettmann Archive, Inc.)

alluring to others. But Marie preferred to explore the nature and origin of Becquerel's spontaneous rays.

The first job Madame Curie set for herself was to measure the extent to which uranium rays ionize the air, that is, make the air a conductor of electricity. Precise measurements were obtained by a highly sensitive electrometer devised by Pierre and his brother Jacques. Within a few weeks, Marie found that nothing affected the "ionization power" of Becquerel rays except the amount of uranium in the samples she used. What was combined with the uranium or the physical conditions of temperature, light, pressure, or anything else just did not matter. In working with uranium salts in air, Madame Curie came to the same conclusion as Becquerel did with photographic plates.

So much for uranium. The question now was this: Do other substances have spontaneous rays? Madame Curie then examined all known chemical elements for radioactivity. Only compounds of thorium, another very heavy element, emitted spontaneous rays. The intensity of radiation was comparable to that of uranium.

Satisfied that only two known elements were radioactive, Madame Curie decided to look for unknown radioactive elements. There was room in Mendeléyev's periodic table for such. She now tried every sample of uranium ore she could obtain. Uranium ores contain other compounds besides uranium salts. Radioactivity from uranium ores could also be due to some unknown element. Excitingly enough, she soon found that pitchblende, a uranium ore from Bohemia, gave off rays with four times the strength of pure uranium. She tried again and again. The results were always the same: The intensity of radiation from pitchblende was much too high to be due to just uranium and thorium. Excitedly she told Pierre: The cause of the extra radioactivity "cannot be a known element because those have already been examined; it must be a new element." Pierre so much shared his wife's enthusiasm that he dropped his own research and joined her in a search for a new radioactive element.

It is one thing to predict radium, a highly radioactive new element, and another to find it. The Curies believed that the task "would be done in several weeks or months." The pair thought that the new element would comprise as much as 1 percent of the pitchblende. They had no idea there was only one part of radium salt to every 2 million parts of ore. And they had no idea of the truly herculean task they faced in obtaining $\frac{1}{300}$th of an ounce of radium crystals from over a ton of ore. It was like going through a huge haystack, straw by straw, to find a needle that was there, far more slender than expected. The search for an isolation of radium salts by the Curies lasted 4 years. And then 7 more years passed before the pure radium was separated from the salts. Once the Curies started, there was no stopping, even though they operated under the worst of conditions, without money or help. Their laboratory was a ramshackle shed with a leaky roof that did not spare them from raindrops or icy weather. To escape dangerous fumes, huge cauldrons often had to be moved into an adjoining courtyard. And with two children to provide for, extra hours had to be spent in tutoring outside of regular teaching and preparations. With much talent, resourcefulness, and confidence in final success, the Curies persevered. Here and there were bright spots, of course, such as the donation by the Austrian government of a ton of needed pitchblende.

Early in the endless boiling, filtering, and crystallizing of materials, a new element, polonium, 300 times more radioactive than uranium, was found. The Curies had removed the uranium salts from the ore and separated various remaining components of pitchblende chemically in order to test each of them for radioactivity. As in the case of detectives in a mystery story, by successive eliminations, they narrowed down the radioactivity to even smaller portions of material. As nonradioactive parts were cast aside, the radioactivity in the remaining material became ever more concentrated. And so on it went until there were only two different radioactive fractions of pitchblende. This meant the existence of two new radioactive elements, not one. In the *Proceedings of the French Academy of Science*, July 1898, a report from the Curies includes the following words:

We believe the substance we have extracted from pitchblende contains a metal not yet observed, related to bismuth by its analytical properties. If the existence of this new metal is confirmed, we propose to call it *polonium* from the name of the original country of one of us.

Polonium was soon "confirmed." But a much more powerfully radioactive element also needed to be run down. The more powerful turned out to be much more difficult because its relative quantity was so very minute. The problem was to isolate enough of the second radioactive element to obtain an atomic weight and other specific traits. Otherwise, all that existed was a hypothesis for a new element without adequate evidence. It was at this point that the Curies turned to the Austrian government for a ton of pitchblende. About the difficult years of effort in this phase of the work, Madame Curie wrote:

I came to treat as many as twenty kilograms of matter at a time, which had the effect of filling the shed with great jars full of precipitates and liquids. It was killing work to carry the receivers, to pour off the liquids and to stir, for hours at a stretch, the boiling matter in a smelting basin.

Eve Curie wrote about her mother in the biography *Madame Curie*:

With her terrible patience, she was able to be every day for four years a physicist, a chemist, a specialized worker, and a laboring man all at once. Thanks to her brain and muscle, the old tables in the shed held more and more concentrated products—products more and more rich in radium. Mme. Curie was approaching the end: ... She was now at the stage of purification and of the fractional crystallization of strongly radioactive solutions. But the poverty of her haphazard equipment hindered her work more than ever . . . .

Then finally one night, there it was:

And in the somber shed where in the absence of cupboard, the precious particles in their tiny glass receivers were placed on tables or on shelves nailed to the wall, their phosphorescent bluish outlines gleamed suspended in the night . . . [like] glowworms.

Madame and Pierre Curie, after 4 years, had prepared $\frac{1}{30}$th of an ounce of pure radium salt from over a ton of pitchblende! The atomic weight of the highly radioactive substance was 226. Needless to say, Madame Curie passed the oral examination of her dissertation. She knew far more about radioactivity than her three examiners—in fact, more than anyone in the world at the time except her husband, Pierre.

The new radioactive element, radium, was 2 million times more active than uranium. One ounce of radium had an energy equivalent of heat from 10 tons of coal. Radium was self-illuminous as well as heat emitting. Its rays ionized air, penetrated solids, and damaged living things. Radium healed surface cancers, killed microbes, and made other things (dust, air, clothes) radioactive, too.

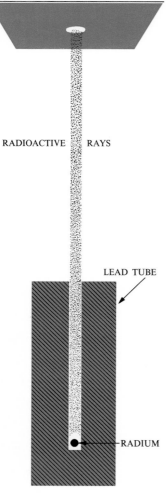

ZINC SULFIDE PLATE

RADIOACTIVE RAYS

LEAD TUBE

RADIUM

A

21–8 Alpha (α), beta (β), and gamma (γ) rays. A radioactive beam is separated into three kinds of rays by electrical plates. Alpha rays are deflected toward the negative plate; beta rays, toward the positive plate. Gamma rays are undeflected.

From their work, the Curies theorized that the origin of spontaneous rays is atomic disintegration. Atoms of uranium, thorium, radium, and polonium—all elements of high atomic weight—break down into other atoms and in the process emit the rays. As Pierre expressed it, "Here we have a veritable theory of the transmutation of simple bodies, but not as the alchemists understood it. Inorganic matter must have evolved necessarily through the ages, and followed immutable laws." Through prodigious experimental detail, the Curies gained insight into the depths and development of atoms. The signals accidentally discovered by Becquerel had begun to be decoded. Atoms do not live up to their name, "indivisibility"; they break down. Radioactivity was here to stay.

In the same year, 1903, that Madame Curie received her doctorate in physical science, she and Pierre obtained the Davy Medal in England and the Nobel prize in Sweden. A long list of international honors began. After Pierre's tragic death in a traffic accident in 1906, the Sorbonne appointed Marie, the first woman professor in its long history, to take her husband's place. But the French Academy of Science, by one vote, missed admitting her as its first woman member. Social biases are overcome as slowly among scientists and professionals as elsewhere.

Seven years after isolating radium chloride, Madame Curie obtained pure radium, shiny "white globules" that tarnished in air. This achievement resulted in a second Nobel prize in 1913. She devoted the remainder of her life to factory production and worldwide distribution of radium for medical purposes. Like her husband earlier, she refused personal patents or money for her discoveries.

Einstein, who knew Marie Curie well, said, "Marie is, of all celebrated beings, the only one whom fame has not corrupted." Occasionally there are such incorruptible individuals. Einstein was another, and Albert Schweitzer, a third. Unfortunately, the great woman and scientist died in 1934 from gradual radium poisoning after considerable illness from it.

ALPHA, BETA, AND GAMMA RAYS

First, cathode rays and positive rays; then X rays and uranium rays. And now radioactive rays from thorium, polonium, and radium. Rays were exciting the scientific world. Here were many clues about the interior of matter: positive charges and negative charges, particles and waves, mass and energy. What new information could radioactive rays add? Do atoms break down into simpler atoms? The British physicist Ernest Rutherford (1871–1937) at the turn of the century decided to find out and started down his road to fame. Figure 21–8 illustrates a noted experiment of this star student of J. J. Thomson. A few grains of radium (or other radioactive source) are at the bottom of a long lead tube. Radioactive rays leave the other end of the tube in a narrow, straight beam to show a glowing spot on a zinc sulfide plate (Fig. 21–8A). A pair of oppositely charged plates is placed parallel to the plane of the beam (Fig. 21–8B). At once, three glowing spots appear. One beam becomes three. The original spot, now less bright, represents a ray not deflected by the magnet. That ray carries no charge. The two new spots are from the rays deflected by the magnet. These rays carry charges. The new spot close to the original one, by its direction, indicates a ray with positively charged particles called *alpha* by Rutherford. Since the deflection is small, the particles are relatively heavy. The third spot is from a ray deflected much further than the second spot and in an opposite direction. The third ray, called *beta* by Rutherford, therefore consists of negatively charged particles much lighter than alpha. Rutherford called the central undeflected ray *gamma*. Alpha (α), beta (β), and gamma (γ) are the Greek letters for *a, b,* and *c.*

Rutherford found that the three rays have different penetrating power. Alpha rays penetrate gold or silver foil 0.001 inch thick, but they are stopped by a sheet of paper or an inch of air. Beta rays penetrate a book or 40 feet of air, but they are stopped by sheet aluminum ⅛ inch thick. It takes a lead plate ½ inch thick to stop gamma rays. Gamma rays turned out to be high-frequency X rays, that is, electromagnetic waves just beyond X rays in the electromagnetic spectrum (Fig. 18–12). All electromagnetic waves travel at the speed of light. Beta particles were found to be identical to electrons in cathode ray tubes by J. J. Thomson. They are emitted at over 160,000 miles per second, almost the speed of light; it is little wonder that beta rays are so penetrating! Alpha particles turned out to be ions of the rare gas helium, the second lightest element, expelled at 10,000 miles per second. Rutherford trapped some alpha particles and amazed his colleagues by showing that the particles were helium atoms with a double positive charge. And so spontaneously bursting out at great speeds from radium and other radioactive elements are helium ions, electrons, and electromagnetic waves!

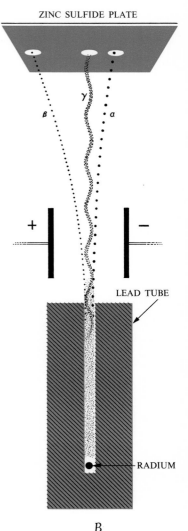

THEORY OF ATOMIC DISINTEGRATION

But something is left behind. Rutherford found a new radioactive gas, radon, remaining with the radium. Radium has an approximate atomic weight of 226; radon, 222; and helium, 4. Notice the balance of atomic weights:

radium $\longrightarrow$ radon + helium
226   =   222 +   4.

Could it be that radium atoms shoot out helium ions as chunks of themselves, and in the process, change into radon atoms? To Rutherford and a brilliant young collaborator, Frederick Soddy (1877–1956), the answer was yes: "The disintegration of the atom and the expulsion of a . . . charged particle leaves behind a new system lighter than before and possessing physical and chemical properties quite different from those of the original parent element." These two British scientists believed they had sufficient experimental evidence for a theory of atomic disintegration. By this time it was also known that polonium, radium, radon, lead, helium, and other elements are always found with uranium minerals. Uranium had the heaviest atoms of all. Rutherford and Soddy, in their theory of atomic disintegration, were confident that uranium atoms are ancestors of a family of naturally radioactive elements. Uranium atoms disintegrated into lighter atoms, which disintegrated into still lighter atoms, and so on in a long series of changes that included radium. When disintegrating, atoms lost either helium ions or electrons and gamma rays. At the end of the line was stable, nonradioactive lead and an accumulation of helium. More details of families of natural radioactivity were soon acquired. Meanwhile, here were the clues to transmutation, the alchemical dream. Nature had been quietly transmuting elements as alchemists feverishly and futilely fired their flames. By going directly to the book of nature, men soon symbolically and literally transmuted mercury into gold. To what avail depends on the values of men.

CHAPTER REVIEW

1. How do each of the following experimental observations suggest that atoms break down and that matter is basically electrical in nature? (a) In the electrolysis of water, hydrogen bubbles always form at the cathode (negative electrode), and oxygen, at the anode (positive electrode). (b) Salt in water conducts a current; dry salt does not. (c) If a metal ore is placed at the anode of an electrolytic cell, pure metal is obtained at the cathode. (d) A paddle wheel within a high-vacuum tube moves away from the negative terminal. (e) A negative electric plate deflects cathode rays away from the plate. (f) Argon in a vacuum tube has a glow different from that of neon. (g) Zinc sulfide powder glows within an operating high-vacuum tube. (h) "Canal" rays stream through holes in the cathode of a Crookes tube. (i) A positive electric plate deflects canal rays away from itself. (j) Metal targets in cathode ray tubes emit X rays. (k) A uranium sample emits rays that "photograph" themselves. (l) Radium and other elements also emit radioactive rays. (m) Radioactive rays consist of positive helium ions, electrons, and electromagnetic waves. (n) Light falling upon certain metals causes electrical currents to flow from them.

2. What is an ion? Illustrate.

3. (a) Show how the ion theory explains the breakdown of table salt

in water into sodium and chlorine ions. (Use a chemical equation.) (b) What is added or subtracted from the atoms in the salt molecule to make them ions? (c) Could atoms be indivisible if something is subtracted from them?

4. Relate the "valence," or chemical combining force, of sodium to its charge as an ion. Do the same for chlorine.

5. Explain the valence of hydrogen and oxygen atoms for each other in water molecules in terms of electrical charge.

6. Explain the valence of carbon and oxygen in CO_2 in terms of electrical charge.

7. (a) What is the evidence that cathode rays consist of electrons, or invisible particles that have a minute mass and a negative charge? (b) What is the evidence that matter spontaneously emits electrons as rays?

8. What does the e/m of an electron mean? Why was this ratio highly significant when determined by J. J. Thomson? How could Thomson determine the ratio of the charge to the mass of a minute invisible particle?

9. How did Millikan determine the charge e of electrons?

10. Why do we believe that all electrons have the same charge?

11. (a) How are positive rays formed in cathode ray tubes? (b) How was it determined that these rays are composed of positive ions heavier than electrons and oppositely charged to them? (c) Support the conclusion that these ions originate from positive parts of gas atoms within the cathode ray tubes.

12. (a) Describe the discovery of X rays by Roentgen. (b) Why was this accidental discovery very significant for the understanding of matter as well as for medical practice?

13. Describe Becquerel's accidental discovery of uranium's "spontaneous rays." Why were these rays even more promising for insights about matter than X rays? Are X rays "spontaneous" rays? Explain.

14. What is meant by the statement that radium is a radioactive element? Is uranium a naturally radioactive element? Do X rays ordinarily denote radioactivity?

15. Describe the experimental search of Marie and Pierre Curie for radioactive elements. Was the cause worth the complete personal sacrifice and devotion of the Curies?

16. What are alpha, beta, and gamma rays? What is the evidence that alpha, beta, and gamma rays are charged particles or electromagnetic waves emitted by matter in natural disintegration?

17. State Rutherford and Soddy's theory of atomic disintegration. Relate this to the Curies' discovery of radium and Rutherford's discovery of alpha, beta, and gamma rays.

18. Illustrate Pasteur's words "Chance favors the prepared mind" with materials in this chapter.

PROBLEMS

1. If the e/m ratio of an electron is 1.76×10^{-8} coulombs per gram and the charge of an electron is 1.6×10^{-19} coulombs, what is the mass of an electron?

2. An electron has never been directly seen. Why do we believe it exists? How can we give it characteristics?

3. Differentiate among the following rays emitted by matter: cathode rays, canal rays, X rays, alpha rays, beta rays, gamma rays, and light rays.

4. Why do we believe that light, X rays, and gamma rays are of the same nature?

5. Distinguish among light, X rays, and gamma rays.

6. How are alpha, beta, and gamma rays separated from one another? Why was the first separation of these rays scientifically significant?

7. Identify alpha, beta, and gamma rays as indicated below:

RAY	SYMBOL	MASS	CHARGE	VELOCITY	GENERAL IDENTITY
Alpha					
Beta					
Gamma					

8. What differences exist between an electron and a photon?

9. Which assumptions of Dalton's atomic theory were seriously challenged by the discovery of the "spontaneous" rays of uranium and radium? Why?

SUGGESTIONS FOR FURTHER READING

Hecht, Selig, *Explaining the Atom,* Viking paperback, New York, 1954, Ch. 2.

Eidinoff, Maxwell Leigh, and Hyman Ruchlis, *Atomics for the Millions,* McGraw-Hill, New York, 1947, Ch. 6.

Feinberg, Joseph G., *Story of Atomic Theory and Atomic Energy,* Dover paperback, New York, 1960, Chs. 7–9.

Curie, Eve, *Madame Curie,* Garden City Publishing, Garden City, N.Y., 1943.

Jaffe, Bernard, *Crucibles: The Story of Chemistry,* Premier paperback, New York, 1960, Chs. 10–11.

Andrade, Edward N. da C., *Rutherford and the Nature of the Atom,* Anchor paperback, Garden City, N.Y., 1964, Chs. 1–4.

22 Special Theory of Relativity

Space by itself and time by itself are doomed to fade away into mere shadows and only a kind of union of the two retains self-independence.

HERMAN MINKOWSKI, 1908

In the early 20th century, excitement and expectation ran high on a number of scientific fronts. Not only were Dalton atoms breaking down and energy becoming corpuscular again, but Newtonian space and time were cracking, too. And strangely enough, in the emerging view, atoms, energy, space, and time lost their independent character. They seemed inseparably intertwined. What do space and time have to do with matter and energy?

ABSOLUTE SPACE AND TIME

Newtonian space was a space of common sense. Like a huge container, it housed all things. Absolute, it existed independently of events. Newton wrote, "Absolute space, in its own nature, without regard to anything external, remains always similar and immovable." Time was absolute, too. "Absolute, true, and mathematical time, of itself and from its own nature, flows equably and without relation to anything external, and by another name is called duration." Time relentlessly rolls on. Robert Burns had

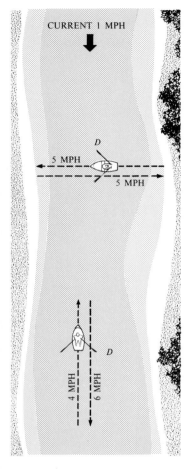

22—1 A rower can move faster across a stream than he can the same distance upstream and back.

the idea: "Nae man can tether time or tide." Or, as Chaucer expressed it,

For though we sleep or wake, or roam or ride,
Ay flees the time, it will no man abide.

If space and time were the setting for all things, they had a commonness, a likeness for everybody. Here, there, and everywhere a second was always a second, a mile always a mile. Space and time were also continuous. Space was a three-dimensional succession of points; and time, a separate one-dimensional succession of instants. Actually, no gaps existed in the continuity of points or instants. And there were no first or last points in space or time. The series of points was mathematically infinite. Space was reversible in direction; it extended right or left, up or down, backward or forward. Time, however, was not reversible. It flowed only one way: forward.

Newton, like Greco-Roman thinkers of old, recognized a universe of motion. Space and time were absolute frameworks in which the motion of all things could be measured. Standard metersticks and clocks guaranteed measurements the same for everybody.

Newtonian mechanics based upon absolute space and time both did very well for over 200 years. Modern technology sprang from it. For all immediate practical purposes, the earth could be treated as stationary, with all objects at rest or in motion upon it. Of course, Huygens's wave theory of light required an unseen, weightless ether as a medium in space for propagation of light waves. But when a fixed ether was necessary also for Faraday's fields and Maxwell's electromagnetic waves, the ether too seemed firmly set in Newton's mechanical universe.

At the end of the last century, scientific progress seemed a matter of improved techniques, a matter of more precision of measurement. Scope, structure, and standards of operation seemed fully achieved. A. A. Michelson expressed typical Newtonian confidence when in 1899 he said, "The more important fundamental laws and facts of physical science have all been discovered, and these are now so firmly established that the possibility of ever being supplanted in consequence of new discoveries is exceedingly remote . . . . Our future discoveries must be looked for in the sixth place of decimals." Little did Michelson realize that an experiment of his own, 18 years before, was a delayed time (and space) bomb soon to rock the physical sciences at their foundations!

THE MICHELSON-MORLEY DILEMMA

In 1881, A. A. Michelson and E. W. Morley tried to "prove" that an ether exists by means of an ingenious device called an interferometer.

A man can row across a river and back sooner than he can row the same distance D upstream and downstream (Fig. 22–1). Suppose the current is 1 mph and the oarsman can race at 5 mph in still water. Upstream, he therefore travels at 4 mph, and downstream, at 6 mph. At first glance, the loss of velocity against the stream seems to be balanced by the gain downstream for an average of $(4 + 6)/2$, or 5 mph. The average is incorrect. Actually, the boat spends *more time* traveling half the distance *at the lower speed* (4 mph) than traveling the other half at 6 mph. His average speed, therefore, will be somewhat less than 5 mph (4.8 mph). Across the current, however, the average speed would come closer to 5 mph (4.9) mph. The boat moves across the current and back faster than upstream and downstream.

In the interferometer, Michelson and Morley substituted a light beam for a boat and an ether "stream" for a water current. If the earth moves in an ether, there would be a relative ether "stream" opposite and equal to the earth's motion. By analogy, a relative wind is felt on a hand stretched out of a moving car even in otherwise still air. From the earth's revolution alone, there should be an ether current of 19 mi/sec. A beam of light is split in the interferometer, and each section sent at right angles through a system of mirrors (Fig. 22–2). The split beams travel equal distances and are reflected back to the same telescope. A beam in the direction of the earth's motion would first move against the ether "current" and then with it. The other beam would be across the ether "current." The analogy is complete. The beam across the ether should complete the round trip before the other. As the two beams are no longer in phase, a changing pattern of light should be observed at the eclipse. The apparatus was sensitive enough to detect a difference of only 2 mi/sec in the speed of the two beams.

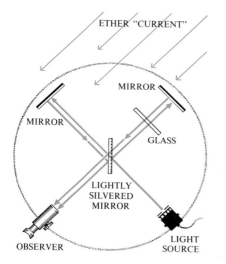

22–2 The Michelson-Morley experiment. Light travels at the same speed whether across an ether stream or upstream and back.

← 19 MI/SEC

19 MI/SEC→

PASSES EARTH AT 186,000 MI/SEC

22–3   The absolute speed of light. Whether the earth moves toward or away from a star, light from the star has a speed of 186,000 mi/sec with respect to the earth.

Michelson and Morley repeated their experiment many times at different angles of rotation and at various times of the day and year. The expected result did *not* occur; the light intensity in the telescope did *not* change. This meant that the velocity of the light beams remained the same regardless of directions. No ether "stream" effects existed. Whether the earth moved toward or away from a star, light from the star would still have a speed of 186,000 mi/sec* with respect to the earth. Suppose car *A* at 80 mph speeds past Car *B* moving at 50 mph on a freeway. At constant velocities the two cars would be either 30 or 130 miles apart in an hour, depending upon whether the cars move in the same or opposite directions. In the case of a light ray passing the earth, whether the earth moves with the ray or against it, the ray is 186,000 miles away at the end of a second (Fig. 22–3). Velocities just did not seem to add up. The Michelson-Morley results violated the principle of addition of velocities at the heart of mechanics. The dilemma was there. What was to be done?

UNTYING THE ETHER KNOT

The ether at the center of the Michelson-Morley dilemma had not been detected. Possible solutions were that (1) both the earth and the ether were stationary, (2) the ether moves with the earth, (3) the earth partially "drags" the ether, (4) the apparatus shrinks in the direction of motion, or (5) ether does not exist.

Established ideas are not easily discarded. The ether was a basic assumption of the mechanical view; to give up the ether was to weaken that view. A stationary earth could save the ether. But nobody cared to become Ptolemaic again. To say that the entire ether moved with the earth was also earth-centered and indefensible. The outermost reaches of the ether would have to move preposterously fast to rotate daily with the earth.

An ether drag concept of Fresnel seemed more feasible. Perhaps the moving earth dragged some ether in its wake much like a ship drags water.

*186,380 mi/sec is a closer approximation than 186,000 mi/sec, but for the purposes of this text, the latter is close enough.

In ether drag, light from a given star would be carried with the ether and could come in from the same direction at all points in the earth's orbit. But unfortunately, back in 1728, the English astronomer James Bradley observed that the direction of starlight *does* vary with the earth's position in its orbit (Fig. 22–4) much as raindrops on the window of a moving vehicle. This *aberration of light* eliminated the ether drag hypothesis.

A more significant alternative to save the ether was the Fitzgerald-Lorentz contraction hypothesis. According to this hypothesis, advanced in 1893 by the Irish physicist George F. Fitzgerald, all objects are shortened in the direction of their motion in the ether. A ball of clay hurled to the ground flattens; why not moving objects opposed by ether? A light ray moving in an interferometer arm against the ether may very well be slowed down by the ether stream. But that light ray would have less far to go if the interferometer arm shrank. The contraction of the arm distance could balance out the lower velocity of the light ray, and both rays could be back at the telescope together. Fitzgerald even developed the following equation to find the necessary contraction of the inter-ferometer arm:

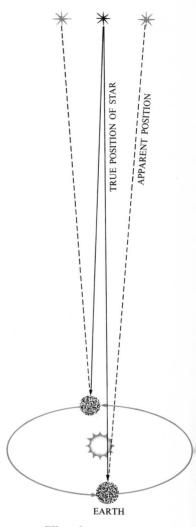

TRUE POSITION OF STAR

APPARENT POSITION

EARTH

$$l = l_o \sqrt{1 - \frac{v^2}{c^2}}, \qquad \text{Equation 22–1}$$

where l_o = the original length of the arm

l = the length when contracted

v = the apparatus velocity in the ether

c = the speed of light.

Note that if $v = 0$, the term $\sqrt{1 - v^2/c^2} = 1$, and $l = l_o$. No apparatus motion, no shrinkage. If $v > 0$, the factor $\sqrt{1 - v^2/c^2}$ is less than 1, and l is a fraction of l_o. Shrinkage of arm length to l depends upon apparatus velocity v in the ether.

Ingenious indeed! Epicycles reconciled Ptolemaic theory with the observed positions of the planets; now contraction of moving substances is suggested to reconcile classical mechanics with the Michelson-Morley results. But Fitzgerald could not specifically explain what causes objects to contract in an ether or why all substances—for example, steel, wood, glass, copper—would flatten equally. In 1895 the great Dutch physicist Hendrik Lorentz (1853–1928) came to Fitzgerald's rescue with an electrical theory of matter: Matter contains electric charges that exert strong forces on each other, he said. The charges are accompanied by electromagnetic fields. An object moving in the ether contracts because the charges and fields within the object interact with the ether stream. A new electrical view of matter was assisting the mechanical view, but

22–4 The aberration of light. The apparent direction of light from a star varies with the direction of the earth's motion in its orbit much as do raindrops on the window of a moving car.

Lorentz's specific field-ether interaction could not be verified. The Lorentz-Fitzgerald contraction hypothesis was on uncertain grounds, but it achieved new meaning with Einstein's relativity.

Einstein with one stroke cut the ether knot; he discarded the ether. All velocities are relative. Nobody knows the absolute velocity of anything. The fixed framework of an assumed ether cannot be detected; the ether is meaningless and unnecessary. Einstein was aware that the mechanical view had run into a number of serious contradictions. Electromagnetic forces between objects worked at right angles rather than in a line of attraction or repulsion (Chapter 16, left-hand rule). Mercury's orbit showed a strange rotation of about 43″ of arc per century (Fig. 22–5) not explainable by Newton's gravitation. And in 1901, W. Kaufmann and J. J. Thomson found that electrons increase in mass the faster they move. In Newtonian mechanics, mass was a fundamental constant of the universe. How could mass increase? What was wrong? To Einstein, classical mechanics had reached its limits. The ether dilemma was only one item in the decline of the mechanical view. The ether was an invention of the mechanical view to transmit electromagnetic waves that Einstein's photon theory (Chapter 18) did not need. In abandoning the ether, Einstein rejected the mechanical view behind it and built a new relativity model of the universe.

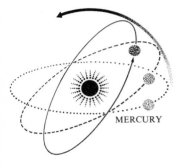

22–5   Rotation of Mercury's orbit around the sun. The orbit of the planet Mercury very slowly rotates in a rosette pattern around the sun at a speed of less than 1′ of arc per century.

BIOGRAPHICAL SKETCH OF EINSTEIN

Einstein was born in Ulm, Germany. He later became a citizen of Switzerland and the United States. Long before Hitler, he remarked with gentle irony: "If my [relativity] theory is proved correct, Germany will hail me as a great German, and the French will hail me as a citizen of the world. If it is proved false, the French will call me a German, and the Germans will call me a Jew." Einstein's scientific ideas had tremendous impact, but the Nazis still labeled them racial.

Newton had his apple, moon, and early farm experiences. Einstein had his magnetic compass and geometry book. When he was 4 or 5 years old, Albert's father showed him a compass. The youngster was indelibly impressed. There was something consistent and alluring about the direction-pointing needle. The wonder led to the mysteries of magnetic fields. Eventually, Einstein successfully extended Maxwell's electromagnetic field equations to gravitation in a universe of four dimensions. But long before that, at 12 years of age, he became fascinated with Euclid's plane geometry for its "purity, lucidity, and certainty of thinking." The young Einstein, in responding to geometry, already was searching for order. Individuals tend to repeat the history of the race. In geometry, the boy Einstein had developed to the period of Greece. But gifted individuals

Albert Einstein in conference with J. Robert Oppenheimer. (The Bettmann Archive, Inc.)

come up to date and leap forward from there. Einstein's early interest in plane Euclidean space led to an unorthodox picture of a mildly curved, non-Euclidean universe (Chapter 25).

As a "gymnasium" (high school–junior college) student, Einstein was not the most promising. He showed no special interest or aptitude in class routines. He was off on imaginative tangents of his own. His "Autobiographical Notes" emphasizes that he "soon learned to ferret out that which was able to lead to fundamentals, and to turn aside from everything else, from the multitude of things which clutter up the mind, and direct it from the essential." Reacting against unrelieved rote routines and deadening details, Einstein continues, "It is, in fact, nothing short of a miracle that the modern methods of instruction have not yet entirely strangled the holy curiosity of inquiry; for this delicate little plant, aside from stimulation, stands mainly in need of freedom; without this the plant goes to wreck and ruin without fail." It was probably during a class reverie that he asked himself whether a student running at the speed of light could see himself in a mirror at arm's length in front of him. This little student-and-mirror barb later flowered into the special theory of relativity. The Michelson-Morley results fell upon prepared and fertile soil. Respect for facts need not mean "cluttering the mind with detail," but rather searching for order through facts.

Einstein obtained a degree in experimental physics at Zurich Polytechnic Institute in 1900 with no special honors. At the Institute he acquired considerable laboratory experience and spent a great deal of time reading current physical theory. In 1902 he became a Swiss patent office examiner, and in 1905 he electrified the world with two papers, one on the special theory of relativity, and the other on the photon theory of light. A third paper that year on Brownian motion (Chapter 13) led to determination of the number of molecules in a given amount of substance. He also completed a doctoral dissertation based on improved technique in determining the size of molecules. He was then invited to lecture at Bern University. In 1909 he became an assistant professor at Zurich Polytechnic, in 1911 a full professor at the German University in Prague, and in 1913 professor of theoretical physics at the Kaiser Wilhelm Institute in Berlin, then one of the world's leading research centers. While there he published his general relativity theory (1916). In 1921 he received the Nobel prize in physics. Einstein was forced out of Nazi Germany and the Wilhelm Institute in 1933. At that time he accepted an invitation to join the Institute for Advanced Studies at Princeton, where he remained for the rest of his life.

Although he became famous, Einstein's personal life, dress, and manner were always exceptionally simple. As expressed in his autobiography, his "major interest disengaged itself to a far-reaching degree from the momentary and the merely personal, and turned toward the striving for a mental grasp of things." Striving for personal prestige and comfort was alien to him. Incorruptible, he was one of those profoundly simple men who create as they search for order.

His last great effort was a unified field theory in which he successfully reduced electromagnetic and gravitational fields to a single set of formulas. Time is still needed to see whether the universe will support that supreme field synthesis. Some time before he died on April 18, 1955, the huge Riverside Church in New York included a statue of him as the only living person among its famous collection of the world's greatest scholars.

SPECIAL THEORY OF RELATIVITY: ASSUMPTIONS

Every theory rests on assumptions. Einstein developed his special theory of relativity from the following three main assumptions.

1. *The velocities of all bodies are relative.* Newton had acknowledged this relativity principle. Let us say that two trains leave a station together at 40 mph. With respect to each other, the trains are not moving. Only by noticing other outside objects (trees, grass, houses) can the passengers be aware of any motion. And that motion, the 40 mph, is *relative* to these observed objects which themselves are moving. The earth bearing them is moving at an unknown absolute velocity. The earth revolves with a speed of 19 mi/sec *relative* to the sun, which revolves with a speed *relative* to the center of the Milky Way, which moves *relative* to other moving

galaxies moving *relative* to one another. There is no fixed framework in space. Absolute velocity is a meaningless concept.

Again, car *A* speeds at 80 mph relative to the earth. Car *A*, however, moves 20 mph relative to Car *B*, which is traveling at 60 mph in the same direction. But the earth also moves. The absolute velocity of the earth and, therefore, of the cars cannot be known unless a fixed ether can be found. But if an ether exists, it is undetectable, said Einstein, and absolute velocities are unknowable. The situation is circular. We had better forget the ether and absolute velocities.

2. *The speed of light is an absolute for all observers at constant velocities.* The velocities of material bodies are relative, but the speed of light is absolute. In Einstein's words, "The velocity of light in empty space always has its standard value, independent of the motion of the source or receiver of light." The speed of light would be measured as 186,000 mi/sec by an astronomer on earth as well as by one the ray overtakes on a spaceship moving 100,000 mi/sec away from the earth. The 100,000 mi/sec of the second observer just would not count. In this postulate, Einstein accepts the Michelson-Morley results as a fact of nature to be used as a starting point for a new system of ideas.

3. *Laws of nature are the same in all systems moving at constant velocity relative to one another.* This assumption expresses a basic confidence in a unity of nature. It is not just mechanical laws but *all* laws of nature that are the same for inertial systems—that is, for systems not changing velocities. Since absolute velocity is unknowable, the constant velocities of systems are expressed as "relative to one another."

All three assumptions involve observers in nonaccelerating, *inertial frames of reference.* The observers move at constant velocity, relative to one another. In his special theory of relativity (1905), Einstein confines himself to natural laws of inertial reference frames.* In his general theory of relativity (1915), Einstein extends his attention to *accelerating reference frames.*

THE RELATIVITY OF
SIMULTANEOUS EVENTS

For ages men assumed that *now* is now everywhere. We see Arcturus in the sky and record its position at this "instant." Actually, the light has traveled 38 years to reach us. Meanwhile, Arcturus has moved on and actually may no longer exist. An observer midway between us and Arcturus would have seen that star in the given position 19 years before we did. The same instant of Arcturus's given position is separated by 19 years for the two observers. *Now* is therefore not absolute, not the same everywhere. In assuming an absolute now, or simultaneity, in the universe,

---

*The earth may be considered an inertial system; its acceleration is negligible.

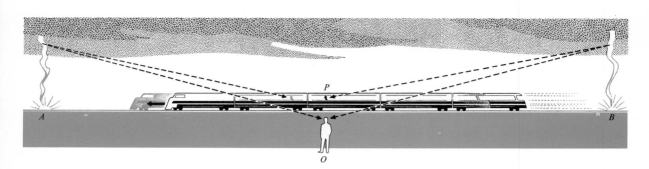

22–6 *Relativity of simul-*
taneous events. For observer
O, the lightning flashes at A
and B occur together. For
passenger P in the moving
train, flash A occurs before
flash B.

men had made no allowance for the speed of light. They had treated light as if it were infinite in speed, whether from Arcturus or anywhere. Einstein concluded that "Every reference body (or coordinate system) has its own particular time; unless we are told the reference body to which the statement of time refers, there is no meaning in a statement of the time of an event."

But there is a bigger problem than that of a different "now" at two different places. There is the problem of two events occurring together as seen from one place, and not together when seen from another place. Two things happening for us here *now* may not be happening together for someone elsewhere. Einstein posed this problem of simultaneity in the following thought experiment.

Two bolts of lightning strike a railroad track at points *A* and *B* (Fig. 22–6). The bolts are simultaneous to an observer *O* situated along the track exactly midway between points *A* and *B*. A fast train moves from *B* to *A* with a passenger *P* directly opposite observer *O* at the time of the flashes. In a mirror arrangement, *P* sees the flash at *A* slightly sooner than the flash at *B* because of his motion toward *A*. In fact, if the train were moving as fast as light, *P* would see only the flash at *A*. The light from the flash at *B* would not catch up to observer *P*. Flashes simultaneous to observer *O* would not be simultaneous to *P*.

Einstein's thought experiment led to his famous relativity principle of simultaneity that events occurring together for one person may not be together for another due to relative motion of the two observers. But if events occur together for one person and not for another, how could time be the same for both? If a lapse of time for one does not exist for the other, how could a second for one be a second for another?

RELATIVITY OF
SPACE AND TIME

The absolute velocity of light is a cornerstone of Einstein's system. No matter how fast an observer moves, he will always find that light travels 186,000 mi/sec with respect to him. The observer may be on earth or on a spaceship leaving the earth at 100,000 mi/sec; light still has a speed of 186,000 mi/sec with respect to him. It is just as if the extra 100,000 mi/sec velocity of the spaceship does not exist. How is this possible? Involved is a contradiction between an absolute speed of light and ordinary addition of velocities.

It was in facing this contradiction that Einstein threw out space and time as absolute entities. Since the observed absolute speed of light would not yield, the space and the time intervals that went to make up the light measurements must. If no matter how fast an observer moves, light always passes him by at 186,000 mi/sec, then perhaps a mile and a second as measured from a spaceship are not the same as they are on earth. Perhaps Newton was incorrect in his assumption that "the duration of an event is independent of the state of motion of the system of reference." Perhaps space and time measurements do depend upon the velocity of an observer. That is, a space or time measurement is a private measurement for a given observer. A value valid for one may not be for another. Determining the velocity of light in miles per second involves measurement of space and time as well as a problem of simultaneity. And simultaneity is relative. Where does all this lead? Clearly, Einstein was faced with the problem of how to correlate clocks and metersticks in one system to those in another. Confident of the possibility of such correlation, he expressed his basic postulate, "All laws of nature are the same for all uniformly moving systems." The Newtonian concept of relativity referred to *mechanical* laws being the same for all uniformly moving systems. To mechanical law, Einstein pointedly added all the other laws of nature, such as laws of light, electromagnetism, or heat. If there is no absolute framework of space or time for moving bodies, there is none for light or other radiation. Consequently, there is no detectable ether. Einstein was also indicating that in a universe where everything is in motion relative to observers also in motion, natural laws exist for correlating all measurements from one system of motion to that of another. Space and time, no longer fixed frameworks, became merely forms of perception or ways of measuring that give different results in different systems. The laws that Einstein sought were relationships between space, time, and other measurements from different systems moving uniformly relative to one another.

But how were these laws or relationships to be found? With space, time, and simultaneity varying from one moving system to another, how could observations of events in one moving system be specifically linked with observations of the same events in a differently moving system? Einstein's clue was the constant velocity of light that started the difficulty. That all observers regardless of motion obtain the same value for the speed of light was an empirical fact. The speed of light replaced space and time as an absolute. The constant c was the key to an orderly universe. If space and time varied from one system to another, the problem narrowed down to these measurements so varying that no matter how relatively fast or slow the observer was going, he always found light to pass him by at the same velocity, 186,000 mi/sec. Mile and second measurements must change accordingly. Unknown to an observer, his clocks must slow down as the velocity of his reference system increases, and his measuring rods must shrink in the direction of motion.

In a sense, Einstein was starting from a set answer ($c = c$ for all) at the back of the book and was working his way to unknown variables of space, time, or mass at the front of the book. In this way, Einstein hoped to link measurements varying from one reference frame to another. And if in the process, the answer at the back of the book became a postulate for a new conceptual model of special relativity, then remember that the new postulate was based upon facts of nature, the Michelson-Morley results.

RELATIVITY TRANSFORMATIONS

Einstein found what he wanted in the Fitzgerald-Lorentz transformation equation (Eq. 22–1), particularly in the contraction factor

$$\sqrt{1 - \frac{v^2}{c^2}}.$$

But he found it with v as the relative velocity between an object and an observer, and c as the constant speed of light with respect to the observer. That is, v the velocity of an object, and c the constant speed of light are with *respect to an observer and not to an undetectable fixed ether.*

By use of the above contraction factor, Einstein found that he could predict the shrinkage of an object's length, a slowing down of clocks, and an increase of an object's mass according to the relative velocity of an observer. Illustrations are in order.

Contraction of Length

Spaceship S returns to the earth at a velocity v of 161,000 mi/sec (Fig. 22–7). The velocity of S is, of course, relative to the earth. An observer in S finds that a light ray passes him at 186,000 mi/sec relative to himself. An earthly observer E finds that the same ray passes him at the same speed relative to himself. The 161,000 mi/sec speed of the spaceship back to the earth makes no difference. For the speed of the light ray to be the same in both places, miles and seconds in them are not the same. There must be a relative shrinkage of metersticks and slowing of clocks in one of the two places for the speed of light to come out the same for both.

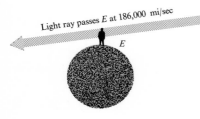

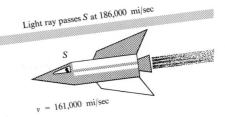

Light ray passes E at 186,000 mi/sec

E

Light ray passes S at 186,000 mi/sec

S

$v = 161,000$ mi/sec

Equation 22–2 is the transformation equation that predicts the appropriate shrinkage of *measuring* rods or objects in a frame of reference.

$$l = l_o \sqrt{1 - \frac{v^2}{c^2}},$$ Equation 22–2

where $l_o =$ the length of an object at rest to an observer

$l =$ the length of the object in relative motion to an observer

$v =$ the relative velocity between object and observer

$c =$ the speed of light.

22–7 A spaceship returns to the earth at 161,000 mi/sec. Regardless of this speed, observers E on earth and S in the spaceship each find that a light ray passes him at 186,000 mi/sec relative to himself.

Suppose observer S measures the length l_o of his spaceship and finds it to be 100 feet. What length l would an observer on earth obtain for the spaceship returning to earth at a velocity v of 161,000 mi/sec? With the speed of light c at 186,000 mi/sec:

$$l = l_o \sqrt{1 - \frac{v^2}{c^2}}$$

$$= 100 \sqrt{1 - \frac{(161,000)^2}{(186,000)^2}} = 100 \sqrt{1 - .75}$$

$$l = 50 \text{ ft.}$$

The spaceship is 100 feet long for the pilot and 50 feet long for observer E. The spaceship pilot is unaware of the contraction of S because his yardstick also shrank to one-half (as observed from the earth). Thus, we see two different measurements, l and l_o, of the length of the same object by observers in two different systems. But $\sqrt{1 - v^2/c^2}$, the relativity factor, permits correlation between the two systems regardless of relative speed. The universe is still one; laws of nature are universal.

Space contraction works both ways. Both observers S and E find that objects flatten in the other frame of reference. The space pilot finds the earth's diameter flattened in the direction of motion from 8,000 miles to

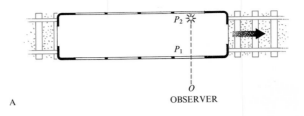

A   OBSERVER

4,000 miles. In Equation 22–2, l_o is the 8,000-mile diameter determined on earth, and l is the 4,000 miles from the spaceship. The ratio $l_o:l$ remains 2:1. The l_o always represents length of an object at rest with respect to an observer.

Contraction of an object is in the direction of its motion *only;* that is, its length. There is no contraction in the other two dimensions, width and height. They remain the same for all observers. That is, where w and w_o, h and h_o are the widths and heights of the spaceship as measured from the earth and spaceship, respectively:

$$w = w_o \qquad\qquad\qquad\qquad\qquad \text{Equation 22–3}$$
$$h = h_o. \qquad\qquad\qquad\qquad\qquad \text{Equation 22–4}$$

When the spaceship is back on earth, the length measurements by observers S and E are the same, 100 feet. With the spaceship velocity v now zero for observer E:

$$l = l_o \sqrt{1 - \frac{v^2}{c^2}} = l_o \sqrt{1 - \frac{0}{c^2}} = l_o\,(1) = 100 \text{ ft.}$$

The situation is now Newtonian and illustrates that when the relative velocity v between an observer and a thing observed is zero or small compared to the speed of light, the Newtonian and Einsteinian answers will be the same or close. Newtonian mechanics is a special case (low relative velocity) of Einstein's relativity.

Now suppose the spaceship could travel away from the earth with the speed of light. The relative velocity v between the spaceship and the earth would equal c. Therefore,

$$l = l_o \sqrt{1 - \frac{v^2}{c^2}} = 100 \sqrt{1 - \frac{c^2}{c^2}} = 100 \sqrt{1 - 1} = 100\,(0)$$
$$= 0.$$

As seen from the earth, the spaceship would have contracted to zero— an impossibility! That is, material objects may closely approach but never

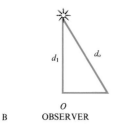

B   OBSERVER

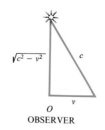

C   OBSERVER

reach the speed of light in a vacuum. Light has the top speed in the universe.

Slowing of Time

Time runs differently for observers moving at constant speed with respect to each other. How does this idea follow from Einstein's postulate that observers at different speeds obtain the same value in measuring the speed of light? In answer, Einstein provides the following thought experiment (Fig. 22–8A). Passenger P_2, riding across the car from passenger P_1, strikes a match the instant they are in line with observer O on the station platform. P_1 clocks the time t_1 for the light to cross the car to him. He also measures the distance d_1 that the light travels. Velocity equals distance d divided by time t. Therefore, for P_1 the velocity of light is $c_1 = d_1/t_1$.

Observer O uses his own watch also to measure the time t_o for the light to cross the car. He also independently determines distance d_o that the light traveled. For observer O, the velocity of light $c_o = d_o/t_o$. By Einstein's postulate, P_1 and observer O should obtain the same answer c for the speed of light. That is,

$$c_1 = c_o \qquad\qquad \text{Equation 22–5}$$

$$\frac{d_1}{t_1} = \frac{d_o}{t_o} .$$

But the train is moving. The distance d_o traveled by the light seen by observer O, therefore, forms a hypotenuse of a right triangle (Fig. 22–8B). The path of light d_1 observed by passenger 1, therefore, is an arm of the same right triangle and is shorter than the hypotenuse d_o seen by O. That is,

$$d_1 < d_o.$$

But the speed of light c is the same in any case. A longer path of light d_o should mean a longer time t_o noted by observer O. By Eq. 22–5 there

22–8 (A) Passengers P_2 and P_1 are in line with observer O when P_2 strikes a match. (B) Because the train is moving, the match light takes a path d_o for observer O, as compared to the path d_1 for passenger P_1. (C) If c is the speed of light on path d_o and v is the velocity of the train, the arm of the right triangle is $\sqrt{c^2-v^2}$. (The square of the hypotenuse of a right triangle equals the sum of the squares of the two sides.)

should be the same ratio between the time intervals noted by the two observers (t_1/t_o) as between distances (d_1/d_o). That is,

$$\frac{d_1}{d_o} = \frac{t_1}{t_o}.$$

Equation 22–6

By the Pythagorean theorem, the square of the hypotenuse of a right triangle equals the sum of the squares of the two sides. (Or, a side squared equals the hypotenuse squared less the other side squared.) The hypotenuse of the illustrated right triangle (Fig. 22–8C) is c, the base is the velocity of the train v, and the third side of the triangle is $\sqrt{c^2 - v^2}$. Therefore, by similar right triangles:

$$\frac{d_1}{d_o} = \sqrt{\frac{c^2 - v^2}{c}}$$

but

$$\frac{d_1}{d_o} = \frac{t_1}{t_o} \text{ (by Eq. 22–6).}$$

Therefore,

$$\frac{t_1}{t_o} = \sqrt{\frac{c^2 - v^2}{c}} = \sqrt{\frac{c^2 - v^2}{c^2}} = \sqrt{1 - \frac{v^2}{c^2}}$$

or

$$t = t_o \sqrt{1 - \frac{v^2}{c^2}},$$

Equation 22–7

where t_o = the time taken for an event *inside* an observer's frame of reference

t = the time taken for an event *outside* an observer's frame

v = the relative velocity of the two reference frames

c = the speed of light.

Equation 22–7 is the famous Lorentz time transformation equation as derived by the Pythagorean theorem. Clocks in different reference frames keep different time in accordance with the motion of the observer. Equation 22–7 links the different clocks together when the motion is uniform.

In further illustration, suppose that identical clocks on spaceship S and on earth are synchronized when together. When S moves away from the earth with a relative velocity v, observer E on earth and S on the spaceship find that the clocks in the two frames of reference do not keep time together. At a relative velocity of 161,000 mi/sec, E finds that S's clock runs half as fast as his. Show this by inserting the values for v

and c in Eq. 22–7 and solving for the ratio t/t_o. Each observer finds that the clock of the other slows down. Paradox indeed!

At a relative velocity of 93,000 mi/sec, each observer finds that the clock of the other runs about nine-tenths as fast as his. If the spaceship should reach the speed of light ($v = c$), time would stop. An upper limit in speed would be reached. At the other extreme, when the spaceship is at rest on earth and its velocity $v = 0$, its clock keeps together with that on earth. That is, Eq. 22–7 reduces to $t = t_o$. The situation is Newtonian; time is the same in both frames of reference.

Let us now add Chaucer's relativistic third line to his lines about time:

> For though we sleep or wake, or roam or ride,
> Ay flees the time, it will no man abide.
> It now depends on how fast we ride.

Relativistic indeed for the 14th century!

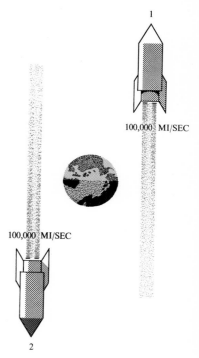

100,000 MI/SEC

100,000 MI/SEC

Adding Velocities in Relativity

Suppose two spaceships, 1 and 2, pass the earth in opposite directions at 100,000 mi/sec (Fig. 22–9). In accordance with Newtonian addition of velocities, the spaceships would have a velocity of 200,000 mi/sec relative to each other:

$$v_3 = v_1 + v_2 = 100{,}000 \text{ mi/sec} + 100{,}000 \text{ mi/sec} = 200{,}000 \text{ mi/sec.}$$

But that is impossible! By the special theory of relativity, no relative speed can exceed that of light, 186,000 mi/sec. The question is, how can the velocities of any two objects be added so as never to be more than the speed of light? The following equation is Einstein's answer:

$$v_3 = \frac{v_1 + v_2}{1 + \dfrac{v_1 v_2}{c^2}} \qquad \text{Equation 22–8}$$

where $v_3 =$ the relative velocity of two objects to each other

$\quad\quad v_1 =$ the relative velocity of one object to a third

$\quad\quad v_2 =$ the relative velocity of the second object to a third.

Let us add the 100,000 mi/sec velocities of spaceships 1 and 2 above by the theory of relativity. Applying Eq. 22–8:

$$v_3 = \frac{v_1 + v_2}{1 + \dfrac{v_1 v_2}{c^2}} = \frac{100{,}000 + 100{,}000}{1 + \dfrac{(100{,}000)\,(100{,}000)}{(186{,}000)^2}} = 155{,}000 \text{ mi/sec.}$$

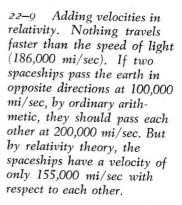

22–9   Adding velocities in relativity. Nothing travels faster than the speed of light (186,000 mi/sec). If two spaceships pass the earth in opposite directions at 100,000 mi/sec, by ordinary arithmetic, they should pass each other at 200,000 mi/sec. But by relativity theory, the spaceships have a velocity of only 155,000 mi/sec with respect to each other.

Although spaceships 1 and 2 pass each other in opposite directions at 100,000 mi/sec with respect to the earth, their velocity relative to each other is 155,000 mi/sec, not 200,000 mi/sec. And 155,000 mi/sec is lower than the speed of light.

Now suppose we take the extreme case and raise the speeds v_1 and v_2 of spaceships 1 and 2 each to the speed of light c. That is, $v_1 = c$ and $v_2 = c$. With Newtonian addition of velocities, $v_3 = v_1 + v_2 = c + c = 2c$. Spaceships 1 and 2 would travel at twice the speed of light relative to each other. Would the relativistic addition of velocities keep v_3 down to a top value of c?

$$v_3 = \frac{v_1 + v_2}{1 + \dfrac{v_1 v_2}{c^2}} = \frac{c + c}{1 + \dfrac{(c)(c)}{c^2}} = \frac{2c}{1 + 1} = c.$$

Although spaceships 1 and 2 are traveling in opposite directions at the speed of light relative to the earth, they are traveling only at the speed of light with respect to each other.

So much for high relative speeds. At low speeds the Newtonian addition of velocities closely approximates the Einsteinian. Suppose two cars zoom past each other at 100 mph relative to a tree. They flash by at 200 mph relative to each other whether by Newton or Einstein.

By Newton: $v_3 = v_1 + v_2 = 100$ mph $+ 100$ mph $= 200$ mph.

By Einstein: $v_3 = \dfrac{v_1 + v_2}{1 + \dfrac{v_1 v_2}{c^2}} = \dfrac{100 + 100}{1 + \dfrac{(100)(100)}{(186,000)^2}} = \dfrac{200}{1.0000003}$

$$v_3 = 200 \text{ mph}.$$

Once again we find that Newtonian principles are special cases of Einsteinian. Newton and Einstein merge for objects at relative speeds below one-tenth that of light. Under the ordinary speed of a train, plane, or rocket, the slowing down of a watch or shrinkage of a ruler is too minute to matter. It is when a relative speed begins to approach that of light that speed really counts. Einstein did not overthrow Newton. Newton's model has a place in the larger picture of relativity.

Mass Increases with Velocity

In 1901 W. Kaufmann and J. J. Thomson discovered that electrons increase in mass with speed. The fact was another challenge to Einstein. Newton's laws certainly did not provide for such changes in an object's mass. Weight is a gravitational force upon an object that changes with distance from the earth. But an object's mass is the "quantity of matter" within it, which supposedly does not change. If, however, an electron's mass *does* increase with speed, so would the mass of anything else. Is an object's mass, like its length, a measurement relative to its speed?

In answer, Einstein proposed that every object has a basic *rest mass* m_o when at rest relative to an observer. When moving, a body acquires extra mass $\triangle m$. A moving object at any time has a total mass m equal to its rest mass m_o plus an extra mass $\triangle m$ from its motion. That is,

$$m = m_o + \triangle m. \hspace{3cm} \text{Equation 22–9}$$

The faster an object moves relative to an observer, the more extra mass $\triangle m$ it acquires and the more total mass m it has.

But just how much does velocity change the mass of an object? Einstein found that the same relativity factor applied to mass as to length or time, only inversely—that is, in the form $1/\sqrt{1 - v^2/c^2}$. If m_o is the rest mass of an object, its total mass m measured when moving at speed v relative to an observer is

$$m = \frac{m_o}{\sqrt{1 - \dfrac{v^2}{c^2}}}. \hspace{3cm} \text{Equation 22–10}$$

From Eq. 22–9, a given object increases in mass with speed relative to a given observer. From the same equation, two or more observers at different speeds obtain different values for the total mass m of that object. Similar differences in measured lengths and travel times of objects for various observers were noticed in Eqs. 22–2 and 22–7. To illustrate, spaceship S has a 1,000-ton rest mass (m_o). S moves away from the earth at 161,000 mi/sec and passes spaceship X at a relative speed of 93,000 mi/sec. By Eq. 22–10, spaceship S at these relative speeds has a mass of 2,000 tons as measured from the earth, and 1,200 tons as determined from spaceship X.

From earth:

$$m = \frac{m_o}{\sqrt{1 - \dfrac{v^2}{c^2}}}$$

$$= \frac{1,000}{\sqrt{1 - \dfrac{161,000^2}{186,000^2}}} = \frac{1,000}{.5}$$

$$m = 2,000 \text{ tons.}$$

From spaceship X:

$$m = \frac{m_o}{\sqrt{1 - \frac{v^2}{c^2}}}$$

$$= \frac{1,000}{\sqrt{1 - \frac{93,000^2}{186,000^2}}} = \frac{1,000}{.833}$$

$$m = 1,200 \text{ tons.}$$

If spaceship S could leave the earth with the speed of light c, its mass would be infinite:

$$m = \frac{m_o}{\sqrt{1 - \frac{v^2}{c^2}}} = \frac{1,000}{\sqrt{1 - \frac{c^2}{c^2}}} = \frac{1,000}{\sqrt{1 - 1}} = \frac{1,000}{0} = \infty .$$

Again, the speed of light is seen as a top speed in the universe. No amount of accelerating force could make an infinite mass move faster. Electrons, however, have been sent swirling at over 0.999999999 the speed of light c, to attain over 40,000 times their mass at rest. For objects at low speeds, the increase in mass is too small to be detected. Masses may then be treated as constant, and Newton's laws applied.

Equivalence of Energy and Mass: $E = mc^2$

But Einstein did not drop relativity of mass at this point. From the idea that objects increase in mass as they go faster, he drew the amazing conclusion that matter and energy are equivalent. After all, mass m did not increase alone; kinetic energy ($\frac{1}{2}mv^2$) also increased with velocity v. Perhaps, said Einstein, matter and energy are different aspects of the same thing. Matter could be a concentrated form of energy. Energy has been distinguished from matter by having no apparent weight. Perhaps energy in free form as light, heat, or kinetic energy has weight, but not enough for detection. Matter as concentrated energy would show weight. In that case, said Einstein, matter has fantastic amounts of concealed energy to be unlocked. Fantastic and yet shockingly real in today's atomic era! Science can be stranger than fiction.

Einstein equated free energy with matter through one of the most significant equations in history:

$$E = mc^2, \qquad \text{Equation 22--11}$$

where E = the free energy in ergs

m = the mass in grams

c^2 = the speed of light squared ($9 \times 10^{20} \text{cm}^2/\text{sec}^2$).

A small amount of mass m as concentrated energy must be multiplied by c^2 to obtain an equivalent in unbound, or free, energy E. The amount of free energy is tremendous because of the c^2.

An iron ball should weigh more when red hot than when cool. Energy has mass (and mass, energy). The heat energy should give the ball extra mass $\triangle m$. Radiation is energy, and should have mass. The sun, stars, or a heated iron ball should lose mass as they radiate.

A 1-pound lump of coal completely converted into free energy would equal all the electric power output in the United States for a month. Conversely, the amount of heat needed to change 30,000 tons of water into steam would weigh only one-thirtieth of an ounce. Very seldom, however, is a total mass m completely converted into its total energy E. The sun, stars, or H bombs lose small portions of mass $\triangle m$ as radiation $\triangle E$. In such cases,

$$\triangle E = \triangle mc^2.$$
Equation 22–12

Equation 22–11 represents total matter-energy transformations, and Eq. 22–12, partial matter-energy transformations.

The law of conservation of energy claims that the total energy of the universe is constant, that energy can be neither created nor destroyed. Does not Einstein's $E = mc^2$ contradict this basic law? When matter changes to free energy, is not energy added to the world? The answer is no. Einstein changed the concepts of matter and energy. Matter is a special form of energy, and all matter is included in the energy total. The law of conservation of energy becomes the law of conservation of matter-energy, more specifically discussed in Chapter 24.

EXPERIMENTAL EVIDENCE OF SPECIAL RELATIVITY

It is one thing to build a mathematical model like relativity, and another for the model to hold in the world of things. Will the universe support ideas of shrinking rods, slowing clocks, and increasing masses? What is the evidence?

Kaufman (in 1901 and 1906) and Bucherer (in 1908) experimented with fast-moving electrons, to find that the higher the speed v of an electron, the more its mass. When, after 1905, they applied Einstein's relativity equation (Eq. 22–10) to their data, they found that all electrons had the same rest mass m_o. That is, when the different values of m and v were appropriately inserted in the equation, m_o came out the same for all electrons. With speed, each electron had increased in mass from a common rest mass as predicted by relativity. Here was Einstein's first evidence. A number of years later, Professor E. O. Lawrence of the University of California found it necessary in the development of his cyclotron to make relativity corrections for the increased mass of his accelerated particles. Electron mass has been measured under various circumstances. The particular speed of electrons in television "picture" tubes gives them an approximate mass increase of 5 percent. Electrons whirled in accelerators at over 0.999999999 the speed of light c have attained 40,000 times their mass at rest, as expected. At the speed of light, the electrons, of course, would have infinite mass. Protons, the nuclei of hydrogen atoms, also have been accelerated to speeds approaching that of light, with the expected increase of mass.

Comets form tails as they swerve around the sun due to pressure of the sun's light. This pressure suggests that radiation has mass. Quantities of metal heated to high temperature have definitely shown slight increases in mass in accordance with $\triangle E = \triangle mc^2$. Heat energy thus shows a mass equivalent. Atom smashing apparatus, atomic power plants, and atomic bombs are much around us. Their processes are everyday evidence for Einstein's idea of the interconversion of matter and energy. For better or worse, Einstein's $\triangle E = \triangle mc^2$ has been successful. Social intelligence can make it far better.

Relativity of time has also been verified. H. E. Ives of Bell Telephone (1936) compared hydrogen atoms at rest to others at high velocity. He found a difference in the vibration frequency of the atoms exactly as predicted by Eq. 22–7. A change in atom vibration frequency is analogous to a change in heartbeat rhythm or in the ticking of a clock. Atomic particles called *mesons* with very short half-lives (Chapter 23) were found in experiments for the purpose (1941) to have a slower rate of aging as they were accelerated to ever higher velocities. In 1956 Professor Frank S. Crawford at the University of California found that the half-lives of some subatomic particles moving through the atmosphere toward earth at high velocities are 15 times as great as those of identical particles at rest.

CLOCK PARADOX

The slowing down of time is reciprocal (Eq. 22–7). To observers S and E moving 161,000 mi/sec relative to each other, time appears slower on the other's spaceship. The heart beats away time, too. All physiological processes are time processes. To S, E should appear to age more slowly than himself; to E, S should appear to age more slowly. Each should find that the other's physiological processes slowed down. S and E were identical twins 30 years of age when S left the earth. When S returns after 20 years, S and E would each expect the other to appear younger than himself by 10 years (Eq. 22–7). How could both be right? This contradiction, the famous clock paradox, seems to disprove relativity. Actually, it does not disprove it; the spaceship accelerates. It accelerates to a high speed on leaving the earth, decelerates and accelerates in reversing direction at a furthermost point, and decelerates again in returning to the earth. Any curved or circular motion also involves acceleration. The special theory of relativity does not cover these periods of acceleration; Einstein's later general theory of relativity does. The paradox, therefore, is no paradox. While the spaceship accelerates, the earth remains an inertial frame. Time effects are reciprocal only when both reference frames are at constant relative velocity. During periods of acceleration, observer S ages less than observer E back home, and S will therefore return home appearing younger to all, including himself.

CERENKOV EFFECT

In 1958 the Soviet scientist P. A. Cerenkov shared the Nobel prize for his discovery of Cerenkov radiation. The speed of light in water is only three-fourths its speed in a vacuum, and in glass only two-thirds. Electrons approach the speed of light in a vacuum. Can electrons travel faster than light in water, air, or another medium where the speed of light drops considerably? Cerenkov successfully sent electrons through water at a speed faster than light in that medium. When this occurred, a cone of light waves, unique in color, showed itself very much like the pattern of bow waves which form when a ship moves faster than water waves. The Cerenkov effect does not contradict Einstein's conclusion that light and other electromagnetic waves are the fastest things in the universe. Electrons or other particles may travel faster than light in material media, but Einstein's reference is to a vacuum.

SIGNIFICANCE
OF SPECIAL RELATIVITY

In summary, Einstein examined classical mechanics at its foundations. No system of ideas is stronger than the assumptions upon which it rests. Could Newtonian assumptions of space, time, mass, energy, force, field, or gravitation be creating difficulties? In examining bedrock concepts and assumptions, Einstein thought his way through to his special (1905) and general (1915) theories of relativity, with resulting revolutionary impact on modern physics, life, and thought. His relativity model solved problems that previous models could not. Relativity ushered in atomic energy. It provided theoretical foundations, and Newtonian mechanics was absorbed as part of a larger picture. Great engineering feats have been achieved with Newtonian principles based on standard clocks and meter-sticks. Under ordinary speeds of autos, planes, or rockets, the slowing down of a watch or the shrinking of a ruler is too infinitesimal to matter. But when atomic particles approach the speed of light, Newtonian principles fall short; and when matter transforms into energy, they fall flat. The physical universe is only partly Newtonian. We now must be concerned about relative motion between an observer and what he observes. And we must now also distinguish between (1) actual events, (2) their signals (light and other radiations), (3) our observations, and (4) our interpretations. Einstein has added to our scientific and philosophic maturity.

CHAPTER REVIEW

1. (a) Define "relative" and "absolute." Illustrate each word. (b) What is meant by the statement that space and time are absolute?

2. Car *A* speeding at 80 mph passes car *B* traveling at 70 mph in the opposite direction. (a) What is the speed of each car with respect to each other? (b) What would be the speed of the two cars with respect to each other if car *A* at 80 mph passes car *B* traveling 70 mph in the same direction?

3. The earth travels at almost 20 mi/sec around the sun. The speed of light is 186,000 mi/sec. (a) When the earth travels toward a given star, with what speed should light from the star pass the earth? (b) When the earth, 6 months later, travels away from the star, with what speed should light from the star pass the earth?

4. Describe the Michelson-Morley experiment. What results were expected? What dilemma resulted?

5. Discuss some of the unsuccessful attempts to resolve the Michelson-Morley dilemma.

6. What was the frame of reference in which light was considered to travel in the Michelson-Morley experiment?

7. (a) In what sense was the ether considered "meaningless" by Einstein? (b) If the ether was really "meaningless," how could its use in physics for centuries be justified?

8. What other serious contradictions besides the Michelson-Morley dilemma did Einstein recognize the mechanical view to have?

9. What former relativity assumption and two new postulates did Einstein substitute for the ether assumption in building his relativity theory? Why wouldn't Einstein's two new postulates also be meaningless?

10. To what are space and time relative in the special theory of relativity? Explain.

11. (a) Express the following equations in words:

$$l = l_o \sqrt{1 - \frac{v^2}{c^2}}$$

$$t = t_o \sqrt{1 - \frac{v^2}{c^2}}$$

$$m = \frac{m_o}{\sqrt{1 - \frac{v^2}{c^2}}}.$$

(b) Explain and illustrate the meaning of these three equations.

12. How do the Lorentz-Einstein transformation equations enable observers with different space, time, and mass measurements of the same objects or events to correlate these measurements?

13. What value is absolute for all observers in the above equations? How so?

14. Use each of the three transformation equations to show that nothing can travel faster than light in a vacuum.

15. What bearing or effects would an infinite speed for light have on the special theory of relativity? (Hint: See the transformation equations.)

16. Do clocks actually slow down with changes in speed relative to an observer? Explain.

17. Do metersticks actually shrink with changes in speed relative to an observer? Explain.

18. (a) What does it mean to say that *now* here is not now everywhere? Illustrate. (b) How can two events happen together for one observer and not be simultaneous for another? Illustrate.

19. What is meant by "each frame of reference has its own space and time measurements and its own definition of simultaneity"?

20. Why is it not possible for an observer on earth and another on Mars to synchronize their clocks just by making allowances for the time it takes for light to get from the earth to Mars and back?

21. (a) Express in words the following addition-of-velocities equation:

$$v_3 = \frac{v_1 + v_2}{1 + \dfrac{v_1 v_2}{c^2}}$$

(b) Explain and illustrate the meaning of this equation.

22. (a) Express the following equation in words:

$$E = mc^2.$$

23. How does $E = mc^2$ (a) revolutionize ideas of matter and energy? (b) Seemingly contradict the law of conservation of matter and the law of conservation of energy?

24. Discuss experimental evidence for the following aspects of the special theory of relativity: (a) increase of the mass of objects with velocity, (b) slowing of clocks with velocity, (c) "shrinking" of rods with velocity, and (d) $E = mc^2$.

25. What is the "clock paradox"? Why is it actually not a paradox?

26. Discuss the Cerenkov effect as a supposed contradiction of the special theory of relativity.

27. Summarize the significance of the special theory of relativity with respect to the following concepts: (a) frames of reference, (b) velocity

of light and an ether, (c) space, (d) time, (e) simultaneity, (f) mass, (g) energy, (h) temperature, and (i) other concepts.

28. In what sense can we say that Newton's mechanics was not eliminated by special relativity but assumed a place in a larger framework of ideas?

29. Use materials from special relativity to illustrate differences among observation, fact, definition, assumption, hypothesis, theory, law, and conceptual model.

30. Explain what you think the following means: "There is more to seeing than meets the eye?" Illustrate.

PROBLEMS

1. How is it possible for an iron ball to weigh more when red hot than when cool?

2. What sense does it make to say that a given yardstick "shrinks" with speed? Or "shrinks" differently for various observers?

3. A spaceship moves away from the earth at 160,000 mi/sec. A light beam is sent after it at 186,000 mi/sec. With what speed does an astronaut within the ship find the light to pass him?

4. A spaceship at rest on earth has a mass of 600 tons, a length of 250 feet, a width of 20 feet, and a height of 10 feet. If the ship moves away from the earth at 37,200 mi/sec ($\frac{1}{5}c$), what is the mass of the ship as determined by (a) an observer on earth? (b) An observer on the ship?

5. What is the length of the ship in problem 4 as determined by (a) an observer on earth? (b) An observer on the ship?

6. What are the width and height of the spaceship in problem 1 for each observer?

7. To an observer on earth, how many hours have passed on the spaceship in problem 4 when 10 hours have elapsed on earth?

8. To an observer on the spaceship in problem 4, how many hours have passed on earth when 10 hours have elapsed on the spaceship?

9. If the spaceship in problem 4 could travel from the earth with the speed of light, to an observer on earth what would be (a) the length of the spaceship? (b) The mass of the spaceship? (c) The time lapse on the spaceship during 1 hour on earth?

10. Suppose the velocity of light were only 100 mph, and a train were moving at 90 mph. If one car of the train was measured as 30 feet long by a passenger, how long would it appear to an outside stationary observer?

11. How fast is an electron traveling if its mass doubles?

12. With what constant speed must a spaceship travel in order that 1 year spent in it should correspond to 2 years on earth?

13. What is the speed of a spaceship that is observed to have 90 percent of its original length on earth?

14. What would be the apparent diameter of the earth from a spaceship approaching the earth at 10 percent of the speed of light ($\frac{1}{10}c$)?

15. (a) What is the energy equivalent of a stationary 1-gram piece of chalk? (b) What is the mass of that chalk when moving at 99 percent of the speed of light (.99c)? (c) What is the energy equivalent of that chalk when moving at .99c?

16. Two spaceships pass each other in opposite directions, each with a speed of 100,000 mi/sec determined from the earth. What is the relative speed of the astronaut in each ship to the other?

SUGGESTIONS FOR FURTHER READING

Coleman, James A., *Relativity for the Layman,* Signet paperpack, New York, 1962, Chs. 2–4.

Einstein, Albert, and Leopold Infeld, *Evolution of Physics,* Simon and Schuster paperback, New York, 1961, Part 3, pp. 129–225.

Einstein, Albert, *Relativity: The Special and General Theory,* Crown paperback, New York, 1961.

Einstein, Albert, *Out of My Later Years,* Philosophical Library, New York, 1950.

Barnett, Lincoln, *The Universe and Dr. Einstein,* Mentor paperback, New York, 1952, pp. 13–84.

Russell, Bertrand, *The ABC of Relativity,* Mentor paperback, New York, 1959, Chs. 1–4 and 6.

Durell, Clement, *Readable Relativity,* Harper paperback, New York, 1960, Chs. 1–7.

Lieber, Lillian R., and Hugh G. Lieber, *Einstein Theory of Relativity,* Farrar, New York, 1945.

Gardner, Martin, *Relativity for the Million,* Macmillan, New York, 1962, Chs. 1–4.

Landau, L. D., and G. S. Rumer, *What Is Relativity?* Basic Books, New York, 1960.

Jaffe, Bernard, *Michelson and the Speed of Light,* Anchor paperback, Garden City, N.Y., 1960.

Reichenbach, Hans, *From Copernicus to Einstein,* Philosophical Library, New York, 1942.

Frank, Philip, *Relativity: A Richer Truth,* Beacon, Boston, 1950.

Bronowski, Joseph, *Common Sense of Science,* Vintage paperback, New York, 1960, Chs. 5–9.

23 Atomic Structure: Theories and Evidence

It was almost as incredible as if you had fired a 15-inch shell at a
piece of tissue paper and it came back and hit you.

LORD RUTHERFORD, 1911

Electrons, ions, X rays, and radioactivity swept aside the Dalton atom.
Data were again outstripping ideas. A century earlier a similar deluge had
revived an indestructible "billiard ball" model of the atom as a prime unit
of matter. And now, a new wave of data was forcing a new model. Electrons were smaller than atoms. Atoms lost or gained electrons to become
ions. Atoms bombarded with electrons emitted X rays. Atoms explosively
emitted alpha and beta particles to transmute themselves spontaneously.
The indestructible atom was shattered.

THOMSON'S ATOMIC
MODEL: ASSUMPTIONS

J. J. Thomson in 1898 proposed a model of the atom with a structure
much like that of a blueberry muffin. Electrons were like small, negatively
charged blueberries distributed in the positively charged body of a muffin.
Inserted in concentric rings, the electrons electrically balanced the rest
of the atom. The loss of an electron or two meant a surplus of positive
charge. The neutral atom then became an ion. Alpha particles flying

from radium were like crumbs shooting out from a muffin. Beta particles from radioactive elements were like blueberries bursting out. Thomson believed that heat, light, X rays, gamma rays, and other radiation from atoms resulted from atomic collisions or other external forces. Such forces caused electrons to vibrate around their regular fixed positions. Fast vibrations meant high-frequency X rays or gamma rays; slower vibrations meant light and heat.

A conceptual model is a big idea that organizes and explains data. Clearly, Thomson's model was no exception. But every idea has assumptions. Thomson's main assumptions were these:

1. The body of an atom consists of a positively charged substance uniformly distributed.
2. Negatively charged electrons are embedded in the positively charged substance.
3. The electrons are stationary relative to the rest of the atom.
4. The positive and negative charges neutralize each other within the atom.
5. No appreciable empty space exists within atoms.

ALPHA PARTICLES AND GOLD LEAF TARGETS

If a single experiment ever decisively overthrew a theory, Rutherford's famous "gold leaf" alpha-scattering experiment did. Thomson's atomic model hardly had a chance to get started before his former star student exploded it and substituted a new one.

Rutherford did not stop with discovering alpha particles and basing a theory of atomic decay upon them. To probe the interior of atoms, he started the use of alpha particles as atomic bullets for bombarding elements. The process continues today, but with mammoth bevatrons smashing atoms at energies up to 300 billion *electron volts*. Rutherford's "gun" was a thick-walled lead tube with a bit of radium at the bottom (Fig. 23–1A). Alpha particles escaped through the open passage at speeds of about 10,000 mi/sec (36 million mph!), more than $\frac{1}{20}$th the speed of light. The energy of the alpha "bullets" was formidable. Expectations were high. But let Rutherford speak for himself:

I remember Geiger coming to me in great excitement and saying, "We have been able to get some of the alpha particles coming backwards." It was quite the most incredible event that has ever happened in my life. It was almost as incredible as if you had fired a 15-inch shell at a piece of tissue paper and it came back and hit you. On consideration, I realized that this scattering backwards must be the result of a

positive charge, however, that came close to a nucleus with its many concentrated positive charges would be considerably deflected by repelling forces. Single planetary electrons, on the other hand, are too light in charge and weight for effecting attraction.

The closer to a nucleus an alpha particle is headed, the more the deflection of the particle. If the particle approaches close enough, the repelling effects of the nucleus can be sufficient to reverse the particle's direction.

If all the space were removed from the atoms composing a giant tree outside your window, the concentrated atomic nuclei and electrons would shrink to a sliver. And yet the weight would remain the same. That matter is mostly space seems fantastic. But how else can Rutherford's alpha-scattering results be explained? Besides, there are definite limitations to our senses. A propeller, when moving fast, appears as "solid" as a disk. The pores in our skin loom large through a shaving mirror. And that is only a first step in magnification. Because we cannot see through a tree trunk does not mean that comparatively vast spaces are not there.

SEARCH FOR THE PROTON

Rutherford's atom had no outer wall. It was just a tiny nucleus in a vast space dotted with planetary electrons. The picture was there, but the details had to be more sharply defined. Were the electrons distributed randomly or in some set order? What was the nucleus like? Were the positive charges imbedded in a single jellylike mass, or was each charge on a separate particle of matter? If on separate particles, did each have the same weight and charge? If so, how would the weight and charge compare to those of electrons? There were many such questions.

No one has ever seen the interior of an atom. But the reasoning and evidence for uniform, positively charged particles ran somewhat as follows.

Atoms are electrically neutral. Electrons, each with a single negative charge, are subatomic particles. There should be positively charged building blocks to offset them. Could the positive components be the doubly charged alpha particles (helium ions) ejected from radioactive atoms? Or would they be lighter particles with a single charge? The only element lighter than helium is hydrogen. A century before, William Prout had suggested that the atoms of all elements are aggregates of hydrogen atoms. Could he have been correct, and all scientists since then, wrong?

J. J. Thomson, even before Rutherford's atomic nucleus idea, believed that Prout may have been right. He said so in his statement "but if we substitute for hydrogen some unknown substance X [today's proton], there is nothing known inconsistent with this [Prout's] hypothesis." To search for "substance X," Thomson in 1907 turned his attention to positive, or "canal," rays (Fig. 21–6). Certain gases in his tube gave him rays with positive charges exactly equal to electrons even if opposite in sign. Other gases resulted in positive particles that had charges *exactly* two, three—or any *whole* number—times the smallest charge (opposite and equal to electrons). Thomson therefore concluded that there is a basic unit of positive as well as negative charge.

Hydrogen ions in Crookes tubes or elsewhere always show the basic unit, or minimum amount, of positive charge. A hydrogen ion is a hydrogen nucleus. Add an electron and the ion becomes an electrically neutral atom. Since hydrogen is the lightest element, Thomson assumed that the single basic positive charge of the ion is neutralized by a single opposite charge of an electron. Thomson then showed that a hydrogen ion is about 1,850 times heavier than an electron. That is, a hydrogen ion has a positive charge equal and opposite to an electron, but a weight 1,850 times greater, and that a hydrogen atom consists of both. All this without a hydrogen atom or an electron actually being seen, let alone individually weighed!

Efforts by Rutherford followed those of Thomson. After discovering the atomic nucleus, Rutherford continued bombarding atom interiors with alpha bullets and succeeded in obtaining hydrogen ions out of other elements. His first success in this direction was in bombarding nitrogen (1919). There was no question that the emitted particles were hydrogen. The ion charge was equal and opposite to that of the electron; the ion mass, or weight, was about 1,850 times greater. Later alpha bombardments of sodium, gold, aluminum, and phosphorus by Rutherford also produced hydrogen ions. These ions certainly seemed to be a common component of atoms of other elements. Rutherford was confident that he and his team had discovered the basic atomic building block that Prout and J. J. Thomson had predicted. He named the particle a proton (1920).

ATOMIC NUMBER
VERSUS ATOMIC WEIGHT

But why settle for the proton as a primary particle? It is about 1,850 times heavier than an electron. Why not first look for an electron with a *positive* charge? Actually, such an opposite twin to the electron, called a *positron,* was later discovered, but it did not replace the proton in importance. Let us see why.

The periodic table provides a first clue. The atomic weights of most elements are close to whole numbers. Take the first nine elements (Table 23–1). Hydrogen is about 1, helium, 4; lithium, 7; beryllium, 9; boron, 11; carbon, 12; nitrogen, 14; oxygen, 16; and fluorine, 19. As we proceed up the periodic table, the amounts that elements increase in atomic weight (column 3) approximate small multiples of the hydrogen nucleus or proton weight unit of 1 rather than of the negligible fraction, the $\frac{1}{1,850}$ unit of the electron. This, of course, is not decisive, just a first rough clue originally used by Prout.

Table 23–1 | ATOMIC NUMBER VERSUS ATOMIC WEIGHT

ATOMIC NUMBER	ELEMENT	APPROXIMATE ATOMIC WEIGHTS	PROTONS ($+$ CHARGES)	ELECTRONS ($-$ CHARGES)
1	H	1	1	1
2	He	4	2	2
3	Li	7	3	3
4	Be	9	4	4
5	B	11	5	5
6	C	12	6	6
7	N	14	7	7
8	O	16	8	8
9	F	19	9	9

Now notice that columns 1, 4, and 5 in Table 23–1 are identical. The order of an element in the periodic table would seem to indicate the number of protons or planetary electrons in the atom of that element. Hydrogen has one proton and one electron; helium, two protons and two electrons; lithium, three protons and three electrons; and so on. A difficulty soon presents itself, however, in the atomic weight column. For example, a hydrogen ion or nucleus has one positive charge and an atomic weight of 1. But a helium ion, with an atomic weight of 4, never has more than two positive charges. If there are only two protons in the nucleus, how can four units of weight be explained? The answer soon given was that the helium nucleus also contains two additional protons, each of which is neutralized by a closely attached electron (Fig. 23–2A). (Remember that the weight of an electron is negligible.) This hypothesis of a combined proton-electron particle in a nucleus soon led to the idea of a third basic atomic particle, an electrically neutral one called a neutron.

That gives us two key concepts to atomic structure: atomic number and atomic weight. The important concept of atomic number was established as the number of protons or planetary electrons in the atom of an element. For example, the lithium atom has an atomic number of 3 and an atomic weight of 7 (Fig. 23–2B). The atomic number gives it three protons and three planetary electrons. The extra four units of weight means four neutrons. Fluorine, atomic number 9 and atomic weight 19, has nine protons, nine electrons, and ten neutrons. All objects in the universe seemed reducible to two basic electrical particles, protons and electrons. Even a third particle, the neutron, was assumed to be a proton-electron composite. First, four Aristotelian elements, then 92 chemical atoms, and then two or three subatomic particles; from simplicity to complexity back to simplicity!

LAW OF ATOMIC NUMBERS

One of Rutherford's most brilliant students, Henry G. Moseley (1887–1915), provided clinching evidence for the association between the order of elements in the periodic table and a one-by-one increase of protons in the atomic nuclei of these elements. He used high-speed electrons to bombard various elements in a cathode ray tube. Different elements emitted X rays of different frequencies. Interested, Moseley found a definite connection between the order of the elements in the periodic table and the frequencies of the X rays they emitted. He noticed that by adding the number "1" successively for each element up the ladder, he could predict the X-ray frequency of that element. He interpreted this successive addition of the digit "1" to be the addition of a positive charge in the atomic nucleus from one element to the next. The unique properties of an element thus became identified with the number of protons or electrons in one of its atoms.

Atomic weight had been a powerful concept in the development of chemistry from Dalton to Mendeléyev and beyond, but now with Rutherford and Moseley, the concept of atomic number was taking over. There had been a few contradictions in the periodic table. Argon, for example, has a higher atomic weight (39.944) than potassium (39.096) and, therefore, should follow the latter in the periodic table (Table 20–4). But argon has properties that should place it in Group 0, inert gases, which *precedes*, not follows, the metal Group I, to which potassium belongs. By atomic weight, potassium should precede argon; by family properties, argon should be first. Moseley applied his high-speed electrons and found that X-ray analysis gave argon an atomic number of 18, and potassium, 19. Argon belonged before potassium in the periodic table in spite of having a larger atomic weight. The positions of cobalt, nickel, iodine, and tellurium in the periodic table were also corrected by Moseley. Atomic number, the number of protons or electrons, was primary to atomic weight in the characteristics of an element. The significant relationship between the properties of elements and the number of protons or electrons in their atoms has been sealed by the designation of a law of atomic numbers. The brilliant future of Moseley, the young founder of the law, was cut short by a Turkish bullet in World War I.

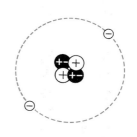

23–2A *The helium atom. Two protons give helium an atomic number of 2. Two neutral particles (neutrons) completing its nucleus give helium an atomic weight of 4. Two planetary electrons of negligible weight electrically balance the protons.*

ELECTRON JUMPS AND LIGHT

Among the many gifted young men in Rutherford's laboratory was Niels Bohr (1885–1962). This great Danish theoretical physicist early tackled the problem of planetary electrons. The problem was how electrons could circle the nucleus without losing energy and spiraling into it—much as an artificial satellite in the earth's atmosphere loses altitude. A revolving electron is an accelerating electric charge; it should radiate electromagnetic

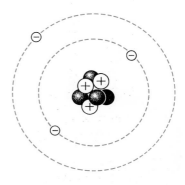

23–2B *The lithium atom. An atomic number of 3 and an atomic weight of 7 means that the lithium atom has three protons (and three planetary electrons) as well as four neutrons.*

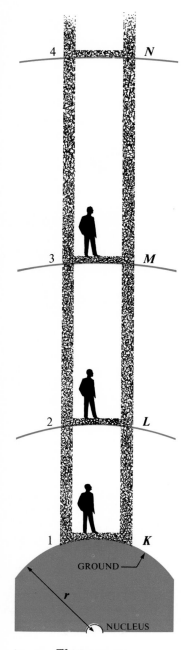

waves (Chapter 18) and lose velocity. But the fact remains that planetary electrons do not end in the nucleus—fortunately! If they did, all atoms and the universe of objects would long ago have collapsed like edifices of bursting balloons. There was also a parallel question for Bohr to face: How could the various colors of a hydrogen bright-line spectrum (Chapter 17) result from a lone planetary electron in a standard fixed orbit within each hydrogen atom?

One way to tackle a dilemma is to modify ideas in terms of existing evidence. If hydrogen atoms emit more than one color, then more than one standard orbit may exist for an electron. If radiation of energy by electrons in fixed orbits means atoms would collapse, then perhaps an electron does not emit radiation when *in* an orbit, but when occasionally jumping *between* orbits.

But how many more than one orbit position would there be? Where would the orbit levels be set? How far apart would the levels be? Bohr first established an innermost *ground* level (*K* level, Fig. 23–3). This was the level at which the electron of a *normal* hydrogen atom orbits. When hydrogen atoms are sufficiently excited through heat or electrical means, an electron may be lifted to higher levels *L, M, N* . . . or even to free space outside an atom. Such an electron absorbs external energy from atomic collisions and heat or other radiation to make the jump. By analogy, energy is required to lift a rock from the ground. The higher the rock is lifted, the more energy is required. Similarly, the higher the electron jump from one level to another, the more external energy is absorbed by the electron for the jump. And like the rock, the higher an electron gets above its ground level, the more potential energy it has. For that reason, Bohr called the electron orbits "energy levels." The further from the nucleus an orbit is, the higher its energy level.

The higher the altitude from which a rock falls, the greater the intensity of the sound it makes when it hits the ground. Electrons also fall back to lower levels, to lose potential energy and emit radiant energy, whether light, infrared rays, ultraviolet rays, or X rays. Bohr visualized this radiant energy to be in the form of Planck's quanta or Einstein's photons. The further an electron falls, the larger the quantum of energy. In general, an infrared quantum or light photon originates in the fall of an electron to the third or the second level, respectively, and an ultraviolet or even X-ray quantum from an electron falling to the first level (Fig. 23–4). Gamma rays, more penetrating than the other rays, result from electrical disturbances in the nucleus rather than from electron jumps.

There is only one photon or quantum for each electron fall, but billions of hydrogen atoms in a glowing tube have electrons falling various distances between different levels. And some free electrons fall into atoms from the outside. These electrons have various amounts of kinetic energy of thermal agitation that they give up when falling into an orbit. The

23–3   Electron energy levels. Bohr believed that electrons orbit only at set distances from an atomic nucleus, starting with an innermost K, or ground, level.

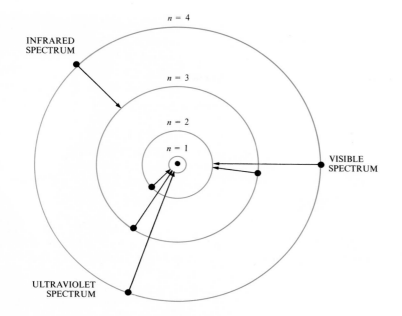

INFRARED
SPECTRUM

n = 4

n = 3

n = 2

n = 1

VISIBLE
SPECTRUM

ULTRAVIOLET
SPECTRUM

variety of colors in a hydrogen spectrum could therefore be expected. But the fact that hydrogen always shows the same colors was significant to Bohr. This meant that orbit levels could not be just anywhere, but at certain fixed positions. Electrons could fall only through distances determined by these fixed levels and, therefore, could emit only corresponding colors. Without changes in distances between levels, there could not be changes in color.

But again, where are the orbit levels to be set? Suppose that wherever set, the orbit levels are designated by numbers instead of letters. The ground level number *n* is 1, and successive levels are 2, 3, 4, 5, 6, and 7. Bohr showed mathematically that he could predict the spectrum colors of hydrogen if he placed the electron orbits to satisfy the following equation:

$$r = Kn^2,$$ Equation 23–1

where r = the radius of a permitted orbit

K = a constant for hydrogen that includes Planck's constant h

n^2 = the orbit number squared.

That is, the radius of an orbit varies according to the square of the particular orbit number (Table 23–2 and Fig. 23–4). Bohr found that the value of K is $\frac{1}{400,000,000}$ inches. If $n = 1$, then r is equal to K in Equation 23–1. Therefore, $r = \frac{1}{400,000,000}$ inches. In such a way can the radius of something unseen be determined! For the second level, $n = 2$

Niels Bohr. (The Bettmann Archive, Inc.)

and $r = 2^2$, or four times the distance to the first level (that is, $4 \cdot \frac{1}{400,000,000}$ or $\frac{1}{100,000,000}$ inches). For the third level, $n = 3$ and $r = 3^2$, or nine times the distance to the first level (that is, $\frac{9}{400,000,000}$ inches). And so on.

Table 23–2 | *RELATIVE DISTANCES TO ORBIT LEVELS*

ORBIT LEVELS			RELATIVE DISTANCES FROM NUCLEUS
n	n^2	$=$	r
1	1^2	$=$	1
2	2^2	$=$	4
3	3^2	$=$	9
4	4^2	$=$	16
5	5^2	$=$	25
6	6^2	$=$	36
7	7^2	$=$	49

In short, the distance to the first level is the radius of the normal hydrogen atom. By knowing that radius, the orbit of an electron that jumps to any other level can be found from Table 23–2. In such a way, scientific models are built with which to probe nature.

The Bohr model clearly is a fusion between a wave and a particle theory of light. The model uses the wave concept of frequency f for light and other electromagnetic radiation emitted from atoms, and yet it also uses photons or other energy particles resulting from electron jumps to explain specific bright-line color spectra. The quantum energy equation $E = hf$ further indicates fusion of the opposing particle and wave concepts. The f indicates wave frequency for radiation, and the h implies radiation particles.

SUCCESSES OF
THE BOHR MODEL

The Bohr model was elegantly designed to explain color frequencies emitted by excited hydrogen atoms. A first significant test was to see if the model could predict accurately in invisible areas of the electromagnetic spectrum below red and beyond violet. The model passed this first test brilliantly. Suitable apparatus showed that glowing hydrogen gas emitted infrared and ultraviolet radiation in frequencies predicted by Bohr's equations. The Bohr theory could explain how light, heat, X rays and other electromagnetic radiation originate. This success for Bohr was also a success for Planck's and Einstein's particle theories of energy incorporated in Bohr's ideas.

The Bohr atom had other successes. Its electrons in orbit could explain magnetic properties of objects. And its electrons could explain chemical behavior. Because of their importance, these successes are described in separate sections.

An Electrical Theory of Magnetism

The planetary model of the atom provides an electrical theory of magnetism. In accordance with this theory, magnetism has its origins in the minute electrical circuits in atoms. Moving electrons within atoms constitute circuits from which magnetic fields arise. If moving charges give magnetic as well as electric fields at an observable level (Rowland's experiment, Chapter 16), why shouldn't moving charges give magnetic fields on a subatomic level? Ampère was the first one to explain how molecules in the molecular theory of magnetism obtain their magnetism. He suggested that molecule-magnets are due to electric currents flowing around them. But Ampère, unaware of electrons, could not explain how his proposed currents started. All innovators are limited by the knowledge of their times. In the planetary theory of the atom, the electron not only revolves around the positively charged nucleus, but also spins on an axis through its center. Supposedly, these motions explain magnetism. But

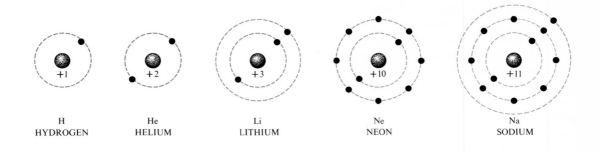

| H | He | Li | Ne | Na |
| HYDROGEN | HELIUM | LITHIUM | NEON | SODIUM |

23–5 *The Bohr-Langmuir atomic model. Electrons are distributed in concentric shells, much like planets in Ptolemaic spheres. More than one electron may exist in a shell: The first shell may have two electrons; the second shell, eight electrons; the third shell, 18 electrons . . . .*

if all atoms have minute interior circuits and magnetic fields, why do very few substances ordinarily show magnetic properties? The answer given is that atoms of highly magnetic substances, like iron or steel, reinforce one another in large groups to form very small magnetized *domains*. The magnetic fields within atoms of "nonmagnetic" substances cancel one another out instead of forming magnetic domains. This electrical theory of the origins of magnetism is known as the domain theory of magnetism.

Electron Shells and Chemical Activity

The question of how many orbital levels there are in the Bohr atom was first successfully handled by an outstanding American chemist, Irving Langmuir (1881–1957). Bohr was a physicist. But chemists were concerned with how planetary electrons could explain such chemical properties of atoms as combining power. Like charges repel each other. A force of repulsion should build up between planetary electrons of two atoms approaching each other. A force of attraction, however, between the nucleus of one atom and the electrons of the other should become increasingly effective as the atoms come closer. Just how do atoms combine? The Bohr model needed more details to explain chemical reactions. Gilbert Lewis, an American chemist, in 1916 had ideas of electrons in cubical shells around a nucleus. But cubical shells contradicted Bohr's circular orbits. Irving Langmuir, the first American industrial chemist to receive a Nobel prize (1932), changed the cubes into concentric shells (Fig. 23–5) much like Ptolemaic spheres. Each shell was spaced to satisfy Bohr energy levels. Into each shell Langmuir placed a fixed number of electrons. The atomic number of an element determined the total number of electrons in the shells of any of its atoms.

Hydrogen has one electron. An electron must be added to the atom of each succeeding element in the periodic table (Table 23–3). But in distributing electrons, what should be the number of electrons in each shell? The inert gases gave Langmuir a clue. These gases, for example, helium and neon, are stable elements that do not form compounds.* They also are in the last column of the periodic table. Perhaps each of these elements should be the cutoff point of an electron shell. For example, helium, atomic number 2, has two electrons, and neon, atomic number 10, has ten electrons. If a helium atom with two electrons is inactive, then perhaps its two electrons in an innermost K shell complete the number

Table 23-3 | *ELECTRON CONFIGURATIONS*

ELECTRONS IN SHELLS	I	II	III	IV	V	VI	VII	VIII
	H							**He**
K shell	1							2
	Li	**Be**	**B**	**C**	**N**	**O**	**F**	**Ne**
K shell	2	2	2	2	2	2	2	2
L shell	1	2	3	4	5	6	7	8
	Na	**Mg**	**Al**	**Si**	**P**	**S**	**Cl**	**Ar**
K shell	2	2	2	2	2	2	2	2
L shell	8	8	8	8	8	8	8	8
M shell	1	2	3	4	5	6	7	8
	K	**Ca**					**Br**	**Kr**
K shell	2	2					2	2
L shell	8	8					8	8
M shell	8	8					18	18
N shell	1	2					7	8

of electrons necessary for electrical balance in that shell (Table 23-3). The one electron of a hydrogen atom, of course, is also in a K shell. And if neon, the next inert gas, is inactive with ten electrons, then perhaps a neon atom has two completed shells, a K shell with two electrons and an L shell with eight more electrons. But immediately after helium is lithium, with three electrons. Its third electron starts the second, or L, shell. With each new element after lithium, an electron is added in the L shell until neon.

All elements between helium and neon are chemically active, as is hydrogen. Therefore, reasoned Langmuir, each atom tends toward outer shell completeness. This tendency results in chemical activity and combination. A hydrogen atom tends to complete its K shell (or lose its lone electron), while atoms of elements 3 to 6 tend to lose all electrons back

*The inert gases xenon and argon recently became exceptions to the rule.

to the *K* shell, and elements 6 to 9 to complete their *L* shells (Table 23–3). The need of hydrogen to take on one electron for chemical stability explains hydrogen's combining power, or valence, of 1. Lithium tends to lose its one electron in the *L* shell. This element is therefore very active, with a valence of 1. Oxygen (atomic number 8) has six electrons in its *L* shell. This shell is two electrons short of completion. Oxygen is therefore chemically active, with a combining power of —2 to complete its *L* shell. Lithium tends to "loan out" one electron, and oxygen, to "borrow" two. Both are then left with a complete outer shell. Similarly, fluorine is short only one electron to complete its *L* shell. Fluorine is therefore very active, with a valence of —1. In general, elements with fewer than four electrons in their outside shell tend to loan them. These are metals and show metallic properties. Elements with more than four electrons tend to gain more. These elements show nonmetallic properties. Elements like carbon, with four electrons in an outer shell, either lose four electrons or borrow four, to show either a +4 or —4 valence.

In the same way, the eight elements in row 3 of the periodic table (Table 23–3) may be associated with a 1-by-1 addition of electrons in an *M* shell. Each of these elements has two electrons to complete a *K* shell and eight electrons to complete an *L* shell. Sodium (atomic number 11) starts the new shell with one electron, and the inert gas argon (atomic number 19) completes the shell with eight electrons.

Table 23–3 shows the basis upon which seven shells are believed to cover the known elements. By the same token, the Lewis-Langmuir shells give the Bohr atom seven basic energy levels.

Members of the same family of elements in the periodic table tend to have the same characteristics and valence because they tend to lose or gain the same number of electrons in outer shells. Valence, other chemical characteristics, and periodic table groupings become identified with electron distribution in shells. Alkali metals have a strong tendency to lose the lone outer electron characteristic of each. The halogens have a strong tendency to pick up the single electron that each needs to complete a shell. Inert gases "stand pat" with completed shells.

Chemical combination involves either outright *transfer* of electrons to form *polar* compounds or the *sharing* of electrons in *nonpolar* compounds.

23–6   Electron transfer in chemical combinations. In losing its single outer electron, the sodium atom becomes positively charged. In gaining the electron, the chlorine atom completes its outer electron shell but becomes negatively charged. In the electron transfer the two atoms become electrically polar and bind each other by electrostatic attraction.

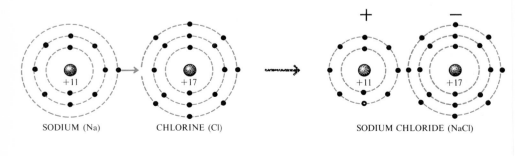

SODIUM (Na)   CHLORINE (Cl)   SODIUM CHLORIDE (NaCl)

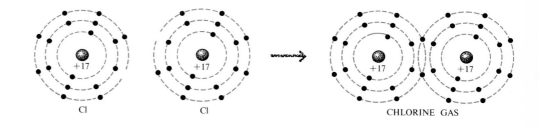

In electron transfer, the atom of a metal loses electrons to a nonmetal. Sodium, an alkali metal, burnt in chlorine, a halogen, forms a polar compound, sodium chloride, by electron transfer. An Na atom tends to dispose of the single electron that the Cl atom needs to complete its outer shell (Fig. 23–6). But in the process, the sodium becomes positively charged, and the chlorine, negatively charged. The two atoms are now polar, or oppositely charged, and bind each other by electrostatic attraction.

On the other hand, two chlorine atoms in a chlorine gas molecule share a pair of electrons to fill in the single gap of each (Fig. 23–7). The shared electrons keep the atoms together.

Clearly, the Lewis-Langmuir shell model gave electron configuration to the Rutherford-Bohr atom and made it a powerful theoretical tool in chemistry. The nuclear atom already had been effective in physics. Now valence, other chemical properties, and periodic table groupings became identified with electron distribution in shells. In such ways, scientific models are built that organize and probe the universe—until the models fall short and give way to more adequate models.

23–7 Electron sharing. Each chlorine atom is short a single electron to complete an outer electron shell. In forming a molecule, two chlorine atoms share a pair of electrons to fill in the single gap of each.

DIFFICULTIES OF THE PLANETARY ATOM

The Rutherford-Bohr atom had early success. It accurately predicted radiation from heated or electrically excited hydrogen gas. It explained the origins of light, X rays, infrared, and ultraviolet radiation. Even now it explains the origin of radio signals from hydrogen in the stars. It accounts for magnetism. And it has served as an effective model to explain chemical behavior and regularities in the periodic table. And yet when the model was used to predict the spectral colors and radiation frequencies from heavier elements than hydrogen, it got into difficulties. Predictions for helium were fairly accurate, but the higher the element, the lower the accuracy. Replacing circular orbits with elliptical worked well for Kepler's planets, but not adequately enough for Bohr's electrons when Arnold Sommerfeld (1868–1951) tried it. Bohr energy levels and electron distributions still serve many purposes, but the concept of "electron cloud," representing the probability of an electron's being in a particular place at a particular time, has replaced Bohr's idea of set electron orbits. The probability concept of electron clouds is beyond the scope of this text, as is the "wavicle" concept of electrons and other material particles having "wavelength" and other wave characteristics as proposed by the great French physicist Louis de Broglie (1892–   ). If light waves can have particle properties, then material particles can possibly have wave properties, thought De Broglie. The electron microscope, based on wave properties of electrons, is now the most powerful of microscopes. Besides, from Einstein's special theory of relativity (Chapter 22), matter and energy are different aspects of the same thing.

As for the size of an electron, Sir James Jeans (1877–1946), an outstanding modern astronomer, remarked, "It is probably as meaningless to discuss how much room an electron takes up as to discuss how much room a fear, an anxiety, or an uncertainty takes up."

In conclusion, Niels Bohr, in his atomic model, seems to conform to a basic creative pattern of reconciliation between the old and the new—to be expected of innovators as human beings. That is, all great men are professionally conditioned by the particular training of their times. They approach new problems with that training. What other way is there, even for gifted humans? Contradictions arise between the traditional and the new, and these men often show their exceptional abilities in reconciling what is contradictory. Copernicus retained uniform circular motion for planets in line with the "perfection of the heavens" doctrine while introducing the sun as the center of the universe in order to solve basic problems. Among other things, he hoped to eliminate the Ptolemaic equant, which he considered contradictory to "perfection of the heavens." It took Kepler to eliminate the epicycles that Copernicus kept because the latter was rooted in tradition even as he innovated. But Kepler "arrived" by way of Copernicus.

Similarly, Galileo showed his Aristotelian training when he considered inertia to be circular. It took Newton to make inertial motion universally straight. But we get to Newton's first law of motion by way of Galileo. Galileo also showed his training when in both of his *Dialogues* he attempts to beat the Aristotelians at their own game of appeal to reason and mathematics rather than directly appealing to and justifying the experimental principles generally associated with his name.

Then again, there were the famous Lorentz transformation equations. Because of his classical background, Lorentz was inhibited from making the breakthrough in interpretation of his own equations that Einstein did in the special theory of relativity.

DISCOVERY OF THE NEUTRON

It was an American physicist, W. D. Harkins, who in 1920 first predicted the existence of the neutron as a third basic particle of matter. The total weight of a nucleus is greater than the total weight of its protons. The presence of neutrons could account for the extra weight. Hydrogen, with only one proton and an atomic weight of 1, was the only atom that needed no neutron. The ten protons of a neon atom gave it an atomic number of 10, but ten neutrons were also needed to explain the atomic mass of neon at 20. The neutron was assumed to be an uncharged particle with a mass about that of a proton.

Twelve years after Harkins' prediction, James Chadwick bombarded beryllium with alpha particles in Rutherford's laboratory. The beryllium emitted an unknown ray of great penetrating power. The ray was composed of uncharged particles with a mass of 1.0087 amu, just slightly more than the mass of a proton. Chadwick had discovered the neutron. Uncharged, these particles are not electrically repelled by orbiting electrons or charged nuclei. They therefore easily penetrate atoms and make excellent "bullets" for atomic bombardments. A thickness of several inches of lead stops only some of them. Neutrons were later found to be unstable outside atoms and to decay into a proton and an electron each. It was therefore assumed that neutrons within nuclei decay into protons and electrons and that the latter leave the scene as fast-moving beta particles. The proton left behind gives a nucleus an extra positive charge. Half of any number of free neutrons become protons in 13 minutes. Protons and neutrons, as the two basic nuclear particles, are called *nucleons*. Just as the number of protons in a nucleus gives the atomic number of an element, the number of nucleons gives the atomic weight.

ISOTOPES

Are the atoms of an element all alike? Dalton assumed they were. It was simpler that way, and simplicity counts. But sometimes small discrepancies lead to big discoveries. Why the .008 in the 1.008 atomic weight of hydrogen if oxygen is 16.000? Or why the extra .18 in the 20.18 atomic weight of neon?

23–8 Discovery of isotopes. A photographic plate at the end of a canal ray tube showed J. J. Thomson and F. W. Aston that neon ions exist with at least two atomic weights. Electric and magnetic fields deflected neon ions to two different spots on the plate. From the amounts of deflection, Thomson concluded that one group of neon atoms has "an atomic weight of 20 and the other of about 22." The lighter atoms were deflected farther than the heavier.

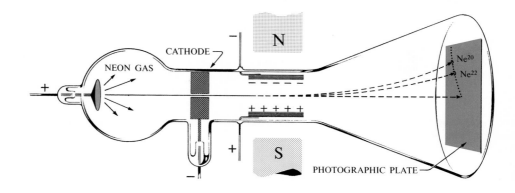

$_{10}Ne^{20}$

$_{10}Ne^{22}$

23–9   *Nuclei of neon iso-*
topes. The isotopes of any
element have the same num-
ber of protons but vary in the
number of neutrons. This
difference in neutron amount
accounts for differences in
atomic weight. Neon isotopes
each have ten protons, but
$_{10}Ne^{20}$ has ten neutrons, and
$_{10}Ne^{22}$ has twelve neutrons.

$_1H^1$

$_1H^2$

$_1H^3$

23–10   *Hydrogen isotopes.*
Hydrogen, with but one
proton, is the only element
that has an isotope ($_1H^1$)
without neutrons.

Back in 1913, J. J. Thomson and a young colleague, F. W. Aston (1877–1945), were working with canal rays. This time, neon gas was in the tube (Fig. 23–8). A photographic plate was at the far end. The neon ions in the red canal rays were deflected by electric and magnetic fields that they crossed. You will recall that the extent of the deflection enabled Thomson to compare the atomic weights of different elements. In this case—repeated many times—upon developing the plate, Thomson and Aston always found a second faint spot above the first as long as neon was in the tube. Thomson's conclusion was that "neon is not a single gas, but a mixture of two gases, one of which has an atomic weight of about 20 and the other of about 22." Thomson and his assistant had discovered *isotopes*. Neon atoms were not identical, just "fraternal" like some twins. Here was an element not necessarily pure, but an atomic mixture in terms of weight. The term "isotope," coined by Soddy, origi-nates in the Greek words *isos,* meaning "equal," and *topos,* meaning "place." Isotopes are atoms in the *same place* in the periodic table, but with different weights. Having the same atomic number, isotopes of any element have the same chemical properties regardless of weight differences.

All neon atoms have the same number of protons (ten) in the nuclei, but their different weights result from different numbers of neutrons (ten and twelve), as in Fig. 23–9 and Table 23–4. Isotopes are symbolized by subscripts and superscripts. The subscript "10" before the "Ne" in $_{10}Ne^{20}$ and $_{10}Ne^{22}$ indicates the common atomic number of neon, and the superscripts "20" and "22" following the "Ne" indicate the two different atomic weights. With a comparatively small number of $_{10}Ne^{22}$ atoms and a large number of $_{10}Ne^{20}$ atoms in ordinary neon gas, we would expect the atomic weight of the gas to be somewhere between the two, and much closer to the 20.* The atomic weight of neon *is* 20.18. If atoms of an element are not necessarily alike but vary in weight, **then** the average atomic weight is not necessarily a whole number.

Since the celebrated experiment of Thomson and Aston, a great majority of elements have been found to contain two or more isotopes. As could be expected, ordinary hydrogen has three isotopes (Fig. 23–10). Whereas most hydrogen atoms are $_1H^1$, with no neutrons, one out of every 4,000 is $_1H^2$ and has a neutron. $_1H^2$ is known as *deuterium* or heavy hydrogen. Another heavy hydrogen is tritium, $_1H^3$, found in a much smaller ratio than even $_1H^2$. For his discovery and work with heavy hydrogen, the great contemporary American chemist Harold Urey became a Nobel laureate (1934). Water contains some molecules with heavy hydrogen. A concentration of water containing heavy hydrogen is called heavy water.

The two elements with the most isotopes are tin and the inert **gas** xenon. Tin has 13 isotopes, ranging from $_{50}Sn^{62}$ to $_{50}Sn^{74}$. Xenon has 17

---

*The 0.27 percent of $_{10}Ne^{21}$ (Table 23–4) is negligible.

Table 23-4 | ISOTOPES OF THREE ELEMENTS

ELEMENT	ISOTOPE SYMBOL	ATOMIC NUMBER	NUMBER OF PROTONS	NUMBER OF NEUTRONS	ATOMIC WEIGHT OF ISOTOPE	RELATIVE AMOUNT OF ISOTOPE (%)	ATOMIC WEIGHT OF ELEMENT
Hydrogen	$_1H^1$	1	1	0	1	99.98	
	$_1H^2$	1	1	1	2	.02	1.008
	$_1H^3$	1	1	2	3	negligible	
Lithium	$_3Li^6$	3	3	3	6	7.9	
	$_3Li^7$	3	3	4	7	92.1	6.940
Neon	$_{10}Ne^{20}$	10	10	10	20	90.00	
	$_{10}Ne^{21}$	10	10	11	21	.27	20.183
	$_{10}Ne^{22}$	10	10	12	22	9.73	

1 OZ RADIUM, NOW

1,600 YEARS

3,200 YEARS

4,800 YEARS

6,400 YEARS

8,000 YEARS

AND SO ON . . .

*23–11 Half-life of radium.
After 1,600 years, only half
of the radium atoms remain in
any sample. The rest decay
into atoms of other elements.
The white area in each circle
represents the comparative
amount of radium left after
each successive 1,600-year
period.*

isotopes, from $_{54}Xe^{70}$ to $_{54}Xe^{86}$. Uranium is famous for its three isotopes, $_{92}U^{234}$, $_{92}U^{235}$, and $_{92}U^{238}$, all radioactive. Aluminum, phosphorus, gold, and iodine are among the elements with one isotope, that is, with atoms all alike.

The great significance of isotopes is that some are radioactive and others are not. $_{1}H^3$ is radioactive, $_{1}H^1$ and $_{1}H^2$ are not. $_{6}C^{14}$ has natural radioactivity; $_{6}C^{12}$ and $_{6}C^{13}$ do not. $_{19}K^{40}$ is radioactive; $_{19}K^{39}$ and $_{19}K^{41}$ are not. Although $_{92}U^{234}$, $_{92}U^{235}$, and $_{92}U^{238}$ are all radioactive isotopes, they vary considerably in the rates at which they decay. Somehow, the number of neutrons in atomic nuclei determines their relative stability. Strangely enough, elements of even atomic numbers have a greater number of isotopes than those of odd numbers. Elements of odd atomic numbers tend to have no more than two stable isotopes.

HALF-LIFE

When atoms break down spontaneously, do they do so at a regular rate? Is there a law of radioactive decay? Rutherford sought a law and found it.

Insurance companies have a concept of "life expectancy." Suppose we say that life expectancy in the United States is 65 years. This means that half the population here reaches age 65. *Half-life* is the life expectancy idea applied to atomic decay; the half-life of a given sample of radium would be the time taken for half the atoms of that sample to break down. If all samples of radium have the same half-life, there is a law of radioactive decay operating for radium. People can be seen and counted. How about atoms? Let us illustrate with radium. A given speck of radium salts can be weighed. Thanks to the work of Avogadro, Madame Curie, and others, the number of radium and other atoms in a given mass of radium salts can be calculated. But how can the rate at which radium atoms break down be counted with precision?

In answer, Rutherford used a very simple setup devised by William Crookes. At one end of a small lead tube, he placed a magnifying lens. A phosphorescent zinc sulfide screen was at the other end. Within the tube close to the screen, Rutherford put a bit of radium salt. Flashes of light appeared like fireflies through the lens of this spinthariscope. *Each flash on the screen meant the decay of a radium atom* and the emission of an alpha particle, as with Rutherford's "gun" (Fig. 23–1A). (Beta particles are not emitted by radium, but by certain atoms before and after it in a family of radioactive elements.) Rutherford counted almost two flashes a second. From the weight of the original speck of radium salt, he calculated that about 35 billion atoms of radium would decay every second from a gram of pure radium.

Various tests with many radium samples have shown a constant rate of decay independent of all outside factors. Every 25 years, radium in any amount anywhere loses about 1 percent of its atoms and becomes radioactive radon gas. This means a half-life of nearly 1,600 years for radium. That is, in each 1,600-year period, the number of undecayed remaining atoms in any radium sample decreases by one-half. Start with 1 ounce of radium today. In 3570 A.D., the amount of radium left will be ½ ounce; in 5160 A.D., ¼ ounce; in 6760 A.D., ⅛ ounce; in 8360 A.D., $\frac{1}{16}$ ounce .... The series seems endless because we always take a half of what is left, that is, ½ of ½ of ½ of ½ ... until the final atom (Fig. 23–11). Uranium salts tested in the same way show a consistent half-life of about 4.4 billion years. The half-life of radon is very short—less than 4 days. Other radioactive materials were found to decay at other constant rates. Flashes on zinc chloride screens led to the recognition of constant radioactive decay and to a mathematical law that embraces all atomic disintegrations.

FAMILIES OF
NATURAL RADIOACTIVITY

Natural radioactivity revolutionized ideas of the atom and its structure. Not only do atoms break down, but they transmute one into another and in families (Table 23–5 and Fig. 23–12). Three families of natural radioactivity appeared out of the patient, piecemeal efforts of dedicated men and women working with alpha and beta particles, gamma rays, atomic numbers, mass numbers, isotopes, neutrons, and half-lives. The beauty of it was that the alpha and beta particles were the key to the nuclear changes that transmuted radium to radon or other elements to lead. Gamma rays were merely secondary effects of nuclear change. Atomic nuclei were not involved in chemical combinations nor in emission of X rays, light, infrared, and ultraviolet radiations. All these complexities narrowed down to planetary electron activity.

Back in 1906 Rutherford and Soddy showed that a radium atom $_{88}Ra^{226}$ emitting an alpha particle $_2He^4$ becomes a radon atom $_{86}Ra^{222}$ (Fig. 23–13) or $_{88}Ra^{226} \longrightarrow _2He^4 + _{86}Rn^{222}$. That is, the loss of an alpha particle moves a radium atom back two places in the periodic table. Alpha particles contain two protons and two neutrons. The atomic number is reduced from 88 to 86 by the loss of the two protons. Atomic number 86 is radon. The atomic weight of the radon is 222; a total of four particles (all atomic weight 1) were lost. The half-life $(T_{1/2})$ of radium is 1,620 years. The radioactive radon that takes its place (Table 23–5) has a half-life of only 3.82 days. Half the number of radon atoms at any instant emit alpha particles and become radioactive polonium $_{84}Po^{218}$. No wonder Madame Curie discovered both polonium and radium in her uranium ore! The polonium, in turn, has a $T_{1/2}$ of only 3.05 minutes. In emitting an alpha particle $_2He^4$, a polonium atom $_{84}Po^{218}$ becomes lead $_{82}Pb^{214}$. This is an

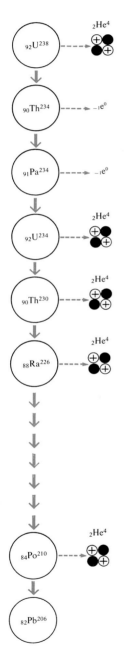

unstable isotope of lead with a half-life of 26.8 minutes. And so the radioactive processes continue (Table 23–5) until the stable isotope of lead $_{82}Pb^{206}$ ends the family line.

But the next question is this: What happens to the nucleus of an atom when a radioactive isotope such as lead-214 emits a beta particle? Or when thorium-234, the daughter of uranium-238, does the same? Soddy, in 1913, was the first to say that the loss of a beta particle moves an atom one place *higher* in the periodic table. That is, the loss of a negative charge from a nucleus is the same as the gain of a positive charge. We have seen that the gain has been explained as the transformation of a neutron into a proton with the emission of a beta particle (electron). Let us illustrate with lead $_{82}Pb^{214}$ (Fig. 23–14). In losing an electron, a lead atom has its 82 protons increased to 83. The periodic table shows that atomic number 83 is the element bismuth $_{83}Bi$. In losing an electron, lead-214 has lost negligible weight. The bismuth atom replacing the lead will have about the same weight 214. Bismuth-214 is a radioactive isotope with a $T_{1/2}$ of 19.7 minutes. Emitting a beta particle, $_{83}B^{214}$ becomes $_{84}Po^{214}$.

Thus, in the natural radioactivity of uranium-238, with a $T_{1/2}$ of 4.4 billion years, we see the start of a radioactive family that includes 15 isotope members. A second radioactive family of elements starts with $_{92}U^{235}$, having a half-life of over 700 million years, and ends with the stable lead isotope $_{82}Pb^{207}$. The isotope thorium, $_{90}Th^{234}$, with a $T_{1/2}$ of 13.4 billion years, heads a radioactive family ending with stable lead $_{82}Pb^{208}$. Notice that all three families are at the upper end of the periodic table. The heavy elements beyond the cherished gold and mercury of the alchemists (atomic numbers 79 and 80) are preponderantly radioactive. No family of natural radioactive elements exists among lighter elements— just a comparatively few isolated elements such as carbon-14 ($T_{1/2} = 5{,}580$ years) or potassium-40 ($T_{1/2} = 1.83$ billion years).

23–12   Uranium-235 family of natural radioactivity. Each radioactive descendant of uranium-235 emits either an alpha particle ($_2He^4$) or a beta particle ($_{-1}e^0$). Each loss of an alpha particle results in a descendant that is two lower in atomic number and four lower in atomic weight. Each loss of a beta particle results in a descendant that is one more in atomic number and about the same in atomic weight.

Table 23–5 | *URANIUM–238 FAMILY OF RADIOACTIVE ELEMENTS*

ELEMENT	SYMBOL	ATOMIC WEIGHT	ATOMIC NUMBER	HALF-LIFE $(T_{1/2})$	PARTICLE EMITTED
Uranium	$_{92}U^{238}$	238	92	4.5 billion yr	alpha
Thorium	$_{90}Th^{234}$	234	90	24.1 days	beta
Protactinium	$_{91}Pa^{234}$	234	91	1.18 min	beta
Uranium	$_{92}U^{234}$	234	92	270,000 yr	alpha
Thorium	$_{90}Th^{230}$	230	90	80,000 yr	alpha
Radium	$_{88}Ra^{226}$	226	88	1,620 yr	alpha
Radon	$_{86}Rn^{222}$	222	86	3.82 days	alpha
Polonium	$_{84}Po^{218}$	218	84	3.05 min	alpha
Lead	$_{82}Pb^{214}$	214	82	26.8 min	beta
Bismuth	$_{83}Bi^{214}$	214	83	19.7 min	beta
Polonium	$_{84}Po^{214}$	214	84	.00015 sec	alpha
Lead	$_{82}Pb^{210}$	210	82	22.2 yr	beta
Bismuth	$_{83}Bi^{210}$	210	83	4.9 days	beta
Polonium	$_{84}Po^{210}$	210	84	138 days	alpha
Lead	$_{82}Pb^{206}$	206	82	infinite	

TIME BY RADIOACTIVITY

Radioactive decay is one of the most constant and reliable processes in the universe. It is not affected by pressure, temperature, or any other physical conditions. Rates of radioactive decay are therefore the most dependable means we have for determining the age of the earth and materials in it. Uranium-238 and carbon-14 have been particularly useful, the uranium for measuring geologic time in hundreds of millions and billions of years, and the carbon for time in centuries.

To understand how a uranium deposit can give the minimum age of the earth, consider again the uranium-238 family of radioactive elements. Over 99 percent of uranium in ore is uranium-238. Amounts of the uranium-234 and uranium-235 isotopes, therefore, are negligible. Around uranium deposits are found considerable amounts of stable lead-206 and helium (from alpha particle emission). Uranium-238 has a very slow rate of decay ($T_{1/2}$ = 4.4 billion years), and its long line of family members have comparatively short half-lives. Only traces of the radioactive isotopes between uranium-238 and the lead end product are found. The more stable lead found in the uranium, the more time has elapsed. If the uranium had been deposited 4.4 billion years ago, then half the uranium would be lead. The amount of uranium, however, still exceeds that of lead. But the oldest uranium deposits do show an age reaching about 4 billion years. This is a minimum age for the earth, since the earth itself

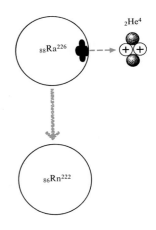

23–13 The decay of radium into radon. A radium nucleus ($_{88}Ra^{226}$) emits an alpha particle. The loss of two protons drops the radium atom two places in the periodic table, to element 86, radon ($_{86}Rn^{222}$). The loss also of two neutrons helps reduce the atomic weight by four units, to 222.

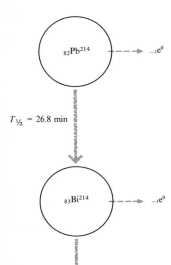

$T_{\frac{1}{2}} = 26.8$ min

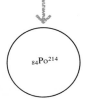

$T_{\frac{1}{2}} = 19.7$ min

23–14   The decay of lead-214 ($_{82}Pb^{214}$) to polonium ($_{84}Po^{214}$). A lead-214 atom loses a beta particle, to raise its atomic number to 83. The new element bismuth-214 ($_{83}Bi^{214}$) also emits a beta particle, to become element 84, polonium-214.

should be older than any of its uranium deposits. Helium deposits near uranium have also been used for determining the earth's age. The more helium, the greater the time lapse. But helium is much less reliable than stable lead. Helium is a gas and escapes more easily.

Carbon-14 has been valuable in dating ancient manuscripts or other materials containing carbon. Carbon dioxide is absorbed by plants. A trace of the carbon is radioactive carbon-14. Animals eat plants. When a plant or animal dies, carbon intake stops. The ratio of radioactive carbon to other carbon atoms is known. At that point, however, the number of radiating atoms decreases. After 5,568 years, half of the radioactive atoms will be gone; the other carbon atoms are stable. In another 5,568 years, the radioactive carbon atoms will be reduced to one-fourth of the original amount. And so on. The total time lapse can be determined from the constantly decreasing ratio of radioactive carbon atoms to stable carbon atoms.

CHAPTER REVIEW

1. Why have early models of the atom been called "billiard ball" models?

2. Show why Thomson's atom may be dubbed a "blueberry muffin" model.

3. Describe the "solar system" atomic model of Rutherford and Bohr.

4. Compare the main assumptions of the above models.

5. The "billiard ball" model was based upon what evidence?

6. How did the following discoveries lead to the breakdown of the "billiard ball" model? (a) Roentgen's discovery of X rays. (b) Becquerel's discovery of radioactivity. (c) The Curies' discovery of radium. (d) Thomson's discovery of electrons. (e) Rutherford's discovery of alpha, beta, and gamma rays. (f) Rutherford's discovery of the proton.

7. What evidence existed for Thomson's "blueberry muffin" model?

8. How did Rutherford's bombardment of gold foil overthrow Thomson's model?

9. What is a proton? How was it discovered? How was the proton's existence predicted before it was discovered?

10. What evidence supported the Rutherford-Bohr "planetary" model?

11. Distinguish between "atomic number" and "atomic weight." Illustrate.

12. Use atomic numbers to show that other atoms may be made up of hydrogen atoms.

13. Why have atomic numbers replaced atomic weights as the organizing principle of the periodic table of elements?

14. What are "energy levels" within atoms? How do energy levels explain the origin of light, X rays, infrared and other radiation of the electromagnetic spectrum?

15. How does the Rutherford-Bohr model explain ions?

16. What are molecules? How does the Bohr model explain what holds atoms together within molecules?

17. How did the Bohr model lead to an electrical theory of magnetism?

18. (a) How does the difference in value between the number and weight of an atom point to the existence of neutrons? (b) How were neutrons discovered?

19. What are isotopes? How does examining values of atomic masses on the periodic chart point to the existence of isotopes?

20. How were isotopes actually discovered?

21. What is meant by radioactive isotopes? Illustrate.

22. Describe what is meant by families of natural radioactivity. Give an illustration of such a family.

23. What does "half-life" mean? Illustrate. Why is this concept important?

24. How can a new atom be predicted from knowledge of the expelled particle of the parent atom?

25. How does knowledge of the half-lives of U^{238} and C^{14} permit dating of the earth or of objects in it?

26. Which of the five main assumptions of the Dalton atom discussed in Chapter 20 are still acceptable today?

27. What difficulties has the Rutherford-Bohr atomic model been unsuccessful in overcoming?

28. What is meant by a model of an atom? What determines whether any model is scientific?

29. Is the atom a hypothesis, theory, or fact? Explain.

PROBLEMS

1. Why have atoms been called miniature solar systems?

2. Why isn't a planetary electron pulled into the positively charged nucleus of its atom by electrical attraction?

3. Explain how elements differ in (a) number of protons and (b) electron distribution in shells.

4. An atom has 79 protons and 118 neutrons. What element is the atom? What is its number and weight? How many electrons does the atom have?

5. Give the number of protons, neutrons, and planetary electrons within atoms of the following isotopes: $_7N^{14}$, $_{13}Al^{27}$, $_{26}Fe^{56}$, $_{10}Ne^{23}$, $_{88}Ra^{226}$, and $_{80}Hg^{200}$.

6. (a) Draw a Bohr model diagram for each of the following isotopes: $_1H^1$, $_1H^3$, $_6C^{14}$, $_8O^{16}$, $_{10}Ne^{20}$, $_{10}Ne^{22}$, and $_{92}U^{235}$. (b) Which of these isotopes are spontaneously radioactive?

7. Explain the difference between the origins of light rays and X rays in terms of Bohr's electron jumps. Between the origins of light rays and radio waves.

8. How does electron theory explain chemical valence? Illustrate with a water molecule.

9. Use a row across the periodic table of elements to show how the outermost ring of an atom determines chemical activities and properties of the element.

10. Use a column down the periodic table to relate the similar chemical and physical properties in a family of elements with similar electron distributions in the outermost ring of atoms of these elements.

11. Radium decays spontaneously into radon and helium, and water decomposes into hydrogen and oxygen. Why is radium considered an element, while water is considered a compound?

12. What does a uranium-238 atom become when it transmutes naturally? Explain.

13. Uranium-238, the heaviest isotope found in nature, is designated as the head of a naturally radioactive family. Could uranium-238 have decayed from a still heavier element? Why?

14. Radioactive carbon has a half-life of 5,600 years. If an ancient wooden tool shows only one-eighth the radioactive carbon count of fresh lumber, how old is the tool?

15. How much radium from a 1-pound sample will be left after 3,200 years? If the sample is sealed, what gases would be found in it? What isotopes of lead?

16. Distinguish between a proton, an electron, an alpha particle, and a beta particle.

17. Use a periodic table to indicate theoretically what an oxygen-12 atom would become if it were to (a) gain a proton only. (b) Lose a proton only. (c) Lose a planetary electron only. (d) Lose a beta particle only. (e) Gain a neutron only. (f) Lose a neutron only. (g) Gain an alpha particle only. (h) Lose an alpha particle only. (i) Emit X rays only. (j) Emit gamma rays only.

18. Use a periodic table to indicate theoretically what a uranium-238 atom would become if it were to (a) gain a proton only. (b) Lose a proton only. (c) Gain a neutron only. (d) Lose a neutron only. (e) Lose a planetary electron only. (f) Lose an alpha particle only. (g) Lose a beta particle only.

19. Can mercury be transmuted into gold through use of the Rutherford-Bohr model of the atom? Explain.

SUGGESTIONS FOR
FURTHER READING

Feinberg, Joseph G., *Story of Atomic Theory and Atomic Energy,* Dover paperback, New York, 1960, Chs. 10–14.

Hecht, Selig, *Explaining the Atom,* Viking paperback, New York, 1954, Chs. 3–4.

Lemon, Harvey B., *From Galileo to the Nuclear Age,* Phoenix paperback, Chicago, 1961, Chs. 33–34.

Jaffe, Bernard, *Crucibles: The Story of Chemistry,* Premier paperback, New York, 1960, Chs. 12–14.

Eidinoff, Maxwell Leigh, and Hyman Ruchlis, *Atomics for the Millions,* McGraw-Hill, New York, 1947, Chs. 6–7 and 10.

Andrade, Edward N. da C., *Rutherford and the Nature of the Atom,* Anchor paperback, Garden City, N.Y., 1964, Chs. 5–6.

24   *Atomic Energy and Power*

> The Moving Finger writes;
>   and, having writ;
> Moves on . . . .
>
> OMAR KHAYYÁM, 12th century

The release of atomic energy has not created a new problem. It has merely made more urgent the necessity of solving an existing one . . . . The discovery of nuclear chain reaction need not bring about the destruction of mankind any more than did the discovery of matches . . . . To have security against bombs . . . we have to prevent war . . . . A new type of thinking is essential if mankind is to survive a move toward higher levels.

ALBERT EINSTEIN, 1950

Einstein had predicted in his $E = mc^2$ that small amounts of matter could be transformed into huge quantities of free energy or vice versa (Chapter 22). Matter was bound energy. A pail of sand could supply the power needs of the United States for several years. The challenge was to find the key that unlocks matter. Tremendous vistas seemed to open for relieving human drudgery. The challenge in the world of ideas was revolutionary, too.

But specifically, how does matter unlock into energy? Einstein suggested radioactivity as a clue. Radioactive atoms show explosive bursts of energy when ejecting alpha and beta particles at thousands of miles a second. Radium crystals generate heat endlessly. Their temperatures are generally 5°F higher than the surrounding atmosphere. Does this heat come from matter transformed in the radioactive process? Does atomic mass disappear in radioactivity?

MODERN ALCHEMY

With such questions in mind, an investigator like Rutherford bombards nitrogen with helium ions and obtains oxygen and hydrogen (Chapter 23). He probes nature and transmutes an element. This process is symbolically shown as follows:

Helium	+	nitrogen	$\longrightarrow$	oxygen	+	hydrogen	
$_2\text{He}^4$	+	$_7\text{N}^{14}$	$\longrightarrow$	$_8\text{O}^{17}$	+	$_1\text{H}^1$.	Equation 24–1

The helium ion $_2\text{He}^4$ hitting a nitrogen nucleus $_7\text{N}^{14}$ upsets the internal electrical balance. The nucleus emits a hydrogen ion or proton $_1\text{H}^1$. The remaining eight protons and nine neutrons are the nucleus of an oxygen isotope $_8\text{O}^{17}$. The usual oxygen atom is $_8\text{O}^{16}$. Notice that the "2" and the "7" subscripts (atomic numbers) in the equation balance the "1" and the "8." Also note that the "4" and the "14" superscripts (atomic weights) balance the "17" and the "1." Where the alchemists failed, Rutherford succeeded in transmuting elements. The unlocking of prodigious amounts of nuclear energy was yet to come.

TRACKING ATOMIC PARTICLES

Imprints in hardened sands tell silent stories of prehistoric life. Tracks on photographic plates also reveal much about unseen atomic particles. Figure 24–1 is a photograph showing Rutherford's transmutation of nitrogen into oxygen. The long thin line diagonally across the upper left-hand corner is the track of an ejected proton. The short, thick line close to the upper right-hand corner is the track of an oxygen nucleus formed after a collision. The many tracks fanning out from the bottom center of the photograph were formed by alpha particles emitted from a radium source. These tracks ended when the particles lost their energies before striking a nucleus. This celebrated first photograph of nuclear decay was taken in Rutherford's laboratory by P. T. M. Blackett, a famous researcher.

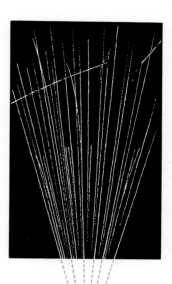

a PARTICLES

RADIUM

24–1 Rutherford's transmutation of nitrogen into oxygen. The many lines fanning out from the bottom are tracks of bombarding alpha particles emitted from the radium source. The long line stretching diagonally across the upper left-hand corner is the track of a proton ejected from a nitrogen atom after collision with an alpha particle. The short, thick track close to the upper right-hand corner is that of an oxygen nucleus formed when another bombarded nitrogen atom emitted a proton. (After photograph by P. T. M. Blackett)

When damp air cools, its water vapor condenses around dust or other particles to form clouds. In 1911, C. T. R. Wilson used this condensation principle of cloud formation to construct an ingenious device for photographing the path of a charged particle. This device, called a *Wilson cloud chamber*, is essentially a radioactive source placed within a metal cylinder C with a glass top T and a piston P bottom (Fig. 24–2). When the piston is lowered, the air within expands and cools, and miniature white clouds appear, each showing the track of an ionizing particle. Any fast-moving electrical particle ionizes or removes electrons from air molecules along its path. Water vapor condenses around these molecules when the piston is lowered. In Wilson's words:

I had in view the possibility that the track of an ionizing particle might be made visible and photographed by condensing water on the ions which it liberates . . . . The first test was made with X rays, and in making an expansion of the proper magnitude for condensation on the ions while the air was exposed to the rays . . . the cloud chamber filled with little wisps and threads of cloud—the tracks of the electrons ejected by the action of the rays. A radium sample was then placed inside the cloud chamber and . . . the clouds condensed along the tracks of the alpha particles were seen for the first time. The long thread-like tracks of fast beta particles were also seen when a suitable source was brought near the cloud chamber.

Other fast-moving ionizing particles show characteristic tracks, as the oxygen ions and protons do in Fig. 24–1. A camera properly attached to the apparatus photographs the trails. So much that we know about subatomic particles and nuclear process is due to Wilson's cloud chamber that by 1927, this powerful research tool earned a Nobel prize in physics for its inventor.

Rutherford early expressed his appreciation of the cloud chamber:

To the period of 1895–1912 belongs the development of an instrument which to my mind is the most original and wonderful in scientific history. I refer to the cloud or expansion chamber of C. T. R. Wilson. . . . It was a wonderful advance to be able to see, so to speak, the details of the adventures of these particles in their flight through the gas. Anyone with imagination who has seen the beautiful stereoscopic photographs of the trails of swift alpha particles, protons, and electrons cannot but marvel at the perfection of detail with which their short but strenuous lives are recorded.

Cambridge physics students sang appreciation of their professors with the following words:

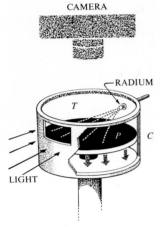

24–2 Wilson cloud chamber. When the piston P is lowered, water vapor condenses around molecules ionized by a charged particle from radium or another source. The condensation shows the particle's path.

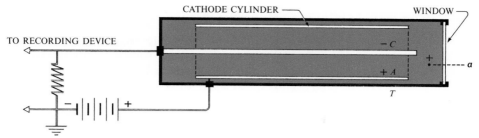

24-3 *The Geiger-Mueller counter. A charged particle entering the window of the counter is attracted to an oppositely charged plate. This attraction completes a circuit connected to a clicking or recording device that indicates the particle's presence.*

Though Crookes at first suspected my [an electron's] presence on the earth
'Twas J. J. [Thomson] that found me—in spite of my tiny girth.
He measured first the "*e* by *m*" of my electric worth.
I love J. J. in a filial way, for he it was gave me birth.

Then Wilson known as C. T. R. his camera brought to bear,
And snapped me (and the Alphas too) by fog tracks in the air.
We like that chap! For a camera snap is a proof beyond compare:
A brilliant star is C. T. R.—we'd follow him anywhere.

Modern cloud chambers are more effective than ever in detecting atomic particles. Instruments extend men's senses.

COUNTING ATOMIC PARTICLES

The combined zinc sulfide screen and microscope (spinthariscope) used by Rutherford for counting alpha or beta particles was described in Chapter 23. The Geiger-Mueller counter (Fig. 24–3) is another famous detector of radioactivity, invented in 1912 as an improvement over the spinthariscope. The special counting tube T is part of an electric current connected to a clicking, lighting, or recording device. The counting tube includes two sealed metal terminals A and C. Even at a fairly high voltage, a current does not flow between electrodes C and A across the tube. However, an alpha or other electrical particle entering the window of the tube ionizes gas molecules within. The electrons forced from gas molecules by the entering alpha particle surge toward the positive electrode A in the tube. For a brief instant, a current is completed, a counting device clicks, and often a light bulb flashes. The charged particle is unseen, but a Geiger counter makes the particle's presence known.

ATOM SMASHERS

In bombarding nitrogen and obtaining oxygen, Rutherford had used natural projectiles, fast-moving alpha particles. Rutherford was ready for the next step: artificially accelerated "bullets." Rutherford asked his young associate John Cockcroft to devise a high-voltage "atom smasher" that could hurl protons at an energy of 1 million electron volts against nuclear targets. Nuclei are positively charged. George Gamow (1904–1968), the brilliant young Russian theoretician at Cambridge, had pointed out that a fast-moving proton should be a more effective projectile than an alpha particle. A proton has one positive charge, not two charges, and therefore has less repulsive force to overcome in approaching a nucleus. Cockcroft and an associate, E. T. S. Walton, in 1932 successfully constructed the world's first atom smasher and directed it at a target of lithium, element 3. Helium resulted. The two researchers had transmuted the third element in the periodic table into the second. This transmutation, the first by particles artificially accelerated, is symbolized as follows:

Hydrogen + lithium ⟶ helium

$$_1H^1 \ + \ _3Li^7 \longrightarrow 2 \ _2He^4.$$

Equation 24–2

A lithium atom hit by a proton *captures* it but splits into two alpha particles.

Boron, atomic number 5, was bombarded by protons with the following results:

Hydrogen + boron ⟶ helium

$$_1H^1 \ + \ _5B^{11} \longrightarrow 3 \ _2He^4.$$

Equation 24–3

A boron atom that captures a proton "bullet" splits into three alpha particles or helium ions. Somehow, two protons and two neutrons tend to break off as a stable helium nucleus when a larger nucleus is disturbed.

The Cockcroft and Walton atom smasher was soon followed by the more powerful Van de Graaf atom smasher. The Van de Graaf electrostatic generator is described in Chapter 15. The running belt delivers the electric charges from the source below to the interior of the huge metal sphere. The buildup of charge results in very high voltages. Ions of an element are accelerated to energies of millions of electron volts by placing them within an accelerating tube and applying the charged Van de Graaf apparatus to the tube. The accelerated ions leave the tube through a slit to strike nuclear targets as a beam.

The Cockcroft-Walton and Van de Graaf atom smashers were but the first two in a series of particle accelerators. A most significant particle accelerator is the cyclotron invented by Ernest Lawrence (1901–1962). This atom smasher and such powerful successors as the bevatron made the Lawrence Radiation Laboratory at the University of California, Berkeley, into a world-famous nuclear research center. Let us describe the cyclotron by analogy. Suppose a volleyball is hung by a string from the top of a Maypole, and two youngsters at opposite sides of the pole hit the ball around. Each time the ball is hit at a half-turn, it moves faster and spirals outward. A number of light blows on the ball have the same cumulative effect as a few heavier swats. Instead of a ball around a Maypole, Lawrence spiraled protons, deuterons, or alpha particles within a circular vacuum chamber (Fig. 24–4). An early model looks like a flat cylindrical can cut into two sections and separated. Since the half-cylindrical chambers looked like D's, they were called "dees." Instead of physical blows, Lawrence gave his particles electrical "kicks." He placed the dees between the poles of a powerful electromagnet and connected the dees to an alternating current of high voltage. The dees are opposite in charge, but the charges alternate. Suppose protons are injected at a center point O between the dees. The positive proton is attracted into the negatively charged dee for a first "kick." But as the proton moves, the magnetic field swerves it into a circular path that returns the particle to point A between the dees. At that instant, the second dee becomes negative, and the first, positive. The proton is now attracted into the second dee. The proton's speed is increased by this second "kick," and

24–4   The "dees" of a cyclotron. Charged particles injected at center point O are sent spiraling in the vacuum chamber by electrical "kicks" and a powerful magnetic field. Each time a particle arrives in the space between the dees, it is further accelerated by another electrical "kick" by the high-voltage alternating current. And the magnetic field ever swerves the particle into a larger circle. By the time the particle reaches the outer edges of the dees, it may reach a speed approaching that of light. The particle leaves a slit in the dees as a high-energy atomic "bullet."

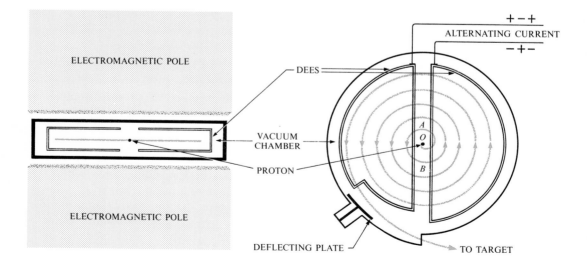

ELECTROMAGNETIC POLE

ELECTROMAGNETIC POLE

DEES

VACUUM CHAMBER

PROTON

+ − +
ALTERNATING CURRENT
− + −

A
O
B

DEFLECTING PLATE

TO TARGET

it is swerved in a larger circle by the magnetic field to point B between the dees. At that instant the dees reverse charges again. This process is repeated many times. The particle spirals outward with increasing speed. Applying 1,000 volts 1,000 times to a particle has the same effect as applying 1 million volts once. Near the outer edge of the dee, the particle is deflected out through a slit as a high energy atomic "bullet." A 60-inch cyclotron at Berkeley sends a deuteron around 100 times in 8.3 millionths of a second to attain a speed of almost 30,000 miles per second—$\frac{1}{6}$ the speed of light—and an energy of 24 million electron volts (24 Mev). At such speeds, the masses of particles increase considerably, and relativity corrections (Chapter 22) must be made in the design of the cyclotron. Otherwise, the particles do not arrive in the space between the dees in time for the alternation of charge. The 184-inch cyclotron at Berkeley has magnetic pole faces 184 inches in diameter. The magnet weighs 4,000 tons. Protons are now accelerated by it to an energy of almost ¾ billion electron volts (Bev).

A bevatron completed at the University of California in 1954 has a magnet containing 10,000 tons of steel and 350 tons of copper. A proton completes 4 million revolutions in 1.8 seconds to travel a distance of 300,000 miles. Such a proton leaves the cyclotron with a speed of 99 percent of that of light and smashes into a nuclear target with 6.2 billion electron volts (Bev) of energy. Accelerators are now being planned in the United States and the Soviet Union to hurl particles at energies of hundreds of billions of electron volts.

Back in 1939, Lawrence received the Nobel award in physics for the cyclotron and its contributions up to that time. It was extending men's fingers, eyes, and insights into the heart of matter. As Lawrence then expressed it: "There lies ahead for exploration a territory with treasures transcending anything thus far unearthed. It [the cyclotron] may be the instrumentality for finding the key to the almost limitless reservoir of energy in the heart of the atom."

NUCLEAR BINDING FORCE

What holds an atomic nucleus together? Like charges repel. If highly concentrated in a small nucleus, positive charges should explosively force each other apart. This should be a far-flung world of only hydrogen atoms. But other atoms and objects do exist. Could there be some unknown short-range binding force within each atomic nucleus that ordinarily offsets the powerful electrical repelling force within it? Is an alpha chunk explosively hurled from a nucleus when an internal balance of forces is upset? How does nature upset its own balance in radioactivity? Answers to these questions are keys to transmutation of elements. They also are keys to fantastic amounts of atomic energy predicted by Einstein's $E = mc^2$.

In 1930 Gamow proposed a liquid droplet model of the nucleus in which "nucleons forming the nucleus are packed closely together much like molecules in a liquid." Analogies often fruitfully explain unknown areas of knowledge—at least at an early stage of investigation. A bicycle moving through a puddle scatters small spherical drops of water in various directions. We say the drops are spherical because of *surface tension*. The drops appear to be bound by a thin elastic membrane in a state of tension. Unbalanced gravitational forces pull inward to give a drop its smallest possible surface, that of a sphere. By analogy, Gamow suggested that an unknown short-range nuclear force could bind an atomic nucleus much like gravitational forces give cohesion to molecules in a drop of water. The nucleus would therefore be spherical, show surface tension, and have other liquid drop characteristics. An alpha particle leaving a nucleus would be like a droplet flying from a disturbed puddle. The emitted alpha particle then achieves its own balance between a cohesive binding force and an internally explosive electrical force. Often the remaining nucleus does, too; otherwise, it radioactively casts out more particles until a balance is reached. The uranium-238 nucleus, heavy and off balance with 238 nucleons, does not achieve stability until becoming lead-206. The uranium-238 atom therefore starts a radioactive family without an outside disturbance.

FREEING MATTER AS BOUND ENERGY

According to Einstein, mass is concentrated energy. Overcoming the binding force of a nucleus means freeing bound or concentrated energy. The reasoning is that the binding force of a nucleus involves *binding energy* that is released when a disturbance upsets the nuclear balance of forces in an atom. When a lithium nucleus is disturbed by a captured proton (Eq. 24–2) and is changed into helium nuclei, some binding energy should be lost, and by $E = mc^2$, some mass, too. But *is* mass lost? As a matter of fact, Cockcroft and Walton did find that some mass disappeared as free energy when they bombarded lithium, shown as follows:

Lithium + hydrogen $\longrightarrow$ helium + *energy*

$$_3Li^7 \quad + \quad _1H^1 \quad \longrightarrow 2 \,_2He^4$$

Mass 7.016 + mass 1.008 $\longrightarrow$ 2 (mass 4.003)

$$\text{mass } 8.024 \longrightarrow \text{mass } 8.006 + energy.$$

Here 0.018 atomic mass units (8.024 − 8.006 amu) disappeared, and an equivalent amount of kinetic energy showed itself in the great speed of alpha particles leaving the scene (about 10,000 miles per second, or 36 million miles per hour).

The explanation is that the $_1H^1$ "bullet" lodges in the $_3Li^7$ atom nucleus and splits into 2 $_2He^4$ nuclei. The four protons and four neutrons of the combined bullet and target are all accounted for in the two helium nuclei. And yet there is an *imbalance* of mass; 8.006 is less than 8.024. *The product helium weighs less than the sum of its parts* (lithium and hydrogen) by about 0.02 mass units. Cockcroft and Walton found that the 0.02 *mass units lost* ($\triangle m$) *equaled the kinetic energy gained* ($\triangle E$) by the swiftly moving helium nuclei in accordance with $\triangle E = \triangle mc^2$ (Eq. 22–12). The great speed of alpha particles in radioactivity clearly is at the expense of atomic mass. Some of the lithium mass is transformed into the kinetic energy of emitted particles. But this is only the start of atomic energy.

ORIGIN OF THE SUN'S ENERGY: NUCLEAR FUSION

Can it be that the sun's energy is nature's testimony to the idea that matter is bound energy? The sun's energy supply is incredible. The earth receives only one two-billionth of the sun's radiation, but that is enough to melt in a year a glacier 175 feet thick encasing the earth. The earth's light bill alone at 3c a kilowatt-hour (Chapter 16) would come to about $50 trillion a day. If the sun were very high-grade coal burning in oxygen, it could maintain its internal temperature of 20,000,000° C for approximately 5,000 years. After that: ashes! But the sun has been relentlessly radiating for billions of years, and it shows every sign of continuing its output of radiant energy for billions of years to come.

A century ago, Julius Mayer concluded that the sun lost mass with its radiation. He even went so far as to estimate that the sun loses about 4 million tons of its mass every second. But how matter and energy as separate entities could be equated Mayer did not know. Scientists in the early 1930s had the benefit of Einstein's $E = mc^2$, but they were no more specific than Mayer about how the sun has maintained its temperature through eons of time.

Hans Bethe (1906–   ) left Nazi Germany in 1933 and became a professor of physics at Cornell University. Supposedly, in the relaxed limbo of a train trip 5 years later, Bethe pondered these questions: Could the sun's energies be nuclear? Are elements transmuted in the sun with vast releases of energy? If so, what elements, and under what conditions? For his answers Bethe received the Nobel prize in 1967. His answers may be summarized as follows. A great deal of hydrogen and helium exist in the sun. At temperatures running into millions of degrees centigrade, atoms within the sun would be stripped of electrons and exist as nuclei. The atomic weight of a hydrogen nucleus or proton $_1H^1$ is 1.0078, and of helium $_2He^4$, 4.0026. A helium nucleus contains two protons and two neutrons. The atomic weight of a neutron is 1.0087. A clue to the sun's abundant energies can be seen in the following analysis of atomic weights:

$$2 \text{ protons} = 2.0156 \text{ amu}$$
$$+ \ 2 \text{ neutrons} = 2.0174$$
$$\text{sum} = 4.0330 \text{ amu}$$
$$- \ _2He^4 = 4.0026$$
$$\text{difference} = .0304 \text{ amu}.$$

The helium nucleus $_2He^4$ weighs 4.0026; the sum of the separate parts that make up the nucleus weighs 4.0330. Somehow the difference of 0.0304 has disappeared. The helium nucleus is a whole that weighs *less* (0.0304 amu) than the sum of its parts! Could the helium nucleus have resulted from a *fusion* of two protons (hydrogen nuclei) and two neutrons that lost mass and therefore radiation energy in the process? But if a neutron is a fused proton-electron particle (Chapter 23), then the helium nucleus basically could involve a fusion of four protons (Fig. 24–5)* possible under conditions of very high temperature. In short, in the sun, hydrogen may be changing into helium, losing mass as energy. If so, 0.03 amu out of 4.03 amu—3 out of 403 parts—or about ¾ of 1 percent of the total hydrogen mass fusing would be lost.

Actually, Bethe postulated a six-stage cycle of transmutations that repeats itself. Notice in Table 24–1 that he starts with carbon-12 and hydrogen and ends with the same carbon and helium. Also notice that nitrogen and oxygen are present in the transition stages of the cycle. For example, in step 1, a proton $_1H^1$ breaks into a carbon nucleus $_6C^{12}$ to become a nitrogen isotope $_7N^{13}$. At millions of degrees centigrade, particle speeds are enormous.

The nitrogen is an unstable, radioactive isotope with a 40,000-year half-life, and it leads to five more nuclear changes that involve the capture of three more protons.† During the last stage, the original carbon nucleus $_6C^{12}$ reappears, and the four captured hydrogen $_1H^1$ have become a helium nucleus $_2H^4$. The net effect of the transformation of hydrogen into helium

24–5 Nuclear fusion of hydrogen into helium. Under solar temperatures of millions of degrees, hydrogen changes into helium, losing mass as energy. A helium nucleus fused from four hydrogen nuclei weighs less than the sum of its parts. The mass lost takes the form of solar radiation (represented by the wavy lines).

* The fusion process involves a number of intermediate steps, discussed later (Table 24–1).

† The $_1e^0$ in the table represents a positively charged electron, discussed in the next section.

Table 24–1 | NUCLEAR FUSION OF HYDROGEN INTO HELIUM

1. $_1H^1 + {_6}C^{12} = {_7}N^{13} + \gamma$ ray
2. $\qquad\qquad\qquad {_7}N^{13} \longrightarrow {_6}C^{13} + {_1}e^0$
3. $_1H^1 + {_6}C^{13} = {_7}N^{14} + \gamma$ ray
4. $_1H^1 + {_7}N^{14} = {_8}O^{15} + \gamma$ ray
5. $\qquad\qquad\qquad {_8}O^{15} \longrightarrow {_7}N^{15} + {_1}e^0$
6. $_1H^1 + {_7}N^{15} = {_6}C^{12} + {_2}He^4$

Net result: $4\ {_1}H^1 \longrightarrow {_2}He^4 + 2\ {_1}e^0 +$ energy

is schematically shown in Fig. 24–5. That the amount of energy released would be tremendous is clear from $E = mc^2$. To illustrate, take the energy E emitted by the sun when it loses a mass m of just 1 gram (or $\frac{1}{28}$ of an ounce). We have seen:

$E = mc^2$

$\qquad = 1(3 \times 10^9)\ (3 \times 10^9) = 9 \times 10^{18}$
$\qquad\qquad\qquad\qquad = 9,000,000,000,000,000,000$ ergs
$E = 9$ billion billion ergs.

Nine billion billion ergs is equal to about 25 million kilowatt-hours, or enough energy to operate 25 million lamps of 100 watts each for 10 hours. Just imagine all this energy transformed from just $\frac{1}{28}$ of an ounce of matter! No wonder the sun and stars can maintain high temperatures for billions of years.

It would seem that atoms not only split into simpler atoms, but in the sun and stars, they fuse into more complex atoms. If so, the universe not only runs down in some places but builds up in others—in basic contradiction to the law of dissipation of energy (Chapter 13). In any case, as long as the sun and stars contain the simplest element, hydrogen, they should form helium as well as shine of their own light.

If matter is energy at a complex level, the transformation from one to the other works both ways. Not only may matter become energy (and be dissipated), but as we shall see, pure energy may concentrate into matter. Stars die, but others form.

DISCOVERY OF POSITIVE ELECTRONS

In 1932 Carl D. Anderson, an American physicist at the California Institute of Technology, discovered positively charged electrons, later called *positrons*. In a cloud chamber photograph an electron track curved in a direction opposite to that of a usual electron (Fig. 24–6). A magnetic field perpendicular to the plane of the figure served to deflect the particle. The ¼-inch lead plate shows that the particle traveled from left to right, from less to greater curvature. A particle, slowed down in passing through a plate, must make a greater curve *after* it leaves the plate. A usual negative electron would have curved downward, not upward, in Anderson's magnetic field.

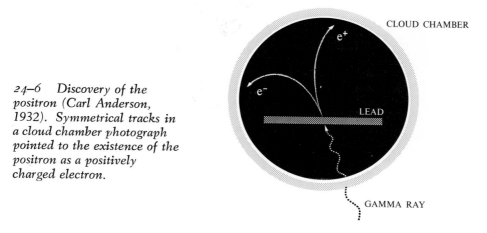

24–6 Discovery of the positron (Carl Anderson, 1932). Symmetrical tracks in a cloud chamber photograph pointed to the existence of the positron as a positively charged electron.

FIRST
ARTIFICIAL RADIOACTIVITY

In 1934 the Joliet-Curies bombarded separate aluminum, boron, and magnesium targets with alpha particles. The targets became artificially radioactive and emitted positrons, or positive electrons. Supposedly, in these cases, when an atom is hit, one of its protons decays into a neutron and emits a positron (Fig. 24–7). This conclusion was supported by the fact that the new elements were one less in atomic number (protons), but the same in atomic weight. The positron was established as a fourth subatomic particle, and Anderson received a Nobel prize for its discovery. Not so basic as the proton, neutron, and electron, the positron showed itself in man-made radioactivity. Positrons were later found

24–7 First artificial radioactivity (Joliet-Curie team, 1934). Aluminum and other atomic nuclei bombarded by alpha particles emit positive electrons. The target atoms, artificially radioactive, decay into simpler atoms.

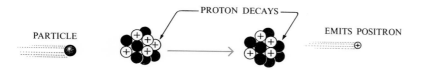

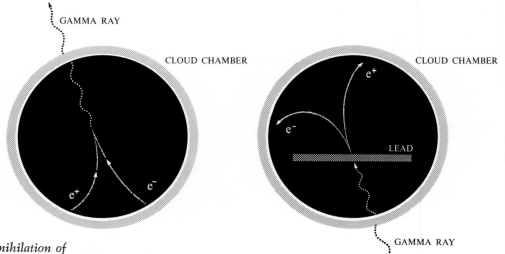

GAMMA RAY

CLOUD CHAMBER

CLOUD CHAMBER

e⁺

e⁻

LEAD

e⁺

e⁻

GAMMA RAY

24–8A Annihilation of matter. Tracks of an electron and a positron are seen to approach each other, unite, and disappear. But a gamma ray appears immediately.

24–8B Creation of matter. The tracks of an electron and a proton here start from a single point and curve away from each other. But first, gamma rays were used to irradiate the metal from which the tracks emerge.

within *cosmic rays,* and to be there in numbers equal to negative electrons. Cosmic rays are discussed later in this chapter.

Curie and Joliet obtained a Nobel prize for the discovery of artificial radioactivity just described and for many other outstanding scientific achievements. Not all man-made transmutations are radioactive. The above Curie and Joliet transmutations were so because particles (the positrons) continued to be emitted and elements transformed *after* target bombardments ceased. Interestingly enough, the first three Nobel awards to women physical scientists were to two Curies, mother and daughter.

POSITRON-ELECTRON ANNIHILATION: ENERGY FROM MATTER

Soon a positron and electron were found to *annihilate* each other. The two are opposite in charge. Tracks of the two particles approach each other and disappear (Fig. 24–8A). But a penetrating gamma ray appears immediately. Two bits of matter vanish from the universe, but a photon of energy takes its place. And the energy E of the photon satisfies $E = mc^2$ where m is the combined mass of the vanished particles. Atomic energy was on its way!

POSITRON-ELECTRON CREATION: MATTER FROM ENERGY

But there is birth of positron-electron pairs as well as annihilation. Matter may arise from pure energy! Photographs were found in which identical symmetrical tracks curve out in opposite directions from a single point (Fig. 24–8B). The lines were typical electron and positron tracks and seemed to indicate the birth of these opposite "twins." Gamma rays had been used experimentally to irradiate carbon, lead, aluminum, or other metals. The energies of the applied gamma ray photons matched the electron-positron masses determined from the tracks. The interpretation is that photons were transformed into electron-positron pairs. Energy is lost and matter gained. But the hapless positron does not last long, about a billionth of a second! Electrons are everywhere, and no sooner does a positron come about than poof, annihilation.

LAW OF CONSERVATION OF MATTER-ENERGY

Chemistry was based on the law of conservation of matter stating that the total amount of matter in the universe is always the same. Physics was based on the law of conservation of energy, stating that the total amount of energy in the universe is constant. But if matter transforms into energy, or energy into matter, then what? Where is the constancy of matter or energy? What happens to the indispensable "=" signs in the equations of the physicist and chemist? What happens to physics and chemistry as "exact" science? Actually, Einstein combined the two conservation laws into one, a law of the conservation of matter *and* energy or of matter-energy: *The total amount of both matter and energy is always the same.* If matter and energy are different forms of the same thing, what difference does the form make in the grand total of that thing? The total amount of money in a child's bank can remain the same regardless of how paper bills are exchanged for coins or vice versa. In the case of matter and energy, $E = mc^2$ takes care of the conversion. It is not just that matter may be transformed into energy, but that a certain amount of matter always transforms into a definite amount of energy. An electron-positron pair as matter always becomes the same definite amount of energy. And by the same conversion scale ($E = mc^2$), every transformable gram of matter should yield 25 million kilowatt-hours of energy. Whatever is lost in matter is gained in energy.

NEPTUNIUM AND PLUTONIUM: MAN-MADE ELEMENTS

The Italian physicist Enrico Fermi (1901–1954) was the first to bombard uranium, the heaviest known natural element, with neutrons and to re-

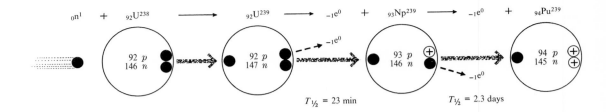

$_0n^1 \quad + \quad _{92}U^{238} \quad \longrightarrow \quad _{92}U^{239} \quad \longrightarrow \quad _{-1}e^0 \quad + \quad _{93}Np^{239} \quad \longrightarrow \quad _{-1}e^0 \quad + \quad _{94}Pu^{239}$

$T_{1/2} = 23$ min $T_{1/2} = 2.3$ days

*24–9   Man-made elements.
A uranium-238 atom captures
a bombarding neutron ($_0n^1$),
to become a radioactive
uranium-239 isotope. The
U^{239} nucleus soon emits a beta
particle ($_{-1}e^0$) and becomes
element 93, neptunium-239.
The Np^{239} nucleus, also
radioactive, emits a beta
particle and transmutes into
element 94, plutonium-239
($_{94}Pu^{239}$).*

port the formation of a heavier element (1934). When the neutron was discovered·in 1932, Fermi immediately recognized its unique possibilities for penetrating nuclei. Uncharged, neutrons would not be electrically repelled by orbiting electrons or charged nuclei of target atoms. By 1933 Fermi showed experimentally that some neutron "bullets" are captured by target nuclei. A captured neutron raises the atomic weight of its host nucleus. Fermi recognized that a captured neutron could disturb the balance, overcome the binding force, and cause transmutation of a nucleus. Fermi also found that slow neutrons are captured more frequently than faster ones. He slowed down neutrons by placing water or paraffin in front of bombarded substances. An alpha or other charged particle needs speed to overcome the electrical barriers of target atoms. But the uncharged neutron has no electrical barrier to meet, and if moving slowly, it has more chance of being captured. The slow neutron projectile was a long step toward tapping nuclear energy, as we shall see.

Fermi then attempted to transform uranium by neutron bombardment. Uranium was the heaviest element, atomic number 92. If a uranium atom $_{92}U^{238}$ captured a neutron $_0n^1$ (charge 0, atomic weight 1), a new uranium isotope $_{92}U^{239}$ would be formed (Fig. 24–9). That is:

Uranium-238 + neutron $\longrightarrow$ uranium-239

$$_{92}U^{238} \quad + \quad _0n^1 \quad \longrightarrow \quad _{92}U^{239}. \qquad \text{Equation 24–4}$$

If this isotope was radioactive as expected and emitted beta particles $_{-1}e^0$, the nuclei would have 93 protons and be *transuranic*—a new, man-made element, atomic number 93, *beyond uranium* (Fig. 24–9). That is,

Uranium-239 $\longrightarrow$ electron + new element

$$_{92}U^{239} \quad \longrightarrow \quad _{-1}e^0 \quad + \quad _{93}Np^{239}, \qquad \text{Equation 24–5}$$

where $_{93}Np^{239}$ would be the new unknown element eventually called neptunium. The beta particle or electron $_{-1}e^0$ has negligible mass; the new element Np would therefore have the same atomic mass 239 as U^{239}.

Fermi conducted an experiment in 1934 and reported his belief that he had discovered a new transuranic element. The scientific world was excited. Scientists in a number of countries, including the Otto Hahn–Lise

Meitner team in Berlin, the Curie-Joliet team in Paris, and eventually Edwin McMillan and Philip Abelson at the University of California, Berkeley, attempted to substantiate the new element by isolating some of it. With the aid of the 60-inch cyclotron at Berkeley, the U.S. team in 1940 accumulated enough of the element to establish its existence and give the element its name, "neptunium." Perturbations of the "outermost" planet, Uranus, led to the discovery of Neptune beyond; instability forced upon the last element, uranium, led to a further element, neptunium. The unstable uranium-239 has a half-life of 23 minutes. But dramatically enough, the new element neptunium was found to be radioactive, with a half-life of 2.3 days! Neptunium emitted a beta particle to form still another artificial transuranic element called plutonium, Pu (Fig. 24–9). That is,

Neptunium-239 $\longrightarrow$ electron + plutonium-239

$$_{93}Np^{239} \longrightarrow _{-1}e^0 + _{94}Pu^{239}. \qquad \text{Equation 24–6}$$

Notice that atomic weights of the plutonium $_{94}Pu^{239}$ and neptunium $_{93}Np^{239}$ are the same, although plutonium, atomic number 94, has one more proton than neptunium. Also notice that the subscripts balance out, since the electron charge is -1.

In 1935 Arthur Dempster at the University of Chicago had discovered that there is a uranium-235 as well as a uranium-238 isotope. However, 99.3 percent of uranium as found in ore is uranium-238. In 1939 McMillan showed beyond doubt that it was uranium-238 rather than uranium-235 that absorbed the neutron to become neptunium. Then Glenn Seaborg, McMillan, J. W. Kennedy, and A. C. Wahl, working with the cyclotron at Berkeley, isolated artificial element 94 and named it plutonium. Plutonium-239 turned out to be quite stable, with a half-life of 24,000 years—relatively stable if left undisturbed by man.

FISSION AND CHAIN REACTION

Lise Meitner, a German-Jewish mathematical physicist at the Karl Wilhelm Institute, near Hitler's chancellery, fled in January 1939 to Sweden just a step ahead of the Storm Troopers. With her she brought a key to unlock the last door to atomic energy. It was an insight that she had gained in her work at Berlin and that could have won the war for Hitler. Instead, she gave her secret to Bohr, who was about to leave for a physics conference in the United States.

Physicist Meitner and chemist Otto Hahn were a highly respected team having much experience with natural radioactivity. Back in 1917, they discovered radioactive protactinium, element number 91. When

Fermi artificially transmuted uranium into neptunium, Hahn and Meitner repeated the experiments and confirmed the results. Then in 1938, joined by Fritz Strassman, they investigated further. An objective was to isolate a minute amount of the new element. But the research bombardments took a strange turn; unexpected atoms showed their tracks. It was at this time, January 1939, that Lise Meitner had to flee from Germany. After her departure, chemists Hahn and Strassman emphasized in a German scientific journal that some uranium atoms do not build up to neptunium but split almost in half. The split nuclei form barium, element number 56, and krypton, element number 36. That is, $_{92}U \longrightarrow$ $_{56}Ba + _{36}Kr$. Meitner, joining a nephew, physicist Otto Frisch, in Sweden, named the splitting of the uranium atom into almost equal parts *atomic fission*. But physicist that she was, she was even more impressed by the 240 million electron volts recorded during the uranium fission in the Berlin research. Here seemed to be not just a strange transmutation of a heavy nucleus into lighter elements, but matter converted to energy on a large scale. We tend to observe what we are trained to see: Chemist Hahn in Germany emphasized the transmutation of elements; physicists Meitner and Frisch pursued the matter-energy conversion.

Bohr reported Meitner's finding to the January 1939 physics conference in Washington, D.C. He suggested that a neutron striking a uranium-235 nucleus caused it to fission, releasing considerable energy, and that a neutron striking a uranium-238 atom transmuted it into an element beyond uranium. Excitement ran high. The atomic energy scent was hot.

Fermi was also at the conference. He had recently left Fascist Italy to become a professor of physics at Columbia University and then at Chicago. Fermi suggested the possibility of chain reaction, a possibility that uranium fission may release one or more neutrons along with split nuclei and energy. Such a chain reaction could *maintain or accelerate a dependable release of atomic energy*. Figure 24–10 illustrates chain reaction of $_{92}U^{235}$. A stray neutron hits a uranium-235 atom, causing it to split into $_{56}Ba$ and $_{36}Kr$, *three* neutrons, and energy. These three neutrons in turn could act as projectiles against three more $_{92}U^{235}$ atoms, which together emit *nine* neutrons and more energy, ... The neutron projectiles and energy emitted multiply like a chain letter in which each person receiving a letter writes three of them. The letter-writing continues as long as there is an average of at least one letter sent out for each one received. Similarly, a nuclear chain reaction is self-sustaining and controlled as long as an average of one neutron emitted in fission causes another fission. Chain reaction in atom splitting is *explosive* when an average of *more than one* emitted neutron causes another fission. The effect can be like that of ping-pong balls set on mousetraps in pairs, and triggered by an odd ping-pong ball thrown into their midst.

For a number of months, research laboratories of several conference participants hummed in checking the above conference ideas. Frisch

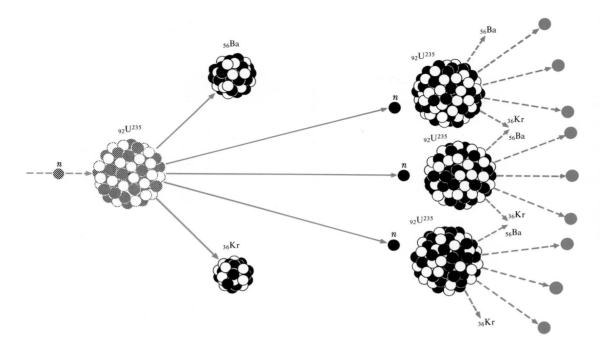

and Joliet independently substantiated the release of large amounts of energy in uranium fission. Fermi, Szilard, and others in the United States explored the possibilities of nuclear chain reactions for military uses. Alfred Nier at the University of Minnesota successfully isolated a small quantity of fissionable uranium-235. It was then that McMillan and Abelson at Berkeley isolated some neptunium, and Glenn Seaborg, McMillan, Wahl, and J. W. Kennedy at Berkeley isolated plutonium. Soon (in 1941) the Seaborg team, joined by Emilio Segré, discovered that plutonium-239 when bombarded by slow neutrons is fissionable. There were now two roads to a chain reaction release of atomic energy: uranium-235—directly fissionable—and plutonium. But there is 140 times more uranium-238 than uranium-235 in ordinary uranium ore. Plutonium, obtainable from the more abundant uranium-238, seemed the better choice. Plutonium is also more easily separated from uranium-238 than is uranium-235. The plutonium direction was followed.

Meanwhile, Einstein had been asked to write to President Roosevelt urging a need for large-scale research and development of an atomic bomb. Although a lifelong pacifist, Einstein did so. He feared that Hitler would secure the bomb first. In his letter to President Roosevelt, Einstein said, "I understand that Germany has actually stopped the sale of uranium from the Czechoslovakian mines which were taken over. That she should have taken such early action might perhaps be understood on the ground that the son of the German Undersecretary of State, von Weizsacker, is

24–10   Nuclear chain reaction. A stray neutron splits a uranium-235 nucleus ($_{92}U^{235}$) into large sections, barium (Ba) and krypton (Kr) nuclei. One or more neutrons also emitted act as projectiles against other U^{235} atoms, which emit other neutrons and energy in a mounting chain process.

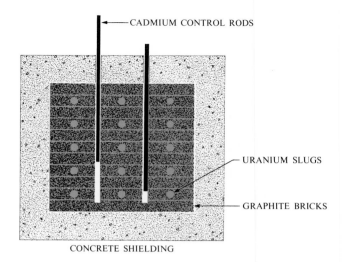

CADMIUM CONTROL RODS

URANIUM SLUGS

GRAPHITE BRICKS

CONCRETE SHIELDING

24–11A *The nuclear reactor. Chunks of uranium are placed in alternate layers of graphite bricks. The graphite bricks slow down fast neutrons emitted by U^{235} atoms, thereby facilitating the capture of neutrons by other U^{235} atoms. Cadmium rods control the chain reaction. Cadmium metal completely absorbs neutrons. A rod inserted further into the reactor absorbs more neutrons and slows down the chain reaction. A chain reaction is sustained when an average of at least one neutron ejected in a U^{235} atom fission induces another fission (see Fig. 24–10). An average higher than one neutron per fission causing another fission results in an explosive reaction.*

attached to the Kaiser Wilhelm Institute in Berlin where some of the American work on uranium is now being repeated." The famous $2 billion Manhattan project was soon started, and military secrecy was clamped down on atomic research and development.

NUCLEAR REACTORS

In 1942 Fermi directed the secret construction of the world's first nuclear reactor under Stagg Field at the University of Chicago. The purpose was twofold: to test the idea of a slow chain reaction on a controlled basis and to investigate the possibilities of producing plutonium on a considerable scale. Fermi's reactor was called a "pile"; 12,400 pounds of graphite bricks were piled one by one into a giant cubic latticework about 24 feet to a side (Fig. 24–11A). Alternate layers of the graphite brick contained chunks of natural uranium. The fissionable U^{235} in the natural uranium would provide neutrons in chain reaction, and the U^{238} would transmute into plutonium (Fig. 24–11B). Graphite consists of carbon atoms. The function of the graphite carbon was to slow down the fast neutrons emitted from U^{235} atoms, so that more of these atoms would absorb neutrons and maintain the chain reaction. The more plentiful U^{238} atoms easily captured the fast neutrons and changed into plutonium.

But it would be deadly for the chain reaction to get out of hand. The metal cadmium completely absorbs neutrons. Cadmium rods were therefore inserted in slots at various places in the pile. An individual rod pushed further into the reactor would absorb more neutrons and slow down the chain reaction as indicated by Geiger counters. A cadmium rod pulled out leaves more neutrons free to fission uranium atoms. On December 2, 1942, with the pile activated and all ten control rods completely inserted, neutron detectors indicated that a self-sustaining chain reaction would start if the rods were removed. Several top scientists in the project, including Fermi, Szilard, Wigner, and Zinn, assembled at the pile. Fermi gave the signal to George Weil to pull out the last control rod. And the first controlled chain reaction took place. Compton called James Conant at Harvard University and said guardedly: "The Italian navigator has landed in the New World." The answer was, "How were the natives?" "Very friendly," was the reply.

FISSION AND THE A-BOMB

The Atomic Age had dawned, but unfortunately in the midst of war; an atomic bomb was wanted. Chain reaction was a fact, and adequate amounts of fissionable material were possible. Needed was a device for solving the problem of *critical mass*. Plutonium or uranium-235, concentrated beyond a certain minimum mass, would explode spontaneously. There were always stray neutrons around to start a chain reaction. A concentration of fissionable material less than the critical mass would not explode; more neutrons would escape than would be replaced in new atom-splitting. Smaller masses therefore could be kept apart so as not to explode. But the problem was to get the lesser pieces to fly together fast enough so as to explode when desired.

Hanford, Washington, was established as a site of suitable safety and security to construct three huge nuclear reactors each five stories high to transmute uranium into plutonium. The Columbia River was used to water-cool the reactors. For separating plutonium from the uranium, a chemical processing complex was also built. Hanford had 60,000 employees at the peak of construction. Oak Ridge, Tennessee, another atomic city, also had a pilot plant, and at one point required 80,000 workers for construction. A Los Alamos Scientific Laboratory was set up at Los Alamos, New Mexico, under J. Robert Oppenheimer (1904–1967), brilliant physicist of the University of California. By July 1945, Oppenheimer and his staff had the first atomic bomb ready to be tested on the New Mexico desert. General Farrell later reported:

> The effects could well be called unprecedented, magnificent, beautiful, stupendous, and terrifying. No man-made phenomenon of such tremendous power had ever occurred before. The lighting effects beggared description. The whole country was lighted by a searing light with the intensity many times that of the midday sun. It was golden, purple, violet, gray, and blue. It lighted every peak, crevasse, and ridge of the nearby mountain range with a clarity and beauty that cannot be described but must be seen to be imagined. It was that beauty the poets dream about but describe most poorly and inadequately.

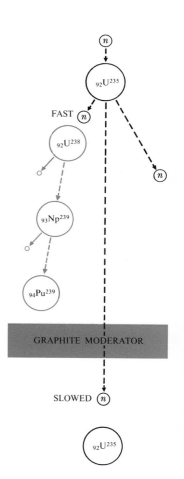

24–11B Production of plutonium. In a nuclear reactor some fast-moving neutrons are easily captured by uranium-238 atoms before reaching the graphite brick moderator. The capture of a neutron transmutes a U^{238} atom into neptunium-239 and then plutonium-239.

Thirty seconds after, the explosion came first, the air blast pressing hard against the people and things, to be followed almost immediately by the strong sustained, awesome roar which warned of doomsday and made us feel that we puny things were blasphemous to dare tamper with [such] forces.

As it turned out, the Nazis placed their main research efforts behind development of rockets rather than A-bombs. Germany surrendered in 1945. Japan was brought to her knees by an atom bomb on Hiroshima and one on Nagasaki. Hiroshima had a population of 245,000. About 85,000 people were killed and another 85,000 maimed by the single bomb, equivalent to many thousands of tons of TNT. Nagasaki had 45,000 people killed and 60,000 injured out of its 195,000 population. The *New York Times* editorialized, "It flashed to the minds of men the most spectacular proof of the Einstein Theory of Relativity which provided the key to the vast treasure house of energy within the atom . . . ." But Einstein, shocked, said, "The world is not yet ready for atomic energy . . . . Had I known that the Germans would not succeed in developing an atomic bomb, I would have done nothing for the bomb . . . . At present atomic energy is not a boon to mankind, but a menace."

FUSION AND THE HYDROGEN BOMB

We have seen that in 1939 Bethe explained that the sun's energies result from the fusion of four hydrogen nuclei into one helium nucleus in six steps (Table 24–1 and Fig. 24–5). Carbon-12 is an agent in the fusion, and positrons $_1e^0$ are emitted, but the end result is matter transformed into vast quantities of energy, as predicted by Einstein.

After World War II, this question arose: Can the fusion process be duplicated on earth for energy purposes? A difficulty was that a temperature of millions of degrees centigrade is necessary to start and maintain a *thermonuclear* process like that on the sun. The process is called *thermonuclear* because it is induced by a great amount of heat. Oppenheimer and his staff at Los Alamos recognized that an A-bomb explosion created for an instant the temperature necessary for a thermonuclear reaction. The A-bomb could be a trigger for a far more devastating hydrogen bomb. As for controlled, peacetime purposes, no techniques were known for controlling a nuclear fusion "furnace" at millions of degrees over a period of time. As a matter primarily of conscience, Oppenheimer argued against the development of the H-bomb, and he was forced from his post in semi-disgrace. The question of the ethical responsibilities of a scientist is still with us. But Hungarian-born Edward Teller, present director of the University of California Radiation Laboratory at Livermore, assumed leadership in creating an H-bomb.

There were several possibilities for man-made thermonuclear reactions. Natural hydrogen was early eliminated as not feasible. Heavy hydrogen isotopes, deuterium $_1H^2$ and tritium $_1H^3$, were found to be effective in combinations, as illustrated below:

Deuterium + deuterium $\longrightarrow$ helium + neutrons + energy

$$_1H^2 \quad + \quad _1H^2 \quad \longrightarrow \quad _2He^4 \quad + \quad n \quad + \quad 3.25 \text{ Mev}$$
Equation 24–7

Tritium + tritium

$$_1H^3 \quad + \quad _1H^3 \quad \longrightarrow \quad _2He^4 \quad + \quad 2n \quad + \quad 11.00 \text{ Mev}$$
Equation 24–8

Deuterium + tritium

$$_1H^2 \quad + \quad _1H^3 \quad \longrightarrow \quad _2He^4 \quad + \quad n \quad + \quad 17.6 \text{ Mev.}$$
Equation 24–9

A comparison of energies emitted shows that a combination of deuterium and tritium (Eq. 24–9) is most effective:

Two deuterium particles (Eq. 24–7) offer 3.25 Mev.
Two tritium particles (Eq. 24–8) offer 11.00 Mev.
Deuterium and tritium combined (Eq. 24–9) offer 17.6 Mev.

The tritium-deuterium combination offers over five times as much energy as deuterium alone and over one and a half times as much as tritium alone.

A successful thermonuclear explosion on November 1, 1952, wiped out an island 30 miles from Eniwetok, the official testing base, according to some reports. An H-bomb has the energy equivalent of *millions* of tons of TNT. (The A-bomb is in the thousands of tons.) At the moment of explosion, there was a flash of light with ten times the glare of the sun, followed by a momentary wave of scorching heat felt even at a distance of 30 miles. A flame 5 miles high and 2 miles wide was seen as thousands of tons of dirt were thrown sky-high. Then a gigantic mushroom cloud appeared, 15 miles high and 30 miles wide.

A year later, Premier Malenkov of the Soviet Union announced that "The government deems it necessary to report to the Supreme Soviet that the United States has no monopoly of the hydrogen bomb." In August 1953, the Soviet Union had its own thermonuclear explosion.

PEACEFUL USES
OF ATOMIC ENERGY

Prometheus braved the wrath of the gods to bring fire to man. Fire warms and fire destroys. Men have learned to benefit from fire and also to

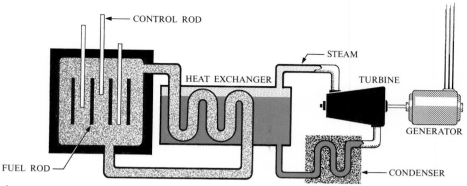

CONTROL ROD

STEAM

HEAT EXCHANGER

TURBINE

GENERATOR

FUEL ROD

CONDENSER

24–12 Electric power from atomic energy. Heat from a nuclear reactor is transferred by water or another coolant into the heat exchanger, where the energy is transformed into steam. The steam spins a turbine, which turns the armature of an electrical generator.

minimize its dangers. Atomic energy also can create and destroy. The problem is an old one. "They shall beat their swords into plowshares, and their spears into pruning hooks," a Biblical quotation counsels. Men have always struggled against hunger and disease. Today nuclear reactors can do much to aid in that struggle. Thinking men can maximize the benefits and avoid the dangers. Nuclear reactors since World War II are playing more and more of a role in supplying electric power, in extending medical diagnosis and treatment, in increasing food and water supply, and in adding to basic knowledge.

Electric Power from Atomic Energy

The coal and oil deposits of the earth took millions of years to form. Estimates are that present reserves will be exhausted in 2 or 3 centuries. The nuclear reactor is the answer to the question of what then. Figure 24–12 illustrates the use of a nuclear reactor for electric power purposes. The reactor contains the atomic fuel that replaces the burning coal or oil. Otherwise, the process of generating electricity is the same as explained in Chapter 16. You will recall that the five basic components of a reactor are these:

    1. A nuclear fuel such as ordinary uranium enriched with U^{235}. Thorium, element 90, has been found to be fissionable, too.
    2. A moderator (graphite, water, or beryllium) for slowing down neutrons.
    3. Control rods made of boron, cadmium, or hafnium.
    4. A coolant, such as water, gas, or a liquid metal.
    5. A lead or concrete shielding.

For manufacturing plutonium at Hanford, Washington, the Columbia River was used as a coolant. A vast amount of heat from the coolant can be transformed into mechanical and then electrical energy. That is, water can be heated to steam which is led to a turbine, which spins the wheels of a generator, which produces electricity.

In 1955 electricity from an experimental reactor of a National Reactor Testing Station lighted Arco, Idaho, for an hour. The first full-scale atomic power plant went into operation at Calder Hall, England, in 1956. The first atomic power plant to supply electricity in the United States was in Shippingport, Pennsylvania, near Pittsburgh, in December 1957. Built jointly by the Atomic Energy Commission and the Duquesne Light Company, the plant had a capacity of 60,000 kilowatts. The Pacific Gas and Electric Company fed 5,000 kilowatts into its power network from a developmental plant in northern California 2 months earlier. In June 1960 the Commonwealth Edison Company sent 180,000 kilowatts over transmission lines to Chicago and northern Illinois. The Atomic Energy Commission anticipates that one-third of all electrical generating capacity in the United States will be nuclear by 1980.

In 1954 the United States sent the Nautilus, the first nuclear powered submarine, to sea. In 1956 the U.S.S.R. completed a nuclear powered icebreaker, and in 1957 an atomic powered whaler. The world's first nuclear powered ocean liner, the N. S. Savannah, was christened in the United States in 1959.

To solve a serious water problem, the U.S. Congress in 1966 authorized a $0.5 billion nuclear desalting and power plant along the California coast. A year later Glenn Seaborg, chairman of the U.S. Atomic Energy Commission, wrote of the project by an Oak Ridge team

> of a nuclear plant capable of generating one million kilowatts of electricity and desalting 400 million gallons of water per day. It is estimated that such a plant could support the daily production of 2,000 tons of ammonia and 360 tons of phosphorus. The food factory in this plant would consist of 200,000 acres irrigated and fertilized by the nuclear plant. On the basis of growing a single high yield grain crop, it is projected that this complex could produce more than one billion pounds of grain annually—enough to feed almost 2.5 million people at a caloric level of 2,400 calories per day. In addition, it could export enough fertilizer to other agricultural areas, where the components other than fertilizer are already available, to cultivate 10 million more acres. It has been estimated that this could provide, even through less scientific agriculture than the "food factory," from 15 billion to 45 billion additional pounds of grain—enough to feed tens of millions of people at the same substantial caloric rate.*

In the middle of 1960, the number of nuclear reactors in the world went well beyond 100, including reactors in Australia, Belgium, Canada, China, England, France, India, Norway, Spain, Sweden, Switzerland, the Soviet Union, and the United States.

*"Need We Fear Our Nuclear Future?", *Bulletin of the Atomic Scientists,* Vol. XXV, No. 7, (January 1969), pp. 38–39.

Particularly in the United States, the Soviet Union, and England, there has been experimentation for some time to obtain energy from a controlled hydrogen fusion. An immense amount of energy then would be available for all mankind. Glenn Seaborg pointed out at the Marie Curie Centenary in Warsaw, Poland, in October 1967, "The heavy hydrogen from the water in the earth's oceans and seas would become available as fuel for the production of energy. The successful development of a controlled thermonuclear fusion reactor would mean the availability of an energy source equal to 500 Pacific Oceans full of high grade petroleum, a truly enormous and staggering quantity of energy." A basic problem is the temperature of fusion. No container could take a temperature of millions of degrees. A concept of a "magnetic bottle" is being pursued. The hydrogen would be in the form of ions. Magnetic fields can confine such electrical particles to limited spaces without container walls. But there are many practical problems and dangers involved that may well take until about 1985 to overcome.

Radioactive Tracers in Medicine, Agriculture, and Research

Atom smashing in cyclotrons and neutron bombardments in reactors resulted in radioactive isotopes—"radioisotopes" for short—undreamed of in variety and amounts. A radioisotope is a radioactive isotope of an element obtained from a man-made nuclear bombardment. Joliet and Curie obtained the first radioisotope in 1934. You will recall that these two scientists bombarded boron with alpha particles and obtained nitrogen. The nitrogen they obtained was not the usual stable nitrogen-14, but a radioactive isotope nitrogen-13. Short a single neutron, a nitrogen-13 atom is very unstable, with a half-life of only 15 minutes. The nitrogen-13 isotope emits positrons. It is a man-made radioactive element.

The metal cobalt, $_{27}Co^{59}$, is one of the few elements in nature that has only one isotope, a nonradioactive one. If a chunk of this stable cobalt-59 is placed in a reactor, part of it becomes an artificially radioactive isotope, cobalt-60. Exposed to neutron bombardment, some of the atoms capture an extra neutron to gain an extra unit of weight and instability. Such atoms show their instability by emitting gamma rays but remain cobalt since the number of protons (27) does not change. The process in the reactor may be shown as:

$$_{27}Co^{59} + _{0}n^{1} \longrightarrow _{27}Co^{60}. \hspace{2cm} \text{Equation 24–10}$$

Artificially radioactive cobalt-60, with a half-life of about 5¼ years, is over 300 times as powerful as naturally radioactive radium. Radioactive cobalt now often is used in place of radium for X-ray therapy in hospitals and is particularly valuable in treating deep-seated cancer, leukemia, goiter, and arthritis.

Cyclotron bombardments of elements by streams of subatomic particles were responsible for many radioisotopes, but a deluge of such isotopes came with nuclear reactors. The great flux of neutrons in reactors resulted in a much greater quantity and variety of radioisotopes at much less cost. Today the number of known isotopes is well beyond 1,000. Of these, about 275 are stable. The rest are mostly man-made radioisotopes. The Atomic Energy Commission by 1960 produced and distributed over 100 radioisotopes to thousands of hospitals and other institutions. These shipments were made for medical, industrial, agricultural, and research purposes in over 30 countries.

Carbon-14 was the first radioisotope delivered from Oak Ridge Laboratory. Carbon-12 and carbon-13 are stable isotopes that occur in nature. An ordinary carbon sample is 98.9 percent carbon-12 and 1.1 percent carbon-13. Carbon-10, carbon-11, and carbon-14 are radioactive isotopes produced in particle accelerators or reactors, with half-lives of 19 seconds, 20 minutes, and 5,360 years, respectively. The first two are too unstable, but carbon-14 is most valuable for medical, agricultural, industrial, and research purposes. Atoms of the stable carbon-13 placed within a reactor absorb neutrons, to become radioactive carbon-14. Elements to be made radioactive are inserted into aluminum cans, which are placed into graphite rods inserted into reactor interiors. Radioisotopes are measured in *milli-curies*. A millicurie is *an amount of a radioisotope that emits as much radiation as a thousandth of a gram of radium.* A millicurie of carbon-14 produced with a cyclotron would cost about $1 million. By contrast, the same amount of carbon-14 produced by the Oak Ridge reactor was about $50 when first produced.

The most valuable uses of radioisotopes are as tracers. A radioactive needle in a haystack can be found by Geiger counters. Radioisotopes can be traced through complex chemical reactions or physiological processes in plants and animals by Geiger or other detectors. Often, cures of diseased tissues can be effected through these radiation-bearing atoms. Cancer cells, for example, multiply much more rapidly than normal cells. Carbon compounds containing some carbon-14 can be used to study the differences in metabolic rate between normal and cancerous cells. Such compounds are fed to animals and traced within them. Cancerous cells will absorb more carbon-14 than normal cells will. This knowledge can lead to checking cancer by starving the rapidly multiplying cells.

Photosynthesis is the process by which plants combine carbon dioxide of the air and water from the soil into sugars and starches with the help of chlorophyll and sunlight. Full understanding and duplication of this natural process offers unlimited possibilities for the artificial manufacture of food. Tagging a small quantity of carbon-14 within carbon dioxide absorbed by plants and tracing this carbon-14 by Geiger counters through

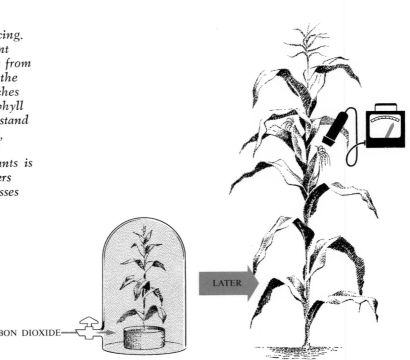

24–13 Radioactive tracing. In photosynthesis a plant combines carbon dioxide from the air and water from the soil into sugars and starches with the help of chlorophyll and sunlight. To understand this production of food, carbon-14 within carbon dioxide absorbed by plants is traced by Geiger counters through chemical processes in plants.

RADIOACTIVE CARBON DIOXIDE

LATER

chemical and physiological processes in these plants has been most revealing (Fig. 24–13) about nature's own recipes for food production.

Radioactive "dating" by carbon-14 has been discussed in Chapter 23. It is believed that fast-moving neutrons in the air bombard nitrogen-14 into radioactive carbon-14 (nature's own atom smashing). Radioactive carbon-14 then combines with oxygen to form radioactive carbon dioxide absorbed by plants and eaten by animals. All living things therefore maintain a small constant ratio of carbon-14 to carbon-12 as part of a life cycle discussed in Chapter 23. When a plant ceases functioning or an animal dies, intake of carbon dioxide from the air stops. As the carbon-14 within the organism decays, the radiation count of the remaining carbon-14 indicates the age of the fallen tree, the manuscript, or what have you. The lower the radiation count, the older the object.

So much for radioactive carbon-14 and cobalt-60. Let us consider a few more examples of radioisotopes significant for health, food, and cultural benefits. Almost all iodine in food makes its way to the thyroid gland in the neck. Patients with possible thyroid trouble are given "atomic cocktails" containing a small amount of radioactive iodine. After a few hours, a counter systematically records the radiation emitted from the thyroid gland area. The concentration of iodine and the size and location of the gland can be determined and compared to normal performances for a medical diagnosis. Secondary cancers due to the thyroid gland also absorb iodine and can therefore be detected.

Radioactive sodium-24 can be incorporated into ordinary table salt. Such a radioactive salt solution is injected into the arm of a possible heart patient and carried by the blood to the heart. A counter near the heart clicks when the tagged blood arrives at the heart. This information of the rate of blood flow to the heart is excellent for diagnosis of heart disease. For example, constrictions in the arteries retard blood flow and can be located, or faulty pumping ability of the heart itself can be identified by tracing tagged atoms through specific heart chambers.

Radioactive phosphorus concentrating in brain tumors permits their detection. Phosphorus in food also makes its way to bones and teeth. The speed with which this is done is easily determined. An animal is fed with a proper radioactive phosphorus compound in its food. A Geiger counter clicks when the radioactive phosphorus arrives in the teeth. Radioactive phosphorus has also aided in agricultural tagging techniques for understanding growth processes in plants. Radioactive phosphates in fertilizers reveal what components and proportions of fertilizer and soil nutrients are absorbed by plant roots and under what circumstances. Also shown are what happens to the phosphorus atoms and to the fertilizer absorbed.

Radioactive phosphorus-32 is used not only to trace living processes but to cure disease. The body manufactures blood cells in bone marrow. In certain blood diseases, radioactive phosphorus taken with food collects in the bones. There the phosphorus emits mild radiation which is often beneficial. The half-life of phosphorus-32 is 14½ days; the radiation is desirably temporary.

Gold has a radioisotope that, arriving in the lymph system, has helped cure diseases there. Even strontium-90, feared as a widely scattered A-bomb product absorbed by plants and animals, has been used with adequate shielding as an electric battery. Heat emitted with weak beta rays from the strontium is converted by a thermocouple into electricity.

ELEMENTS BEYOND URANIUM

Neptune and Pluto became the outermost planets, but neptunium and plutonium did not complete the list of man-made elements. Berkeley research teams headed most often by Seaborg detected the eleven man-made elements 93–103, generally with the aid of the cyclotron.

Three years after creating plutonium, Seaborg and his Berkeley team, A. Ghiorso, R. A. James, and L. O. Morgan, discovered element 95. The group intensely bombarded plutonium with neutrons in nuclear reactors at the University of Chicago to find the new element, which they named americium (Am) after the Americas. Americium is produced in gram quantities at most.

In 1945 Seaborg, Ghiorso, and James bombarded plutonium with alpha particles from the 60-inch cyclotron at Berkeley. The result was element 96, curium (Cm), named after the Curies. This element can be collected only as minute specks with a half-life of 19 years.

Element 97, berkelium (Bk), resulted in 1949 when americium, element 95, was bombarded with alpha particles from the cyclotron. The new element honored Berkeley, the birthplace of many new elements. Samples of berkelium are infinitesimal.

When Seaborg and his colleagues in 1950 bombarded curium, element 96, with alpha particles, they obtained element 98, californium (Cf), in extremely minute amounts. The element, of course, was named after the state.

Elements 99 and 100 were discovered in radioactive dust of the first H-bomb explosion in 1952. The discoveries were made when tons of radioactive coral near the blast were independently analyzed by Seaborg and his colleagues, by a group at the Los Alamos Laboratory in New Mexico, and by a team at the Argonne National Laboratory in Illinois. The elements were named einsteinium and fermium after Einstein and Fermi. Einsteinium was later created in nuclear reactors, but in amounts too small to be weighed. Fermium has so short a half-life—3 hours—that serious doubt exists that enough of that element will ever be collected for weighing.

Seaborg and his group bombarded einsteinium with alpha particles in 1955, to obtain element 101, mendelevium, named after Mendeléyev.

A new heavy-ion linear accelerator at Berkeley enabled a group under A. Ghiorso in 1958 to bombard curium with carbon ions and to obtain element 102, called nobelium after Alfred Nobel.

In 1961 californium was bombarded with boron ions to produce element 103, named lawrencium after the inventor of the cyclotron.

Not only the collectable amounts of the man-made elements after plutonium become successively smaller, but the half-lives, too. Plutonium has a half-life of 24,000 years; curium, 19 years; californium, 55 days; fermium, 3 hours; and nobelium, 3 seconds. Discovery of further elements now becomes difficult indeed when the quantities created are so small that they must be counted as atoms by detectors, and when these atoms themselves are expected to have half-lives in small fractions of a second.

For his work with plutonium and leadership in creation of man-made elements, Seaborg has received many honors and awards, including a Nobel prize. Considered one of the outstanding living nuclear chemists in the United States, he has received honorary degrees from twenty universities, has been chancellor of the University of California, Berkeley, and has been the chairman of the Atomic Energy Commission through the 1960s.

COSMIC RAYS AND
OTHER NUCLEAR PARTICLES

That there should be alpha, beta, and other particles in the atmosphere is not surprising. Uranium, thorium, and other radioactive deposits have been emitting rays for billions of years. What is surprising is that the farther we ascend from the earth's surface, the more ionized are the particles found in the air. Considerable balloon experimentation just before World War I made inescapable the conclusion that ionizing rays are bombarding the earth's atmosphere from outer space. Later investigations showed that these *cosmic rays* approach the earth from all directions.

In time this radiation bombardment from outer space was divided into primary and secondary cosmic rays. The primary rays are the original rays before they reach the earth's atmosphere. The primary rays have been found to be mostly protons traveling almost as fast as light. But helium, carbon, nitrogen, oxygen—in fact, almost all known elements—are included in this rain of ions from outer space. Cosmic rays are primarily atomic nuclei that have left their orbital electrons far behind. Estimates are that more than a billion billion primary cosmic particles approach the earth each second.

The origin of cosmic rays is a matter of hypothesis. Undoubtedly some protons and other particles do arrive from the sun as a "solar wind." But the earth turns. If most of the cosmic rays were from the sun, sharp day-and-night differences in cosmic ray intensity would be observed. Intensity would certainly be much greater during the day. Actually, observed day-and-night differences are negligible. Cosmic rays from the sun are like a slight spray of moisture from a running stream during a heavy cloud-burst. There is some reason to believe that cosmic rays originate within our galaxy, the Milky Way. Our galaxy rotates; that means our solar system is a speck moving in it. The front of a moving car receives more raindrops than the back does. If cosmic rays come from outside the Milky Way, the front side of the earth in its galactic motion would be hit by more rays than the back would. But cosmic ray intensity is about equal on all sides of the earth. The most likely hypothesis is that cosmic rays are bits of matter hurled out in explosions of *supernovae* within our galaxy, and seen about once a century.

Moving electrical particles are deflected by magnetic fields. As cosmic particles approach, the earth's magnetic field deflects the slower ones toward higher latitudes. The faster particles rain in everywhere. Recent rocket and artificial satellite probes showed unexpected zones of trapped particles oscillating around the earth. These zones comprise the Van Allen Belt, named after their discoverer, James Van Allen.

Cosmic ray particles strike the earth's atmosphere at tremendous energies. The fastest, traveling at almost 186,000 miles per second (670 million miles per hour), reach energies of more than 1 billion Bev (1 billion billion electron volts). Imagine the havoc among molecules in the upper atmosphere hit by such "bullets"! The most powerful atom smashers of man have yet to reach a thousand Bev, let alone a billion Bev. Bevatron particles are comparable to the least energetic cosmic radiation.

Cosmic ray particles hit nitrogen and oxygen molecules in the air with such force that cascades of secondary particles result. A single primary "bullet" may smash many nuclei, which in turn are hurtled into other nuclei like bowling pins into each other. The primary particles get lost, but about eight secondary particles reach each square inch of the earth at sea level each minute. These secondary particles have been found to fit into five main categories: (1) nucleons, (2) electrons (positive and negative), (3) gamma rays, (4) mesons, and (5) hyperons.

Nucleons among secondary cosmic ray particles are protons and neutrons smashed out of atoms by primary cosmic rays or other secondaries. Some neutrons emit beta particles and decay into protons. Other neutrons are captured by nitrogen atoms that decay into radioactive carbon-14 and protons exactly as in nuclear reactors.

Neutron + nitrogen-14 $\longrightarrow$ carbon-14 + proton

$$_0n^1 \quad + \quad _7N^{14} \quad \longrightarrow \quad _6C^{14} \quad + \quad _1H^1. \qquad \text{Equation 24–11}$$

Carbon-14 unites with oxygen molecules, to give traces of radioactive carbon dioxide in the air and in plants and animals as described in sections on radioactive "dating" (Chapter 23) and on radioactive tracers.

Gamma rays, or *photons,* are expected wherever atomic nuclei are seriously disturbed or smashed, as in the atmosphere. They are also expected where both positrons and electrons exist to annihilate each other.

Electrons among cosmic rays are both negative and positive (positrons). Negative electrons result in the air when neutrons decay into protons. Also recall that some gamma rays (photons) when striking targets become electron-positron pairs. The process, of course, works both ways; gamma rays create electron pairs, and the pairs create gamma rays. High-energy photons create fast-moving electron pairs, and fast pairs create high-energy photons. In the reciprocal process the number of photon and electron pairs multiplies, but each new photon has less energy, and the new electron pairs have less speed. The cascade generally ends in the absorption of the end products by air molecules considerably above the earth. Electrons and gamma rays also arise in meson decay within secondary cosmic rays, described next.

Mesons were independently discovered in 1937 by Anderson and Nedermeyer at the California Institute of Technology and by Street and Stevenson at Harvard. Both research teams observed strange traces (Fig. 24–14) among cosmic ray tracks photographed in Wilson cloud chambers.

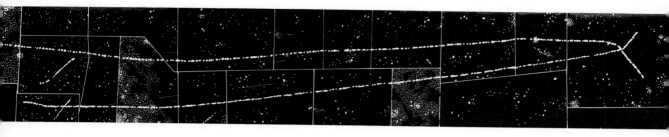

These traces indicated particles about 200 times heavier than electrons among debris of atoms shattered by cosmic rays. Researchers soon carried instruments to high mountain peaks and up in planes and balloons and found many more such particles. Protons entering the atmosphere from outer space at nearly the speed of light were pounding out mesons from air molecules. Free mesons were found to be very short-lived. In the unimaginably short time of 0.000002 seconds, half of them were gone. They decay into electrons, gamma rays, and into another new particle, the *neutrino* of no charge and no (or negligible) weight. Two years before the discovery of mesons, the Japanese physicist Yakawa theorized their existence within atomic nuclei. Such particles could explain the binding force within atomic nuclei that ordinarily keeps nuclei from electrically exploding apart. Yakawa's idea was that individual protons and neutrons do not maintain their identities, but change one into the other by continuous exchange of a positively charged meson between a proton and a neutron. Whichever particle at any moment has the positively charged meson is the proton. It is like a game in which hot potatoes are thrown around, and whoever is tagged with a potato is "it." Or, by another analogy, two or four tennis players are unified in a game by hitting a ball back and forth according to rules; an atomic nucleus is also bound together by to and fro motions of meson balls. To determine rules for tennis balls is, of course, easier than for mesons. But to come up with rules for nature is a long-term objective of science.

Yakawa went so far as to predict the existence of negative and neutral as well as positive mesons. In this way, he could explain bonds between proton and proton and between neutron and neutron as well as between proton and neutron. And true enough, negatively charged and neutral mesons were found. But once the simplicity of the atomic nucleus was broken, the nucleus really became complicated. Mesons were also found that varied in weight. Not only were there *mu* (μ) mesons with + or − charges and with a 2.2 millionths of a second half-life, but there were also *pi* (π) mesons, positive or negative in charge, with a 0.25 billionths of a second half-life (Table 24–2). The mu mesons were found at sea level with a mass 207 times an electron mass, and the pi mesons had a mass of 273 electron masses. A neutral pi meson had a mass of 264 electron masses. Found at altitudes where primary cosmic rays smash oxygen and nitrogen atoms, pi mesons rather than mu mesons are con-

24–14   Meson tracks. Such tracks traced in composite cosmic ray photographs indicate that particles about 200 times heavier than electrons exist in the debris of atoms shattered by cosmic rays. (After composite photographs taken at the University of California, Berkeley)

Table 24-2 | ELEMENTARY PARTICLES

FAMILY NAME	PARTICLE NAME	SYMBOL	ANTI-PARTICLE	MASS (ELECTRON MASS = 1)	HALF-LIFE (SEC)	STABILITY OR DECAY
	Photon	γ (gamma ray)	(γ)	0	Infinite	Stable
	Graviton			0	Infinite	Stable
Electron	Neutrino (of electron)	ν_e	$\bar{\nu}_e$	0	Infinite	Stable
	Electron	e^-	e^+ (positron)	1	Infinite	Stable
Muon	Neutrino (of muon)	ν_u	$\bar{\nu}_u$	0	Infinite	Stable
	Muon	u^-	u^+	207	2.2×10^{-6} (.0000022 sec)	Decays into electron and two neutrinos.
Meson	Pion	π^+	π^-	273	2.6×10^{-8}	Decays into muon and neutrino.
		π^0	(π^0)	264	$.9 \times 10^{-16}$	Decays into two photons.
	Kaon	K^+	$\bar{K}^+$	966	1.2×10^{-8}	Decays into two pions.
		K_1^0	$\bar{K}_1^0$	974	$.9 \times 10^{-10}$	Decays into two pions.
		K_2^0	$\bar{K}_2^0$	974	5.7×10^{-8}	Decays into two pions.
	Eta	η	$(\bar{\eta})$	1,074	Over 10^{-22}	Decays into two photons.
Nucleon	Proton	p^+	p^- (antiproton)	1,836	Infinite	Stable
	Neutron	n^0	$\bar{n}^0$	1,839	1,010 (17 min)	Unstable when free. Decays into proton, electron, and neutrino.
Hyperon	Lambda	Λ^0	$\bar{\Lambda}^0$	2,183	2.5×10^{-10}	Decays into proton and pion.
	Sigma	Σ^+	$\bar{\Sigma}^+$	2,328	8.1×10^{-11}	Decays into neutron and pion.
		Σ^-	$\bar{\Sigma}^-$	2,343	1.6×10^{-10}	Decays into neutron and pion.
		Σ^0	$\bar{\Sigma}^0$	2,334	About 10^{-20}	Decays into lambda hyperon and photon.
	Xi	Ξ^-	$\bar{\Xi}^-$	2,586	1.75×10^{-10}	Decays into lambda hyperon and pion.
		Ξ^0	$\bar{\Xi}^0$	2,573	3.0×10^{-10}	Decays into lambda hyperon and pion.
	Omega	Ω^-	$\bar{\Omega}^-$	3,276	1.5×10^{-10}	Decays into xi hyperon and pion.

sidered to be the "hot potato" binding force within atom nuclei. As shown in Table 24–2, mu mesons form when pi mesons decay outside of atoms. And then much heavier K mesons (Table 24–2) were found with about half the mass of protons. Some K mesons decay into pi mesons.

Over 200 different atomic particles have been found among debris shattered by powerful atom smashers operating at billions of electron volt energies. Among these particles are the *hyperons*. Hyperons are a group of unstable particles with masses greater than protons (Table 24–2). Early discoveries of hyperons were among cosmic rays. But most of the later discoveries were by atom smashers. With cyclotrons and other accelerators, atoms are smashed where they can be observed. With cosmic rays, a research team must wait until nature obliges. More and more powerful atom smashers are therefore being built everywhere.

ANTIPARTICLES
AND AN ANTIUNIVERSE

It is beyond the scope of this text to describe the many atomic subparticles in detail. But we do wish to point out that among these particles are antiparticles (Table 24–2, column 3). The positron has already been discussed as an antiparticle of the electron. The two particles are identical except for an opposite charge, and they annihilate each other to form gamma rays as shown in Wilson cloud chamber photographs. Emilio Segré and collaborators working with the Berkeley cyclotron were the first to artificially create in 1955 an antiparticle called an antiproton. The antiproton had the same mass as a proton but a negative charge (Fig. 24–15). The particles were created when protons were accelerated in the bevatron to an energy of 6.2 billion electron volts. When one of these protons hit a neutron in a target atom, an antiproton and a new proton were created. About 2 billion electron volts of the pure energy of the projectile particle disappeared, and two new particles of matter appeared. Man was creating matter by checking ideas against observations. Dr. Lawrence enthusiastically stated at the time: "Recalling that at the beginning of the past quarter-century the discovery of the positive electron set off the remarkable developments in nuclear physics that followed, one cannot help but wonder whether the discovery of the antiproton likewise is a milestone on the road to a whole new realm of physics that are coming in the days and years ahead."

Before Segré's man-made creation of an antiproton, tracks in separate studies by G. Retallack at Indiana University in 1951 and by B. Rossi at the Massachusetts Institute of Technology in 1954 pointed to antiprotons. The tracks were identical to those of protons except that they curved in a direction expected of a negatively charged particle. And in 1954, M. Schein at the University of Chicago showed evidence in a

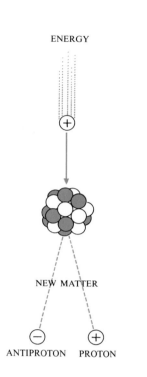

ENERGY

NEW MATTER

ANTIPROTON   PROTON

24–15   Artificial creation of an antiproton (Segré, 1955). The energy of high-speed protons directed at a target was transformed by Segré and collaborators into matter. Tracks show that particles identical to protons but opposite in charge replaced the "pure" kinetic energy of the original "bullets."

photograph emulsion flown at 100,000-foot altitude of the mutual annihilation of a proton and antiproton as the latter came in from outer space.

The value of the discovery of the creation and annihilation of antiprotons so far has been that of basic research, that of understanding the universe around and within us. The Latin origin of the word "science" is "to know." Spurred by the existence of particle polarity and annihilation in the case of electrons and protons, researchers and atom smashers sought and found antiparticles for neutrons, neutrinos, mesons, and hyperons, as listed in Table 24–2. Speculation has gone so far as the existence of an antiuniverse far from our own. It had better be far because matter and antimatter would totally annihilate each other on contact and would release enough energy to start reactions elsewhere.

The Bohr antiatom in such a universe would involve positive electrons (positrons) revolving around nuclei of negative protons (antiprotons) instead of electrons around protons. A proton and planetary electron compose a hydrogen atom. An antiproton and planetary positron would form an antihydrogen atom. Hydrogen atoms form a hydrogen molecule by sharing electrons (Chapter 20). Antihydrogen atoms would form an antihydrogen molecule by sharing positrons. Further antielements would be built up in a periodic table by adding antiprotons one by one to nuclei. Antioxygen, for example, would contain a nucleus of eight antiprotons and eight antineutrons. Eight positrons would surround the nucleus. The various antielements would form hundreds of thousands of compounds to compose the antiuniverse. In such an antiworld, antilife conceivably could emerge. And if electrons and positrons as well as protons and antiprotons annihilate each other, then what about the universe and an antiuniverse, or life and antilife in proximity?

To conclude, back in our universe, on the tiny frame of reference we call earth, experimental facts of atom smashers and cosmic rays have outstripped theory. New theories are needed, and paradoxically, ever more powerful atom smashers are being devised to gain new data and insights for such new unifying theories. Protons, electrons, and neutrons remain as workable stable entities within atomic nuclei, but these particles, like photons of light, have been shown to have wave as well as particle characteristics. Electron microscopes based on wave properties of electrons are far more effective than optical microscopes based on light waves.

CHAPTER REVIEW

1. How are cloud chamber photographs similar to fossil imprints in hardened sand? Illustrate.

2. How does a Geiger-Mueller counter count atomic particles?

3. Is matter a concentrated form of energy? How is this indicated by $E = mc^2$?

4. Why is the natural radioactivity taking place within the sun called fusion? How is this process opposite to that within the "three families of natural radioactivity"? (Chapter 23).

5. What is meant by nuclear binding force or energy? How does this binding force ordinarily enable the atomic nucleus to remain intact in spite of the electrical repulsion of nuclear protons?

6. How can the helium atom weigh less than the four hydrogen atoms that form it?

7. How does the law of conservation of matter-energy combine the formerly separate laws of conservation of matter and conservation of energy?

8. How in its natural radioactivity is the sun a bridge of understanding between atoms and the universe?

9. How did Rutherford transmute ordinary nitrogen into oxygen?

10. How was lithium first artificially transmuted into helium?

11. Show how the transmutation of lithium into helium illustrates the law of conservation of matter-energy.

12. (a) What is artificial radioactivity? Illustrate. (b) Why is the artificial transmutation of nitrogen into oxygen not a case of artificial radioactivity?

13. How is the cyclotron used as an atom "smasher"?

14. What is a positron? How was it first detected?

15. Is the neutron a combined proton and electron or is the proton a combined neutron and positron? Explain.

16. Discuss positron-electron annihilation as the transformation of matter into energy.

17. Discuss positron-electron creation as the transformation of energy into matter.

18. (a) Discuss the transmutation of neptuniun and plutonium from uranium-238 as creation of man-made radioactive elements not found in nature. (b) Write the nuclear equations representing the transmutations resulting in these two new radioactive elements.

19. Differentiate between the natural radioactivity and the artificial radioactivity of uranium-238.

20. What is atomic fission? Illustrate the differences between atomic fission and fusion.

21. What is atomic chain reaction? Describe its discovery.

22. How did the discovery of fission and chain reaction lead to the A-bomb?

23. Relate the hydrogen bomb to nuclear fusion in the sun.

24. Describe the nuclear reactor.

25. How can the nuclear reactor be used to extend the benefits of electrical power?

26. What are radioactive isotopes? Radioactive tracers? How are they obtained artificially?

27. Illustrate how radioactive tracers permit advances in (a) medicine, agriculture, and industry, (b) knowledge of ancient cultures, and (c) knowledge of the age of the earth.

28. Describe the man-made transmutation of elements beyond plutonium. Of what importance are such transmutations?

29. What are cosmic rays? From where do they come?

30. What are mesons? Relate them to the nuclear binding force of atoms.

31. About how many different atomic particles have been discovered? Under what conditions are they generally found?

32. Why search for more atomic particles? Why not return to Dalton's simple model of an indivisible atom?

33. Discuss the antiproton as matter created from "pure" energy.

34. What is an antiuniverse? Why build such a conceptual model?

35. Is science a Frankenstein monster or a Prometheus bringing gifts?

PROBLEMS

1. Use $E = mc^2$ to find the energy equivalent in calories of 1 gram of chalk.

2. For each pound that the sun loses in mass, how much energy (in Btu's) does it radiate?

3. How much energy does the sun radiate each year if it loses 4 million tons of mass each second?

4. How much energy is formed when only four hydrogen atoms fuse into helium?

5. What is a thermonuclear reactor? Relate efforts to develop a thermonuclear reactor to the fusion of the sun's hydrogen atoms into helium.

6. Why in investigating matter are neutrons often used as "bullets" instead of alpha or other particles?

7. Is there any danger of the earth's exploding from a stray neutron striking a uranium deposit? Why?

8. How much energy is released when an electron and a positron annihilate each other? How much energy is needed to form a positron-electron pair?

9. How does the Wilson cloud chamber photograph transformations of invisible atoms or particles?

10. Which elementary particles listed in Table 24–2 have half-lives less than a millionth of a second? How can such short periods of time be measured?

11. In Table 24–2, photons and neutrinos are indicated as having a mass of 0. How is that possible?

12. The mu meson is listed as having a mass of 207. What is the unit?

13. Which particles are larger than protons? What are these larger particles called?

14. What evidence is there for thinking that hyperons are not stable particles ordinarily existing in atoms?

15. Write the symbols for an electron, a positron, a proton, a neutron, and an alpha particle.

16. Express the following in words:

$$_2He^4 + {_7}N^{14} \longrightarrow {_8}O^{17} + {_1}H^1$$

$$_3Li^7 + {_1}H^1 \longrightarrow 2\,{_2}He^4 + energy.$$

17. Why is each equation in problem 16 famous?

18. Express the following in words:

$$_0n^1 + {_{92}}U^{238} \longrightarrow {_{92}}U^{239}$$

$$_{92}U^{239} \longrightarrow {_{-1}}e^0 + {_{93}}Np^{239}$$

$$_{93}Np^{239} \longrightarrow {_{-1}}e^0 + {_{94}}Pu^{239}$$

$$_{92}U^{235} + {_0}n^1 \longrightarrow {_{56}}Ba^{141} + {_{36}}Kr^{92} + 3\,{_0}n^1 + energy.$$

19. Why is each nuclear equation in problem 18 famous?

20. (a) What do the following equations represent?

$$_1H^2 + {_1}H^2 \longrightarrow {_2}He^3 + {_0}n^1 + 3.25\ Mev$$

$$_1H^2 + {_1}H^3 \longrightarrow {_2}He^4 + {_0}n^1 + 17.6\ Mev.$$

(b) Express the above equations in words.

21. Describe the following processes as constructive applications of nuclear materials: (a) radioactive dating by carbon-14, (b) determining the age of the earth through uranium-238, (c) injecting sodium-24 into the arm of a heart patient, (d) imbibing radioactive phosphorus to detect brain tumors or cure cancer, (c) imbibing "atomic cocktails" of radioactive iodine to detect thyroid gland difficulties, (f) using radioactive cobalt treatments to cure cancer, and (g) using radioactive tracers to investigate photosynthesis in plants.

SUGGESTIONS FOR FURTHER READING

Hecht, Selig, *Explaining the Atom,* Viking paperback, New York, 1954, Chs. 5–12.

Eidinoff, Maxwell Leigh, and Hyman Ruchlis, *Atomics for the Millions,* McGraw-Hill, New York, 1947, Chs. 8–9 and 11–25.

Feinberg, Joseph G., *Story of Atomic Theory and Atomic Energy,* Dover paperback, New York, 1960, Chs. 10–14.

Jaffe, Bernard, *Crucibles: The Story of Chemistry,* Premier paperback, New York, 1964, Chs. 15–16.

American Foundation for Continuing Education, *Mystery of Matter,* ed. Louise B. Young, Oxford Univ. Press, New York, 1965, pp. 135–204 and 580–665.

Einstein, Albert, and Leopold Infeld, *Evolution of Physics,* Simon and Schuster paperback, New York, 1961, Part 4.

Conant, James, *Science and Common Sense,* Yale Univ. Press paperback, New Haven, Conn., 1962, Chs. 11–12.

Bronowski, Jacob, *The Common Sense of Science,* Vintage paperback, New York, 1953, Chs. 6–9.

25   *General Theory of Relativity*

The universe is not a rigid and inimitable edifice where independent matter is housed in independent space and time; it is an amorphous continuum without any fixed architecture, plastic and variable, constantly subject to change and distortion. Wherever there is matter and motion, the continuum is disturbed. Just as a fish swimming in the sea agitates the water around it, so a star, a comet, or a galaxy distorts the geometry of the space-time through which it moves.

LINCOLN BARNETT, 1948

FOUR-DIMENSIONAL SPACE-TIME

The great Russian mathematician Hermann Minkowski was exceedingly impressed by the relativity of space and time. This former professor of Einstein opened a science meeting (Cologne, 1908) with these words: "The views of space and time which I wish to lay before you have sprung from the soil of experimental physics, and therein lies their strength. They are radical. Henceforth space by itself and time by itself are doomed to fade into mere shadows, and only a kind of *union* of the two retains an independent reality." Minkowski proposed a new concept, space-time. He combined the three dimensions of "shadowy" space, and an independent dimension of time into a four-dimensional space-time.

25–1A   A rock's fall in space and time.

There is nothing mystical about compounding space and time, whether in mathematical models of the universe or in everyday life. Many simple examples show time hidden in the fabric of space, or better still, show space and time as part of the same space-time fabric of events. Solar system motions and distances determine calendars and clocks. The earth completes an orbit to mark off a year. Other planets with shorter or longer orbits (distances) have shorter or longer years (time). At noon, the sun is more directly overhead; a point in time is set by the sun's relative position in space. A day is determined by the rotation of a point on the earth through a full circle. A day on the moon is over 27 times longer than ours; a point on the moon's surface completes a different circle at a different rate. The complete swing of a pendulum (time) varies with a changing acceleration of gravity at different places (space) on earth. Seasons (time) are due to an angle of inclination of the earth's axis as the earth moves in orbit.

If we say that a star is 200 light-years away, we are indicating not only distance but time. The light we see now left the star 200 years ago and indicates the star's *position then*. Meanwhile the star has moved on. The only proper frame of reference for the physical reality of that star is a combined space-time reference, a "four-dimensional space-time continuum." Space or distance has meaning or reality only in terms of time, in terms of when.

A train schedule is a good example of the necessity for describing position in terms of time. We are interested not merely in the route of a train, but *where* it will be *when*. In that sense, the train schedule is a "two-dimensional space-time continuum," with the railroad track just a one-dimensional space component. The distances can be plotted against the time.

On the same basis, a sea captain is concerned with his two-dimensional space continuum of latitude and longitude against time, thus involving a "three-dimensional space-time continuum." An air pilot has a four-dimensional space-time situation. He is concerned not only with his three-dimensional space continuum of latitude, longitude, and altitude as such, but with these in the four-dimensional where-when of his schedule.

Einstein was greatly impressed by Minkowski's concept of space-time. The idea provided insights into the world of events and had promise for the extension of Einstein's relativity theory. The space-time concept is made graphic by plotting space against time. Every event may have a point in a space-time graph. Suppose a rock is dropped from a 400-foot cliff. Figure 25–1A shows the rock's fall in space and in time; Fig. 25–1B, the rock's fall in space-time. Point *A* (Fig. 25–1B) is the position of the rock 400 feet above ground at time 0; point *B*, 16 feet lower, 1 second later; point *C*, 64 feet from the top, 2 seconds later; point *D*, ... These points and any points between them are called *point-events* in space-time.

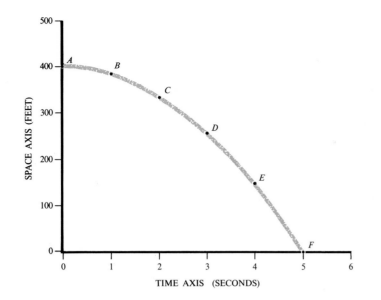

25–1B   A rock's fall in space-time. Points A through F are point-events of this fall. (For comparison with Fig. 25–1A, only the space axis here is vertical. Frequently in a space-time graph, only the time axis is vertical.)

A single point represents the place of an event in a combined space-time graph or coordinate system.

A succession of point-events in a curve is called a *world line*. Curve *AF* is the world line in space-time of the rock during its fall. In this case, one of uniform acceleration of gravity, the world line is a parabolic curve. If a rock fell or moved at constant velocity, its world line would be a straight line. Figure 25–2 illustrates the straight world line (in space-time) of an auto traveling at 100 feet per second for 5 seconds. This world line is a diagonal. Every object in the universe has a world line. Even a parked car would show a horizontal line on a space-time graph. Its "fixed" position has duration in time. Particularly significant for Einstein was the fact that acceleration could be identified with curved lines in space-time. In the development of general relativity, he was interested in gravity and acceleration.

EINSTEIN INTERVAL

People incorrectly believe that there is nothing absolute in relativity. Actually, space-time became an absolute, an entity that gave the same values to everybody regardless of circumstances, like the speed of light in the special theory of relativity. Einstein showed that observers with different relative values for the space and time of an event obtain the same value for space-time distance in the world line of the event. A simplified

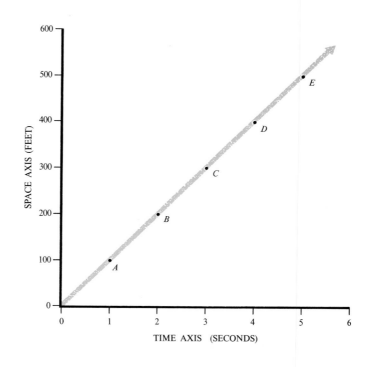

25–2 *The world line in space-time of a car traveling at 100 feet per second for 5 seconds. Points A through E are point-events in this world line. (The diagonal may be extended in its given direction for as long as the velocity is constant.)*

explanation of this absolute, called the *Einstein interval,* is centered around Fig. 25–3A–D.

1. One (space) dimension: $OB = x$. An object travels a distance OB in one dimension x.

2. Two (space) dimensions: $OB = \sqrt{x^2 + y^2}$. An object travels a distance OB in two space dimensions x and y. The Pythagorean theorem is involved: The square of the hypotenuse of a right triangle equals the sum of the squares of the two sides. OB is the hypotenuse, and x and y are the two sides.

3. Three (space) dimensions: $OB = \sqrt{x^2 + y^2 + z^2}$. An object travels a distance OB in three space dimensions x, y, and z. The Pythagorean theorem as applied to three dimensions is involved.

4. Four (space-time) dimensions: $OB = \sqrt{x^2 + y^2 + z^2 - c^2t^2}$.

Equation 25–1

An object travels a distance OB in four-dimensional space-time, x, y, z, and ct. The equation here also has the Pythagorean theorem form (except for the minus sign before c^2t^2). The time, or fourth dimension, factor is in ct, the distance light travels at velocity c in time t. (Distance equals velocity multiplied by time.)

OB, in Equation 25–1 is the Einstein interval, a distance between two points on a world line. Each observer of the motion of an object may obtain a different space measurement *x*, *y*, or *z*, and time measurement *t*. Each inserts different space and time values in Equation 25–1 but obtains the same value for *OB* in space-time. Thanks to Minkowski, Einstein's Equation 25–1 was not a mathematical device for an absolute quantity *OB* but a reflection of the world "as a four-dimensional space-time continuum." Relative space and time became local aspects of a more basic common space-time developed by Einstein into a common, universal frame of reference in a general theory of relativity.

BASIC PROBLEM OF GENERAL RELATIVITY: STRANGE WORLD OF ACCELERATION

Space and time are flickering "shadows." But we have seen (Chapter 22) that when systems move at constant velocity relative to each other, the different values for space, time, or mass can be equated (Eqs. 22–2, 22–7, and 22–10). Correspondence between systems exists and nature seems orderly. But these relativity equations do not apply when systems accelerate. What relationships exist that include accelerating systems? That was Einstein's basic problem in general relativity. There could not be one set of laws for uniformly moving reference frames and another for accelerating systems. Einstein expressed his confidence in the unity of nature in his *general relativity postulate: Laws of nature are the same for all systems regardless of their state of motion.* Einstein, assuming order, proceeded to create order through a general theory of relativity.

Newton's laws of motion emphasize *individual objects* moving at constant velocity (law of inertia) or with acceleration (law of acceleration) in a fixed space and time. But Einstein's focus is on *reference frames* of observers that are inertial or that accelerate. Newton's laws and special relativity apply to inertial frames of reference and not to accelerating frames. Let us see why.

A stationary disk is an inertial frame of reference. An object can remain at rest on it, and Newton's laws apply to it as on the earth. But the same disk when rotating is an *accelerating* frame of reference. Objects do not tend to remain at rest on it, but to move off. An observer on it feels a strange force tugging at him. A ball rolled from the center curves away from the radius. Objects on a rotating disk do not move freely in a Newtonian sense of inertia. Newton's laws no longer apply on the disk. In accelerating frames of reference, inertia becomes a force commonly felt in trains rounding curves or buses sharply stopping or starting. The earth is an inertial frame. Its very slow rotation once a day and revolution

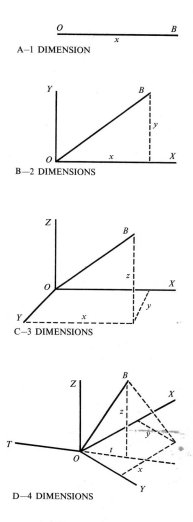

25–3   The distance *OB* in terms of 1 to 4 dimensions.

A. 1 (space) dimension:
$OB = x.$
B. 2 (space) dimensions:
$OB = \sqrt{x^2 + y^2}.$
C. 3 (space) dimensions:
$OB = \sqrt{x^2 + y^2 + z^2}.$
D. 4 (space-time) dimensions:
$OB = \sqrt{x^2 + y^2 + z^2 - c^2 t^2}.$
OB here represents distance in space-time (the Einstein interval).

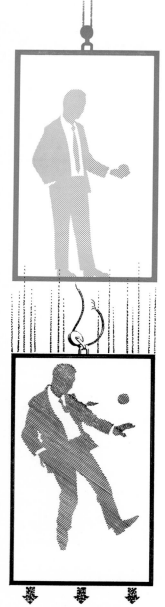

once a year may be ignored; objects can remain at rest or at constant velocity on it, and Newton's laws apply for objects at speeds considerably lower than that of light.*

Briefly, we know of no frame of reference that is inertial in an absolute sense. Any definition of one is operational—that is, based on experience. We operate on the earth, and Newton's laws generally apply here. Other reference frames moving at constant velocities relative to the earth are considered inertial frames, too; Newton's laws should apply there also. These laws and Einstein's special relativity corrections, however, do not apply in accelerated reference frames and therefore are not universal.

In the special relativity theory, Einstein started from the Michelson-Morley experiment and the constant speed of light. In the general theory, Einstein had no direct experiments as a base—only idealized thought experiments of falling elevators and rotating disks. Both are accelerating frames of reference; an elevator accelerates in speed and a disk accelerates in direction. The Lorentz equations (Chapter 22) do not apply between observers there and on the earth. What principles exist to equate all reference frames? Einstein peopled elevators and disks, and he introduced light rays for clues.

Accelerating Elevators and Curving Light Rays

The world appears different in accelerating systems than in inertial systems. If strange forces appear on rotating disks, weightlessness occurs in falling elevators. Most of us have experienced "sinking" sensations in elevators suddenly starting (accelerating) downward. The floor recedes from under us, so that we do not get the full back force on our feet. This is the beginning of weightlessness. The greater the acceleration of the elevator, the less back force we get and the less weight shown on a platform scale under us. If the cable snaps, the acceleration of the elevator and of ourselves is free fall, and there is no back force from the floor. We are weightless. By blowing downward, we could even rise to the ceiling of the elevator. A person born and raised in such a freely falling elevator world would not observe any gravitational effects. A ball released from his hand would not drop to the floor; it would float with him (Fig. 25–4A). This is the gravityless world he knows. To an observer on earth, the elevator occupant and objects freely fall together because of the gravitational pull of the earth. What is gravity from the earth as a reference frame is inertia in the elevator. Einstein said that

25–4A A freely falling elevator is a gravityless world. After the cable snaps, there is no back force from the elevator floor, and the man feels weightless. The ball apparently floats with the man.

*Small inertial forces on earth can be observed, however, as *Coriolus forces* causing westerly and easterly planetary wind belts or as slight, unfelt centrifugal forces of less than an ounce pulling on our bodies against gravity.

both points of view are correct. What is gravity force and accelerated motion from the earth is not force and motion within the elevator. Force is relative to frames of reference. Gravity forces acting at a distance was Newton's assumption in a great advance of ideas. But since Newton, the mechanical view has run into difficulties.

Suppose instead of freely falling to earth, the elevator accelerates upward (Fig. 25–4B). The floor presses strongly against the passenger's feet. The passenger feels heavy. He says that there is a strong gravitational attraction between him and the floor of his elevator world. And any objects released from his hand are on the floor quickly. To an observer on earth, the effects in the elevator were not due to gravity but to accelerated motion. What were gravity effects from one frame of reference were accelerated motion from another. Highly significant to Einstein was that within the accelerating elevator world, there is no way to tell the difference between accelerated motion and gravity effects. Whether up or down in an elevator, acceleration effects are felt as weight effects. Einstein therefore enumerated his famous *principle of equivalence: At any point in space, the effects of gravitation and accelerated motion are equivalent and cannot be distinguished from each other.* This principle also applies to the earth, since it is not an absolute or fixed reference frame, just a convenient frame for us. Because it is an inertial frame, laws from it are limited and not necessarily universal. Einstein's deep insight was to use this equivalence principle as a bridge between inertial frames and accelerated frames of reference. This was facilitated by introducing light beams into his thought experiment. After all, light was unique in inertial frames of reference; its speed was absolute. Light may also be unique in accelerating frames.

Now imagine a light ray passing through the glass walls of a stationary elevator above the earth's surface. An observer on earth and one within the elevator would agree that the path of the ray is straight (Fig. 25–5A). The two frames are inertial. Now let the elevator accelerate upward at 32 feet per second per second. With respect to the earth, the path of the ray is still a straight line. With respect to the observer in the elevator, the path of the light ray is a parabolic curve (Fig. 25–5B), like that of a cannonball fired horizontally on earth. A meteor streaking across the elevator would also form a parabolic curve. To the elevator observer, the floor of the elevator seems to have a gravitational force on the light ray and meteor identical to the gravity of the earth on a stone thrown horizontally. The observer on earth claims that the parabolic curves apparent in the elevator are due to the accelerated motion of the elevator. But there is no way within the elevator world to tell the difference between accelerated motion effects of the elevator and any apparent gravitational effects. By assuming gravity, the elevator scientist is assuming what Newton assumed on earth. And there is no preferred or absolute frame. Again, we have an illustration of Einstein's equivalence principle. But

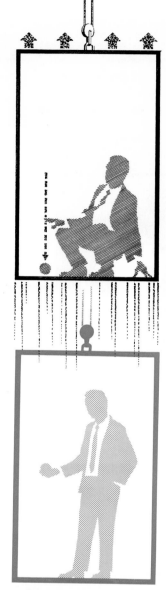

25–4B   The floor of an elevator accelerating upward presses strongly against the passenger's feet, the passenger feels particularly heavy, and the ball appears to fall faster than usual. A strong gravitational force seems to operate from the floor.

effect on the astronauts would be the same as if a huge asteroid suddenly loomed behind them (Fig. 25–7). Einstein spoke of gravitational fields and equivalent inertial fields. To him, fields were real; his main professional objective was to unify all fields—gravitational, inertial, and electromagnetic.

For future space travel, Einstein's principle of equivalence is taken for granted. Spaceships will spin considerably while moving toward destinations. Rotational effects keeping passengers along sides of enclosures will be equivalent to gravitational effects. Weightlessness would be overcome. The sides of the enclosures will be designed as floors of rooms. Although originating from thought experiments, Einstein's equivalence principle is here to stay.

Rotating Disks, Lagging Clocks, and Curving Rulers

Disks rotating at high speed show distortion of space and time within. The further from the center of the disk, the faster a point on it moves (Fig. 25–8). Point 4 on radius OA moves much more quickly than point 1. The direction of motion at any point is perpendicular to the radius, shown by arrows. By the Lorentz transformation principle (Eq. 22–2), objects shrink *in the direction of motion:* The higher the velocity, the more the shrinkage. Therefore, a very small shrinkage existing near the center of the disk at a tangent increases with distance from the center. On the other hand, no shrinkage exists in the direction of a radius, since that is *perpendicular* to the direction of motion. An observer on the rotating disk should find that the circumference C_1 of a small circle through point 1 almost equals $2\pi r_1$ ($C = 2\pi r_1$); the large shrunken circumference C_4 does *not* equal $2\pi r_4$ ($C \neq 2\pi r_4$). The shape of the disk, the space on it, is distorted. A basic proposition in Euclidean geometry is that $C = 2\pi r$. Einstein was convinced that Euclidean geometry does not apply on accelerating frames of reference.

Now place synchronized clocks on points 1, 2, 3, and 4 on the rotating disk (Fig. 25–9). By special relativity transformation, the further the clocks are from the center, the more they slow down. Increased velocity slows clocks (Eq. 22–7). Time is also distorted on the disk.

In summary, by Einstein's principle of equivalence, gravitational mass effects are equivalent to accelerated motion effects. The disk thought experiment represents accelerated motion. Therefore, if rotating disks show distorted space and time, then large masses, such as the sun and stars, should show distortions of space and time around them. Euclidean geometry, therefore, would not apply close to large masses. And light, like matter, would also take a curved path on a rotating disk and near the sun and stars. All this from thought experiments about elevators and disks!

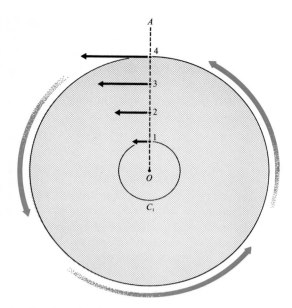

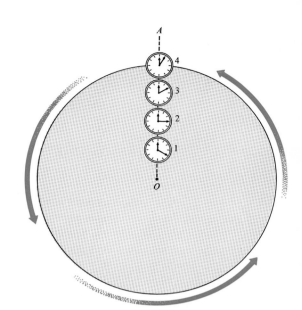

25–8 The further a point is from the center of a rotating disk, the faster the point moves and the greater is the disk's shrinkage.

25–9 Increased velocity slows clocks. The further a clock is from the center of a rotating disk, the more the clock slows down.

But if ordinary "flat" geometry does not apply to irregularities of space, then what kind of geometry does? Such great mathematicians as the Hungarian John Bolyai (1802–1860), the Russian Nicholas Lobachevsky (1793–1856), and the German G. F. B. Riemann (1826-1866) had developed non-Euclidean systems of geometry, but no scientist until Einstein had seriously applied non-Euclidean geometry to the physical universe.

GEOMETRY, AN ORANGE, AND A SADDLE

In Euclidean geometry, the sum of the angles of a triangle equals 180°. Like all statements, this one has assumptions and limitations. A basic assumption here is that the triangle is on a flat surface. The sum of the angles of a triangle drawn on an orange equals *more* than 180° (Riemann, Table 25–1). Or, on certain areas of a saddle, *less* than 180° (Lobachevsky, Table 25–1). The smaller the orange, the larger the sum of the degrees of the triangle. The larger the orange, the closer the angles approach a 180° sum. A small triangle on an orange the size of the earth would have the sum of its angles very slightly more than 180°. And so space even on the earth's surface is not what it seems.

On a spherical surface like the earth, an arc of a great circle, or longitudinal line, is the shortest distance between two points, not a Euclidean straight line. Great circles or "polar routes" for planes are easier in the nature of things than digging tunnels through the earth

Table 25–1 | *FLAT VERSUS CURVED SURFACES*

	EUCLID (EUCLIDEAN GEOMETRY)	RIEMANN (ELLIPTICAL GEOMETRY)	LOBACHEVSKY (HYPERBOLIC GEOMETRY)
Fifth Postulate	One and only one line can be drawn through a point parallel to a given line.*	No line can be drawn through a point parallel to a given line.	Two lines can be drawn through a point parallel to a given line.
Surface	Plane	Sphere	Pseudosphere
Curvature	Zero	Positive	Negative
Triangles	The sum of the angles of a triangle equals 180°	The sum of the angles of a triangle is greater than 180°.	The sum of the angles of a triangle is less than 180°.
Ratio of Circumference to Diameter	Pi (π)	Less than pi ($< \pi$)	Greater than pi ($> \pi$)

*This is an equivalent statement to Euclid's fifth postulate.

between various points on the surface. A *geodesic* is the term for a line that is the shortest distance between two points on a surface or in space, regardless of the shape of the line. At the equator, great circles, or lines of longitude, are parallel and, according to Euclid, should not meet. By the nature of the earth's spherical surface, these lines *do* meet at the poles, the sum of the angles of a triangle drawn anywhere on the earth's surface *is* more than 180°, and $C \neq \pi D$ (or $C/D < \pi$), as emphasized in Riemann's geometry.

In his geometry, Lobachevsky used a pseudosphere—for example, a saddle (Table 25–1), as a model. He proved that there are cases on such models where *two* lines can be drawn through a point parallel to a given line, the sum of the angles of a triangle is less than 180°, and $C/D > \pi$. Euclidean "flat" geometry, with its Euclidean straight lines and 180° triangles, applies to space that is not curved: Riemann's "spherical" geometry, to positively curved reaches of space; and Lobachevsky's geometry, to negatively curved space.

But what could be meant by curved space? And how could such space be detected? Light enters on the second question. If space is curved, light would follow the curve and reveal it just as in an accelerated elevator. If, for example, space is curved around the sun because of its large mass, then light from a distant star would curve around the sun. Einstein's principle of equivalence predicts that gravity affects the path of light. Deflection of light should be observable during a solar eclipse (Figs. 25–10 and 25–17) and should involve triangles with curved sides, as on the earth's surface (Riemann's geometry). Euclidean geometry, of course, would be inappropriate. But the first question, the *nature* of curved space, is more difficult.

Take points A and B near the sun. A ray from star S would be deflected from a straight-line path BC' to curve around the sun to BC (Fig. 25–10). A ray from another star T would be deflected near the sun from BA' to BA. A third ray from star U would take the curved path AC. The triangle formed would clearly be of the Riemann type: The sum of the angles would be more than 180°.

Space is appreciably distorted on very fast disks and near large masses. Time is not uniform on disks rotating speedily. By the underlying principle of equivalence, clocks or any rhythmic process should be slowed down in small amounts in gravitational fields near large masses.

Euclidean, or flat, geometry does not apply on rotating disks. The shortest distances on them are not Euclidean straight lines but curves.

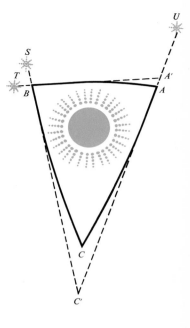

25–10 Curvature of the paths of starlight around the sun. The triangles formed are like those on the surface of a huge orange.

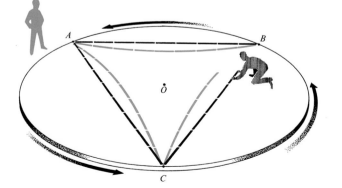

25–11 What appears as a straight line of rulers to an observer on a quickly rotating disk appears as a curved line to an outside observer.

What kind of curves? Take points *A, B,* and *C* on a rotating disk (Fig. 25–11). When the disk is stationary, an observer on it would find that the shortest distance would be the dashed lines *AB, BC,* and *CA.* The smallest number of rulers he would need end to end would be along Euclidean straight lines. Once the disk rotates, an outside observer should see the inside observer curving in from *A* to *B, B* to *C,* and *C* to *A* as he sought to triangulate with the smallest number of rulers. The explanation is relativistic contraction of length of the rulers: Moving a ruler closer to the center gives it a smaller linear velocity and therefore less shrinkage. A ruler would cover more ground by curving inward. Up to a point, the added distance from the point of view of an outside observer is more than balanced by less shrinkage. A curve becomes a shorter distance. And the faster the disk rotates, the more the bending inward for the geodesic. The curve in this case would be Lobachevskian; the sum of the angles of the triangle would be less than 180°. And since light also propagates along the shortest path, light would show the nature of the curve or the space.

To further illustrate that Euclidean measurements do not apply in non-Euclidean space, consider the street plans in Chicago and San Francisco. The Chicago area is flat; the street plan is highly rectangular and regular. Madison Street is a straight-line axis separating the north side from the south side. State Street is a straight line separating east from west. Almost all city streets are parallel to these two, and all numbering starts from the two axes. The city street plan has the uniformity of a Cartesian coordinate system (Fig. 25–12A) based on "flat" Euclidean geometry. Some streets in San Francisco follow the contours

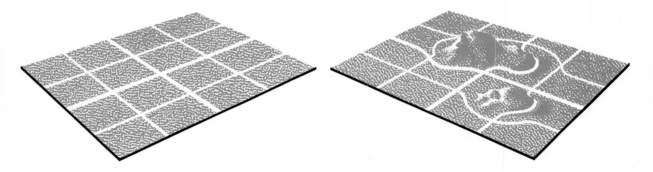

25–12A Rectangular street system. Chicago streets are parallel to State Street and Madison Avenue, main street axes. Such Cartesian systems are effective in flat areas.

25–12B Contoured street system. Some San Francisco streets follow contours around high hills. Such "wavy" lines of streets are more feasible in mountainous areas than are rectangular patterns.

of its high hills, at least in part. To force the flat Cartesian plan, excellent for Chicago, upon San Francisco would be folly. It would mean streets tunneled into hills. Curved surfaces are often more adequately handled and numbered by a Gaussian coordinate system of wavy distended lines (Fig. 25–12B) adjusted to fit specific situations.

WORLDS OF DIFFERENT DIMENSIONS

The mildly curved space in the universe is "shaped by masses and their velocities," said Einstein. "The geometrical properties of space are not independent, but are determined by matter." Basically, space is a sequence of objects, and time, a sequence of events. Without objects or events, space or time does not exist. Just nothing, a zero with the rim knocked off. But objects endure in time and therefore become events. Space and time are to be taken as space-time. Just as electric fields and magnetic fields become electromagnetic fields, separate space and time were inseparably linked in Minkowski's concept of space-time. Therefore, space distortions and time distortions around large masses become combined space-time distortions, a four-dimensional concept. And Einstein preferred to consider gravity as a continuous field in four-dimensional space-time than as a Newtonian force acting at a distance in three dimensions of space separate from time. Difficulties in understanding this, said Einstein, may be that we are three-dimensional creatures in a four-dimensional world and must compensate mathematically for our physical limitations. Two lines of sight from two eyes give us depth, the third dimension of vision. One eye would give us only two dimensions. Physiological, mechanical, and astronomical rhythms give us a separate awareness of time. Our physiological mechanisms do not combine space and time. Einstein suggests analogies of one-dimensional creatures in a two-dimensional world and two-dimensional creatures in a three-dimensional world.

A one-dimensional creature in a one-dimensional world is confined to a straight line. Without sight, he is limited to that line with a "feeler," much like a streetcar to an electric line by a trolley. The 1–d creature can only move forward or backward. Sideways or up and down do not exist in his vocabulary. If his straight line has terminals, 1–d lives in a *finite* and *bounded* world—finite because the line has a fixed length and bounded because of the stopping points (Fig. 25–13A). Without terminals, 1–d would have an infinite and unbounded world, even though of one dimension.

Suppose our one-dimensional creature 1–d were placed on a two-dimensional world, a circle (Fig. 25–13B). The circle is so large that, like an earthling going around the equator, he may believe he is always on a straight line. With the best of intelligence, it would be difficult for

A – FINITE & BOUNDED

B – FINITE & UNBOUNDED

25–13   (A) One-dimensional creature in a one-dimensional world. (B) One-dimensional creature in a two-dimensional world.

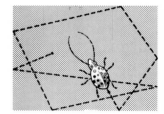
A – FINITE & BOUNDED

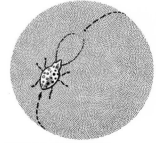
B – FINITE & UNBOUNDED

25–14   (A) Two-dimensional creature in a two-dimensional world. (B) Two-dimensional creature on a three-dimensional world.

1–d to understand how he could always move forward in one direction and eventually find himself in his starting place. Visualization of a second dimension would not happen by everyday experience alone, but only by mathematical imagination. If 1–d previously had experienced a circle as a mathematical game of two dimensions, he could transcend his one-dimensional limitations and explain how he could move only in one direction and return to a starting point. He would understand how his world could be *finite* (the circumference of a circle) and still be *unbounded* (no end points).

A two-dimensional creature 2–d in a two-dimensional world would be much like a creature on a flat movie screen. Thickness would not exist, just length and width (Fig. 25–14A). The world would really be flat, and 2–d, one-eyed. Circles could be seen and understood, but spheres would be seen as circles. Euclidean plane geometry could exist and apply to the world, but Euclidean solid (three-dimensional) geometry would be only a game of logic for imaginative mathematicians. As a huge screen, the world would be finite and bounded. If our one-eyed creature was rooted to the earth, railroad tracks would appear as coming to a point, and trains as monsters that puffed up or shrank in size rather than approaching or departing. Even Euclidean plane geometry would not directly apply to his observable world if 2–d observed parallel lines to come to a point.

Now place a movable 2–d on a curved screen, in fact, on a gigantic spherical screen, and remember that thickness is not observable to 2–d (Fig. 25–14B). Only a mathematical 2–d could visualize how he could start off in any direction on his spherical screen in a straight line and land at his starting place. Or how the screen world could be *finite* (a limited measurable surface area) but *unbounded* (no boundaries on that area). Once again, mathematics would transcend the physical limitations of an observing creature.

Einstein's point, of course, is that if we are three-dimensional creatures in an assumed four-dimensional space-time world, we are physically handicapped. We visualize in three dimensions, not four. A mathematical model involving non-Euclidean (curved) geometry and flexible, wavy Gaussian coordinate systems could overcome physical limitations.

GRAVITY IN A FOUR-DIMENSIONAL WORLD

Newton's gravitational force between two masses depended upon the distance between them ($F = G \, Mm/d^2$). Masses and the distance between them had the same values for all observers. Matter had mass; energy did not. The gravitation idea had successfully explained the heavens and worked marvels on earth—with one serious exception. The theory could not fully explain why the orbit of Mercury, the planet closest to the sun, slowly rotates about one-sixth of 1° a century (Fig. 25–15).

Could the closeness of the sun to Mercury be a disturbing factor? The sun is massive, and huge masses have effects equivalent to those of accelerated frames of reference. Light rays curved in Einstein's accelerating elevator (Fig. 25–5B), whether due to gravity as the passenger thought, or to the elevator's motion, as the earthly observer thought. The earth is an inertial frame of reference; the sun is not. The huge mass of the sun would give its immediate surroundings effects equivalent to those on a quickly rotating disk or in an accelerating elevator. Newton's laws would not apply, and understanding Mercury's rotating orbit requires a concept of gravity appropriate near massive objects.

What could such a gravity concept be? A basic postulate of optics is that light always takes the shortest path. In inertial frames and near small masses, the shortest path is a Euclidean straight line or very nearly so. But near large masses, light should curve just as on a rotary disk or in an accelerating elevator. These light ray curves are the shortest paths, or geodesics, just as great circle arcs on earth are the shortest distances between points. That is, light rays or meteors, in taking these curved paths, are taking the easiest paths and are therefore in natural motion; no forces are acting on them. Einstein reversed the picture. Instead of saying that gravity is a force acting equally on material objects and light to give them the same curved path, he says that no forces act on either.

But if no forces act, then why the *curve* near large masses, and what is gravity? The answer is field. Gravity is a field, not a force acting at a distance. That answer returns us to space-time and curved (Gaussian) coordinate systems. Einstein explained the curved path of a ray as an effect of space-time distortions around masses noticeable when masses are large. The sun is accompanied by distortions in space and time forming space-time fields, much like moving magnets surrounded by electromagnetic fields. Such space-time distortions or gravitational fields structure our four-dimensional space-time universe. The four-dimensional gravitational field is there whether objects and light wander in or not.

When a meteor or light ray does wander in, it is guided by the four-dimensional gravitational lines, or "grooves," already there. The particular line taken becomes the shortest path of the object or ray in space-time. Far from the sun or any mass, the "guiding lines" become Euclidean straight ones. All these "guiding lines" are considered as forming a continuous pattern or model called a "space-time continuum," whether "straight" and flat in empty space or "curved" where matter is concentrated. If matter is properly concentrated in the universe, light can curve around enough to return to a starting place and provide a glimpse into primeval history.

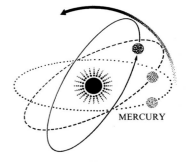

25–15   Rotation of Mercury's orbit around the sun. The orbit of the planet Mercury very slowly rotates in a rosette pattern around the sun at a speed of less than 1' of arc per century.

EINSTEIN'S
GENERAL LAW OF MOTION

The entire discussion in this chapter builds up to *Einstein's* one *general law of motion: All free bodies pursue geodesics, or straight paths, through space-time, regardless of whether they are near matter or remote from it.* This law is a combined law of motion and gravitation that relates all frames of reference, accelerated and inertial. When the "free body" is remote from other matter, the geodesic follows a Euclidean straight line in four-dimensional space-time and also in three-dimensional space if observed from an inertial frame of reference. If the body is near matter, the geodesic is curved in space-time and, therefore, also in space. The earth moving around the sun is therefore a "free body" in the same sense that a meteor is in far-off space. Each follows the space-time structure in its vicinity. Space-time is curved near the sun. The natural path, or world line, of the earth in space-time is therefore curved (Fig. 25–16). Far from matter, the world line of the meteor is straight. Thus, in general relativity, a force is not necessary to explain the orbit of a planet or moon. A planet or moon follows a structured path as the natural, easiest path, whether near or far from matter. Gravity is the four-dimensional field in space-time structuring the paths of objects and radiation. These paths, world lines, or geodesics are curved near matter, less curved away, and straight (Euclidean) far off in empty space in accordance with the distortions of the gravitational field by large masses. But curved or straight, the paths are continuous. Briefly, gravity is a continuous field in space-time, influencing and being influenced by matter. The special theory of relativity is a special case of the general theory in which space-time paths, undistorted by large masses, are straight and gravitational influence is negligible.

The huge space-time continuum is an absolute connecting everything in the universe. Individual measurements of separate space and time are relative, as emphasized in Einstein's special theory; each observer has his own local values. But an Einstein interval, or distance between point-events on the world line of an object, is the same for all observers everywhere. An absolute four-dimensional space-time continuum was the scientist Einstein's answer to the artist Goethe's conviction that "in nature we will never see anything isolated, but everything in connection with something else which is before it, beside it, under it, and over it." There was much of the artist in Einstein's work, just as there was the scientist in much of Goethe's.

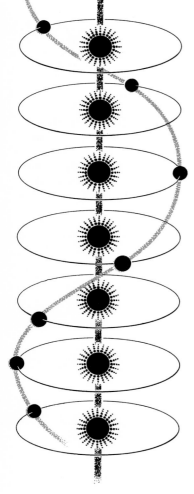

25–16   The world line, or natural path, of the earth in space-time.

GENERAL
RELATIVITY EVIDENCES

Does Einstein's space-time model really fit the universe? What is the evidence?

Solar Eclipse Evidence

If gravity affects the path of light, the sun's mass should deflect starlight that grazes the sun. To test this prediction of Einstein, A. S. Eddington (1882–1944), one of the world's great astronomers, led a British astronomical expedition to a West African island, Principe, to observe the solar eclipse of May 29, 1919. Another British expedition, under A. C. Crommelin, went to northern Brazil for the same purpose. Ordinarily, the sun is too bright for starlight to be seen. During a solar eclipse, the moon blots out the sun, and starlight grazing the sun can be photographed (Fig. 25–17). Since the relative position of a given star to other stars is known, the bending of its rays is easily determined. Einstein's four-dimensional gravitational field equation gave 1.74″ of arc as the deflection of a light beam grazing the sun. Newton's law of gravitation ($F = GMm/d^2$) gave a deflection value of 0.87″ of arc. The relativistic mass m of light energy E ($E = mc^2$) was used for m in Newton's equation.

Einstein stated in advance that the eclipse test was crucial for his general relativity idea of space distortion by masses even if not for his special relativity concept of $E = mc^2$. If there were no deflection of starlight at all, the general theory of relativity was out, and the $E = mc^2$ matter-energy equivalence principle was seriously shaken. If a deflection near 0.87″ of arc was found, the general relativity theory of gravitation was out, Newton's concept of gravitational forces at a distance strengthened, and $E = mc^2$ upheld. If a deflection near 1.74″ of arc was found, Einstein's concept of gravity as a field in space-time deserved further exploration. It would be showing far more accuracy and scope than Newton's concept. Scientific excitement ran high in May 1919 and even higher when solar expedition photographs gave average deflections close to Einstein's predicted value. Other solar eclipse data since 1919 have further confirmed Einstein's space-time concepts of gravitation.

Rotation of Mercury's Orbit

We have already noticed that the slight rotation of Mercury's orbit could not be fully explained by Newtonian gravitation. The gravitational effect of known planets accounted for only 531 of the 574″ (about $\frac{1}{6}°$) of arc of this rotation. A new planet, Vulcan, was hypothesized as near Mercury. But Vulcan was never found. The excess rotation of Mercury's orbit remained unexplained until Einstein's relativity. Mercury has more speed when closer to the sun than when further away. Einstein's special relativity predicts a variation of Mercury's mass with speed. This variation of mass accounts for 7 of the 43 unexplained seconds of arc per century. General relativity mathematics accurately accounts for the remaining 36″ of arc. This successful explanation of the rotation of Mercury's orbit is perhaps the best evidence so far for Einstein's theory of gravity.

Gravitational Effects on Time

A clock slows down with its increased velocity whether in an inertial reference frame, in an accelerating frame of a rotating disk, or in an accelerating spaceship. By Einstein's principle of equivalence between accelerated motion and gravitational effects, time should also slow down appreciably on or near gravitational masses. If time "stretches," then space-time should, too. Einstein figured that a second on the sun should be 1.000002 earth seconds because of the sun's greater mass. Jupiter's mass is larger than the earth's but smaller than the sun's. A second on Jupiter should also be between that of the earth and that of the sun in length. Vibrating atoms act as clocks. Vibrations of hydrogen atoms, for example, on the sun or stars should be slower than hydrogen atom vibrations on earth. This can be tested by color analysis of starlight dispersed in prisms (Fig. 17–12C). Glowing hydrogen gas has its characteristic colors. If vibration frequencies of hydrogen atoms decrease, the colors due to hydrogen will shift toward the red, or lower frequency, end of the spectrum. This reduction in frequency, due to presence of large masses, is known as the *relativistic* or *Einstein red shift* to separate it from red shifts due to other causes. The Einstein shift was first found on white dwarf stars much more dense than the sun. Sirius B, twin star of the Dog star, Sirius, with a diameter about one-thirtieth that of the sun has a density over 25,000 times greater. A handful of material from the interior of that star would weigh tons. The astronomer Adams, in 1925, was the first to find a relativistic shift on Sirius B that matched the predicted amount.

Among other evidences for the slowing down of time processes by gravitational fields is an experiment at Harvard in 1960. Two extremely precise "atomic clocks" were placed at the base and top of a 70-foot tower. As expected from general relativity predictions, the time on the ground was very slightly slower than the time 70 feet above the earth's surface; the earth's mass definitely affects time!

SIGNIFICANCE OF RELATIVITY

Perhaps more time is needed to realize the full impact of relativity. For better or worse, our atom-smashing age substantiates the special relativity theory. Accelerated particles increase in mass, matter is converted into energy, and atomic bombs hang heavy over our heads. With civilization at the crossroads, it is imperative that men with human values influence the choice of the road. In the closing years of his life, Einstein was aware of the dangers and helped educate against them. As for the general theory of relativity, evidence is still sparse but favorable. More time is needed for solid substantiation.

Meanwhile, relativity compels us to ask: If such basic and solid assumptions as Newton's absolute time and space could go toppling, what assumptions do we hold today that the future will also cast aside? That opens up the justification of questioning all assumptions, definitions, concepts, and systems of scientific as well as other ideas. Also justified is that type of thinking which, while encouraging free play of the imagination in "calling the world to order," still insists upon testing imaginative ideas.

Relativity is now a conceptual model that has absorbed Ptolemaic and Copernican-Newtonian models into itself as partial pictures. The earth is an organizing center from which thinking men worked their way from immediate, private, relativistic pictures of the universe to a common space-time model. To repeat Minkowski: "Space by itself and time by itself are doomed to fade away into mere shadows and only a kind of union of the two retains self-independence." But, of course, shadows are part of reality, too. The Ptolemaic and Copernican-Newtonian models are three-dimensional partial pictures of Einstein's larger four-dimensional model. Men can work outward only from where they are. From the earth as a frame of reference, geocentric (Ptolemaic) models were in order for sea and air navigation. But for space travel, the sun is a basic frame of reference, and sun-centered (Copernican) models are preferable. But difficulties arise in the relativism of different frames of reference. From the earth, the orbit of the moon is nearly a circle; from the sun, it is not. A circular orbit from one frame is not from another. And in an absolute sense, there is no "more correct" frame. Where everything moves, absolute velocities are unknown. There is no preferred frame of reference for universal laws.

Observers on the earth, sun, or anywhere, however, can have common world lines of the moon in space-time. The space-time model is a larger reference relating all observers. The immediate three-dimensional Ptolemaic and Copernican-Newtonian models are facets in a more basic, four-dimensional model.

In this way, through big, unifying ideas, scientific man makes his way outward in a search for order in a complex, changing world. His big ideas run into contradictions, face more promising ideas, and are eclipsed. But each big idea has its own expansive effect. The broadening effect of Einstein's model in specific concepts of space, time, matter, energy, gravity, or geodesics has already been emphasized. So has Einstein's frames of reference approach to the universe. Einstein's space-time is not likely to be the final model of the universe. It is the best so far. In turn, it may become a facet in a still larger framework, but meanwhile, like previous models, it helps man creatively project himself outward.

CHAPTER REVIEW

1. (a) Explain how observing the heavens means observing time as well as space. (b) What does it mean to say that space and time are part of the same space-time fabric of events?

2. (a) Describe a train schedule as "a two-dimensional space-time continuum." (b) Describe the three space dimensions and the fourth dimension of time in a plane schedule.

3. What is a point-event? A world line?

4. (a) Show a parked car as a point-event in a space-time graph. (b) Draw the world line of a parked car.

5. Draw the world line of a car traveling at 30 meters per second for 5 seconds.

6. Draw the world line of a rock falling 5 seconds from rest.

7. What did Minkowski mean by "Space and time are flickering shadows. Only a kind of union of the two retains an independent reality"?

8. Explain the Einstein interval OB in the following equation as an absolute that gives all observers with different space and time values of an event the same value for distance in the world line of the event:

$$OB = \sqrt{x^2 + y^2 + z^2 - c^2 t^2}.$$

9. What is an inertial frame of reference? An accelerated frame of reference? How do an elevator and a rotating disk illustrate accelerating frames? When is a disk, a moving elevator, and a moving spaceship an inertial frame?

10. (a) The earth rotates. Why is it considered an *inertial* frame of reference? (b) Why would Newton's laws not apply on the earth if it rotated 100 times faster?

11. Why can't the Lorentz-Einstein transformation equations (Chapter 22) apply in an accelerated frame of reference?

12. How did Einstein use an accelerating elevator in a thought experiment to show the following? (a) The path of light rays in an accelerating frame of reference curves like that of a material object. (b) The light ray path that curves in the accelerating frame may appear straight to an outside observer. (c) Gravity to an observer in an accelerating reference frame may be inertia to an outside observer. (d) Inertia in an accelerating frame may be gravity to an outside observer.

13. Use a rotating disk in a thought experiment to show the following: (a) A straight line to an accelerating observer may be a curved line to an outside observer. (b) Centrifugal force and gravity are equivalent. (c) Clocks keep time at a slower pace in an accelerating system than in an inertial system.

14. Use a spaceship in a thought experiment to illustrate Einstein's idea of the equivalence between gravitational forces and inertial forces.

15. In the general theory of relativity, to what are space and time relative?

16. Use the following to show that a straight line is not necessarily the shortest distance between two points: (a) the surface of the earth and (b) a rotating disk.

17. Use the following to show that the sum of the angles of a triangle may be more than or less than 180°: (a) the surface of an orange, (b) the surface of the earth, (c) the surface of a saddle, and (d) a rotating disk.

18. Use the earth's surface to show that parallel lines may meet.

19. (a) Does light necessarily travel in a straight line? If not, when can we be sure we have a straight line? (b) What are other difficulties in determining a straight line?

20. How does the concept of "geodesic" solve the problem of a straight line?

21. What is meant by a "distortion of space or space-time"?

22. How does starlight observed curving around the sun during a solar eclipse reveal space distortions?

23. What is Einstein's general law of motion? Explain how this law relates all frames of reference, inertial and accelerated.

24. Why did Einstein consider the moon in orbit to be in free motion? Did Newton think so, too?

25. Why is the general theory of relativity called Einstein's theory of gravitation?

26. Describe the following as experimental evidences for the general theory of relativity: (a) rotation of Mercury's orbit around the sun, (b)

deflection of starlight during solar eclipses, (c) the Einstein red shift, and (d) a speeding up of "atomic clocks" with altitude above the earth's surface.

27. Consider the implications of general relativity upon the following: (a) ideas of space and time, (b) ideas of force, field, and gravitation, (c) ideas of absolutes in the universe, (d) the nature of the path of light in the universe, (e) the general nature of the universe, (f) habits of continually questioning and re-examining all assumptions, definitions, concepts, and theories in all areas of knowledge, (g) the free play of imagination and thought in "calling the world to order," but on a testable basis, (h) application of the frames of reference concept to other areas of human experience, and (i) the idea that men are not observing but interacting in the process of gaining knowledge.

PROBLEMS

Explain, illustrate, and give relativistic implications of the following statements:

1. Time does not run at the same rate for all observers.
2. A clock at sea level runs more slowly than one on a mountaintop.
3. Two observers appearing to move at constant velocity relative to each other cannot tell which one is at rest.
4. The moon's path observed from the sun is not an ellipse.
5. Straight lines and parallel lines are not self-evident.
6. The shortest distance between two points is not always a straight line.
7. A geodesic is the shortest distance between two points.
8. Light is deflected around the sun.
9. Space near a large mass is curved.
10. Space-time near a large mass is curved.
11. Nothing exists in space to determine absolutely a straight line.
12. Gravitational force is relative.
13. Centrifugal force and gravitation are equivalent.
14. Inertial mass and gravitational mass are equivalent.
15. Gravitation is a field in space-time rather than a force acting across space.
16. The charge of an electron is an absolute.
17. Space-time is an absolute.
18. Light travels in geodesics; its paths show how space and space-time are shaped by the distribution of matter in the universe.

SUGGESTIONS FOR
FURTHER READING

Einstein, Albert, and Leopold Infeld, *Evolution of Physics,* Simon and Schuster paperback, New York, 1961, Part 3, pp. 210–260.

Einstein, Albert, *Relativity: The Special and General Theory,* Crown paperback, New York, 1961.

Gamow, George, *One, Two, Three . . . Infinity,* Mentor paperback, New York, 1953.

Coleman, James A., *Relativity for the Layman,* Signet paperback, New York, 1962, Chs. 5–7.

Barnett, Lincoln, *The Universe and Dr. Einstein,* Mentor paperback, New York, 1952, Chs. 10–15.

Russell, Bertrand, *The ABC of Relativity,* Mentor paperback, New York, 1959, Chs. 5, 7–9, and 12–15.

Gardner, Martin, *Relativity for the Million,* Macmillan, New York, 1962, Chs. 5–10.

26   Recapitulation: Science as a Human Enterprise

Not the Power Man, not the Profit Man, not the Mechanical Man, but the Whole Man, Man in Person, so to say, must be the central actor in the new drama of civilization . . . . If Technics is not to play a wholly destructive part in the future of Western Civilization, we must ask ourselves, for the first time, what sort of society and what kind of man are we seeking to produce?

LEWIS MUMFORD, 1954

Science is not a cut-and-dried proposition. It is not technology alone. Nor is it merely a set of equations by and for a small group of eggheads. It is a dynamic interplay between man and his surroundings embodying his attempts to understand, predict, and control nature. Science arose out of our efforts to survive, our natural curiosity, and our search for order in a seemingly capricious, hostile world. Like art or government, science is a human enterprise that reflects men. Its strengths and limitations are those of its human originators. Knowledge and perspective of science in relation to other human endeavors are vital to the future of our culture.

Anthropologists are well aware that technology arose mainly from man's efforts to survive, whether he shaped flint and clubs for protection, built fires for warmth, or devised calendars to anticipate events. Tools and technology became extensions of man's body, mind, and imagination. The hammer, the wheel, and the engine are extensions of man's muscles. The telescope, radio, and microscope are extensions of the senses to perceive distant or minute objects. Calendars and computers are extensions of man's mind. And no science or technology would exist without human imagination.

Today's technology has changed the face of the earth. Skyscrapers and highways replace hamlets and wilderness; jet planes challenge the birds their skies. And even now rockets reach for the moon, planets, and stars. But there are also H-bombs, population explosions, and radioactive fallout. In helping us master nature, is technology a gift-bearing Prometheus, or has it become a Frankenstein monster? Does the danger reside in technological advance or in a lack of social intelligence? Will man be dehumanized by automation and a highly structured society? What about population pressures and natural resources?

Ancient Babylonia, Egypt, Greece, and Rome were highly structured civilizations based on slavery. Medieval serfdom survived in Europe into this century. There were chattel slaves in the United States a century ago. If chattel slaves are no longer prevalent, it isn't that we are more moral but that our technology has allowed us to substitute machines for bodies. In that sense, technology is a humanistic influence.

Technology can help us increase labor productivity, relieve drudgery, prevent and heal sickness, control birth, extend life, and can aid us to free ourselves for living with dignity, enlightenment, and wisdom. Technology in the service of man can mean more humanism. Men need not be slaves to machines; the problem of technological advance is primarily one of an accompanying social reorganization in accordance with human values.

But science is more than technology, more than an accumulation of facts, principles, and gadgets. It is also a dynamic investigation of nature in a challenging search for order. It is an open-minded, systematic, and critical approach to the universe that insists on evidence. Early questions put to nature led to facts and theories. Facts and theories led to further questions in a continuing, reciprocal process that ever extends horizons. Modern probing of atoms, chromosomes, and cancer cells; of the moon, planets, and stars; or of man himself reveals science as a human enterprise that constantly pushes the boundaries of the known into the unknown. In the dynamic search for order, an understanding of individual objects has developed that unfortunately does not yet extend to human relationships. A science of man is needed.

Men have minds and imagination as well as senses. They not only learn, adapt, and invent, they build systems of ideas as well as of things. Philosophy, mathematics, religion, literature, music, art, economics, politics, and social theory are some of the idea systems built by men. And, of course, we have houses, ships, and bridges when men build systems of things. None of these tangible products, however, is possible without the ideas behind them. Science is a synthesis of the world of ideas and of things, and man is the synthesizer. In astronomy, when men grouped stars into constellations and projected domes or spheres upon the heavens in order to locate moving objects there, they were scientifically system building. They were projecting ideas upon nature to systematize nature.

The heavens above are a vast natural laboratory with sparkle, beauty, and mystery. And even the earliest men could see that celestial motions were generally periodic and regular. It wasn't that the sun moved, but that it did so daily across the same belt in the sky. It wasn't that the moon had phases, but that the phases exactly repeated themselves. Spring always followed winter; and summer, spring. Such regularities suggested order, natural law, and system. They encouraged calendar and chart making; they stimulated questions and man-made conceptual models of the world. And the same sky that stimulated men to develop systems of astronomy and mathematics stimulated religious systems, poetry, and art.

In his interactions with nature, man, whether in everyday life, art, science, philosophy, or religion, uses his mind, imagination, or senses. But none of these faculties can be trusted alone. For example, although indispensable, *our senses cannot be trusted alone.* Olives appear larger in brine than in air; a spoon appears to bend when dipped in tea. The sun seems to move across the sky. A golf ball appears to have little, if any, empty space within it. Things are not always as they appear directly to our senses. Plato suggested a cave analogy (now famous) that our senses give us only flickering shadows of reality. According to Plato, we are like men in a cave at night with our backs to a fire at the cave entrance. All that we get of the outside world through our senses are flickering shadows on the cave wall before us. To Plato, the senses give us superficial, fleeting shadows of events rather than events themselves. He therefore minimized the importance of the senses and fell back upon the mind for knowledge of the world. Logic and ideas, not shadowy sensations, were to be depended upon for understanding nature.

But *the mind alone cannot be trusted.* Life is bigger than any system of logic, whether in philosophy, religion, science, or mathematics. So far, systems of logic have been like traps through which natural processes somehow ooze as if through sieves. Also, every idea or instance of reasoning involves one or more assumptions and can be no more valid than its original assumptions. Every idea or system of reasoning is vulnerable at the level of assumptions no matter how internally consistent it may be. In arithmetic, for example, we learn that $3 + 4 = 7$, but actually, $3 + 4$ may $= 5$. If we walk 3 miles due west and 4 miles due north, we are only 5 miles from where we started. The statement that 3 miles $+ 4$ miles $= 7$ miles involves the assumption that direction or change of direction does not matter. The total walk is 7 miles, regardless of direction. But if direction *is* important and does count, then 3 miles $+ 4$ miles geometrically gives only 5 miles, the actual final distance from the starting point. The statement that $3 + 4 = 7$ does not cover all cases and therefore applies as logic only in special, arithmetic situations.

Similarly, *imagination alone cannot be trusted.* Imagination alone cannot differentiate fact from fancy. Alone, imagination can breed illusions and delusions, and it is therefore often on the other side of the same coin as sensory illusions.

Since neither senses, mind, nor imagination can be trusted alone, man must use everything he has in a system of checks and balances. At least, that is the position of science in its basic method of inquiry, hypothesis testing. Forming a new hypothesis requires imagination (courage, too!). This was certainly true for the Copernican idea that the earth moves around the sun, particularly at a time when tradition as well as appearances favored an earth-centered universe. It also took imagination as well as observation and reasoning to propose that men evolved from simpler forms of life. But it takes additional reasoning and observation to test hypotheses or theories once they are formed. Generally, in hypothesis testing, events are predicted (that is, reasoned through in advance) from the hypothesis. Actual events are then observed and compared to the predictions. If the *observed* results *match* the *predicted* results, the underlying hypothesis is tentatively accepted; otherwise, it is rejected. Thus, hypothesis formation and testing generally involve imagination, reasoning, and observation in checks and balances.

There is a fable of several blind men who came upon an elephant. None of them had previous knowledge of or experience with an elephant, and each one, upon examining the animal, came in contact with a different part of its body. The first man touched the elephant's tail and decided that the elephant was ropelike. The second blind individual came in contact with its side and decided that the elephant was wall-like. To the third man, who contacted the leg, the elephant was stumplike; whereas to the fourth, who touched the trunk, the object was snakelike.

In our approach to reality, we are often like the blind men. We have limited ideas based upon limited knowledge and experience. Yet we are in the habit of projecting our limited concepts upon the universe and then identifying these premature concepts as the final answers to the universe itself. We do not distinguish between our concepts of reality and reality itself. Our ideas become final and absolute instead of merely the best approximation of reality under circumstances of limited senses, limited knowledge, limited tools, limited experience. We constantly form concepts based upon that part of the elephant with which we happen to be in contact throughout particular professional, religious, racial, or national groupings. If we are unwise, we call our own particular incomplete picture the final reality; we call the tail the elephant, and the elephant a rope. The danger of premature absolutes is that we shut ourselves off from possibilities of additional knowledge, more complete pictures, and a closer approach to reality itself. Worse than that, we perpetuate professional, religious, racial, and national walls, and we set ourselves in motion against one another.

Science, too, has been caught in this entanglement of not distinguishing between concepts of reality and reality itself. We encounter instances in which even outstanding men of science too often show a disappointing lack of an open minded, systematic, and critical approach to problems out-side their own field. We can even find illustrations in science itself. At the close of the last century, a group of prominent scientists meeting at an Eastern university resolved that the physical sciences had attained full scope in Newtonian mechanics. That is, Sir Isaac Newton's laws of motion and of gravitation fully covered a universe in which an absolute space provided a fixed framework. A second was always a second; a mile always a mile. All that was claimed necessary was more and more precision, not structure or scope.

Consequently, like a bombshell in 1905 came Einstein's special theory of relativity, revealing that Newtonian mechanics is only part of a larger picture in which space, time, and simultaneity of events are not absolute and fixed, but relative to the observer; that metersticks shrink and clocks slow down when the motion of the system on which they are located increases, and that the mass or quantity of matter of any object increases as its velocity increases. The props of the formerly firm mechanics were shaken, holding only under limited conditions. Science was embarrassed; science was caught short. Why? Science, like other areas of human experience, had not sufficiently differentiated between concepts of reality and reality itself. Science had projected its concepts of an absolute time and an absolute space upon the universe and had then identified its own concepts as realities or properties of the universe itself.

How then is science, or how is man, to bridge the gap between concepts and reality? The first step is to recognize that the difference exists, to recognize that on the one hand is man with his senses, physical tools, mental tools, feelings, imagination, and the ideas based upon all of these; and on the other hand, existing independently of concepts, is the universe.

The second step toward a mature approach to reality is recognition that our senses, our tools, our experiences, our knowledge, and consequently our concepts are of a limited, a selective, a relative character. First of all, we are limited to the particular receiving mechanisms of the sensory and mental apparatus that we possess. Reality and the universe are sending out their signals in many, many ways, some known and some unknown to us. Waves would be one example. We catch only those messages or waves for which we have receiving mechanisms. For example, by virtue of our eyes and an accompanying nervous system, we receive waves in a range of from about 3,500–7,000 angstroms to give us light, sight, and color. The range of frequencies involved here is a very narrow one in a very broad band of electromagnetic waves including, for example, ultraviolet, X rays, gamma rays, infrared, and even radio waves. Yet our eyes are not delicate enough instruments to catch any wavelength longer than red light or shorter than violet, just as we are not aware of sound waves below or above a certain pitch or frequency. Yet these waves exist. Japanese experts in earthquake phenomena have reported a sensitivity of animals to earth-quake waves that human beings would ordinarily be unaware of except through instruments. Radio waves are constantly passing all around us;

we are aware of them only when we set up the proper receiving mechanisms. Man has extended his senses through such tools as the radio and seismograph, but the number and diversity of these receiving mechanisms are as yet small. There should be many, many more to come. Most that we now have can become much more precise. Present-day tools do not give us information that later tools will. They involve and select only the particular types of messages and knowledge for which they are designed. Meanwhile, we form concepts based upon limited and partial knowledge, concepts that only begin to approach reality.

Further, if the nature of our knowledge depends on the nature of the senses and the tools we have, then the nature of our tools depends on accumulated past knowledge in a selective process. A great deal of data on atoms and atomic power has been obtained through cyclotrons, bevatrons, or synchrotrons. However, these powerful tools of artificial radioactivity have been possible only because the previous discovery and knowledge of radium and other naturally radioactive substances pointed to their development.

Granted our recognition of the incomplete and selective character of our factual knowledge and therefore of our ideas or concepts of reality, we are still left with the problem of reconciling our ideas of reality with reality itself. How can we keep our ideas in line with reality as we attempt to approach it? How can we minimize being embarrassed by reality as we try to form ideas about it? "Operationalism" and "frames of reference" are terms that have arisen in attempted answer to this question. Operationalism as first emphasized by P. W. Bridgman contends that concepts or ideas—for example, space, time, democracy—should be defined and qualified functionally, that is, in terms of the evidence behind the concept. Since evidence generally arises through observations, tools, processes, and practices, *these* must enter into the definition of an idea. That is, the definition of an idea should be a working definition. For example, 1 calorie is operationally defined as that amount of heat that will raise the temperature of 1 gram of water from 15° C to 16° C. Or, a year, as time, would be understandable in terms of one revolution of the earth around the sun. Concepts thus become defined in terms of actual processes that occur rather than absolute, fixed properties imposed upon things. Light becomes understandable in terms of waves when associated with diffraction gratings but, on the other hand, as corpuscles or photons when photoelectric cells are used. Perhaps waves and photons will be seen as different aspects of the same thing or else as parts of a larger picture when more knowledge becomes available. Meanwhile, as Bridgman stated it, "If experience is defined in terms of commonly shared and commonly verified experience, there will always be correspondence between experience and our description of it." And meanwhile, prematurely set *a priori* principles need not exist to limit possibilities of the new experiences and new knowledge that may give the larger picture.

Last of all, for a mature, scientific approach to reality we might mention, thanks to Einstein, frames of reference broadly as that aspect of the relativity of knowledge arising from the particular background or system of motion in which an individual observer is located. If the year of time is determined by a complete revolution of the planet on which the observer happens to be, then a year to an observer on Mars would not be the same as to an observer on earth; Mars is hardly halfway around its orbit when the earth is all the way around its own. Or again, if "up" is the direction away from the center of the earth, then because the earth is spherical, to the observer in the United States "up" is in almost the opposite direction in space than it is to the observer in China. It depends on where the observer happens to be. And a bigger frame of reference may help: We are all on one spaceship, the earth, moving in space—who knows where?

C. P. Snow emphasized two separate traditions or cultures, the literary and the scientific, and decried the chasm between them. To Snow's literary and scientific traditions, I would add a third, a *social* tradition, and would emphasize that in actuality, these three cultural traditions are parts of the same cloth spun by man that in turn drapes and shapes him. That is, man creates his traditions, which in turn influence him. The three cultural traditions, the literary, the scientific, and the social, have common origins in the makeup and interactions of men with their surroundings and one another. For example, science insists upon *common evidence* for ideas and appeals to the senses that men have in common, whereas art bases itself upon *individual differences* in the apparatus, impressions, and insights of men. But both science and art are products of men, and both the common evidences of science and the individual differences of art are based on the nervous systems, minds, and senses that characterize men. Man has evolved from nature; and science, literature, and government from man. If man is a conscious part of nature interacting with the rest of nature in everyday life, science, art, music, or social theory, then none of these cultural products of man exists in isolation. Inter-related, they affect and reflect one another in their developments and in man's development, too. A science of man is needed in the fullest sense of the words.

Galileo, in his Copernican writings and Inquisition difficulties, brought to a dramatic focus crosscurrents of the scientific, the literary, and the socioreligious. Since the time of Galileo, knowledge has multiplied and required increased specialization. This process has tended to narrow and deepen professional interests and to create artificial boundaries. More professional generalists are therefore necessary now within and between disciplines. This is already recognized in medicine. The internist serves the role of the professional generalist in medical practice. Life and personality are bigger than the immediate interests of the best specialists in the sciences, arts, or social sciences. Yet professionally, as otherwise, we are often like the blind men and the elephant. Professionally also, we have limited ideas based upon limited knowledge and experience. We form concepts based upon that part of the elephant with which we happen to be in contact through our particular professional grouping. If we are not careful, our own particular partial picture becomes the complete one. Work long enough upon the elephant's ear, and it may become the elephant. Specialists have much to gain through interdisciplinary sharing of experiences.

There is also a need for people in the natural sciences, social sciences, and humanities to work toward one another. A science of man is possible through common effort. And somewhere in the educational process, too, provisions must be made to present things in their larger frameworks. Without specialization we are superficial; without perspective, provincial. Both specialization and perspective, analysis and synthesis, are necessary for an educated man.

The concluding materials below are meant merely to suggest an approach to a science of man leading from the natural sciences. In this we take a cue from the idea of the ancient Greeks that each of us is a microcosm or miniature universe. But we emphasize that as microcosms, we exist at various inter-related levels of activity, and that we are not island universes; we interact with other microcosms. We have surroundings that shape us and that are shaped by us. And as with the rest of nature, there is no artificial separation within us of physics, chemistry, biology, psychology, or sociology. We incorporate almost all the sciences, the social sciences, and the humanities, too.

To be specific, let us start with the following three propositions:

1. The human personality includes energy mechanisms adapted for change in a world of change on levels that may be designated as subatomic, chemical, physical, physiological, biological, psychological, social, and cultural.

2. The activities at these various levels are inter-related. Variations in activity at one level affect activities at other levels.

3. The internal activities, interactions, and changes of the human microcosm can be understood and often predicted in terms of basic laws within and between the various levels of organization, including the sociocultural.

These three propositions may be reinforced by such generalizations as the following:

1. The matter making up our bodies has the same electrical basis and is subject to the same subatomic, electrical laws as other objects around us.

2. The body in its locomotive apparatus, temperature regulation, and sensory apparatus is equipped for dynamic physical relationships with a changing environment and is subject to universal laws of mechanics, thermodynamics, light, and sound.

3. The body through its own composition, through its cellular activity, and through its digestive, respiratory, and glandular systems performs chemical transformations for its own needs.

4. The cells, tissues, organs, nervous system, and brain with their specialized functions form a complex integration of activity for the well-being of the human organism.

5. Associated with the various activities above, biological, neurological, psychological, social, and cultural mechanisms condition the goal-seeking interactions of the human personality and society with its environment.

In any case, science is an enterprise *of* human beings, about humans as a part of nature, and we hope, for human beings. The extent to which science and technology become increasingly more *for* human beings is a social problem to be socially determined.

Appendixes

Appendix A

CONVERSION OF UNITS

	ENGLISH SYSTEM	METRIC SYSTEM	INTERCONVERSIONS
LENGTH	*Foot (ft)* 1 ft = 12 in. 1 yd = 3 ft 1 mi = 5,280 ft	*Meter (m)* 1 km = 1,000 m 1 m = 100 cm = 1,000 mm 1 A = 10^{-8} cm	1 in. = 2.54 cm 1 m = 39.37 in. 1 km = .62 mi
MASS	*Pound (lb)* 1 lb = 16 oz. 1 t = 2,000 lb	*Kilogram (kg)* 1 kg = 1,000 g 1 g = 1,000 mg	1 kg = 2.2 lb 1 lb = 453.6 g
TIME	*Second (sec)* 1 sec = 1/86,400 aver. solar day	*Second (sec)* Same as in English system	
VOLUME	1 cu ft = 1,728 cu in. 1 gal = 231 cu in. 1 gal = 4 qt = 8 pt	1 cu m = 10^6 cc 1 liter = 1,000 cc	1 liter = 1.06 qt 1 cu ft = 28.35 liters
FORCE	1 lb = 32.2 poundals (pdl) 1 slug = 32.2 lb	1 newton = 9.8 kg = 10^5 dynes 1 g = 980 dynes	1 kg = 2.2 lb 1 lb = 453.6 g
ENERGY	1 Btu = 778 ft-lb 1 kwhr = 1,000 whr 1 electron volt = 1.074×10^{-9} amu	1 joule (j) = 10^7 ergs = 2.4×10^{-4} kcal 1 cal = 4.187 joules 1 kwhr = 3.6×10^{13} ergs	1 joule = 23.73 ft-pdl 1 Btu = 252 cal = 60.2 joules 1 amu = 1.67×10^{-27} kg = 931 Mev 1 electron volt = 1.6×10^{-19} joules = $1.07 \cdot 10^{-9}$ amu
POWER	1 hp = 550 ft-lb/sec	1 w = 10^7 ergs/sec = 1 joule/sec	1 hp = 746 w
TEMPERATURE			1° C = 1.80° F
ELECTRIC CHARGE			1 coul = 3.0×10^9 esu 1 statcoul (esu) = 3.34×10^{-10} coul

Appendix B

POWERS OF TEN

Very large and very small numbers are often expressed in powers of 10 as follows:

LARGE NUMBERS

$10^0 = 1$	Decimal point is just after the 1.
$10^1 = 10$	Decimal point is moved 1 place to the *right* of the 1.
$10^2 = 100$	Decimal point is moved 2 places to the right.
$10^3 = 1,000$	Decimal point is moved 3 places to the right.
$10^4 = 10,000$	Decimal point is moved 4 places to the right.
$10^5 = 100,000$	Decimal point is moved 5 places to the right.
$10^6 = 1,000,000$	Decimal point is moved 6 places to the right.

and so on.

The power of 10 in each case above indicates the number of places that the decimal point is moved to the right.

Any large number may be expressed in terms of a power of 10. For example:

$$3,000,000 = 3.0 \times 10^6 \quad \text{(decimal point moved 6 places)}$$
$$670,000,000 = 67 \times 10^7 \quad \text{(decimal point moved 7 places)}$$

or

$$6.7 \times 10^8 \quad \text{(decimal point moved 8 places)}$$
$$475,000 = 4.75 \times 10^5 \quad \text{(decimal point moved 5 places)}.$$

SMALL NUMBERS

$10^0 = 1$	Decimal point is just after the 1.
$10^{-1} = 1/10^1 = .1$	Decimal point is moved 1 place to the *left* of the 1.
$10^{-2} = 1/10^2 = 1/100 = .01$	Decimal point is moved 2 places to the left.
$10^{-3} = 1/10^3 = 1/1,000 = .001$	Decimal point is moved 3 places to the left.
$\cdots$	
$10^{-6} = 1/10^6 = 1/1,000,000 = .000001$	Decimal point is moved 6 places to the left.
$\cdots$	
$10^{-9} = .000000001$	Decimal point is moved 9 places to the left.

and so on.

The negative power of 10 in each case above indicates the number of places that the decimal point is moved to the left.

Any small number may be expressed in terms of a (negative) power of 10. For example:

$$.0003 = 3 \times 10^{-4} \quad \text{(decimal point moved 4 places)}$$
$$.0067 = 67 \times 10^{-4} \quad \text{(decimal point moved 4 places)}$$

or

$$6.7 \times 10^{-3} \quad \text{(decimal point moved 3 places)}$$
$$.0000475 = 4.75 \times 10^{-5} \quad \text{(decimal point moved 5 places)}.$$

Appendix C

TABLE OF PHYSICAL CONSTANTS

SYMBOL	MEANING	VALUE (3 SIGNIFICANT FIGURE ACCURACY)
c	Velocity of light in a vacuum	3.00×10^8 m/sec or 186,000 mi/sec
e	Electron charge	1.60×10^{-19} coul
g	Acceleration of gravity at earth's surface	9.8 m/sec² or 32.2 ft/sec²
F	Faraday's constant	96,500 coul
G	Universal gravitational constant	6.67×10^{-11} newton · m²/kg²
h	Planck's constant	6.63×10^{-34} joule · sec
j	Mechanical equivalent of heat	4.19 joules/cal
k	Coulomb's law constant	9.00×10^9 n · m²/coul²
k	Boltzmann's constant	1.38×10^{-23} joule/°K
m_e	Electron rest mass	9.11×10^{-31} kg
m_p	Proton rest mass	1.67×10^{-27} kg
m_o	Neutron rest mass	1.67×10^{-27} kg
N	Avogadro's number	6.02×10^{23}/mole
R	Universal gas constant	8.32 joules/mole/°K
—	Absolute zero temperature	−273°C (−273.16°C) or −460°F (−459.69°F)
—	Molar volume of ideal gas at 0° C and 1 atm pressure	22.4 liters

Appendix D

Falling Bodies

Chapter 7 dealt with the simplest cases of falling bodies, those cases in which an object accelerates *from rest* (Equations 7-1–7-3). What if the object has an initial speed? A stone thrown down from a cliff should arrive faster than one merely dropped. How can allowances be made for the initial speed in determining the time of fall? What happens to the relationships among the velocity v, time t, and distance d fallen of the stone? Equations A-1–A-3 give these desired relationships. Compare these three equations to Equations 7-1–7-3, respectively.

The terms in boldface type designate the allowances for an initial velocity (v_o):

$$v_f = \mathbf{v_0} + gt \qquad\qquad\qquad \text{Equation A–1}$$

$$d = \mathbf{v_0 t} + \tfrac{1}{2}gt^2 \qquad\qquad\qquad \text{Equation A–2}$$

$$v_f^2 = \mathbf{v_0^2} + 2gh. \qquad\qquad\qquad \text{Equation A–3}$$

In general, what happens to the relationships among the velocity v, time t, and distance d moved, whether an object falls freely, rolls downhill, or otherwise uniformly accelerates from an initial velocity v_0? Equations A-4–A-6 give these relationships. Compare Equations A-4–A-6 to Equations A-1–A-3, respectively, and notice that the acceleration of gravity g in Equations A-1–A-3 is just a special case of uniform acceleration a in Equations A-4–A-6.

$$v_f = \mathbf{v_0} + at \qquad\qquad\qquad \text{Equation A–4}$$

$$d = \mathbf{v_0 t} + \tfrac{1}{2}at^2 \qquad\qquad\qquad \text{Equation A–5}$$

$$v_f^2 = \mathbf{v_0^2} + 2ad. \qquad\qquad\qquad \text{Equation A–6}$$

Glossary

These glossary statements are intended as a quick reference for basic technical terms used in the text. For fuller descriptions or illustrations, see the index.

A

Abberation of light. The apparent slight displacement of an object in the sky due to the earth's motion. The earth's motion affects the direction from which light seems to reach us just as the motion of a train affects the angle of raindrops on a window pane.

A-bomb. See *Fission bomb.*

Absolute motion. Motion relative to a fixed ether or other supposedly universal, set frame of reference.

Absolute zero (0°K). The lowest temperature possible; the temperature at which all thermal molecular motion theoretically stops: 0°K or −273.16°C or −459.69°F.

Acceleration. Change of speed and/or direction in a unit of time.

Accelerator. A device for imparting very high velocity to charged particles such as electrons or protons. Each time a particle passes properly placed electrodes, the particle is given an additional forward "kick" and velocity.

Acid. A substance with a sour taste that turns blue litmus paper red; that contains hydrogen replaceable by a metal to form a salt; or that liberates hydrogen ions in solution.

Ad hoc hypothesis. A tentative, working explanation of a particular set of observations.

Alchemy. An ancient art that attempted to transmute baser metals into gold and to prolong human life.

Alkali or *base.* A substance that turns red litmus paper blue; that neutralizes an acid to form a salt; or that produces negatively charged hydroxyl ions (OH⁻) in solution.

Alpha particle (α). A small, positively charged particle thrown off at a high velocity by many radioactive materials. Composed of two protons and two neutrons, the particle is identical with the helium nucleus.

Alpha rays (α rays). Streams of fast-moving *alpha particles* (described above) emitted from some radioactive substances.

Alternating current (AC). An electric current that reverses its direction regularly.

Altitude (astron). The angular distance of a celestial object above the horizon.

Ampere. The unit of electric current equal to a flow of 1 coulomb per second, or about 6×10^{18} electrons per second.

Angle of incidence. The angle at which a light ray strikes a surface, measured between the incoming ray and a perpendicular to the surface.

Angle of reflection. The angle at which a light ray is reflected from a surface, measured between the reflected ray and a perpendicular to the surface.

Angle of refraction. The angle at which a light ray enters a second transparent medium upon bending when passing from a first medium of different density. The angle is measured between the refracted ray and a perpendicular to the surfaces of the two media at the point of incidence.

Angstrom unit (A). The unit of very short lengths, used for wavelengths in the electromagnetic spectrum. One $A = 10^{-8}$ cm.

Anode. The positive electrode of a battery or vacuum tube, as compared to the *cathode* or negative electrode.

Antimatter. Matter composed of antiparticles, in which positrons supposedly would revolve around negative protons rather than electrons around usual (positive) protons. For example, an antihydrogen atom would consist of a positron revolving around an antiproton.

Antineutron. A particle identical to a neutron except for its spin being opposite in direction.

Antiparticles. Pairs of particles opposite in charge or in direction of spin but otherwise identical. The usual electron (− in charge) and the positron (a + charged electron) are called an electron pair.

Antiproton. A negatively charged proton. That is, a particle with a mass equal to that of a proton, but with an opposite charge.

Aphelion. The point in the earth's orbit farthest from the sun.

Apogee. The point in the moon's orbit farthest from the earth.

Artificial radioactivity. Radioactivity induced in stable elements by bombardment with high-energy particles or other radiation.

Asteroids. See *Planetoids.*

Astrology. The ancient practice of predicting the course of human destinies from the positions and motions of the heavenly bodies.

Astronomical unit. The average distance between the earth and the sun, about 93 million mi.

Atom. The smallest portion of an element that can take part in a chemical reaction.

Atomic energy. Nuclear energy. Energy released in nuclear reactions as mass is converted into energy.

Atomic nucleus. The positively charged center of an atom, in which most of the atomic mass is concentrated.

Atomic number. The number of protons (positively charged particles) found in an atom's nucleus. This number of protons within an atom of an element designates the element's order in the periodic table.

Atomic pile. See *Nuclear reactor.*

Atomic weight. The relative weight of an atom of an element compared to a standard particle, originally to the hydrogen atom (base 1), then to oxygen (base 16), and now to carbon-12. In any case, the approximate sum of the number of protons and neutrons in the nucleus of an atom.

Atom smasher. A machine (called an accelerator) that speeds up atomic and subatomic particles so that they can be used as projectiles to shatter the nuclei of other atoms.

Avogadro's law. Equal volumes of all gases at the same temperature and pressure have equal numbers of molecules.

Avogadro's number. The actual number of molecules in a mole, or gram-molecular weight, of any substance: 6.023×10^{23}.

Azimuth. The angular distance west of an object from the south (or north) point on the horizon.

B

Barometer. A device that measures atmospheric pressure. The pressure is determined from the varying height of a column of mercury that the changing atmospheric pressure is able to support. The mercury column is in a long tube, closed at one end, that had been filled with mercury and inverted in a mercury-containing vessel. A vacuum exists above the mercury column in the tube.

Baryons. Heavier atomic particles including protons, neutrons, hyperons, and their antiparticles.

Base. See *Alkali.*

Beta particle (β). An electron ejected at high speed by a radioactive nucleus. Beta particles do not exist *within a nucleus* but form at the instant of emission.

Beta ray. A stream of electrons emitted by some radioactive substances. Traveling close to the speed of light, beta rays are very penetrative.

Bev. A billion electron-volts. An electron with this much energy travels with a speed close to that of light.

Bevatron. A huge, circular accelerator, such as the one at the University of California. Protons are whirled through the 160-ft "doughnut" between the poles of a magnet weighing 13,000 tons. It is designed to produce energies of 10 billion electron-volts.

Binding energy. The energy needed to break up an atomic nucleus into constituent particles. This equals the energy emitted in the formation of the nucleus.

Breeding (phys.). The process of creating fissionable materials in a nuclear reactor.

Brownian motion. Random motions of small particles suspended in a medium due to continuous irregular bombardment by molecules of the surrounding medium.

Brushes (electrical). Fixed terminals in contact with the sliprings or commutator of a rotating coil in an electrical generator or motor.

C

Caloric. A supposedly weightless fluid once thought to constitute heat.

Calorie. A unit of energy. The amount of

heat necessary to raise the temperature of 1 g of water from 15°C to 16°C.

Catalyst. A substance that increases the rate of a chemical reaction but which is itself unchanged at the end of the reaction.

Cathode. The negative electrode of a battery or vacuum tube, as compared to the *anode* or positive electrode. The cathode is the electrode that emits electrons in a circuit.

Cathode rays. Streams of electrons moving from the negative to the positive electrode in a vacuum tube.

Celestial equator. The great circle on the celestial sphere exactly halfway between the celestial poles. The celestial and earth equators are on the same plane.

Celestial latitude. The distance of a celestial body from the ecliptic in degrees along a great circle passing through the ecliptic poles and the body.

Celestial longitude. The distance of a celestial object along the ecliptic in degrees from the vernal equinox.

Celestial meridian. The great circle on the celestial sphere passing through the observer's zenith, nadir, and both celestial poles.

Celestial sphere. An imaginary sphere on which celestial objects appear to be located. The observer is supposedly at the center of the sphere.

Centrifugal force. An outward force acting on a body in circular motion. This force is opposite and equal to the *centripetal force* described below.

Centripetal force. A force tending to pull a body toward the center of its circular motion.

Cerenkov radiation. An eerie blue glow given off by electrons traveling in a transparent material such as water.

Chain reaction. Successive nuclear reactions in a self-sustaining process. A fissionable nucleus split by a neutron releases energy and one or more neutrons. These neutrons split other fissionable nuclei, thus releasing more energy and more neutrons, and so on.

Chemical change. A change in a substance due to decrease, increase, or rearrangement of atoms within its molecules.

Chemical compound. A substance of two or more elements in definite proportions by weight that has properties distinctly different from those of its constituent elements.

Chlorophyll. The green pigment in plants that absorbs sunlight to start the process of *photo-synthesis,* by which plants produce sugars and starches from carbon dioxide and water.

Cloud chamber. A glass-walled device for tracking charged particles. Visible droplets condense from a supersaturated vapor on ions formed along the path of a charged particle within the device.

Cobalt-60 $(_{27}Co^{60})$. A radioactive isotope of the element cobalt, widely used in research as a source of gamma radiation.

Combustion. Burning. A rapid combination of a substance with oxygen that produces heat and light.

Complementary colors. Two spectral colors that added together make white or gray.

Compton effect. The glancing collision of a gamma ray with an electron. The gamma ray gives up part of its energy to the electron.

Conjunction. A planet or other body in a line of centers with the sun and earth. *Inferior conjunction* exists when the body is between the earth and sun; *superior conjunction,* when the body is on the other side of the sun from the earth.

Conservation of energy. The principle that energy cannot be created nor destroyed but merely transformed. The total amount of energy in the universe remains the same regardless of energy transformations.

Conservation of matter. The principle that matter can neither be created nor destroyed but merely transformed in a chemical reaction. The total weight of the reacting substances (reactants) equals the total weight of the products.

Conservation of matter-energy. The principle that the total amount of mass-energy in the universe remains constant. By relativity theory, matter and energy are different aspects of the same thing. Matter may change into energy or energy into matter, but the total amount of both in the universe remains the same.

Control rod. A rod used to control nuclear reactors by absorbing neutrons otherwise free to split fissionable atoms of the fuel. Pushed further into the reactor, the rod increases the number of neutrons absorbed and thus reduces the amount of fission. Pulling more of the rod out decreases the number of neutrons absorbed and thus increases the amount of fission.

Convection current. The circulation process in which the lower section of a gas or liquid is heated, expands, and rises to be replaced by cooler upper sections that descend.

Coordinate system. A background reference frame involving sets of numbers for locating a point or object. One set of numbers locates a point on a line; two sets locate a point on a plane; three sets in three-dimensional space; and four sets in space-time.

Coriolus force. The rightward deflection of winds in the Northern Hemisphere and leftward deflection in the Southern Hemisphere, due to the earth's rotation.

Corona. The very hot, diffuse gas extending hundreds of thousands of miles beyond the sun's atmosphere. The corona is seen during a total eclipse when the *photosphere* or main body of the sun is covered by the moon.

Cosmic rays. Protons, other high-energy charged particles, and photons showering the earth's atmosphere from outer space.

Cosmotron. A huge accelerator at Brookhaven National Laboratory that speeds up subatomic particles to billions of electron-volts.

Critical mass. The minimum mass of nuclear fuel necessary to sustain a chain reaction. With a smaller "chunk" too many neutrons stray, and the reaction dies out.

Crystallize. To form a solid, especially from a solution, in a definite geometric pattern.

Curie. A unit of measure for the rate at which a radioactive substance emits particles: The radioactivity of 1 g of radium or 3.7×10^{10} disintegrations per second.

Curvature. Deviation from "straightness" or "flatness" of a line, surface, or space.

Cycloid. The curved path taken by a point on the circumference of a circle which rolls on a straight line.

Cyclotron. A particle accelerator in which atomic particles, whirled around in a spiral between the ends of a huge magnet, gain speed with each rotation in preparation for bombarding target material.

D

Decay (radioactive). The disintegration of a radioactive atom in becoming the atom of a new element.

Deceleration. Negative acceleration, or rate of decrease of velocity.

Declination. Angular distance north or south of the celestial equator.

Deferent. The main circle on which another circle or system of circles move.

Density. The mass per unit volume of a substance ($D = m/v$).

Deuterium ($_1H^2$). A heavy hydrogen isotope with an atomic weight of 2 and a charge of $+1$. The weight is due to one proton and one neutron; the charge to the proton. The nucleus of an ordinary hydrogen atom consists of a proton only.

Diffraction. The spreading of light around the edges of an obstacle. Colored bands are seen on a screen when a beam of white light passes through small openings or across edges of opaque obstacles; alternate light and dark bands are seen when a beam of monochromatic light passes through.

Diffraction grating. A transparent or reflecting surface ruled with many parallel lines that produces a color spectrum by means of interference.

Diffusion of gases. Spontaneous intermingling of two or more gases due to random motion of molecules, as when an odor spreads through a room.

Diffusion of light. The scattering or irregular change of direction of light rays as caused by irregular reflection at rough surfaces or transmission through fog or frosted glass.

Disintegration (nuclear). The spontaneous emission of a charged particle from the nucleus of a radioactive element. The remaining nucleus changes in charge and atomic number to form a new element.

Dispersion of light. The separation of light into a spectrum of component colors or wavelengths through refraction.

Divalent. Capable of uniting with two atoms of hydrogen or their equivalent. Also see *Monovalent* and *Trivalent*.

Doppler effect. A change in the apparent wavelength of sound, light, or other electromagnetic waves due to the relative motion of an observer toward or away from a wave source.

Dyne. A force that imparts an acceleration of 1 cm/sec/sec to a 1-g mass (cgs system).

E

Eccentric circle (or *sphere*). A circle (or sphere) that is off-center.

Eclipse. The passage of one nonluminous body into the shadow of another. In a *lunar eclipse,* the moon passes into the shadow of the earth. In a *solar eclipse,* the shadow of the moon falls on part of the earth.

Ecliptic. The sun's apparent annual path in the zodiacal belt of stars. This path is a great circle formed by the intersection of the plane of the earth's orbit on the celestial sphere.

Electric current. A stream of moving electrons or other electric charges.

Electric field. Region of electric lines of force around electric charges or moving magnets.

Electrode. A conductor through which an electric current enters or leaves a gas (as in an electric discharge tube) or a liquid (as in an electrolytic cell).

Electrolysis. The dissociation of a chemical compound into positive and negative ions by an electric current. The substance that dissociates into ions and conducts the current is called an *electrolyte.*

Electrolytes. Substances that conduct a current when in water or another solution and that are simultaneously decomposed by the current.

Electromagnetic field. The combined electric and magnetic fields surrounding an electric current.

Electromagnetic spectrum. The range of frequencies of electromagnetic waves. In order of increasing frequencies, electromagnetic waves are differentiated into radio waves, infrared radiation, light, ultraviolet radiation, X rays, gamma rays, and cosmic rays. All electromagnetic waves travel at the speed of light, 186,000 mi/sec.

Electromagnetic wave. A transverse wave consisting of electric and magnetic fields that oscillate at right angles to each other and to the direction of wave motion. All electromagnetic waves travel at the speed of light.

Electron. The smallest known particle with an electric charge.

Electron-volt (ev). The energy gained by an electron accelerating through a potential difference of 1 volt.

Element. A substance which cannot be decomposed into simpler substances by chemical means.

Ellipse. The locus of a point such that the sum of the distances of the point from two fixed points (foci) is constant.

Emission spectrum. A pattern of sharp, bright lines seen when light from a glowing, heated substance passes through a prism or grating. Each heated substance shows a pattern of bright lines characteristic of itself in colors and arrangement.

Energy. Ability to do work. Among forms of energy are mechanical energy, heat, light, electrical energy, chemical energy, and atomic energy.

Energy level. Energy associated with specific orbits of electrons in an atom. Each electron has an amount of energy that depends upon the particular position or level of its orbit around the atomic nucleus.

Epicycle. A circle whose center moves on another circle.

Equant. A point off a deferent center about which an epicycle center moves with uniform circular motion in the Ptolemaic system.

Equinoxes ("equal nights"). A time when days and nights are equal in length (12 hrs) all over the earth. This time occurs twice a year as the sun crosses the celestial equator. One point of crossing, the *vernal equinox,* determines the first day of spring (March 21), and the other point, the *autumnal equinox,* determines the first day of fall (September 23). The vernal equinox is also a point of 0° longitude and 0° latitude on the celestial sphere.

Erg. The work done by a force of 1 dyne acting through a distance of 1 cm.

Escape velocity. The minimum speed needed by an object to escape from the gravitational attraction of a given planet or moon. A speed of 7 ft/sec, or about 25,000 mi/hr, is needed to escape from the earth.

Ether. An elastic but weightless substance formerly assumed to fill empty space and to serve as a medium of travel for light and other electromagnetic waves.

Ether wind. Relative motion of the ether past a body traveling through it.

Evaporation. Change of a liquid into a gas without its necessarily reaching the boiling point. Molecules in random motion escape from the body of the liquid at the liquid surface.

Extrapolation. The mathematical technique by which data in a given range are projected for inferences about data beyond that range.

F

Fields of force. Regions around a magnet (magnetic field), an electrically charged object (electric field), or any body (gravitational field) in which these bodies exert influence or force. Fields are conceptual models involving lines of force that depict how forces can exist between bodies across space.

Fission. The release of nuclear energy as atomic nuclei split into two roughly equal parts. Fission reactions happen only with heavy elements such as uranium or plutonium.

Fission bomb or *A-bomb.* The bomb in which uranium or plutonium nuclei are split into about equal chunks, with neutrons in chain reaction to release huge quantities of nuclear energy.

Fluid. A substance that takes the shape of the vessel containing it. A liquid or gas is a fluid.

Fluorescence. The property of absorbing light of one wavelength and emitting it at another wavelength.

Force. That action which changes the velocity or momentum of an object.

Formula. Chemical representation of a molecule in which symbols of atoms of elements composing molecular compounds are placed side by side.

Fourth dimension. In general, a fourth set of numbers in a coordinate system. In relativity theory, time provides a fourth set of numbers in a combined space-time coordinate system.

Frame of reference. A coordinate system or other background for indicating the location, direction of motion, or relevant characteristic of an object.

Free fall. The motion of an object in space which is subject to gravity forces only.

Friction. Forces that resist motion between surfaces in contact.

Fusion bomb or *H-bomb.* The bomb that uses the A-bomb for the millions of degrees temperature needed to fuse hydrogen into helium, thus releasing tremendous energies. The energies result from the mass lost in the fusion of hydrogen nuclei into helium nuclei.

Fusion (nuclear). The uniting of light atomic nuclei, with the accompanying loss of mass and release of nuclear energy. Hydrogen nuclei in the sun unite at millions of degrees to form fewer but heavier helium nuclei and release huge amounts of energy. The energies result from the mass lost in the fusion of the hydrogen nuclei.

G

g. An acceleration of gravity (or centrifugal force) of 32.2 ft/sec, or 9.80 m/sec.

Galaxy. A group of billions of stars, often disk-shaped or lens-shaped, moving as a unit through space.

Galilean system. See *Inertial frame.*

Gamma rays (γ). Highly penetrating electromagnetic waves emitted from some radioactive atomic nuclei with wavelengths just shorter (or frequencies just higher) than X rays.

General relativity. Basically, Einstein's theory of gravitation that generalizes his special theory to include accelerated motion, gravity, and centrifugal force. See *Special relativity.*

Geocentric. Refers to an *earth-centered* world system.

Geodesic. The shortest line between two points on a spherical or other surface or in space or space-time.

Gravitation (or *gravity*). Mutual attraction between any two objects. According to Newton, the attraction is a force that varies directly with the product of the masses of the two objects and inversely with the square of the distance between them. According to Einstein, gravitation is the tendency of material bodies to move through space-time along geodesics determined by the distribution of other material bodies.

H

Half-life. The period of time required for one-half of any sample of a radioactive element to decay.

H-bomb. See *Fusion bomb.*

Heat of fusion. Amount of heat needed to change 1 kg of a substance from a solid to a liquid at its freezing point. The same amount of heat is freed when 1 kg of the substance changes from a liquid to a solid at its freezing point.

Heat of vaporization. Amount of heat needed to change 1 kg of a substance from a liquid to a vapor at its boiling point. The same amount of heat is freed when 1 kg of the substance changes from a vapor to a liquid at its boiling point.

Heavy hydrogen ($_1H^2$ or $_1H^3$). Hydrogen isotopes with one neutron (deuterium) or two neutrons (tritium).

Heavy water (D_2O). A concentration of water containing the heavy hydrogen isotope $_1H^2$ (that is, D, deuterium) rather than ordinary hydrogen $_1H^1$.

Heliacal rising. The appearance of a given star with the sun at the eastern horizon.

Heliocentric. Refers to a sun-centered (or solar) planetary system.

Horizon. That great circle where the earth and sky seem to meet.

Horsepower. A 550 ft-lb/sec rate of doing work.

Hydrogen bomb (H-bomb). See *Fusion bomb.*

Hyperbola. The locus of a point on a plane such that the difference of the distances of the point from two fixed points (foci) is a constant.

Hyperon. A particle with a mass greater than that of a proton or neutron.

I

Impulse (Fxt). The product of an accelerating force and the time that the force takes to act to give a body a change of momentum.

Inert gases (or noble gases). Those gases composed of atoms whose outer electron shells are ordinarily complete. Supposed to have been chemically inactive, in recent years inert gases have been found that are chemically active.

Inertia. The resistance of a body to any change in its state of rest or in its speed or direction of motion.

Inertial frame. A coordinate system moving through space at constant velocity relative to all other inertial systems.

Interference of light. The combined effect of overlapping light waves. Bright bands form when intersecting waves reinforce each other, crest to crest and trough to trough. Dark bands form when waves cancel each other, crest to trough.

Interpolation. A mathematical process of finding intermediate values between known values in a series.

Ion. An atom or group of atoms that have become electrically charged by gaining or losing one or more electrons.

Ionization. The process of ion formation.

Isomers. Molecules with the same combinations of atoms but different structural arrangement.

Isotopes. Atoms of the same element with different atomic weights. Such variants have almost identical chemical properties. Isotopes have the same number of protons but a different number of neutrons. All hydrogen atoms, for example, have one proton. But most hydrogen

atoms have no neutrons; some have one neutron; and relatively few have two neutrons.

J

Joule. Unit of work or energy. That work done in a second by a current of 1 amp flowing through a resistance of 1 ohm. A w-sec. (1 joule $= 10^7$ ergs).

K

Kilowatt-hour. The work done or energy provided by a power source of 1,000 watts (kilowatt) operating for 1 hr.

Kinetic theory of gases. A model that explains gas behavior on the assumption that gases consist of widely separated molecules in rapid, random motion.

L

Latent heat. The heat energy needed to change a solid into a liquid or a liquid into a gas without an increase in temperature.

Latitude (celestial). Angular distance of a celestial object from the ecliptic, as compared to *terrestial latitude,* the angular distance of a location above or below the earth's equator.

Latitude (terrestial). Distance in degrees north or south of the equator.

Lattice pile. The interspaced graphite and uranium blocks structuring nuclear reactors.

Leptons. Particles lighter than protons that include neutrinos, electrons, muons, and their antiparticles.

Levity. A supposed tendency that enabled light objects to rise, as contrasted by ancient Greeks to the fall caused by gravity.

Libration. Apparent oscillation of the moon or another body.

Light-year. The distance that light travels in a year, about 6 trillion mi.

Lodestone. A naturally magnetic mineral called magnetite, an iron oxide.

Longitude (celestial). Angular distance along the ecliptic from the vernal equinox to the point of intersection of a great circle, passing through a given object and the ecliptic poles. The angular distance is measured westward from the vernal equinox as a 0° point.

Longitudinal wave. A wave in which particles of the wave oscillate in the same direction that the wave itself moves. Compressional waves in a spring are longitudinal waves. For comparison, see *Transverse wave.*

M

Magnetic field. Region of magnetic lines of force around a magnet or electric current.

Magnetic pole. Imaginary centers where magnetic lines of force apparently concentrate in entering a magnet or fan out in leaving it. Lines of force are considered to leave a magnet from a *north magnetic pole* and to enter from a *south magnetic pole.*

Mass. Quantity of matter in a body as determined by the amount of force (f) required to give it unit acceleration (f/a). Mass may also be considered to be equivalent to the inertia of a body, that is, the resistance of a body to change of motion or acceleration. Weight is generally used as a measure of mass related to the earth's gravitational pull on an object.

Mass spectograph. An instrument that separates and indicates isotopes according to their weights.

Mechanical equivalent of heat. The number of mechanical energy units in one unit of heat; for example, 4,185 joules per kcal (mks system).

Megaton. A million tons. This unit is applied to nuclear explosions with energy equivalents of a million tons of TNT.

Meridian, celestial. The great circle of the celestial sphere passing through the zenith and the celestial poles.

Meson. Any subatomic particle with a mass between that of an electron and that of a proton. Mesons may be positive or negative in charge. A *mu-meson (muon)* has about 200 times an electron's mass; a *pi-meson (pion),* about 270 times an electron's mass.

Meteor. A solid body from outer space. Heat of friction of the earth's atmosphere causes meteors to glow as "shooting stars" in the earth's atmosphere.

Meteorite. The unburned portion of a meteor originally large enough to get through the atmosphere and land on the earth.

Mev. Million electron-volts.

Micron. One-millionth of a meter, or 10,000 angstrom units.

Millimicron. 1/1,000 micron; 10^{-7} cm.

Minute of arc. One-sixtieth of a degree of arc.

Mixture. A substance composed of two or more elements or compounds that keep their individual properties when together.

Moderator. Material used in nuclear reactors to slow down neutrons. Graphite (carbon), heavy water, or beryllium is generally used.

Mole. Gram-molecular weight. A unit of weight of a substance equal to its molecular weight in grams.

Molecule. Smallest particle of a substance with an independent existence that retains the chemical properties of that substance.

Momentum $(m \ x \ v)$. The product of the mass and velocity of a body.

Monovalent. Capable of uniting with one atom of hydrogen or its equivalent. *Divalent* and *trivalent* refer to the capacity of uniting with two atoms and three atoms of hydrogen or their equivalents, respectively.

Mu-meson (muon). See *Meson.*

N

Nadir. The point on the celestial sphere opposite to an observer's zenith.

Neap tide. The lowest tides in the month at half-moon phases when the tidal effects of sun and moon oppose each other.

Neptunium (Np). The artificially produced element of atomic number 93, just after uranium in the periodic table.

Neutrino. An elementary particle with no electric charge or mass emitted with beta or other particles during radioactive decay. First postulated to preserve conservation laws of mass-energy and of momentum.

Neutron. A basic nuclear particle electrically neutral with a mass slightly greater than that of a proton. Found with protons in all atomic nuclei except in ordinary hydrogen. Both neutrons and protons are called *nucleons.*

Neutron capture. The taking in of a neutron by an atomic nucleus.

Newton. A force that imparts an acceleration of 1 m/sec/sec to a 1 kg-mass (mks system).

Noble gases. See *Inert gases.*

Nova. A star that suddenly becomes 5,000

to 10,000 times more luminous than usual and then slowly returns to its former brightness. The nova brilliance is believed due to an explosion in which up to one percent of the star's mass is ejected as a gas cloud. See *Supernova*.

Nuclear energy. See *Atomic energy*.

Nuclear fission. The process in which a heavy nucleus splits into two or more lighter nuclei with emission of much energy.

Nuclear fusion. The process in which light nuclei unite to form a heavier nucleus with emission of much energy.

Nuclear reactor. An atomic pile or device that maintains and controls nuclear fission reactions to produce nuclear energy, radioactive isotopes, or artificial elements.

Nuclear transmutation. The change of atoms of an element into atoms of another element by nuclear reactions.

Nucleon. A basic nuclear particle, that is, a proton or neutron.

O

Ohm. Unit of electrical resistance. The resistance to a current flow of a column of mercury 106.3 cm long and 1 sq. mm cross-section at 0°C.

Ohm's law. The intensity of an electric current (amperes) along a conductor equals the potential difference (volts) divided by the resistance (ohms). $I = V/R$.

Operationalism. Definition of anything in terms of a process or operation in which it is found. For example, see *Calorie*.

Opposition (astron). Relative positions in which the earth is between the sun and an outer planet or the moon.

Oxidation. The chemical combination of a substance with oxygen. More generally, any chemical reaction that involves the loss of electrons from an atom.

Oxide. Compound of an element or group of elements with oxygen.

Ozone (O_3). A form of oxygen with three atoms to a molecule.

P

Packing loss. The difference between the mass of a nucleus and the sum of the masses of its components taken separately.

Pair production. Conversion of gamma ray energy (photons) into "opposite twin" particles of matter, i.e., electrons and positrons.

Parabola. The locus of a point equidistant from a fixed point (focus) and a fixed line (directrix).

Parallax. The angle made at an object by two lines of sight. Annual *stellar parallax* is the apparent yearly shift of a star relative to more distant stars due to the revolution of the earth.

Parsec. The astronomical distance to a point that has a parallax of 1″ of arc (about 3.3 light years or 19 trillion mi).

Perigee. The point in the moon's orbit nearest to the earth.

Perihelion. The point in the earth's orbit nearest the sun.

Periodic law. The generalization established by Mendeléyev in 1869 that "properties of elements are in periodic dependence upon their atomic weights." See *Periodic table*.

Periodic table. A classification of the chemical elements in order of their atomic number, that is, number of protons in a nucleus. Elements with similar properties occur in this classification at regular intervals to form families of related elements such as alkali metals, halogens, or noble gases. The relatedness is identified with similar electron grouping in the outer shells of the atoms of the particular elements. Elements having the same number of electrons in outer shells are similar in chemical properties.

Period of revolution. Time taken for a complete revolution of an object.

Perturbation. Deviation of a planet or satellite from its regular elliptical path due to the proximity of another celestial body.

Phase of moon or planet. The amount and form of the body's lit disk that is visible.

Phlogiston. A substance supposed in the 18th century to be released from a burning object in its flame.

Photoelectric effect. The ejection of free electrons from a metal exposed to light or other electromagnetic radiation.

Photons. Tiny packets or quanta of energy without rest mass, assumed to compose light rays or other electromagnetic radiation and to move at a fixed speed with a wave motion. A photon has energy, $E = hn$, where h is *Planck's constant* and n is the frequency of the wave.

Photosynthesis. The process by which green plants produce carbohydrates from carbon dioxide and water in the presence of sunlight ($6CO_2 + 6H_2O \longrightarrow C_6H_{12}O_6 + 6O_2$).

Physical change. Any change in a substance not involving change in chemical composition, such as ice changing to water.

Pile. See *Nuclear reactor.* Early reactors consisted of "piles" of graphite (carbon) blocks and uranium slugs.

Pi-meson (pion). See *Meson.*

Planck's constant (h). A universal constant that when multiplied by the frequency n of any electromagnetic radiation (for example, light or X rays) gives the energy $E = hn$ of a quantum of that radiation. See *Photon.*

Planetoids or asteroids. Several thousand small bodies revolving around the sun, mostly between Mars and Jupiter.

Plutonium (Pu). The artificially produced element of atomic number 94, just after neptunium in the periodic table.

Polarized light. Light waves vibrating in one plane rather than in all directions. Wave components formerly vibrating in other planes have been filtered out by passage through or reflection from special materials.

Positron. A positive electron, that is, a particle identical to the electron except for its opposite but equal charge.

Postulate. An assumption upon which a mathematical or other logical system is based.

Potential difference. The difference in the electrical states at two points which causes a current to flow between these points.

Poundal. A force that imparts an acceleration of 1 ft/sec/sec to a 1-lb mass (fps system).

Power. Rate of doing work. The *watt* (1 joule/sec) is the metric unit of power; the *horsepower* (550 ft lb/sec) is the British unit. 1 hp = 746 w.

Precession of the equinoxes. The very slow westward motion of the equinox points around the celestial equator (26,000 years for one cycle). The equinox points are the two at which the sun apparently crosses the celestial equator. An implication is that every calendar day has the opportunity to be the first day of spring (or of fall) every 26,000 years.

Pressure. Force per unit area.

Probability. The relative frequency of an event as determined by the ratio of the favorable occurrences of the event to the total occurrences possible. "Heads" would be a favorable possibility five times in throwing up a coin ten times.

Proton. A basic, positively charged particle with a mass about 1,840 times that of an electron and a charge numerically opposite but equal to that of the electron. A proton is the nucleus of hydrogen ($_1H^1$), the simplest of atoms.

Q

Quanta. Discrete units or packets into which all electromagnetic waves are reduced. Each packet is considered to have an energy $E = hn$, where h is *Planck's constant* and n is the *frequency* of the wave.

R

Radiation. Streams of atomic particles or electromagnetic waves.

Radical (chem.). A group of two or more atoms entering into chemical combination as a unit but usually incapable of independent existence as a molecule.

Radioactive fallout. Radioactive isotopes scattered into the atmosphere by nuclear explosions and often carried long distances by winds before settling to the ground.

Radioactive series. A series of disintegrations affecting a radioactive isotope until reaching a stable state.

Radioactive tracer ("tagged" atoms). A radioactive isotope used within an object to trace chemical processes, often by means of radiation counters.

Radioactivity. Spontaneous emission of alpha, beta, gamma, or other radiation from atomic nuclei.

Radioelements. Radioactive isotopes artificially produced in nuclear reactors and not ordinarily found in nature.

Radioisotope. A radioactive isotope of an element. Radioisotopes are often used as tracers in research and industry. These isotopes may be artificially produced by placing substances in a nuclear reactor for bombardment with neutrons.

Radon. An inert (noble) gas found when radium disintegrates.

Red shift. A shift toward the red in the wavelength of light due to relative motion of the source away from the observer or to influence of a strong gravitational field around a large mass.

Reduction. The removal of oxygen from a substance or the addition of hydrogen to it. In general, any chemical reaction in which an atom or ion gains electrons.

Reflection of light. The casting back of light from a surface. The *law of reflection of light* holds that: (1) The incident ray, the reflected ray, and the perpendicular or normal to the reflecting surface at the point of incidence lie at the same plane. (2) The angle of incidence (between the incident ray and the normal) equals the angle of reflection (between the reflected ray and the normal).

Refraction. The bending of light or another ray from a straight line as it passes obliquely from one medium to another. Bending takes place at the surfaces between the media in accordance with *laws of refraction* given below.

Refraction, laws of. (1) The incident ray, the refracted ray, and the perpendicular to the surfaces of the two media at the point of incidence are in the same plane. (2) The ratio of the sine of the angle of refraction is constant for any two media. This constant is called the *index of refraction.*

Relativity, general. See *General relativity.*

Relativity, special. See *Special relativity.*

Relativity of length. The variation in the measured length of an object according to the relative speed of an observer.

Relativity of mass. The variation in the measured mass of an object according to the relative speed of an observer.

Relativity of time. The variation in the measured time interval of a clock according to the relative speed of an observer.

Resolving power of a telescope. The ability of a telescope to separate two adjacent points seen as one point.

Rest energy. The energy of an object at rest relative to an observer. This energy equals the product of an object's mass when at rest and the square of the speed of light ($E_o = m_o c^2$).

Rest mass. The mass of an object at rest relative to an observer.

Resultant. The combined or total effect of two or more vector quantities.

Retrograde motion. Reversed (westward) motion of the planets in relation to the stars.

Revolution. The motion of an object around an outside center, such as the earth's yearly motion around the sun.

Roentgen unit. A unit for measuring the amount of absorbed radiation in accordance with the ionization produced. A roentgen produces ions carrying one electrostatic unit (esu) of electricity in 1 cc of dry air.

Rotation. The motion of an object around its own axis, such as the daily turning of the earth on its north-south axis.

S

Salt. An ionic compound formed by the reaction of an acid and base. In general, a compound resulting from the replacement of one or more hydrogen atoms of an acid by metal atoms or electropositive radicals.

Scattering of light. Deflection of light by small particles, most pronounced for blue and other high frequencies, as shown by the blueness of the sky.

Sidereal day. Twenty-four hours as determined by a rotation of the earth in respect to the stars rather than to the sun.

Sine (of an angle). A trigonometric function equal to the ratio of the side opposite that angle in a right triangle to the hypotenuse of the triangle.

Solar wind. A steady stream of gas moving from the sun to the earth and other reaches of space.

Solenoid. A coil of wire around a soft iron core much greater in length than diameter. A current through the coil creates a magnetic field through and around the coil.

Solstices. The longest and shortest days of the year. On these days, June 22 and December 22, the sun is at its northernmost and southernmost points respectively from the celestial equator, to initiate summer or winter.

Space-time. The four-dimensional coordinate system of relativity involving three space dimensions and one time dimension.

Space-time interval. The distance between two events in space-time. Observers with different local measurements of space and time obtain the same absolute value for an Einsteinian space-time interval.

Special relativity. Einstein's initial relativity theory, concerned with the relative space, time, mass, and other measurements by observers moving in inertial frames only.

Specific gravity. Ratio of the density of a substance to the density of water at 4°C. *Density* is the mass of a substance divided by its volume ($D = m/V$).

Specific heat. The heat required to raise the temperature of 1 g of a substance by 1°C.

Spectroscope. A device for analyzing a ray of light into its component colors.

Spectrum. An arrangement of electromagnetic radiations in the order of their wavelengths or frequencies. The visible region of light waves are represented by the rainbow colors—red, orange, yellow, green, blue, indigo, and violet—in order of decreasing wavelength. An unbroken or *continuous spectrum* of color results when a beam of white light from a heated solid, liquid, or very hot gas at high density passes through a prism or diffraction grating. A *bright line or emission spectrum* of sharp, discrete lines of color is emitted from heated gases at ordinary pressures. Each gas has its characteristic emission lines of color. A *dark line or absorption spectrum* results when white light passes through a gas medium. (Certain color frequencies are absorbed from the white light spectrum characteristic of the given gas medium.) The gas medium absorbs its characteristic colors from the transmitted white light to leave dark lines in the resulting spectrum.

Spectrum analysis. The chemical analysis of a substance by observation of its spectrum.

Speed. Distance covered in a unit of time.

Speed of light (c). About 186,000 mi (300,000 km) per sec.

Spring tide. The highest tides in the month at new and full moon phases, when the tidal effects of the sun and moon reinforce each other.

Steady state theory. The theory that the universe has no beginning or end in time, but keeps a uniform state of density as new matter constantly forms to replace other matter moving outward with the expansion of the universe.

Stellar parallax. See *Parallax.*

Sublimation. The direct change of a solid into a vapor without its passing through the liquid state.

Supernova. A star believed to completely explode with a maximum brightness 100 million times that of the sun. The supernova, many times brighter than a *nova,* does not return to its original luminosity. The phenomenon is believed to result when a star runs out of hydrogen and collapses under its own gravitational field.

Surface tension. The state of tension shown by the open surface of a liquid, much like that of a stretched elastic film over the liquid. The tension results from forces of attraction between molecules of the liquid.

Synodic period of the moon. Time needed for the moon to make one turn around the earth in respect to the sun.

T

Temperature. The degree of hotness of a body with respect to an arbitrary zero (as in the centigrade or Fahrenheit scales) or to an absolute zero (as in the Kelvin scale). Temperature is thus a property of a body that determines the rate at which heat will be transferred to or from it.

Thermal equilibrium. The state of uniform temperature finally reached when bodies at different temperatures are placed in contact or mixed, and heat flows from bodies of higher to lower temperatures.

Thermonuclear reaction. The fusion of hydrogen or other light atomic nuclei into nuclei of heavier elements at a very high temperature. This reaction occurs in the sun and stars naturally and in hydrogen bombs artificially.

Tracer. See *Radioactive tracer.*

Transformation equations. Equations relating the coordinates of two different systems.

Transformer. A device through which the energy of an alternating current is transferred from one coil to another by electromagnetic induction.

Transit. The motion of an apparently smaller celestial body across the face of a larger one.

Translucent. The property of transmitting light diffusely or imperfectly, as in the case of frosted glass.

Transmutation. See *Nuclear transmutation.*

Transparent. The property of a substance of transmitting light so that objects can be seen through it clearly.

Transuranic elements. Elements beyond uranium, that is, with atomic numbers greater than 92.

Transverse wave. A wave in which particles of the wave oscillate *at right angles* to the direction that the wave itself moves. The end of a horizontally stretched spring shaken vertically causes waves that move horizontally. For comparison, see *Longitudinal wave.*

Triangulation. The process of determining a larger distance by measuring a short base line and angles of sight.

Tritium ($_1H^3$). The radioactive, extra-heavy isotope of hydrogen with atomic weight 3, that is, with a nucleus of one proton and two neutrons.

Trivalent. Capable of uniting with three atoms of hydrogen or their equivalent. Also see *Monovalent* and *Divalent.*

U

Ultraviolet light. Invisible electromagnetic radiation just beyond violet in the color spectrum. The wavelength of ultraviolet light is just too short for visibility or eye response.

Uncertainty principle. Refers to the impossibility of simultaneously determining accurate values for both the position and velocity of a particle or both the energy and time of an event. These values are thus considered in terms of probabilities rather than certainties.

Unified field theory. A theory unifying gravity and electromagnetism by a single set of equations.

Uniform circular motion. Motion in a circle at constant speed.

V

Valence. The combining ability of an atom or atomic group; specifically the number of hydrogen atoms another atom or group will combine with or replace. For example, the valence of oxygen in water (H_2O) is 2.

Valence electrons. Electrons in an atom's outermost shell.

Vapor pressure. The maximum pressure of a confined vapor in contact with its liquid form. The pressure is due to the vapor molecules which, evaporated from the liquid surface, have saturated the space above the liquid. Saturated vapor pressure increases with rise in temperature.

Vector quantity. A quantity that has both magnitude and direction, as represented by an arrow and its length drawn to scale. A vector is in contrast to a *scalar* quantity, in which only magnitude and not direction is considered. Velocity is a vector quantity; speed is scalar.

Velocity. Speed in a given direction.

Velocity of light (c). 3×10^8 m/sec or 186,000 mi/sec.

Viscosity. The property of a fluid by which it tends to resist relative motion within itself or change of shape.

Voltage. The value of the electromotive force or potential difference expressed in volts.

Voltaic cell. A source of electric current composed primarily of two different metals in contact with an electrolyte.

W

Wave. The propagation in a medium of a periodic disturbance-carrying energy. Along the path of a wave motion, a particle or point of medium vibrates periodically about a central position, somewhat as a molecule in a water wave vertically vibrates as the wave itself moves horizontally.

Wave frequency. The number of waves per second.

Wavelength. The distance between two points in the same phase on adjacent waves, as from crest to crest.

Weight. The force of attraction of the earth upon an object.

Work. The product of a force acting on an object and the distance through which the force acts.

World line. The path of an object in four-dimensional space-time.

X

X rays. Electromagnetic waves of very short wavelength between ultraviolet and gamma rays. X rays result from bombardment of metal targets by electron beams and give shadow pictures of denser parts of objects they penetrate. X rays arise from disturbances in planetary electrons in atoms rather than in disturbances of nuclei.

Z

Zenith. The point in the celestial sphere directly above an observer's head.

Zodiac. A belt in the celestial sphere extending 9° on each side of the ecliptic. This belt, containing the paths of all the planets, the moon, and the sun, is divided equally lengthwise into twelve *signs of the zodiac,* each named after a constellation.

Name Index

Subject Index

mechanical equivalent of heat, 249–250, 253–254

Jupiter, 50, 93, 368–369

K

Kelvin, Lord (William Thomson), 110, 274–275
Kelvin temperature scale, 274–275
Kepler, Johann, 70, 71
  laws of planetary motion, 71–76, 90
    first: law of ellipse, 71
    second: law of equal areas, 72, 73
    third: harmonic law, 73–76
  mathematical hypothesis testing, 78
  "On Celestial Harmonies," 74
  and the parsimony principle, 76–78
Kilocalorie, 231
Kilogram, 158–159
Kilowatt, 336
Kinetic energy, 212–214, 217–220
  units, 214
Kinetic molecular assumptions, 266–268
Kinetic molecular evidence, 265–266
  Brownian motion, 265–266
Kinetic molecular explanations, 268–280
  of change of state, 270–273
  of diffusion, 278–279
  of heat, 269–270
  of pressure of gases, 273
  of temperature, 269–270
  of transfer of heat, 268–269
Kinetic molecular theory of heat, 266–268
Kinetic theory of gases, 264–266

L

Langmuir, Irving, 508–511
  Lewis–Langmuir shell model of atom, 508–511
Laplace, Pierre S., 257, 261
Latent heat, 272, 273
  boiling and condensation, 239–240
  melting and freezing, 237–238
Latitude, 6, 7, 10
Lavoisier, Antoine L., 413–415, 418–419
  and law of conservation of matter, 413–415
  modern chemical nomenclature, 419
  theory of burning, 413–414
Lawrence, Ernest, 529–530

cyclotron, 529–530
Laws, physical science:
  conservation of charge, 318
  conservation of energy, 251–257
  conservation of matter, 405, 413–415, 430–434
  conservation of matter-energy, 537
  conservation of momentum, 196, 206–207
  definite proportions, 424–425
  dissipation of energy, 280–282
  electrostatic force, 320–321, 323
  gravitation, 174, 185–186
  independence of velocities, 150
  magnetic force, 297–298
  motion, 155–163, 580
  multiple proportions, 425–426
  pendulum, 145–146
  planetary motion, 71–76, 90
  reflection of light, 352–353
  refraction of light, 354–355
Leeuwenhoek, Antony van, 82
Left-hand rules, 338–340
Leibnitz, Gottfried W., 205–207, 214, 257
Leonardo da Vinci, 375
Leucippus, 397, 399, 404
Levity, 111
Leyden jar, 311–312
Libration of moon, 99
Light, 471
  aberration of, 473
  absolute speed of, 471–472
  curved paths in accelerating elevators, 568–570
  diffraction, 381–382, 390
  dispersion (color), 382
  and the electromagnetic spectrum, 385–389
  experiments, speed of light, 368–370
    Fizeau's mirror technique, 369–370
    Galileo's experiment, 368
    Michaelson's interferometer techniques, 370
    Roemer's observations, 368–370
  interference principle, 381–385
  origin of, 507
  photoelectric cells, 390
  photoelectric effect, 389–390
  photoelectric equation, 389–390
  reflection, 352–353, 376, 380
  refraction, 353–355, 376, 380–381
  theories of nature of light:
    corpuscular (Newton), 376
    early theories, 374–375
    electromagnetic waves (Maxwell), 385–387
    photon (Einstein), 385, 389
    waves (Huygens-Young), 379–382
Lightning:
  experiments, 312–315

rods, 313, 314
Lines of force, 321
  electrostatic, 321
  gravitational, 322–323
  magnetic, 294–297
Liquids:
  boiling point of, 239, 271–272
  freezing point of, 238
  kinetic molecular theory of, 270–271
  vapor pressure of, 272
Lobachevsky, Nicholas, 573–575
Lodestone, 287–288
Lomonosov, Mikhail, 257, 260–261
Longitudinal waves, 377–378
Lorentz, Hendrik, 473–474
  Fitzgerald-Lorentz contraction hypothesis,
    473–474, 480
Lucretius, 205, 397, 399, 401, 405
Lunar eclipse, 7, 16, 41–42, 59

M

Magnetic attraction, 288
  law of, 291–292
Magnetic compasses, 290
Magnetic declination, 292–294
Magnetic dip, 293–294
Magnetic fields, 294–297
  of electric current, 337–338
  experiments, 294–296
  lines of force in, 294–297
Magnetic induction, 289
Magnetic poles, 289–290, 291–292
Magnetic repulsion, 290–292
  law of, 291–292
Magnetism:
  of earth, 294
  experiments, 288–292, 294
  law of force, 297–298
  lines of force, 295
  theories, 298
    domain, 300, 507–508
    molecular, 298–300
Magnets, 287–292
Marconi, Guglielmo, 387
Mars, 50, 95
Mass:
  of earth, 188–189
  and energy, 488–489, 531–532
  and inertia, 159–160
  law of conservation of, 251–257
  relativity of, 486–488

and weight, 160–161
Mass-energy:
  conservation of, 537
  equivalence, 488–489, 531–532
Matter:
  ancient theories, 396–408
  annihilation of, 536, 557–558
  atoms, 398, 404–406
  change of state, 236–240, 270–273, 417–418
  chemical changes, 417–418, 430–434
  conservation of, 405, 413–415
  and energy equivalents, 488–489, 531–532
  four elements, 401–403, 405–406
  four qualities of matter, 399, 402
  innumerable elements, 403–404
  one basic element, 396–401
  physical changes of, 417–418
Matter-waves, 423
Maxwell, James Clerk, 385–388
Mayer, Julius Robert, 246–247, 254–256
Mechanical equivalent of heat, 249–250, 255
Mechanical view, 204–205, 323–324, 347
  decline of, 347
Meitner, Lise, 539–540
Melting points, 238
Mendeleyev, Dimitri Ivanovich, 436–445
  periodic classification of elements, 438–445
    chart, 440–441
Mercury, 14, 40, 48, 50, 57, 94
  rotation of orbit, 474, 579, 582
Meridian, prime, 20
Meson, 554–557
Meteor, 102–103
Meteorite, 99, 102–103
Method of mixtures, 234, 236
Meyer, Lothar, 433–436
Michell, John, 186
Michelson, Albert A., 351, 368, 370, 470
  Michelson-Morley experiment, 470–472
Millicurie, 549
Millikan, Robert A., 455–456
  oil drop experiment, 455–456
Minkowski, Hermann, 563
Mirror experiments, 352–353
Mixtures, 415–416
  versus compounds, 416
Molecular formulas, 429–430
Molecular weight, 435
Molecules:
  and atoms, 428, 430
  Avogadro's hypothesis, 433–435
  Brownian motion of, 265–266, 476
Momentum, 163, 205
  conservation, 206–207